Date Due

Fundamentals of Mathematics
from an Advanced Viewpoint

Volumes 3 and 4

Geometry and Geometric Analysis
Solid Geometry and Spherical Trigonometry

Fundamentals of Mathematics from an Advanced Viewpoint:

Fundamentals of Mathematics from an Advanced Viewpoint

Geometry and Geometric Analysis
Solid Geometry and Spherical Trigonometry

by

E. G. KOGBETLIANTZ

The Rockefeller University

GORDON AND BREACH SCIENCE PUBLISHERS
NEW YORK · LONDON · PARIS

TO MY WIFE, EUGENIA

Contents

Volume IV   Solid Geometry and Spherical Trigonometry

Volume II   Algebra and Analysis: Determinants – Equations – Logarithms

CHAPTER 13

Euclid's Axioms

*"By the use of Mathematics, that most nearly
perfect and most immaterial tool of the human
mind, we try to transcend as much as possible
the limitation imposed by our finiteness and
materiality and to penetrate ever nearer to the
understanding of the mysterious unity of the
Kosmos."*

Kosmos, Willem de Sitter (1872–1934)

The elaboration of thought undoubtedly represents the highest point
reached by life in its evolution on our planet up to now. Human thinking, in
particular, reveals itself as the best tool for the preservation of life through
understanding of our natural environment. This environment consists not
only of the physical universe around us but also of human society. Evolved
especially to perceive the physical world, the human brain is not nearly as
well adapted to understand our social environment as it is to study the
physical universe. Its fundamental device of locating perceptions in a time–
space frame, which works wonderfully well in the study of the physical world,
seems to be of no value for the understanding of psychological phenomena
which govern our social life.

The citation from the book of the Dutch astronomer de Sitter concerns
only the understanding of the physical universe, and, with this limitation,
it emphasizes well the importance of mathematics in the study of the cosmos,
human society excluded. From this point of view, geometry was the first
branch of mathematics elaborated by the human mind for a better understanding of the exterior world.

We are living in a continually changing, ever-flowing world and have to
deal in our experience with unstable, oscillating forms. There is nothing invariable or fixed around us. A sentence attributed to the Greek philosopher
Heraclitus, "Everything is flowing," well expresses this fundamental feature
of our environment. We try to organize this flowing world by measuring it,

1 Kogbetliantz

but a measure can be performed only with respect to some fixed invariable frame of reference. We need, therefore, absolutely rigid standards to which we can refer our ever-changing, flowing surroundings. Since no rigid standards can be found in our environment, we create such invariant solids in our thought. They are called geometric figures or configurations, and their study is the purpose of geometry.

Geometric configurations are thought to be located in an empty space which is considered in itself, independently of, and as having no relation at all to the physical space into which our mind projects its perceptions. This abstract geometrical space is needed as a frame of reference for the idealized and completely rigid, fictitious forms studied in geometry. Time is excluded from geometry and, with it, the concept of motion. Geometric configurations may undergo displacements in geometrical space, but their changes of position are to be considered as unrelated to time and motion.

Geometrical space is a pure abstraction and, in itself, is devoid of any properties. But the study of geometric configurations which exist in this space is based on certain assumptions, called axioms or postulates, which govern mutual relations of the simple elements (points, straight lines, planes) involved in these configurations. The choice of these fundamental assumptions fixes the kind of geometry considered and endows the geometrical space with definite properties.

Geometry is a study of abstract forms which have nothing in common with the real world as we perceive it. It is based on the idea of rigidity, which also is a completely abstract notion, a human invention, as is the idea of number, the foundation of algebra. Now, when the precision of our instruments and the accuracy of our measurements have enormously increased, we know not only that gaseous and liquid bodies change their shape when moved, but also that so-called solid physical bodies have no fixed boundaries and vary their size and form when they undergo a displacement in space.

The axioms of geometry ensure the rigidity of geometric figures so that their properties become completely independent of their position in space and are unaffected by displacements. This alone shows us clearly that geometric facts, called theorems, are independent of our experience. They can be neither deduced from it nor explained by it.

In a certain sense, these geometric facts even precede and prepare our experience. To understand what we see, hear, and feel, we must interpret our perceptions, and this cannot be done without using a reference frame constituted by time and space. To become conscious of our perceptions, to know that we are seeing something, for example, we need this frame of reference. Therefore, both the interpretation of our perceptions and the meaning for us of our experience depend on the fundamental properties we ascribe, consciously or subconsciously, to space. Thus, it is geometry which helps the human mind to discover the intrinsic structure of the physical environment, suggesting the fundamental properties of the physical space on which are based the interpretations of our experience. It is sufficient to mention the relativistic interpretation of the physical world to become convinced that not only the exact sciences, but science in general, is based on geometry.

Geometry is a purely deductive science developed as a logical chain of syllogisms from a system of basic assumptions called *postulates* or *axioms*. Since to a certain extent there is a freedom in the choice of axioms, many different geometries can be constructed. Among them, Euclidean geometry and its two generalizations, Riemannian geometry and the geometry of Lobachevsky, known as *non-Euclidean* geometries, are particularly important. These geometries have grown up quite naturally, since Euclid's ten axioms, the first system of axioms explicitly formulated by the human mind as the foundation of geometry, were not invented arbitrarily. They were suggested by experience, so that Euclidean geometry reflects, in an idealized form, our experience.

It is of interest to recall how this geometry arose. We begin our study of geometry by discussing the origin of one of the most famous books in the history of human thought, *Elements*, by Euclid.

The first Greek geometers learned rudimentary geometrical facts in Egypt where, forty-five centuries ago (*circa* 2500 B.C.), some practical geometric rules were already known. After every Nile flood, these rules served to re-establish the boundary lines of property destroyed by the floods. In the Ahmes Papyrus (an old papyrus manuscript written about 1650 B.C. but based on a still older manuscript which dates back to about 2500 B.C.) we find some examples of these Egyptian rules: the area of an isosceles triangle with base b and equal sides a is erroneously expressed by the formula $ab/2$ instead of $bh/2$, h being the altitude of the isosceles triangle; the area of a circle with diameter d is represented by $64d^2/81$, being thus thought of as equal to that of a square with sides $8d/9$, which is also incorrect. Replacing the diameter d by 2R (R = radius) and comparing $256R^2/81 = 3.1605 \cdots R^2$ to the exact expression of the area, that is, to $\pi R^2 = 3.14159 \cdots R^2$, we find, indeed, a relative error which is less than 1 %, while in the Bible (II Chronicles 4:2) the number three is substituted for the correct factor π, which causes an error of nearly 5 %. Nevertheless, the fundamental fact that the area of a circle increases (or decreases) as the square of its radius R was known to the Egyptians forty-five centuries ago.

In the Ahmes Papyrus we also find the origin of the famous Pythagorean theorem: to construct a right angle, a rope twelve units in length was used with two knots A and B at distances of three and five units from both ends. By fixing the knots A and B to the earth and bringing together the two ends of the rope at C (see Figure 1), a physical realization of an ideal right triangle ABC with the right angle at the point B was constructed. This Egyptian rule is exact. It is a particular case of the Pythagorean Theorem since $AB = 4$, $BC = 3$, $AC = 5$, and, thus, $AC^2 = AB^2 + BC^2$.

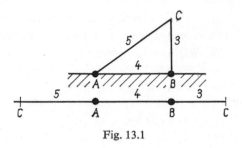

Fig. 13.1

All Egyptian geometrical knowledge consisted of such pragmatic rules without any proof or systematization. In the seventh century B.C., a rich Greek trader and merchant, Thales of Miletus, who often visited Egypt for his business, became interested in Egyptian geometry, studied it, and founded in Greece a school of philosophy where he taught geometry. Among his disciples was Pythagoras of Samos, whom Thales also sent to Egypt to study geometry.

In the five geometric theorems attributed to Thales, we already find the concept of an idealized straight line which has only one dimension, namely, length, and no thickness at all. Such a straight line is a pure abstraction: in our experience all lines have three dimensions. Their sections are areas, maybe very small, but areas which cannot be reduced to dimensionless points. But the section of a straight line as defined by Thales is a mathematical point which has no extension at all.

Here are the five propositions discovered by Thales: (1) a circle is bisected by its diameter; (2) two angles at the base of an isosceles triangle are equal; (3) the opposite *(vertical)* angles formed by two intersecting straight lines are equal; (4) the angle inscribed in a semicircle is a right angle; (5) there is only one triangle having a given side included between two given angles. The validity of the last proposition depends on many important assumptions, but more than three centuries passed before these assumptions were understood and formulated by Greek thinkers and before Euclid gave (*circa* 300 B.C.) to geometry its present beautiful structure of a purely logical deductive science based on definitions and axioms.

In the meantime, between Thales and Euclid, Pythagoras (580–500 B.C.), Antiphon of Athens (480–411 B.C.), Plato (429–348 B.C.), Eudoxus of Cnidus (408–355 B.C.), and many others explored plane and solid geometry and discovered most of the theorems systematized by Euclid in his famous treatise *Elements*.

Among Greek mathematicians after Euclid, the most important contributions to geometry were made by Archimedes (287–212 B.C.) and Apollonius (*circa* 200 B.C.). Archimedes defined exactly the number π and computed some areas bounded by curves as a limit. We are indebted to him for the expressions for the volume and surface of a sphere in terms of its radius. Apollonius wrote a treatise on conic sections and discovered many of their properties, thus preparing the work of Copernicus and Kepler.

We will now discuss the ten axioms of Euclid's Plane Geometry given in *Elements* in two groups of five under the titles Common Notions and Postulates. This discussion is not a study of axioms in themselves. It is, rather, a kind of introduction in which the reader may become acquainted with some important definitions, concepts and ideas of geometry.

Euclid's Definitions and Axioms

The configurations of plane geometry involve points and straight lines as fundamental or simple elements with the aid of which they are constructed. From a purely logical point of view, the simple elements need not to be defined directly. In modern geometry, they are introduced as undefined fundamental elements which must satisfy certain relations described completely in the axioms. In this way, geometry is completely abstracted from our experience and becomes a purely logical deductive structure of great generality. Therefore, if a set S of things can be shown to verify the axioms of geometry when these things are interpreted as "points" and "straight lines," all geometric theorems hold for this set S, and their content describes the mutual relations and properties of the things which are members of the set S.

But for us it is of interest to follow, at the beginning, the less general but more intuitive way of approach to geometry as it is exemplified in *Elements*.

Euclid's definition of a point is as follows (Definition I): "*A point is that which has no part.*"

From this, it follows that a point can have neither volume nor area nor length because each one of these magnitudes, as a part of space, is infinitely divisible as is the space itself, and has, therefore, parts. By definition, a point has no dimensions at all and is, as any other geometrical object, a fiction to which nothing in our experience or in our physical environment corresponds.

What is significant in Definition I is the implicit antithesis between the infinitely divisible space and its last, indivisible element, a point. As we saw already in volume I, a non-denumerable infinity, at least a continuum, of points is needed to form a length, an area, or a volume. This is so precisely because a point has no dimension.

The concept of point is abstracted from the perceptions of very small objects such as, for instance, a pencil dot. Diminishing incessantly in our imagination its size, at the limit when the shape and size of the dot disappear, we obtain at the place where was the dot an ideal object called a geometric point. It has neither shape nor dimension but occupies in space a definite position: a point may be on a line, in a plane, or in a three-dimensional space, etc.

The physical reality which by idealization generates the concept of a straight line is a tightly stretched thread or a ray of light. Decreasing incessantly in our imagination the thickness of the thread or string and passing to the limit, we obtain a geometric object called a line which has no thickness at all. A line is defined in *Elements* as "breadthless length" (Definition II) and a *straight* line is defined as a line which "lies evenly with the points on itself" (Definition IV).

Thus, a straight line as defined by Euclid appears first as a finite one-dimensional object. It has length but no area or volume, so that it is what we now call a *segment* of a straight line. But, using this definition in his first two axioms, Euclid develops further the concept of a straight line as follows:

AXIOM I: *A straight line can be drawn from any point to any point.*

AXIOM II: *A straight line may be produced, that is, extended indefinitely in a straight line.*

The second axiom, together with Definition IV, ensures the uniqueness of a straight line drawn between two given points, the existence of which is postulated by the first axiom. Since a straight line can be extended in both directions in a straight line, if it is extended in *two* different straight lines, these two straight lines would have a common segment. Furthermore, "a straight line lies evenly with the points on itself," so that both lines would have to lie evenly with the points of this common segment and would consequently be indistinguishable.

Thus, the meaning of the first two axioms is clear: two given points define one and only one straight line. In other words, through two given points can be drawn only one straight line. In these axioms, a point appears as the fundamental element, and a straight line is definable in terms of points because a straight line is determined completely by any two of its points. Moreover, the second axiom ascribes to a straight line an infinite length. It asserts that, given a finite segment of a straight line, this segment can be extended *indefinitely*. Thus, the process of its extension cannot be stopped and, as result, a straight line extends infinitely in both directions. There is no last point on the line in either direction.

Here, at the very first step of geometry, we meet again the idea of infinity. Moreover, the infinity implied in the concept of a straight line of infinite length must be an *absolute* infinity since, if, to the contrary, the straight line is considered in the process of its extension only (potential infinity), as it is in the second axiom, the concept of straight line becomes vague and not well determined: a line forever increasing is a variable and, therefore, indetermined object. We can obtain the entire and complete straight line, considering it as a perfectly determined entity, only when the line does not vary more, the effect of its endless successive extensions according to the second axiom being already *exhausted*. In other words, if we want to form the static and well-determined concept of a straight line as an entity in itself, we must apply the same passage to the limit that we used with the infinite sequence of integers, creating the first transfinite number aleph-null. Refusing to follow in our thinking the endless extension of a line step by step, we jump in our imagination to the final result of this infinite but denumerable chain of finite extensions and, thus, obtain at the limit a perfectly *static* image of an actually infinite and well-determined straight line.

Another important fact is implicitly contained in the first two axioms: two distinct straight lines cannot have more than one point in common, for if they had two common points they could not be different lines, since two given points define one and only one straight line through them. Given two straight lines which belong to the same plane (we do not discuss solid geometry here), two cases are possible: these two lines intersect each other and thus define, considered together, a unique point, their point of intersection; or, being extended indefinitely in both directions, the two lines do not meet one another in either direction. By Euclid's Definition XXIII, two straight lines which,

thus produced, do not meet are called *parallel* straight lines. We shall now
consider the former case.

Dedekind's Axiom of Continuity. Euclid implicitly assuemd the existence of
a common point when two straight lines intersect. In modern geometry,
this assumption is explicitly formulated as a separate Axiom of Continuity:

DEDEKIND'S AXIOM. *If all points of a straight line fall into two classes such
that every point of the first class lies to the left of every point of the second
class, then there exists one and only one point on the line which separates all
the other points into two classes.*

The existence of a point common to two intersecting lines can be deduced
from this axiom. If AB and CD are two intersecting lines (Fig. 2), the points
on the line AB fall into two classes: by definition, points to the left of the
line CD will be said to belong to the first class (such is, for example, the
point A), while points to the right of CD will form the second class. Every
point of the first class is to the left of every point of the second class. Therefore, applying the axiom of continuity, we are sure that a point X exists on
the line AB separating both classes, so that every point to the left of X belongs to the first class and every point of AB to the right of X is a member
of the second class.

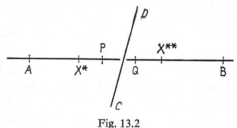

Fig. 13.2

To prove that the point X lies on the line CD, we have to show that it can
be neither to the right nor to the left of this line. Assume to the contrary
that X lies on AB to the left of CD, at X*, for example, and choose on AB
a point P between X* and CD. This point P must belong to the second class
since it is to the right of X*, but being to the left of CD it must also belong
to the first class. We obtain a contradiction, and this contradiction proves
that the point X cannot be to the left of CD. Were it to the right of CD,
at X**, for instance, the choice of a point Q between X** and CD would
lead again to a contradiction. Therefore, being neither to the left nor to the
right of CD, the point X lies on the line CD, and, thus, the existence of a
point X common to two intersecting lines AB and CD is proved.

Dedekind's Axiom formulates explicitly an important structural feature of the straight line, namely, the perfect density of the continuum of points forming the straight line. The points are so dense on the line that there are no gaps whatever between them. This is why two lines cannot cross each other without having a common intersection point. The idea that a straight line is continuous is familiar to us. The axiom of continuity defines the precise content of this idea, transforming it into the concept of a *continuous* straight line.

The lack of this axiom in *Elements* constitutes a very important logical omission, for without this axiom it is not at all certain that two intersecting lines always define a point, and no geometry is possible without this fundamental fact.

Relations of Incidence and Non-Incidence

A point and a straight line can form only two configurations: they may lie outside each other or be *incident* with each other. They are said to be incident when the point belongs to the line, the line passing through the point. The relation of incidence can also take place for a point and a plane or for a straight line and a plane: a point (a line) and a plane are incident with each other if the point (the line) belongs to the plane, the plane passing through the point (the line). Modern geometry uses the term *incident* instead of the expressions "belongs to," "is on," or "passes through" because the relation referred to is symmetrical with respect to elements involved in it, while the latter expressions ascribe an active role to one of the two elements in incidence.

The concept of non-incidence is related intrinsically to the construction of simple elements. If two given points are incident with each other, they coincide and cannot define a straight line. Given two *non-incident* points, they define a perfectly determined straight line incident with them. Let us consider now a straight line and a point. If they are incident, nothing more can be said, but a straight line and a point non-incident with each other define one and only one *plane* incident with them. When we say that a point P is non-incident with a straight line AB, we postulate the existence of a space surrounding the straight line and having therefore more than one dimension. In other words, we think of the non-incident point and line as immersed in a higher space S. To define the plane P–AB incident with the point P and the straight line AB, we draw all the straight lines incident with the point P and any one of the points on the line AB. The set of all these straight lines can be described as the totality of all positions of a variable straight line MP (Fig. 3) which passes through the fixed point P while the second point M slides on the line AB. When M describes the whole line AB, the line PM performs half a revolution about the point P and sweeps the whole plane P–AB, so that this plane can be defined as the set of all straight lines incident with the point P and any one of the points on the line AB. Thus, adding to a straight line a point non-incident with it, we create a plane containing the line and the point. In other words, as the non-incidence of two points defines one and only one straight line, the non-incidence of a point and line defines one and only one plane.

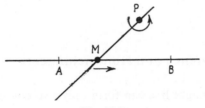

Fig. 13.3

Introducing the notation s_k to denote a space of k dimensions, we can describe a straight line as a one-dimensional space s_1, a plane being the two-dimensional space s_2. Thus, our result just obtained can be formulated as follows: a point and a one-dimensional space s_1 non-incident with each other define a two-dimensional space s_2.

We consider now a point and a plane s_2. They may be incident with each other or they may lie outside of each other. If they are non-incident, they belong to a higher space whose number of dimensions exceeds two. In this higher space, a point and a plane non-incident with each other define one and only one three-dimensional space which contains both point and plane. Indeed, joining all the points lying in the given plane s_2 by straight lines to the given point and considering the continuum of points incident with all these straight lines, we obtain all the points of the three-dimensional space s_3, to which belong the given point and the given plane s_2 non-incident with each other. Thus, again a point and a two-dimensional space s_2 non-incident with each other define a three-dimensional space s_3, so that the relation of non-incidence between a point and a space s_2 leads to the definition of a space s_3 whose number of dimensions is one unit greater than that of the space s_2 non-incident with the point. By adding to s_2 an extraneous point non-incident with it, we create s_3.

Now what can be said about the relation of non-incidence between a point P and a three-dimensional space s_3? Human imagination is strongly influenced by the idea of physical space. Our mind can project its perceptions only into a three-dimensional space, that is, for us, an event takes place always in some part of the three-dimensional *physical* space in which we feel ourselves immersed. In studying geometry, we must first of all get rid of this feeling and liberate our thinking and imagination from limitations imposed on our mind by the obsession of physical space.

The abstract continuum of dimensionless points forming a geometrical space can have any number of dimensions. If it is one-dimensional, a line is formed and it can be considered as existing by itself, without being thought of as immersed in a higher space, such as s_2 (plane) or s_3 (our three-dimensional space). A two-dimensional continuum of points s_2 is a plane, and, again, it may be considered in itself without being thought of as a part of the three-dimensional space s_3.

A three-dimensional space s_3 is an abstraction, as are a straight line s_1 and a plane s_2. It is a fiction created by our imagination and, as such, can be conceived of as lying completely outside of a given point. In other words, a point P may be incident or may not be incident with a given space s_3, as is the case with a point and straight line or a point and plane. The relation of incidence is in no way more compulsory for a point and a space s_3 than it is for a point and a straight line or a point and a plane.

The assumption that P lies outside of s_3 locates this point somewhere in a more extensive space which contains both P and s_3 and of which s_3 is a part only. This *higher* (that is, more extensive) space must have at least four dimensions. We assume that P and s_3 non-incident with each other are immersed in a four-dimensional space s_4. Such a space s_4 cannot be visualized because our sense of vision ascribes to the physical space around us three dimensions only, so that we cannot "see" more than three-dimensional objects. But a continuum of points s_4 can be built up with the aid of the same construction which we used to prove that a point and a plane define an s_3, provided they are not incident.

Given an s_3 and a point P outside it, we can join any point M lying in s_3 to P by an infinite straight line PM passing through these two points P and M. It is possible because, according to the first two axioms, two distinct points define one and only one straight line. On the line PM there is only one point, namely, the point M, which belongs to the three-dimensional space s_3. If there were two points on PM which were in s_3, the whole line would belong to the space s_3, and this is impossible because, as we know, the straight line PM passes through the point P which is outside s_3. Therefore, the line PM intersects the three-dimensional space s_3 at the only point M, all the rest of its points being located outside of s_3.

This fact proves incidentally that a three-dimensional space immersed in a higher space has no thickness at all in this higher space because it is pierced by a straight line in just one point. This circumstance is analogous to the fact that a plane has no thickness when considered as a part of the three-dimensional space in which it is immersed. To a hypothetical, perfectly flat, two-dimensional, thinking being, living in a plane world, our assertion that his universe-plane has no thickness for us would seem as unrealistic as the statement just formulated about our three-dimensional space s_3 may seem to us. Having not the slightest idea about the existence of the third dimension, this hypothetical being would be reluctant to believe that his world has no thickness since it would contradict his experience. The fact that a three-dimensional space s_3 has no thickness when considered as a part of s_4 also contradicts our experience, but the important thing is that geometry is an abstract science in no way limited by our experience and must, therefore, be accepted, even if its truth contradicts our experience.

Thus, a straight line imbedded in a four-dimensional space s_4 and non-incident with a three-dimensional space s_3 belonging also to s_4 intersects the space s_3 in a point and is, therefore, divided by s_3 into two half-lines separated by the space s_3. We now join *every* point lying in s_3 to the point P by a straight line. We obtain as many straight lines through P as points in s_3. The set S of all these straight lines can be described as the totality of all positions of a variable straight line MP which turns around the fixed point P as on a pivot when the variable point M sweeps the whole space s_3. Consider now the continuum of points formed by points on all these straight lines belonging to the set S. This continuum of points is a space in which is located s_3 as its part. This higher space has four dimensions: it is divided by the three-dimensional space s_3 into two halves since through every point of s_3 pass straight lines belonging to this higher space. Given any point Q in the new space, we can characterize its location by joining it to some known point K of s_3 and measuring the distance KQ. The position of Q inside s_3 is fixed by the values of three coordinates of K, and the distance KQ is the fourth datum, so that the location of Q inside the new space can be characterized by four numbers, coordinates of Q. Therefore, the new space is an s_4, that is, a four-dimensional space.

Thus, given a point and a three-dimensional space, they define one and only one four-dimensional space, provided they are not incident with each other. This process of recurrent definition of higher spaces can be continued, and nothing can stop it: if a point and an s_4 are non-incident, they define one and only one five-dimensional space s_5; a non-incident point and s_5 define one and only one s_6, etc. Our discussion of the relation of non-incidence leads us to the following generalization of the first two axioms of Euclid: *A point and an N-dimensional space s_N considered together and non-incident define one and only one $(N+1)$ dimensional space s_{N+1}.*

This proposition, which can be proved by mathematical induction and with the aid of the same construction we used for $N = 2$ and $N = 3$, is, as a matter of fact, a recurrent definition of spaces of all dimensions, beginning even with the case of the straight line for which N must be taken equal to zero. A point indeed may be called s_0 because the subscript zero means no dimensions at all and a point is the unique dimensionless element in geometry. Therefore, the symbol s_0 denotes a space with no dimension, and such a space degenerates into a point. For $N = 0$, our proposition reads as follows: two non-incident points define one and only one s_1, that is, a straight line.

Collinear and Coplanar Points

A straight line is completely determined by any two of its points. Therefore, the definition of a plane by non-incident point and line can be rephrased as follows: *Three points define a plane, provided they are not incident with the same straight line.*

Given three points, they can form three different configurations consisting each of a line and a point. If all three points are incident with the same straight line, they are called *collinear*, and, in this case, they cannot define a plane. But, if they do not belong to the same straight line, in which case they are called *non-collinear*, they define three different straight lines and a plane incident with these three straight lines. Since three non-collinear points always define a plane, we can say that three non-collinear points are always *coplanar*, which means that they belong to one and the same plane.

The situation is different when *four* points are considered. They may be collinear, and then they do not define anything except the line to which they belong. If four points are non-collinear and, thus, define at least a plane, they may be coplanar. In this case, they define the plane to which all four belong and nothing else. But, given four distinct points, in general they are not coplanar, each one of them being non-incident with the plane defined by three other points. Such a group of four *non-coplanar* points defines a three-dimensional space, because any three of them define a plane, and this plane, considered together with the fourth point (which is non-incident with the plane because otherwise the four points would be coplanar), define an s_3. Thus, rephrasing the definition of s_3 by non-incident point and plane we can say that four non-coplanar points define one and only one three-dimensional space s_3 to which they all belong.

Given *five* points, it may happen that all five belong to the same three-dimensional space s_3 (in which case they are said to be *cospatial*), but it may be also that any one of them is non-incident with the three-dimensional space defined by the four other points. In this important case of five *non-cospatial* points, a four-dimensional space s_4 is defined as the only s_4 to which belong all five given points.

In general, it can be stated that given $N + 1$ distinct points which do not belong together to the same $(N - 1)$dimensional space s_{N-1}, they define an N-dimensional space s_N which contains all $N + 1$ points.

We postpone the study of three- and four-dimensional configurations which dwell in an s_3 or s_4, our aim here being only to emphasize the existence of multidimensional spaces in pure geometry and to show their relation to the concept of non-incidence. We return now to plane geometry.

Do Parallel Straight Lines Define a Point?

We saw that, just as two points define only one straight line, two *intersecting* straight lines define one and only one point. In other words, each two points are incident with a unique straight line, and each two lines are incident with a unique point, *provided they are not parallel*. What strikes us in this proposition is the limitation "provided they are not parallel," qualifying the case of two straight lines, whereas there is no exception for two points. Without this limitation, the roles played by a point and by a straight line at the very beginnings of geometry would be identical because to the axiomatic definition of a straight line by two points would correspond the similar definition of a point by two straight lines.

The enormous advantage of such a logical duality is clear. Suppose it is established. In general, one fundamental element only is sufficient to build up all geometric configurations. In plane geometry, it may be a point or a straight line: if a point is considered as the fundamental element, straight lines are defined as pairs of points; if a straight line is chosen as the fundamental element, points are defined as pairs of straight lines. All this, of course, presupposes that a point and a line may play in geometry the same logical role. If so, they can be interchanged in every logical deduction without destroying its logical validity, so that every theorem becomes transformable into another theorem, its dual companion, by simple replacement in its enunciation of the word "point" by "straight line" and *vice versa.*

It must be pointed out that a perfect duality with complete interchangeability of point and straight line is unattainable in Euclidean geometry. We will see that the perfect duality is incompatible with the existence of similar figures, having the same shape (and, therefore, equal corresponding angles) but different size. Or, the existence of similar figures is the most characteristic and distinctive feature of Euclidean geometry since the two non-Euclidean geometries, those of Lobachevsky and Riemann, have no similar figures at all.

Although perfect duality is realized only in non-Euclidean geometries, nevertheless a kind of restricted duality can also be discovered in Euclidean geometry, provided that the limitation mentioned above and related to the case of two parallel straight lines is removed. We shall, therefore, discuss more closely Euclid's definition of parallelism.

Precisely what does it mean that two parallels "do not meet when extended indefinitely in both directions"? In this sentence, the word "indefinitely" means a potentially infinite sequence of successive extensions, a finite segment of a straight line undergoing a finite extension at each step. If we imagine a motionless observer located at some fixed point in the plane of two parallel lines, for this observer the successive extensions are performed, at every step of their infinite sequence, at a finite distance from him, and everything remains, therefore, in the finite region of the plane, the term "finite region" meaning all points which are at a finite distance from the observer. The same observer is always introduced implicitly under the guise of a fixed point O, the origin of distances or the origin of coordinates. We prefer to state explicitly his existence in geometry, the discrimination between a finite region and a region at infinity of a plane being based on the introduction of an observer.

Thus, Euclid's definition of parallelism implies that no point common to two parallel straight lines can be found in the *finite* region of the plane. What happens to two parallel straight lines at infinity is neither stated nor implied in their definition. The important conclusion we can draw from this discussion is that we are free to fix the behavior of parallel lines at an infinite distance from the observer as we choose, provided we respect the symmetry which characterizes the configuration formed by two parallel lines and their common perpendicular. In other words, the behavior of two parallel lines at infinity to the right must be the same as their behavior at infinity to the left because two parallel lines are symmetric with respect to their common perpendicular.

Right Angle. Perpendicular

We are using a commonly known term, "perpendicular", which we must now define. Any point O incident with a straight line L infinite in two directions divides L into two half-lines called *rays*, so that a ray is infinite in one direction only. Consider two rays belonging to the same line and separated by their common extremity O, such as OA and OB (Fig. 4a). Rotating one of them around the point O clockwise or counterclockwise through 180° (half a revolution), we make it coincide with the other ray. Likewise, a straight line AB divides the whole plane into two half-planes. Any two points P, Q of a half-plane bounded by AB can be joined by a continuous path of finite length which does not cross AB, but no two points lying in two different half-planes separated by AB can be joined by such a path, and every line passing through such two points, M and N for example, necessarily crosses the line AB.

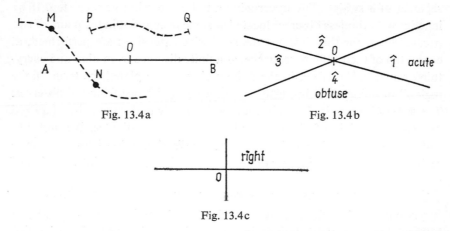

Fig. 13.4a   Fig. 13.4b

Fig. 13.4c

Two straight lines intersecting at O divide their plane into four infinite regions, each of which is bounded by two rays emanating from O (Fig. 4b). Such a region is called *angle*, the rays are two *sides* of the angle, and their common point is its *vertex*. The four angles around their common vertex O and denoted by $\hat{1}, \hat{2}, \hat{3}, \hat{4}$ (Fig. 4b) may be grouped into two pairs of opposite angles. Two opposite angles *(vertical angles)* are equal: $\hat{1} = \hat{3}$ as well as $\hat{2} = \hat{4}$. To justify this, we rotate one of them through 180° (half a revolution) around its vertex. It will then be seen to coincide with the other.

In general, two adjacent angles, such as $\hat{1}$ and $\hat{2}$, or $\hat{2}$ and $\hat{3}$, are unequal, but their sum is always a half-plane, which is also considered as an angle, notwithstanding the fact that the rays forming its two sides belong to the same straight line. An angle equal to a half-plane is called a *straight* angle, so that the angular space around a point in a plane is equal to two straight angles. Since we count 360° around a point, the measure of a straight angle in degrees is equal to 180°.

If two intersecting straight lines divide the plane in such a way that adjacent angles are equal and, therefore, since vertical angles are equal, all four angles are equal, these lines are said to be *perpendicular*, and each of the four equal angles is called a *right* angle (Fig. 4c). In other words, an angle bounded by two perpendicular rays and equal to a quarter of the plane is a right angle and it is equal to half a straight angle, that is, to 90°.

Two intersecting non-perpendicular lines form two unequal pairs of equal vertical angles, the angles of the one pair being greater and the angles of the other pair being smaller than a right angle. An angle greater than a right angle is called *obtuse*, an angle smaller than a right angle is called *acute*.

Fifth Postulate and Playfair's Axiom

Before studying the behavior of two parallel lines at infinity, it is logical to prove, first of all, their existence. Euclid's definition of parallel lines does not establish their existence. An explicit statement that parallels do exist in Euclidean geometry is Proposition 27 of the First Book of *Elements*, namely,

THEOREM I: *If a straight line intersecting two other straight lines makes the alternate interior angles equal to one another, the two straight lines are parallel to one another.*

In Fig. 4d, the straight line AB, called *transversal*, makes with two lines, AC and BD, four *interior* angles $\hat{1}, \hat{2}, \hat{3}, \hat{4}$. Their sum is equal to four right angles, i.e., $\hat{1} + \hat{2} + \hat{3} + \hat{4} = 360°$ since $\hat{1} + \hat{4} = \hat{3} + \hat{2} = 180°$. The angles

2 Kogbetliantz

$\hat{1}$ and $\hat{3}$ on the one hand and $\hat{2}$ and $\hat{4}$ on the other hand are called *alternate interior* angles.

Theorem I assumes that $\hat{1} = \hat{3}$ or $\hat{2} = \hat{4}$, which does not make a difference since $\hat{1} + \hat{4} = \hat{3} + \hat{2}$, so that $\hat{1} = \hat{3}$ and $\hat{2} = \hat{4}$ imply each other.

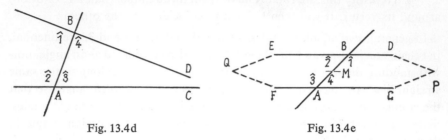

Fig. 13.4d   Fig. 13.4e

To prove Theorem I, we use the indirect method, that is, we assume, to the contrary, that the lines FAC and EBD, cut by the transversal AB, intersect to the right of AB in some point P at a finite distance from AB (see Fig. 4e) and denote by M the midpoint of the segment AB, so that AM = MB. Now rotate Fig. 4e about the point M through 180°. This rotation brings the intersection point P into a new position Q to the left of AB and interchanges the points A and B and the straight lines FAC and EBD because the alternate interior angles are equal. After the rotation, the ray AC coincides with the ray BE, and the ray BD coincides with the ray AF, so that it becomes clear that the rays BE and AF must intersect at Q to the left of AB, if AC and BD intersect at P to the right of AB. Therefore, the existence of an intersection point P of two straight lines FC and ED to the right of AB would entail their intersection to the left of AB in a second common point Q. This, however, is impossible because two distinct lines cannot have more than one common point. The same reasoning proves that the existence of an intersection point to the left of AB entails a second intersection to the right of AB.

Therefore, if the alternate interior angles are equal, the straight lines FC and ED cannot have an intersection point either to the left or to the right of AB, that is, they are parallel. Thus, the theorem is proved. We apply this result to the following question: Given a point E and a line AC (see Fig. 5), non-incident with each other, draw through E a parallel to the line AC. Drawing through E any line EF which intersects AC in a point B, we form at B an angle EBC. Now we can construct at the point E an angle BEK equal to the angle EBC. The straight line KEH will be parallel to AC since the alternate interior angles EBC and BEK are equal. Therefore, through a given point non-incident with a given line at least one parallel can be drawn.

This important conclusion does not preclude the existence of many other straight lines passing through the point E and non-intersecting the straight line AC. The behavior of two parallel straight lines at infinity depends on the choice between two equally possible postulates: (1) a *unique* parallel through E to AC in both directions, to the right and to the left, or (2) *two* different parallels, both of which pass through E and are parallel to AC, but each of which is parallel to AC in one direction only, so that one must distinguish between a righthand parallel and a lefthand parallel to AC.

Euclid's choice was the *unique* parallel through a given point to a given line, and this choice fixed the most important and characteristic properties of the Euclidean plane and of Euclidean geometry. Case (2) corresponds, as we will show later, to a kind of non-Euclidean geometry which is called hyperbolic or Lobachevsky's geometry.

Euclid's choice is formulated in his famous Fifth Postulate, which reads:

FIFTH POSTULATE. *If a straight line intersecting two other straight lines makes the sum of interior angles on the same side less than two right angles, the two straight lines, if extended indefinitely, intersect on that side on which are the angles with sum less than two right angles.*

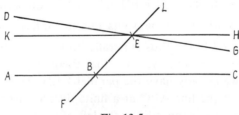

Fig. 13.5

The uniqueness of the parallel is easily deduced from this postulate. Consider (Fig. 5) two parallel lines AC and KH cut by a transversal FL at points B and E, respectively, and having a sum of interior angles equal to 180°. Suppose that there is a second parallel to AC through E and draw it as a straight line DEG distinct from KH. It cuts the first parallel KH at the point E, and, therefore, on one side of the transversal FL, it is between the lines AC and KH, while on the other side it is separated from AC by the line KH. On the side where DG is between KH and AC (in Fig. 5, on the right side), the angle $\widehat{GEB}$ it makes with the transversal EB is a part of the angle $\widehat{HEB}$, so that $\widehat{GEB} < \widehat{HEB}$. Therefore, the sum of two interior angles on this side, $\widehat{GEB} + \widehat{CBE}$, is less than the sum $\widehat{HEB} + \widehat{CBE} = 180°$. Applying the Fifth Postulate, we come to a contradiction: a parallel DG must intersect the line to which it is parallel. This contradiction proves that our initial assumption, the existence of more than one parallel to AC through E, is incompatible with the Fifth Postulate: granted the Fifth Postulate, there can be only one parallel to a given line through a given point non-incident with the given line.

The uniqueness of parallel was shown by Proclus (fifth century A.D.) to be equivalent to Euclid's Fifth Postulate, either statement being deducible from the other. This substitute for the Fifth Postulate is known as

PLAYFAIR'S AXIOM. *Through a given point not more than one parallel can be drawn to a given line non-incident with this point.*

To justify the equivalence of Playfair's Axiom and the Fifth Postulate, it remains to deduce the Fifth Postulate from the Axiom. We consider again Fig. 5. Given two straight lines AC and DG and a transversal FL such that the sum of the two interior angles to the right of FL, $\overparen{CBE} + \overparen{BEG}$, is less than two right angles, we replace the angle $\overparen{BEG}$ by a greater angle $\overparen{BEH}$ such that the sum $\overparen{CBE} + \overparen{BEH}$ is equal to two right angles and draw through E a fourth straight line KEH. This straight line makes with FL an interior angle $\overparen{KEB}$, which is equal to its alternate interior angle $\overparen{CBE}$: $\overparen{KEB}$ = 180° − BEH = $\overparen{CBE}$ and thus is parallel to the line ABC.

Applying Playfair's Axiom, we state that there can be no other parallel to ABC because we already have the parallel KEH. Thus, the straight line DEG *must* intersect the line ABC at a finite distance from FL. The intersection point, moreover, cannot lie to the left of the transversal FL because in this direction the secant line DEG is separated from ABC by the parallel KEH, which does not meet ABC. Thus, the intersection point is to the right of FL, that is, on the side where two interior angles have a sum less than two right angles. We see, therefore, that the Fifth Postulate may be deduced from Playfair's Axiom.

Now, if a transversal makes a right angle with one of two parallels, being perpendicular to it, this transversal will be perpendicular to the other parallel as well, because the sum of two interior angles cannot be different from two right angles. Thus, the symmetry displayed by two parallel straight lines with respect to their common perpendicular is proved.

Parallel as the Limit of a Secant

To determine the behavior of two parallel lines at infinity, we consider two intersecting lines: a fixed line CD and a variable straight line HBM, passing through a fixed point B and intersecting the first straight line at a variable point M (Fig. 6). Dropping from the point B a perpendicular BA on the fixed straight line CD, we form at A a right angle BAD. Through the point B on the secant line HM passes the unique parallel EBF to CD making a right angle ABF with the transversal AB. As the point M moves on the line CD to the right, the secant line HBM rotates counterclockwise about the point B, approaching the parallel EBF. At the limit, when the point M is at infinity to the right of A, becoming, thus, the *point at infinity* of the line CD, the acute angle $\widehat{ABM}$ becomes equal to the right angle $\widehat{ABF}$, and the secant HBM coincides with and is transformed into the parallel EBF.

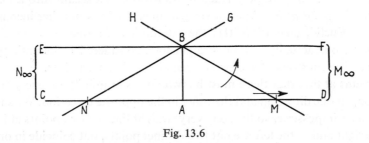

Fig. 13.6

Hence, a parallel may be considered as the limit of a secant. But a secant, in all its positions, always has a common point M with the base line CD. When we pass to the limit, rotating the secant, only the *position* of M on the line CD changes, its *existence* being independent of the position of the secant. Therefore, the passage to the limit can change only the position of M and cannot make it vanish. At the limit, when the secant becomes a parallel to CD, it does not lose its common point with CD. The only difference between a secant and a parallel consists in the location of the point common with CD with respect to the observer: whereas for the secant this common point is at a finite distance from the point A (that is, in fact from the observer at A), in the case of the parallel, the common point is at an infinite distance from A (that is, from the observer at A). If we change our point of reference A, shifting our observer to the point at infinity where the point M now is, he will see in this region at infinity of the plane two *intersecting* lines which are the same two lines CD and EF, parallel to each other for an observer at A.

Euclid's discrimination between two intersecting and two parallel straight lines is based on the elimination of the region at infinity of the essentially infinite Euclidean plane. Or, the unique difference between the finite region and the region at infinity is indeed their relative location with respect to the reference point around which is concentrated our attention, that is, the attention of an observer. Thus, the refusal to consider and study the behavior of geometric configurations at infinity is a disguised introduction into geometry of a human element, the observer.

Point at Infinity

We must emphasize once more that a new element is introduced by the passage to the limit we performed in transforming a secant into a parallel, namely the *point at infinity* of a straight line. There is nothing inconsistent because (Euclid, Definition III) "the extremities of a line are points," and, therefore, our actually infinite straight line, considered in its entirety as a static entity, must also have two extremities which are points.

It seems at first that there must be two points at infinity on every straight line, one in one direction and the other in the opposite direction. We shall see that this is impossible, so that on every straight line the two points at infinity to the right and to the left are not two distinct points, but coincide in one and the same *unique* point at infinity.

To show that the introduction of the point at infinity by passage to the limit implies its uniqueness we consider (Fig. 6) two symmetric secant lines HBM and GBN such that the variable and increasing segments AM and AN always remain equal, AM = AN, notwithstanding their variation. Letting AN and AM increase together, the point N moves to the left and, at the limit, disappears from our sight into infinity on the left, while M moves to the right and disappears into infinity on the right.

Both secants HM and GN tend to the unique parallel EF, and, at the limit, when M and N disappear away from sight and become points at infinity of the line CD, the two secants coincide with the parallel EF which is thus their common ultimate position, i.e., their limit. Denoting the ultimate positions of points M and N by M_∞ and N_∞, respectively, we ascertain that each one of these two points at infinity M_∞, N_∞ is incident with *both* parallel lines CD and EF, which, by hypothesis, are two distinct straight lines.

But, as we know, the first two axioms imply that no two distinct straight lines can have more than one point in common. Therefore, the points M_∞ and N_∞ cannot be distinct and must coincide in order to avoid a contradiction. We are thus led to accept the identity of two points at infinity, that is, the *uniqueness* of the point at infinity on every straight line.

We complete now the definition of a straight line by introducing on every straight line its unique point at infinity. This point can be reached either from the left, appearing then as the point at infinity to the right, or from the right, appearing then as the point at infinity to the left.

The introduction of a unique point at infinity on every straight line removes the limitation "provided they are not parallel," discussed above, and we can state that any two straight lines (naturally, if coplanar) define a point in complete analogy to the definition of a straight line by two points. If two lines are parallel, their common point is at infinity and, conversely, if two straight lines have their common point at infinity, they are parallel, the fact that two distinct straight lines have the same point at infinity being thus equivalent to their parallelism.

On the other hand, what two parallel lines have in common for an observer to whom they appear as parallel is their *direction*. They are parallel for this observer precisely because they have the same direction. Thus, the introduction of the point at infinity is another way of characterizing the direction of a straight line. Two infinite sets, the set of all directions and the set of all points at infinity on all straight lines of the Euclidean plane, are related to each other by a one-to-one correspondence: prescribing the incidence of a straight line with a given point at infinity, that is, choosing its point at infinity, we in fact determine the direction of this straight line and, *vice versa*, all parallel lines having the same direction have in common the same point at infinity. Choosing a direction, we in fact determine the point at infinity.

Thus, we complete the fundamental plane which contains the configurations of plane geometry, adding to the ordinary points located in its finite region the set of all points at infinity in all directions. In such a completed plane, any two straight lines, parallel or not, always define one and only one point, which lies in the finite region of the fundamental plane if the two lines intersect each other, but which is one of the points at infinity if the two lines are parallel.

Do two Points always Define a Line?

The introduction of points at infinity, however, necessitates a review of the proposition "any two points define one and only one straight line", because this statement was originally made only for two points belonging to the finite region of the plane, that is, for two ordinary points. Euclid did not consider points at infinity, but we do and, therefore, we have to study the meaning of the proposition "two points define a straight line" when (1) one of two given points is a point at infinity, the other lying in the finite region of the plane, and (2) both given points are points at infinity.

CASE (1). How can we construct a straight line incident with a given point at infinity and another given point which is at a finite distance from the observer? When a point at infinity is considered as a *given* point, it can mean only one thing: it is a point at infinity of a straight line whose direction is known. Any straight line incident with this point at infinity will have the same direction and thus will be parallel to a line having the same and known direction. Drawing a line L having this known direction, we conclude that a straight line incident with an ordinary point P and with the point at infinity on the line L can be drawn as a parallel to the line L passing through the point P. This problem of construction, solved in *Elements* admits of only one solution, and, therefore can be only one straight line incident with a given point at infinity and an ordinary point.

Euclid's solution of this construction problem as well as our introduction of the unique point at infinity are based on the assumption of a unique parallel to a given line through a given point. The fact that two given points, one of which is a point at infinity, define one and only one straight line is also a corollary of this assumption, the validity of which is based, as we saw, on the Fifth Postulate of Euclid.

CASE (2). We pass now to the study of the second case, where both given points are points at infinity. Since to each of them corresponds a direction, no ordinary straight line, that is, a straight line passing through the finite region of the plane, can be defined by two distinct points at infinity because every ordinary straight line has only one direction and passes through one point at infinity only.

Nevertheless, two distinct points at infinity do define a perfectly determined straight line, a straight line of a very special kind: all its points are points at infinity. This special straight line is entirely rejected into the infinite

part of the plane and has no part of it in the finite region. To show its existence, we will apply again the passage to the limit. Consider (Fig. 7) two
ordinary straight lines AO and BO intersecting at an ordinary point O. Draw
through the point M on AO and the point N on BO a straight line MN and
suppose that the points M and N move on their respective lines away from O,
the distances OM and ON remaining equal and increasing without limit,
$OM = ON \to \infty$. The straight line MN moves away from O, and, when
at the limit the points M and N disappear into infinity and become points at
infinity M_∞, N_∞ on their respective lines, the line $M_\infty N_\infty$ they will define is
rejected into infinity in its entirety. For, if there were an ordinary point (call
it Q) on this line, then one and the same line $M_\infty N_\infty$ should be parallel to AO
and to BO ($QM_\infty \parallel AO$ and $QN_\infty \parallel BO$), which is impossible. In other words,
if two points of a straight line are points at infinity, all the points of this line
are points at infinity.

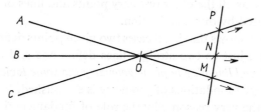

Fig. 13.7

The straight line just defined and introduced plays an important role in
plane geometry and is called the *straight line at infinity* of the plane. Just as
in plane geometry every straight line has its point at infinity, in solid geometry every plane has its straight line at infinity. And just as a line has only
one point at infinity, in every plane there is only one line at infinity. To show
this, we have to prove that the line at infinity of a plane contains all the
points at infinity of this plane. It is sufficient to prove that any point at infinity we choose is on the line $M_\infty N_\infty$.

Choose a determined point at infinity P_∞ and draw through the point O
(Fig. 7) a line CO for which P_∞ is its point at infinity. This line CO and the
line MN, whose ultimate position $M_\infty N_\infty$ is the line at infinity, intersect at
a point P. Now, when $M \to M_\infty$ and $N \to N_\infty$, the line MN becoming at the
limit the line at infinity $M_\infty N_\infty$, the point P also is rejected into infinity and
coincides with the point at infinity P_∞ of the line CO. Thus, the point at
infinity P_∞ we chose arbitrarily is shown to belong to the line at infinity
$M_\infty N_\infty$, which means that this line at infinity contains all the points at in-

finity which are its intersection points with all ordinary straight lines of the fundamental plane.

In geometry, the set of all points which verify the same geometrical condition is called a *locus*. Usingt his terminology, we can say that the straight line at infinity is the locus of all the points at infinity of the plane. It has in common with each ordinary straight line its point at infinity and, therefore, seems to be parallel to all ordinary straight lines simultaneously. This paradoxical conclusion is eliminated by observing that the concept of parallelism is well defined for, and can be applied to ordinary lines only because it characterizes their behavior in the *finite* region of the plane and the line at infinity does not pass through the finite region at all.

We see that the introduction of points at infinity entails the introduction of the line at infinity, and, thus, this line must be added to the rest of the straight lines of the plane. Points and line at infinity have the same mathematical existence as all the other ordinary points and lines of the plane: they are fictions created by our imagination.

This discussion shows that in all cases two given points define one and only one straight line, just as two straight lines define one and only one point. Therefore *point and line play in plane geometry the same logical role*, and the duality in the very foundations of geometry is established. It is of interest to throw light on the very reason why the role of fundamental element can be played by point or by straight line without any difference in the logical deductions and proofs of theorems.

Circle

This reason can be found by discussing Euclid's Third Axiom, which concerns the circle. The concept of circle is introduced in Definitions XV and XVI, which can be summed up as follows: a circle is a closed curve such that all the straight lines falling upon it from a point among those lying within this curve are equal, this point being called the center of the circle. In other words, a circle is the locus of points equidistant from an interior point called the center. We formulate now the Third Axiom:

AXIOM III: *A circle can be drawn with its center at any point and with any radius.*

The Euclidean plane is necessarily an infinite surface because it contains straight lines of infinite length. This important and characteristic feature of the Euclidean plane is implicitly contained in the Third Axiom also. There is no limitation whatsoever on the value of the *radius* (the distance from the center of the circle to any point on its circumference). The radius can be chosen as large as we please, and this is possible only if the plane is infinite.

We ask now what happens to a circle when its radius becomes infinite? To study the limiting form a circle as its radius increases without limit, we choose a fixed point C and consider all of the straight lines incident with the point C. Such a configuration is called a *pencil of lines (*or *sheaf of lines)*, and the point C is the *vertex* of the pencil. This concept of a pencil of lines is the dual companion of the concept of a straight line: transforming by duality a straight line with an infinite set (continuum) of points incident with this straight line, we obtain a point (dual image of a straight line) with all the straight lines incident with this point, that is, a pencil of lines because the dual image of a point is a straight line. Thus, a pencil of lines P with its vertex C and the points of a straight line *c* considered together with this straight line are, so to speak, two faces of the same coin. Every line *a* of the pencil is the dual image of a point A on the line and *vice versa*. The point C itself, vertex of the pencil, is the dual image of the straight line *c*. If the vertex of a pencil of straight lines moves away and finally disappears becoming a point at infinity, the pencil is gradually transformed into a family of parallel straight lines with this point at infinity as their common point. Thus, a family of parallel lines is a particular case of a pencil of lines, namely a pencil with its vertex at infinity. Disregarding this special case, it can be said that the vertex of a pencil divides every line of this pencil into two rays.

Marking on each ray of a pencil of lines a point at a distance R, the same for all rays, from the vertex C of the pencil, a circle with center C and radius R is obtained. We now let R increase without limit, the center C of the circle remaining fixed. As R increases, the points of the circumference move on the rays of our pencil further and further away from the center C and finally disappear into infinity, when at the limit R becomes infinite.

Thus, a circle of infinite radius whose center C lies in the finite region of the plane is the locus of all points at infinity in all directions. But we saw that this locus is a straight line, namely, the straight line at infinity. Therefore, a circle of infinite radius and with its center at an ordinary point is the straight line at infinity. We learn that *a circle of infinite radius is nothing more than a straight line.*

We now want to show that this transformation of a circle into a straight line when its radius becomes infinite is independent of the fact that, in our reasoning, the center of the circle remained fixed. Let us draw a circle of radius R which is tangent at the point B to a fixed straight line ABC (Fig. 8). The center O of this circle is on the perpendicular BD to the line AC and at a distance BO = R above the contact point B. In this statement, we assume a theorem which will be proved later, namely, that the radius of the contact point is perpendicular to the tangent line.

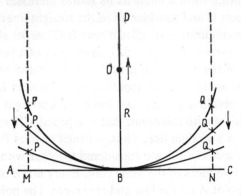

Fig. 13.8

Suppose now that the tangent line AC and the contact point B remain fixed, but that the center of the circle O climbs upwards along the line BD so that the radius $R = BO$ increases without limit. Choosing on the line AC an interval MBN symmetrical with respect to the contact point B and as large as we want, we find out that the arc PBQ of our variable circle above the segment MBN opens more and more as R increases, the points of the arc approaching those of the interval MBN.

In other words, the arc PBQ flattens out, and the amount of its bending decreases when the circle's radius increases. For a circle, the amount of bending (*curvature*) is the same everywhere on the circumference, and this is the reason why a circle, if rotated about its center, can slide on itself without any hindrance. We say that the circle is a curve of constant curvature, meaning that the curvature of a circle is the same at all of its points. No other curve has this property, which is a characteristic feature of the circle, and, therefore, no curve except the circle can slide on itself.

But a straight line possesses the same characteristic property as a circle because it can slide on itself without hindrance. A straight line, of course, has no curvature at all (it is *straight* at all of its points) and therefore it has, as a circle, a constant curvature. The difference between the constant curvature of a straight line and that of a circle consists precisely in the fact that a circle is a curve of a constant *non-zero* curvature, while a straight line has a constant curvature equal to zero.

Thus, the flattening of the circular arc PBQ as its radius increases shows that throughout the whole circle the curvature decreases when the radius increases. At the limit, when the center O disappears into infinity and the radius R becomes infinite, the arc PBQ coincides completely with the segment MN of the straight line AC. This means that the curvature of the arc PBQ vanishes at the limit and with it vanishes the curvature of the whole circle because it is the same everywhere on the circumference. Thus, the circle is transformed at the limit into the infinite straight line AC to which it remains tangent at B during the transformation. Therefore, it can be stated that a circle of infinite radius is a straight line which shows that straight line can be considered as a particular (limiting) case of a circle, namely a circle of infinite radius. A circle is a closed curve and therefore its limiting form, a straight line, must also be closed. This agrees well with the fact that a straight line possesses only one point at infinity which can be reached by going either to the left or to the right, in two opposite directions.

Another important particular case of a circle, obtained also as a limiting form, is the point. To transform a circle into a point, it is sufficient to let its radius R approach zero. At the limit, when R vanishes, all that remains of a circle is its center, that is, a point so that point is a circle of radius zero. Thus, point and straight line appear as two limiting forms of the same general curve, the circle. This is why both of them can play the same role of fundamental element, being interchangeable by duality.

The concept of a straight line of *infinite* length is based on the following arithmetical axiom:

AXIOM OF ARCHIMEDES: *Given two numbers n and m < n, there is always a finite integer N such that the multiple Nm of the smaller number is greater than the larger number n, that is, Nm > n.*

The geometrical equivalent of this axiom reads as follows:

Given two unequal segments of a straight line, there is always a finite multiple of the smaller such that it is greater than the larger segment.

In this geometric form, the axiom is formulated more than half a century before Archimedes in *Elements*, by Euclid, who took it over, like so many of his theorems, from Eudoxus of Cnidus.

It is this axiom which is implicitly used when we state that the endless repetition of extensions according to Axiom II increases the length of a line without limit, giving it as great a length as we want. To make our ideas precise, suppose that at every step of the extension process the length of the segment increases by k units of length. Given a length L as large as we want, we can extend our segment to a length greater than L precisely because the Axiom of Archimedes ensures the existence of a finite integer n such that $nk > L$.

The existence of such an integer n is based also on an important property of the geometrical space we use in Euclidean geometry. Indeed, the axiom of Archimedes alone cannot insure the inequality $nk > L$, and with it the infinitude of the straight line. There is something more to be postulated, if we want to be certain that the product nk is actually the measure of the total increase of length achieved by n successive extensions of k units of length each. The extension of a given segment is performed by adding at its end another segment of length k. To perform such additions many times, we have to move the length k at every extension-step farther and farther. In doing so, we implicitly postulate and use the invariance of length of a segment under motion in the plane because we accept as valid the hypothesis that a length k remains the same after we displace it.

Suppose, to the contrary, that each time we shift a segment of length H through k units of length, its length is reduced in a constant ratio r (where r is less than one) and becomes equal to rH. Extending a given segment k units each time and repeating the extensions an infinite number of times, we will never be able to realize a straight line of infinite length. Instead, the total extension achieved as the final result of an infinite number (aleph-null) operations will have a finite length of $k/(1 - r)$ units only because it will be equal to the sum of the following geometric progression:

$$k + kr + kr^2 + kr^3 + \cdots + kr^n + \cdots = k/(1 - r)$$

This example illustrates well the importance of the axiom of rigidity, that is, the axiom which ensures the indeformability of geometric configurations by displacements. This idea was not explicitly formulated by Euclid, but the meaning of his Fourth Axiom clearly seems to refer to the indeformability of angles by displacement:

AXIOM IV: *All right angles are equal to one another.*

In discussing this axiom, we state that, for Euclid, the equality of two figures can be proved only by their congruence. In the group of five axioms entitled „Common Notions" we find

COMMON NOTION IV: *Things which coincide with one another are equal.*

Therefore, the equality referred to in the Fourth Axiom implies the comparison of right angles constructed at different points by superposition only.

On the other hand, according to Euclid's definition of a right angle, the equality of all right angles in themselves is immediately evident (Definition X): *When a straight line set up on a straight line makes the adjacent angles equal to one another, each of the equal angles is right, and the straight line standing on the other is called perpendicular.* It follows from this definition that all right angles intrinsically, without comparison by displacement and congruence, must be equal because a right angle is a quarter of the whole plane, whatever the position of its vertex. Indeed, according to Definition VII, a plane is a surface which "lies evenly with the straight lines on itself" and "a straight line lies evenly with the points on itself" (Definition IV). Therefore, a plane lies evenly with the points on itself, which means that in all of its parts the plane has identical structure and is homogeneous. Thus, at every point there is the same angular space around it and its quarter (right angle) is the same at all points of the plane.

Thus, Euclid's reason for enunciating explicitly the Fourth Axiom can be understood only if we recall that for Euclid things are equal when they may be made to coincide. The true meaning of the Fourth Axiom consists in the statement that two right angles are *congruent,* that is, they coincide by superposition. But superposition necessitates a displacement so that the equality of two essentially identical figures after one of them was moved and superposed on the other proves that a displacement cannot generate a deformation or distortion of geometric figures.

Sometimes this principle is included in the system of axioms and stated as a separate axiom as follows:

AXIOM OF RIGIDITY: *A geometric figure may be moved to a new position without changing its size or shape.*

We observe that the Axiom of Rigidity was already used implicitly when we rotated geometric configurations. In modern geometry, the Euclidean method of superposition is no longer used. Displacements of geometric figures are not considered, and the concept of congruence is defined with the aid of a set of postulates of congruence, thus eliminating the need for superposition. In this book, we will not follow the modern geometers and will use Euclidean method of superposition based on the Axiom of Rigidity.

This axiom, together with the Axiom of Archimedes, insures the infinite length of a straight line. It is of interest to compare this abstract concept with our perception and measurement of physical length. We carry out our measurements with the aid of a meter or some other measuring instrument which we apply to the object whose length is to be measured. In other words, we use the method of superposition and are thus obliged to move and carry about our meter. In doing so, however, we do not care about what happens to it as result of the motion. Perhaps, when the meter is undergoing a displacement its real length changes (we could cite as an example the Lorentz transformation considered in physics), its length may depend on the position of the meter in the plane, or it may remain unchanged and not depend either on the location of the meter or on the velocity of its motion. In any case, the method of superposition works well and everything goes on just as if length were an invariant.

Suppose, for instance, that physical length does depend on velocity. Measurements by superposition are always performed at relative rest, when the meter and the length being measured have the same velocity. Consequently, they will change in the same ratio, and the fact of congruence will not depend on their motion. If the length of objects depends on the particular location, it means that there is a coefficient c attached to every location in the plane which characterizes the contraction $(c < 1)$ or the expansion $(c > 1)$ of an object when and because it occupies this particular location. Such coefficients define a physical property of *space*, and, therefore, they cannot depend on the objects, being the same for all of them. Because things will change equally if they are at the same location, we come again to the conclusion that the fact of congruence is independent of location, so that the definition of equality by superposition must work well in this case, too.

These considerations lead us to a surprising conclusion: we would be unable to discover the variations of length caused by motion if there were such variations because we ourselves and our instruments would then undergo the same variations. Returning to our example of the contraction of length in a definite ratio r by displacement, so that a unit of length at the origin O, when shifted through nk units, shrinks to a length of r^n units, we find that we would be unable to perceive this phenomenon because everything, our meter and ourselves included, would contract in the same ratio when displaced. A finite length equal to $k/(1 - r)$ would appear to our mind as infinite and our universe would seem to us an infinite world, being, in fact, limited by a sphere of finite radius $R = k/(1 - r)$.

The study of physical space does not belong to geometry. It is a problem of physics. But the comparison of a purely geometrical concept of an infinite straight line with our perception of finite physical length is interesting because it shows that a profound knowledge of all possible structures of abstract geometrical space is necessary for a better understanding of the more complex physical space. The history of physics proves that to every progress in geometry corresponds a development of our knowledge of physical world around us. The discovery of the structure of the solar system by Copernicus, Kepler, and Newton, Newton's law of universal gravitation included, was possible only because a pure mathematician, Apollonius, discovered purely theoretical geometrical properties of conical sections (ellipse, hyperbola, parabola). Another example is Einstein's Theory of Relativity, based on theoretical research by Riemann and Christoffel, who were studying abstract properties of geometrical space.

Straight Line's Segment as Shortest Path

The fact that the shortest path between two given points is a segment of straight line is so familiar to us that it seems to be a self-evident truth which does not depend on any assumption and does not need discussion.

Nevertheless, this idea is not as simple as it seems to be, and in what follows we will try to examine some of the implications included in it which reveal an important structural feature of the Euclidean Plane and Euclidean spaces in general. The full meaning of the proposition "a segment AB is the shortest path between two points A and B" will become clear when we complete our discussion of Euclid's concept of a straight line, analyzing what Euclid means by the word "evenly" used in the definitions of straight line (Definition IV):

A straight line is a line which lies evenly with the points on itself,

and of a plane (Definition VII):

A plane is a surface which lies evenly with the straight lines on itself.

In Definition IV, the word "line" means any line, that is, a curve. The word "evenly" may be interpreted in two ways. A curve which "lies evenly with the points on itself" may be considered as a plane curve viewed in its plane from the outside, and then the word "evenly" means perfect flatness, that is, the absence of curvature, the curve having the same direction at all its points. The logical impossibility of such an interpretation consists in the vicious circle which follows if we accept it. To view a straight line from the outside, we must locate it in a plane and therefore define first the concept of a plane independently from that of a straight line. But the definition of a

3 Kogbetliantz

plane follows that of a straight line and is based on it. We well know how sensitive the Greek thinking was to logical errors of this sort, and, therefore, we must reject this first interpretation.

Another way of interpreting Definition IV, is to consider a curve in itself, unrelated to a plane. Then, "evenly" means that a straight line considered in itself is the same at all of its points, i.e., it is identical in all of its parts.

We are obliged to accept this second interpretation of the word "evenly" but there is an objection to it which must be studied. The sameness at all points characterizes not only straight lines but also circles. Circles and straight lines are the only plane curves which can slide smoothly on themselves without any hindrance because they are the only curves of constant curvature and possess, therefore, a sameness at all of their points, the curvature of all other curves being variable from point to point.

Therefore, Definition IV considered alone covers not only straight lines but also circles. The same remarks also hold for Definition VII of plane. When considered from the outside as located in a three-dimensional space, a plane as defined by Euclid is the absolutely flat surface devoid of curvature which is familiar to us. But this interpretation of the word "evenly" presupposes a definition of a flat three-dimensional space which is defined in *Elements* with the aid of the concept of plane, again involving us in a vicious circle.

The only possible interpretation of the word "evenly" used in Definition VII is related to the concept of a plane viewed from the inside, as a two-dimensional surface not immersed in a three-dimensional space. Thus, a plane, as defined in *Elements*, appears as a homogeneous surface, the same in all its parts, identical at all of its points, that is, as a surface of constant curvature.

But we know that this property holds not only for a plane but for the sphere as well, the only distinction being the *value* of the constant curvature: it is greater than zero for the sphere and is zero for the plane which has no curvature. Indeed, a plane is the limiting form of a sphere when the radius of the sphere becomes infinite, its curvature vanishing. To see this, rotate the Fig. 8 about the straight line BD as the rotation axis. The line AC generates a plane perpendicular to BD, while the various circles tangent to AC and tending to it generate spheres tangent to this plane at B and tending to it when the radius increases. Then, when the radius becomes infinite just as the circle becomes a straight line, the sphere opens completely and coincides with the plane. Thus, a plane is a sphere of infinite radius and, as such, is a surface of constant and vanishing curvature. Among all surfaces, only the sphere and the plane possess constant curvature. This is why a plane can turn and slide on itself and a sphere can rotate about any of its diameters, sliding smoothly on itself without any hindrance. We now see clearly that Definition VII considered alone covers not only the plane but also the sphere.

It is now clear that Euclid's definitions, if isolated and considered in themselves, define geometrical entities more general than the straight line and plane, namely, the circle and sphere. One could substitute a spherical surface with circles drawn on it for the plane with its straight lines if the concepts introduced by Definitions IV and VII did not also have to verify the system of Euclid's axioms. It is interesting to discuss how these axioms eliminate the sphere and circle as a possible interpretation of Definitions VII and IV. But before this can be done, we must describe two kinds of circles (*small* and *great* circles) which can be drawn on a spherical surface of finite radius.

Circles are drawn on a sphere with the aid of a compass exactly as they are on a plane. The fixed leg AC of a compass CAM (Fig. 9) defines the center C of a spherical circle MPQM the circumference of which is described by the other leg AM. A spherical circle, like a plane circle, is also the locus of points equidistant from its center C, but in this proposition the word distance means *spherical distance*, which is defined as the shortest path on the spherical surface between two given points.

Thus, a spherical distance is an arc of a curve drawn on the surface of the sphere and it must not be confused with the rectilinear chord subtending it. This chord is also a shortest path between the same two points, but in the three-dimensional space surrounding the sphere and not on the sphere itself. In studying the geometry of the spherical surface we do not consider it as immersed in a higher space. For a flat, two-dimensional thinking being crawling on the sphere and studying its geometry, as we study plane geometry, three-dimensional space does not exist, and, therefore, spherical distance realizes the shortest distance.

To consider an example illustrating the distinction between small and great circles of a sphere, let us recall the geographic maps of our globe. They are based on the oversimplified assumption that the earth is a perfect sphere, so that the spherical curves of constant geographical longitude (meridians) as well as those of constant geographical latitude (parallel circles) are circles drawn on a sphere. The parallel circles (called, by abbreviation, *parallels*) form a family of concentric circles of various size with their common center at a pole of the globe. Their radii are arcs of meridians such as NB (see Fig. 9) and the largest parallel circle is the equator. It is equidistant from both poles and is as large as a meridian circle.

The meridians and the parallels are different types of spherical circles. A meridian circle (and the equator) bisects the sphere's surface into two halves, called hemispheres, while a parallel circle (except the equator) divides it into two unequal parts. Thus, meridians (and the equator) are the greatest circles of the sphere. This is why they belong to *great circles* of the sphere, while

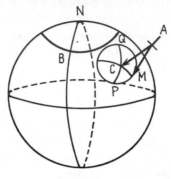

Fig. 13.9

every parallel circle, except the equator, is one of the *small circles* of the sphere. The distinction between great and small circles is important because on the surface of a sphere great circles play the role of straight lines in a plane. Walking on a sphere, always in the same direction (for instance, to the north on the earth), one follows an arc of a great circle, so that the shortest path between two points A and B on the sphere (Fig. 10a) is the arc AB of the

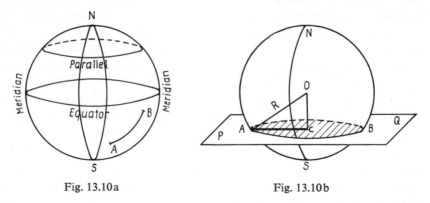

Fig. 13.10a   Fig. 13.10b

great circle passing through these two points. Moreover, a great circle through two given points is unique. Two points on the sphere define one and only one great circle incident with them, just as two points on a plane define one and only one straight line. There is however one exception: if two given points are diametrically opposite on the sphere, being two endpoints of a diameter (antipodes), they do not define a unique great circle, and there are an infinite number of great circles passing through them. An example is given by the north and south poles with all the meridians.

To prove this important point, we consider the intersection of a sphere with a plane. Each spherical circle, great or small, defines a plane to which it belongs as the intersection curve of this plane with the sphere. Therefore, considered as a plane circle, it has a center C and a radius AC in its plane PQ (Fig. 10b). On the other hand, considered as a spherical circle drawn on the surface of the sphere, the same circle has another center (S or N) and another spherical radius (SA or NA) lying in the spherical surface. Denoting the radius of the sphere by R, we find that, in general, the circle's radius in the plane, AC, is smaller than the radius of the sphere $R: AC < AO = R$, The spherical circles with radii smaller than R are obtained as intersection circles of the sphere with planes which do not pass through the center O of the sphere, and they are called *small* circles of the sphere.

But when the sphere is cut by a plane passing through its center O, its surface is bisected by this plane into two hemispheres, and the center C of a great circle in its plane coincides with the center O of the sphere, so that the circle's radius in the plane, AC, reaches its maximum value $AO = R$ and becomes equal to the sphere's radius R. Such circles are called *great* circles of the sphere.

We saw that three points are necessary and sufficient to define a plane in a three-dimensional space, provided that these three points are not collinear. To define a spherical circle, it is sufficient to define the plane passing through it because a circle drawn on a sphere is always the intersection curve of a plane with this sphere. Therefore, to define a small circle, we need three points on the sphere's surface, provided they do not belong to a great circle. But the plane of a great circle is known to pass through the center of the sphere, so that one of three points is already given. Therefore, to define a great circle, it is sufficient to give only two points on the sphere's surface. These two points, together with the center of the sphere, define, in general, only one plane, whose intersection with the sphere is the great circle passing through two given points. The exceptional case of two diametrally opposite points which do not define a unique great circle is now clear: three points can define a plane only if they are not collinear, and two diametrically opposite points considered together with the center of the sphere form precisely a group of three collinear points.

Returning now to Definition IV of a straight line, we already see that the small circles of a sphere are eliminated by the First and Second Axioms as possible interpretations of Definition IV because through two given points on the sphere pass many different small circles, while a straight line is uniquely determined by two of its points. On a sphere, the small circles play the role of ordinary circles in a plane: they are defined by three points and are the loci of points equidistant from a given point.

The First and Second Axioms do not preclude the substitution of great circles for straight lines because they are defined by two points and can be extended indefinitely, being unbounded as any closed curve.

It is the Third Axiom which eliminates the possibility of using a sphere with its great circles instead of a plane with its straight lines as the fundamental domain of "plane" two-dimensional geometry characterized by Definitions IV and VII. The third axiom states (1) that a center can be chosen at any point and (2) that the radius can be as large as we want. Part (1) does not preclude a sphere, but statement (2) characterizes an infinite plane and does not hold for a sphere with its finite extension. When the spherical radius of a spherical circle increases, its circumference approaches the antipode (diametrically opposite point) of its center and degenerates into a circle-point at the antipode for a maximum value πR of the spherical radius.

If the spherical radius is equal to a quarter of a great circle's circumference, a great circle is obtained. If the radius exceeds this critical value, the great circle shrinks back to a small circle, which again contracts further with increasing radius. When, finally, the spherical radius of a spherical circle reaches its maximum value, which is equal to one half the circumference of a great circle, the small circle shrinks to a single point diametrically opposite its center. There is, indeed, only one point on the surface of a sphere whose distance from a given point is equal to one half the circumference of a great circle, and this distance is the maximum spherical distance between two points on a sphere.

We thus see that Definitions IV and VII combined with the first three axioms do define uniquely the straight line and the flat plane because the Third Axiom ensures the infinitude of the plane and thus contradicts the existence on a spherical surface of a maximum for a spherical distance between two points.

W. K. Clifford, in his work *The Common Sense of the Exact Sciences*, states that, from the point of view of practical experience, a constant non-zero curvature of the physical space around us could not be perceived as such and would remain for us completely undistinguishable from the absence of the curvature, that is, from perfect flatness. If the perceiving mind (we will call it the *observer*) is not able to perceive the curved space from the outside, but remains in his perceptions always inside it and has no means for considering his evenly curved space as immersed in a higher-dimensional space, he never will perceive the non-zero constant curvature of his universe as a physical property of space inside which it lives.

Clifford's reasoning is based on the assumption that the observer can explore every part of his universe but is incapable of recognizing a point in it where he has already been. The reasoning remains valid if we replace Clifford's assumption by another, namely that the observer is so small with respect to the dimensions of the universe or so short-lived that he cannot make a round trip and thus discover the finiteness of his world. Our assumption is of a purely physical nature as is the question raised by Clifford, and this assumption is verified in the case of mankind.

We consider first a one-dimensional world of constant curvature, representing it by an infinitely thin circular tube of finite radius within which dwells a linear and conscious being W (Clifford's *worm*). This being cannot imagine anything outside his own tubular space in which he can circulate and observe. Moving back and forth inside his linear world, W always experiences the same amount of bending, which he associates quite naturally with his own physical constitution because this feeling does not vary and remains the same everywhere and all the time. Therefore, W will never be able to perceive the curvature of the world in which he dwells as a geometric property of space and thus will be led to ascribe a perfect straightness to a circle, perceiving it as a straight line. His displacements in both directions never being restrained, our linear observer W will perceive his space as an infinite world, though in reality this space is a finite circle. The shortest path between any two points A and B in this one-dimensional and circular universe is an arc AB. It is not a straight line, but to W, who knows nothing about the existence of a second or third dimension, this curved path will appear as devoid of curvature, as a segment of a straight line appears to our mind.

Passing now to a two-dimensional world which has lengths and areas but neither thickness nor volume, we suppose that an infinitely thin and conscious being F (Clifford's *flatfish*) is living on a spherical surface so that his two-dimensional universe has a constant curvature. Assuming that this observer F cannot perceive anything outside his own space and has no knowledge of the existence of space interior and exterior to the surface of the sphere on which he dwells, F will naturally come to the same conclusions as W.

The surface of the sphere will appear to F as perfectly flat because he ascribes the feeling of constant curvature to the peculiar structure of his body. The unboundedness of the spherical surface will seem to him infinite extent. The great circles of the sphere will be straight lines for F, and since, by hypothesis, our observer is unable to complete a trip around his world, he will say that his straight lines are infinite and verify the first two axioms of Euclid.

If now F, guided by his experience, which, under our assumption of limited travel, is related to a small part of his world, tries to build up a geometry, he may erroneously assume that the Third Axiom and the Fifth Postulate hold for the "straight lines" and "circles" of his spherical universe. But if F can invent and use in the study of his two-dimensional environment physical instruments which extend considerably the region of space accessible to his measures and thus replace by these measures the direct exploration of space by travel, he will soon understand that no two "straight lines" of his world can be parallel because two great circles of a sphere always intersect each other.

Thus, F will be obliged to correct his first interpretation of physical space around him and substitute for the Fifth Postulate of Euclidean geometry the corresponding fundamental assumption of *Riemannian* Geometry:

> *Any two straight lines intersect when extended*

or the related form of Playfair's Axiom which it takes in Riemannian geometry and which reads as follows:

> *Given a point and a line non-incident with it, any straight line through the given point intersects the given straight line.*

There are, therefore, three possible and logically equivalent choices for the axiom of parallels: (1) no parallel lines at all (Riemann); (2) one and the same parallel to the right and to the left (Euclid); and, (3) two parallels through a point to a straight line, namely, one to the left and another to the right (Lobatchevsky).

In case (3) of hyperbolic geometry, no straight line lying between the two parallels can meet the given line. Such straight lines are called *ultraparallels*. We emphasize also that Riemannian geometry is not at all the geometry of great circles on a sphere. It merely happens that, interpreting the great circles of a sphere as analogous to straight lines of a Riemannian plane, we can construct in Euclidean space a *model* of Riemannian plane geometry and, thus, visualize the content of its theorems in terms of Euclidean configurations drawn on a curved surface. This visualization is based on the fact that both straight lines in a Riemannian plane and great circles on a sphere, are the shortest paths on their respective surfaces and verify the axiom of Riemannian geometry, which postulates that two straight lines always intersect each other at a finite distance from the observer.

Other similar visualizations can be constructed, as, for instance, that of Euclidean geometry on a curved surface in the three-dimensional hyperbolic space of Lobachevsky, as well as the model of the plane hyperbolic geometry of Lobachevsky on a curved surface in ordinary Euclidean space.

In such visualizations, the curves which are the shortest paths between two points play the role of straight lines. They are called *geodesics*, and every surface has its own geodesics. Thus, great circles are geodesics of a sphere just as straight lines are geodesics of a plane.

Are two Symmetric Figures Equal?

At first, the answer to this question is "no", as the example of two gloves of the same pair seems to show: to be equal, two figures must be congruent, and the right glove does not appear to our mind as congruent to the left glove, unless we turn it inside out, which is a forbidden deformation.

Nevertheless, the answer to this question is not as simple as it seems to be, and the last part of this chapter will be devoted to a discussion of the concept of symmetry. We begin this discussion by the one-dimensional case of two configurations formed by points of a straight line and symmetric with respect to a point O. Symmetric configurations can be obtained by reflection in a mirror. Given three points A, B, C on the one side of the origin O, such that B is between A and C but does not coincide with the midpoint of the interval AC, we construct a configuration symmetric to that formed by the points A, B, C by reflecting these three points in the point mirror O. Denoting the points symmetric to A, B, C by A*, B*, C*, respectively, we thus obtain two symmetric configurations ABC and A*B*C* (Fig. 11).

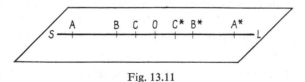

Fig. 13.11

We now try to bring A*B*C* into congruence with ABC without using a second dimension and limiting, therefore, displacements to translations along the straight line SL incident with our symmetric configurations. Naturally we fail because, if the points C*, A* coincide with A and C respectively, the point B* does not coincide with B. We can make coincide only parts of our two symmetric figures. Thus, if C*B* coincides with BC, B*A* and AB are not superposed, while if they are then C*B* and BC are not. Therefore, if we do not want to immerse our symmetric figures into a higher space of more than one dimension, they cannot be considered as congruent figures, and in a one-dimensional space SL two symmetric figures are not equal, but only symmetric, although they have all the parts of one figure equal separately to corresponding parts of the other.

If, however, the line SL is considered as immersed in a plane, the ray OL can be made to coincide with the ray OS by a rotation through 180° about the point O. Since, by definition, OA = OA*, OB = OB*, and OC = OC*, this rotation brings two symmetric configurations into a perfect congruence. Thus, introducing a supplementary dimension and immersing the one-dimensional space SL in a higher space s_2 (plane), we succeed in showing that a symmetry in s_1 (straight line SL) is simply an identity in s_2.

We state that there is no intrinsic difference between two symmetric configurations ABC and A*B*C*. They are, rather, two different positions of one and the same configuration because a displacement is sufficient to bring them into coincidence. Thus, our idea of symmetry as a non-identical disposition of identical parts is relative to the number of dimensions we have at our disposal. In other words, the concept of symmetry does not express an intrinsic geometric property of two symmetric figures which are, in fact, identical for an observer using one dimension more.

Considering now figures symmetric in a plane s_2, two points P and P′ (Fig. 12) are said to be symmetric with respect to the straight line MM (mirror) if this line MM is perpendicular to the line PP′ and bisects the segment PP′, so that the intersection point Q is the midpoint of PP′. Two figures are said to be symmetric with respect to MM if all their points are symmetric point by point.

By reflecting three non-collinear points A, B, C in the linear mirror MM, a triangle A′B′C′ symmetrical to the triangle ABC is obtained. A triangle is, by definition, a configuration formed by three non-collinear points, called *vertices* of the triangle, and by three straight lines defined by the three non-collinear vertices. These lines are *sides* of the triangle, and they intersect at vertices, forming three *interior angles* and three *exterior angles*. An exterior angle together with the adjacent interior anlge form a straight angle equal to 180°. Comparing separately each part of the triangle ABC to the corresponding symmetric part of the image A′B′C′, we see that they are identical because they are congruent when isolated from their respective triangles. The congruence of corresponding parts can be achieved by a displacement in the plane to which our two triangles belong.

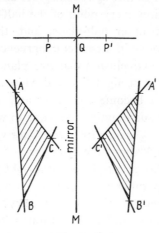

Fig. 13.12

But if we try to bring the two triangles ABC and A'B'C' considered as *entities* into coincidence using only displacements in the plane, we fail. The dissimilar arrangement of identical parts in these two symmetric configurations is an obstacle to the realization of their congruence: if one pair of equal sides coincides, the other two do not (Fig. 13).

But, if we decide to use the third dimension and move one triangle through three-dimensional space s_3 surrounding our plane s_2, we can superpose it on

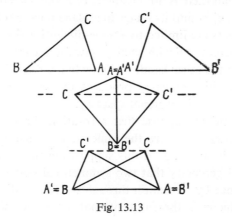

Fig. 13.13

the other and thus realize a perfect congruence, each point of one coinciding with its symmetric point of the other of two symmetric triangles.

To achieve the congruence, it is sufficient to rotate the half-plane which contains the triangle A′B′C′ through 180 degrees about the straight line MM because after this rotation every point of the half-plane coincides with its symmetric point in the other half-plane, and, thus, the triangle A′B′C′ falls upon ABC from above in a perfect congruence.

We come again to the conclusion that two plane figures which are symmetrical with respect to a straight line and which, therefore, are non-congruent inside their plane become congruent and are thus identical in the three-dimensional space surrounding the plane to which they belong: *What is a symmetry in a plane s_2 is identity in the space s_3.*

Now what can be said about the symmetry of solid bodies in a three-dimensional space s_3? Are a left glove and a right glove of the same shape and size two structurally different objects which happen to be symmetrical to each other with respect to a plane of symmetry? Or are they one and the same object observed in two different positions with respect to an observer? We know that the image of a left glove formed by a reflection in a plane mirror is a right glove of the same shape and size, that is, of the same pair of gloves. Is a three-dimensional configuration congruent and therefore identical to its image in a plane mirror, and, if so, what kind of motion can achieve this congruence? In other words, is the symmetry in an s_3 with respect to a plane a phenomenon related to two different positions of the same body or is there an intrinsic, structural dissimilarity in two symmetric bodies? The importance of these questions for organic chemistry with its symmetrical molecules cannot be exaggerated.

We emphasize that there is no possibility of making a left and a right glove or, in general, an object and its image in a plane mirror coincide by motion, if their displacements are limited to a three-dimensional space to which they belong. This fact agrees well with what we saw for linear and plane symmetric configurations. On the other hand, we know that a reflection in a line mirror which is performed in a plane s_2 produces the same effect as a rotation through 180° in a threedimensional space s_3.

It is quite natural to suppose that a rotation through 180° in a four-dimensional space s_4 may have the same effect as a reflection in a plane mirror performed in an s_3. And this supposition turns out to be true: we will prove in solid geometry that two symmetrical bodies are brought into a perfect congruence by a rotation through the fourth dimension.

Therefore, symmetry in three-dimensional space does not involve a structural dissimilarity of two symmetric configurations. In other words, the left glove is identical to the right glove, and, if you want to put it on your right hand without turning it inside out, you have only to rotate it through 180° about a plane in the four-dimensional space which includes our three-dimensional universe as its part.

Unfortunately, we do not know how to do this, and, moreover, we are not at all sure that there is in our physical environment such an unknown and yet undiscovered feature as a fourth dimension. If it does exist, its discovery would mean as profound a revolution in our life and in our conception of the universe as was the passage from two-dimensional to three-dimensional mentality in the evolution and gradual development of the animal mind of our ancestors.

But in pure geometry, which deals with fictions, there is no doubt about the existence of a fourth dimension, and, for this abstract science, the only difference between a left and a right glove is their position with respect to the observer. This example shows how closely the interpretation of our experience depends on the fundamental geometrical assumptions implied in the structure of the spatial frame into which our mind projects its impressions. It is not excluded that the instinctive reluctance with which children react to our teaching of left and right stems from the artificiality of the concept of symmetry because the child's mind is nearer to nature than is the thinking of an adult man.

The ten axioms of Euclid discussed in this chapter do not form a complete system of geometrical axioms. Our discussion was also far from being complete, and this first chapter on geometry is to be considered as a kind of general introduction, stressing some important definitions and questions which have to be more closely studied in what follows.

CHAPTER 14

Triangle. Duality

In Chapter 13 we stated that the concept of straight line can be deduced from that of a point and *vice versa*. We will now describe how this is done. Given any three distinct points A, B, C, we can define three straight lines AB, BC, CA, each incident with two points. The configuration formed by these three points may be of two different kinds:

(1) If three lines AB, BC, CA are distinct straight lines, forming a triangle, the points are said to be non-collinear because in this case there exists no straight line incident with all three points A, B, C.

(2) If two of these straight lines, for instance, AB and BC, coincide, then the three points are incident with the line ABC, and the third line AC also coincides with ABC because one and only one straight line can be drawn through two points A and C. We know that in this second case the points A B, C are said to be collinear.

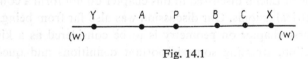

Fig. 14.1

Three collinear points A, B, C (Fig. 1) exhibit a relation of order symbolized by (ABC) and expressed with the aid of the word *between:* the point B is *between* the points A and C. Given three distinct collinear points A, B, and C, three different arrangements are possible, so that one and only one of the three relations (ABC), (BCA), and (CAB) holds. The sense of orientation is not related to the concept of betweenness, so that the relations (ABC) and (CBA) are equivalent. If we have (ABC) or (CBA), then (BCA) = (ACB) and (CAB) = (BAC) do not hold. By definition, the relation of betweenness is essentially limited to the *finite* part of a straight line.

We now introduce the concept of a segment of a straight line AB formed by two end points A and B: we call a *segment* AB the set (or class, or collection) of all points P collinear with A and B and such that (APB) is true, that is, P is between A and B. The set of all points X such that (ABX) is true is called *ray* BW, where W is the symbol of the point at infinity of the straight line AB. Likewise, the set of all points Y such that (YAB) holds is called ray WA. We note that the end points of a segment or of a ray are *not* included.

The rays WA, BW and the segment AB together with the three points A, B, W form the entire straight line defined by two points A and B. Thus, the concept of a straight line as a set of points is derived from that of a point with the aid of the relation of betweenness. We add that the two rays WA and BW considered together with the point at infinity W form an infinite *exterior* segment BWA with end points A and B, because the Euclidean straight line has only one point at infinity and is, therefore, a closed line. The relation of betweenness does not apply to such infinite segments, so that, for example, the point C is not between B and A although it is interior to the infinite segment BWA.

Considering a straight line as the fundamental element and applying to the above construction the transformation by duality, we can also deduce the concept of a point as a pencil of lines from that of straight line. As we have shown in Chapter 13 two straight lines always define a point. Three distinct straight lines *a, b, c* (we will systematically denote points by capital letters and their dual transforms, straight lines, by the same but small letters) define, in general, three distinct intersection points D(b, c), E(c, a), and F(a, b), which are vertices of a triangle DEF.

Eliminating this general case of three non-concurrent lines, let us consider a pencil of straight lines with a vertex F defined as the intersection point of two fundamental lines *a* and *b* (Fig. 2). The dual image of F, *a, b* consists of a straight line *f* with two points A, B marked on it. The lines *a* and *b* form at F two pairs of equal vertical angles, $\hat{1}$ and $\hat{2}$, and it is sufficient to consider one of two equal acute angles $\hat{1}$ as well as one of two equal obtuse angles $\hat{2}$, disregarding, for instance, the angles lying below and to the left of the straight line *b*.

The length of a segment AB is a measure of the distance between its two end points A and B. Likewise, the measure of the angular distance between the two straight lines *a* and *b* is the magnitude of the angle they form at the intersection point F. Thus, angle and segment are dual companions, as are point and straight line.

The two angles $\hat{1}$ and $\hat{2}$ in Fig. 2 are dual transforms of segments AB (interior) and BWA (exterior), where W is the point at infinity on the line *f*.

Therefore, a line *x* of our pencil such that it belongs to angle $\hat{1}$ is said to be *between a* and *b*, in symbols (*bxa*), while, if a line *y* is in angle $\hat{2}$, we will say that *a* is between *b* and *y* and denote it by (*bay*). The dual transformation of points on the line *f* into lines through the point F and *vice versa* can be easily realized by drawing any straight line non-incident with the vertex F of the pencil, as is done in Fig. 2. We therefore define angle $\hat{1}$ as the set of all lines *x* concurrent with *a* and *b* such that (*bxa*) is true, that is, *x* is between *a* and *b*,

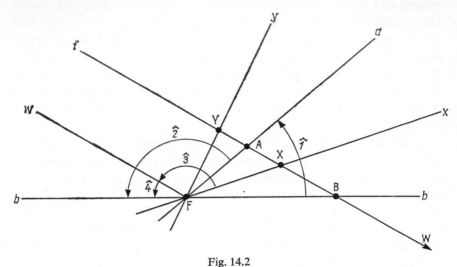

Fig. 14.2

the set of all lines *y* concurrent with *a* and *b* and such that for them holds the relation (*bay*) forming angle $\hat{2}$. In the Fig. 2 the dual image of any straight line through F is its intersection point with the line *f* and, *vice versa*, to each point of the line *f* corresponds as its dual transform the line of the pencil which passes through this point. The line *w* of the pencil parallel to the line *f* is the dual companion of the point at infinity W on the line *f* which is the common point of two parallel lines *w* and *f*. The two angles $\hat{3}$ and $\hat{4}$ into which the line *w* subdivides the obtuse angle $\hat{2}$ are dual transforms of two rays AW and BW of the line *f*.

The straight lines belonging to two angles $\hat{1}$ and $\hat{2}$, considered together with the two fundamental lines *a* and *b*, form the entity called point F, so that the concept of point is equivalent to that of the pencil of straight lines with the vertex at this point: a point, as dual companion to a straight line, includes all straight lines incident with it, as a straight line is composed of all points incident with this line.

Triangle

The configuration formed by three non-collinear points, called a triangle, is a most important geometric figure because all rectilinear configurations can be conceived as composed of triangles. To build up a triangle, imagine three mutually adjacent angles around their common vertex O, so that their sides are three rays of a pencil of lines with a vertex at O (Fig. 3). Choosing

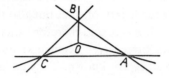

Fig. 14.3.

three points A, B, C, one on each of the three rays, and joining them by straight lines, we form three adjacent triangles AOB, BOC, COA with the common vertex O. Considered together, they add up to a large triangle ABC. This construction may be generalized: consider n rays emanating from O and mark off n points, one on each ray, no three of them being collinear. Joining the points on adjacent rays by straight lines, we form n adjacent triangles around the common vertex O (Fig. 4). These n triangles appear then as parts of a larger rectilinear figure bounded by n sides and having n vertices. Such a rectilinear figure bounded by n straight lines is

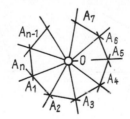

Fig. 14.4

called an n-sided *polygon*, a Greek word meaning many-angled. Thus, a triangle is a simplest kind of polygon having only three sides, while other polygons have more than three sides. Polygons with four, five, six, seven, and eight sides are called quadrangle (or also quadrilateral), pentagon, hexagon, heptagon and octagon, respectively.

4 Kogbetliantz

Triangles are widely used in building constructions as essential links of a frame. The geometrical reason for this is that the triangle is the only polygon whose size and shape are determined by the length of its sides. Even four segments of given length may form an infinite number of different quadrangles of various shapes. If four lengths of material are hinged together, they are free to rotate around vertices turning on the hinges. The same is true for all polygons except triangles. Their shape remains indetermined when the sides only are prescribed because their angles can vary without any variation of the length of their sides. To fix the shape of a convex polygon with n sides, one must know not only the length of sides but also the values of $n - 3$ of its n angles. But, for a triangle $n = 3$, and therefore there can be only one triangle having as its sides three given segments: its angles are completely determined, if the three sides are known. They cannot vary without corresponding variation in the length of the sides, so that the triangle is the only undeformable polygon.

The dual transform of a triangle is again another triangle, so that the triangle is a *self-dual* figure. The vertices $A(n, p)$; $B(p, m)$; $C(m, n)$ of a triangle (Fig. 5) are the intersection points of the straight lines m, n, p, and they are transformed by duality into three straight lines a, b, c, which form a triangle MNP, dual companion to the triangle ABC. The vertices $M(b, c)$; $N(c, a)$; $P(a, b)$ are dual transforms of straight lines m, n, p which form the sides of the triangle ABC. The angles at the vertices A, B, C are transformed into segments NP, PM, MN, respectively, and the sides AB, BC, CA become angles at the vertices P, M, N.

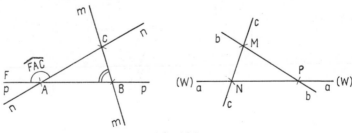

Fig. 14.5

It is important to emphasize, however, that the dual image of the interior of one triangle is the *exterior* of the other. Therefore, when we state that a segment such as NP, for instance, is transformed into an angle, here an angle at A formed by the two straight lines n and p, we must be careful in choosing between the interior angle $\overset{\frown}{BAC}$ and its supplement to 180°, the exterior angle $\overparen{FAC}$. Because, as will be shown later, the interior of ABC corresponds dually to the exterior of MNP, the interior angle $\overparen{BAC}$ is the dual image of the infinite *exterior* segment NWP of the line *a*, joining the points N and P through the point at infinity W on the line *a*. The finite segment NP (a side of the triangle MNP) is the dual transform of the *exterior* angle at the point A, namely angle $\overparen{FAC}$. This is a general rule: *The sides of a triangle are dual images of exterior angles of the dual triangle.*

We said before that a triangle is uniquely determined by the length of its sides. We cannot say, however, that any three lengths always form a triangle. A segment of a straight line is the shortest path between its two end points, and, therefore, given a triangle ABC, we must have the three following inequalities:

$$AB + BC > CA; \quad BC + CA > AB; \quad CA + AB > BC$$

Transposing BC in the first and CA in the third inequality to the right, we deduce for the side AB the two other inequalities, namely, $AB > CA - BC$ and $AB > BC - CA$, whose righthand members $CA - BC$ and $BC - CA$ differ from each other only in sign, one being the negative of the other. Denoting their common absolute value by $|CA - BC| = |BC - CA|$, we can disregard the inequality whose righthand member is negative (it is always verified because AB as a length is positive) and write the other inequality as follows:

$$AB > |BC - CA|; \quad BC > |CA - AB|; \quad CA > |AB - BC|$$

with similar inequalities for the two other sides CA and BC.

These two sets of inequalities show that three given segments can form a triangle if and only if each one of them is greater than the difference of two others, but less than their sum. Thus, segments of length 7, 11, and 15 do form a triangle, but those of 7, 11, and 20 do not since 20 is greater than $7 + 11 = 18$ and 11 is less than $20 - 7 = 13$. Therefore, when we assert that three sides determine a triangle, we assume that their lengths verify the necessary conditions just described.

Furthermore, as we will prove later (Theorem VIII, this chapter), there can be only one triangle having three given lengths AB, CD, EF as its sides. It is easy to construct it, provided they verify the necessary inequalities. The construction which follows is based on the fact that two circles intersect in two points only, these points being symmetric with respect to the line of centers.

Suppose that the largest of three segments, AB, verifies the condition $|CD - EF| < AB < CD + EF$ and draw (Fig. 6) two circles with radii CD and EF around the end points A and B of the segment AB as centers of the two circles. The two circles cannot be exterior to each other because, were it so, we should have the sum of their radii CD + EF less than the distance of their centers AB, and we know that it is greater because AB < CD + EF.

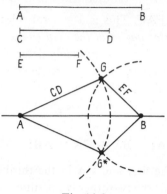

Fig. 14.6

Since the difference of their radii, |CD − EF|, is smaller than the distance AB of their centers, the smaller circle cannot be interior to the larger one. The two circles cannot be tangent to each other, either externally or internally, because otherwise we should have AB = CD + EF or AB = |CD − EF|, respectively. Therefore, the condition |CD − EF| < AB < CD + EF, which is necessary for the existence of a triangle with sides AB, CD, EF, is at the same time sufficient to ensure the intersection of our two circles. Denoting the two intersection points by G and G*, we obtain the two triangles ABG and ABG*, which have the three given segments as their sides. The solution thus obtained is, in fact, unique because these two triangles, being symmetrical, are equal.

Sum of Angles of a Triangle

Guided by the idea of duality, we might be tempted to guess that the proposition "There is only one triangle having three given segments as its sides" must have its dual companion theorem, namely, "There is only one triangle having three given angles as its exterior angles". We observe immediately that an exterior angle supplements the adjacent interior angle to 180° and, therefore, it will make no difference if we consider interior angles as given instead of exterior ones, enunciating our guess as follows: *There is only one triangle having three given angles as its angles.*

This theorem is perfectly true in both non-Euclidean geometries, and it is the most striking peculiarity of Euclidean geometry that it does not hold in this geometry.

In Euclidean geometry, any triangle can be amplified or reduced in size without changing its shape, and, therefore, there are an infinite number of triangles having all their angles the same, but differing in size. Such triangles are called *similar*, and the existence of similar triangles and similar figures in general is a characteristic feature of Euclidean geometry. This feature is a corollary of the Fifth Postulate, and it well illustrates the fact that, in Euclidean geometry, the duality is of restricted kind and does not always hold. In particular, the duality does not apply to theorems related to the Fifth Postulate and based on it.

Just as there are certain conditions which govern the choice of lengths to be used in constructing a triangle, so three angles of a triangle cannot be chosen completely at random. Given any three angles, it is, in general, impossible to build a triangle having these as its interior angles. In Euclidean geometry for all triangles, the sum of the three angles is the same, does not depend on the size of the triangle, and is always equal to two right angles, that is, to 180°.

It is of interest to note that this numerical value, 180°, of the sum of three angles of a triangle can be easily deduced from the simpler fact that it is a constant, the same for all triangles. Denoting this unknown constant by the symbol s, let us consider Fig. 3 with its three triangles AOB, BOC, and COA. The nine angles of these three triangles added yield a sum equal to $3s$ because they belong to three triangles. On the other hand, this sum represents the sum of three angles of the large triangle ABC plus 360° around the point O, so that it may also be expressed as $s + 360°$. Thus, our unknown s must verify the equation $3s = s + 360°$, the solution of which is $s = 180°$.

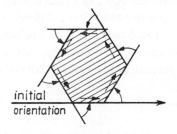

initial
orientation

Fig. 14.7

Applying the same reasoning to Fig. 4 in which an n-sided polygon is decomposed into n adjacent triangles with their common vertex at an interior point O, we conclude that, for this polygon, the sum of its angles is equal to the sum of angles of all the n triangles less the 360° which represent the sum of all the angles around the point O. Therefore, the sum of angles of an n-sided polygon is $180° \cdot n - 360° = 180°(n - 2)$. Furthermore, at each of the n vertices of this polygon we may form an exterior angle supplementing the adjacent interior angle to 180° (Fig. 7). Therefore, the sum of all the exterior and interior angles of the polygon is equal to $180° \cdot n$, which proves that *the sum of exterior angles is 360°:* since $180° \cdot n - [180° \cdot n - 360°] = 360°$. The sum of exterior angles does not depend on the number of sides, and it is the same for all polygons. What is interesting in this result is its generality: walking counterclockwise along the perimeter of any polygon and turning at every vertex to the left through the corresponding exterior angle in order to be able to continue along the next side, at the end of our travel and after the last turn, so that we are looking again in the same direction in which we were looking at the beginning of our trip, we have completed a whole revolution through 360°, because the sum of all exterior angles is equal to 360°. Since a closed curve can be approximated with any prescribed accuracy by polygons, the same conclusion holds for any closed path on the Euclidean plane: returning to the initial starting point, we find ourselves looking in the same direction as at the start, knowing that we have turned to the left in all through 360°. Strange as it may seem, here again we meet a situation characteristic for Euclidean geometry and which is not true in non-Euclidean geometries. On the sphere, for instance, returning on a closed path to the initial point and orientation, one had to turn, in all, less than 360° and the difference increases with the area included in the interior of the closed path. If one follows a great circle, he does not turn at all, so that this difference reaches 360°, the area bounded by a great circle being equal to that of the hemisphere. Thus, in Riemannian geometry the sum of all turns is variable and always less than 360°. In Lobachevsky's geometry this sum is, to the contrary, always greater than 360°, difference again increasing with the area bounded by the closed path. Only in Euclidean geometry is the sum of all turns constant and equal to 360° and this fact is a corollary of the Fifth Postulate because it is related to the value (180°) of the sum of angles of a triangle.

We now shall discuss the proof of

THEOREM II: *The sum of the interior angles of any triangle is two right angles.*

This is another alternative form of the Fifth Postulate. To justify this we have not only to prove that Theorem II follows from the Fifth Postulate, but have also to deduce this postulate from Theorem II. We begin by proving the converse of the Theorem I (Chapter 13, p. 565), (Proposition XXIX, Book I of *Elements*): *The alternate interior angles a transversal makes with two parallel lines are equal*, which is needed in the proof of Theorem II. Suppose that MN and KL (Fig. 8) are parallel to each other but the angle $\widehat{KCA}$ the transversal AC makes with KL is greater than the angle $\widehat{CAN}$, $\widehat{CAN} < \widehat{KCA}$.

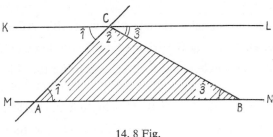

14. 8 Fig.

Since $\widehat{KCA} + \widehat{ACL} = 180°$, it follows that $\widehat{CAN} + \widehat{ACL}$ is less than 180° and, therefore (Fifth Postulate), the lines MN and KL must intersect each other to the right of the transversal AC. This contradiction (parallels do not intersect) proves that, if MN and KL are parallel, the two alternate interior angles cannot be unequal, so that the converse of Theorem I is proved.

PROOF OF THEOREM II: Given a triangle ABC with the angles $\widehat{BAC} = \hat{1}$, $\widehat{ACB} = \hat{2}$, and $\widehat{CBA} = \hat{3}$ (Fig. 8), draw through the vertex C a parallel KL to the side AB. This construction is possible only if the parallel in question is perfectly determined, and in Euclidean geometry it is so because there can be only one parallel to a given line through a given point not on this line (Playfair's Axiom). The alternate interior angles a transversal makes with two parallels being equal, we have, on one hand, $\widehat{NAC} = \hat{1} = \widehat{ACK}$ (transversal AC) and, on the other hand, $\widehat{MBC} = \hat{3} = \widehat{BCL}$ (transversal BC). Therefore,

$$\hat{1} + \hat{2} + \hat{3} = \widehat{CAN} + \widehat{ACB} + \widehat{MBC} = \widehat{ACK} + \widehat{ACB} + \widehat{BCL} = 180°$$

which completes the proof of Theorem II. The construction of the parallel KL being based on the Playfair's Axiom, our proof stands or fails with the Fifth Postulate.

The deduction of Playfair's Axiom from Theorem II is much more complicated than the proof of Theorem II just completed, but it is worth studying as an excellent example of geometric reasoning. This deduction is based on two propositions. The first one is a particular case of the Theorem I: two straight lines perpendicular to a third straight line are parallel. The second proposition concerns triangles with two equal sides, called *isosceles*, and it reads as follows:

THEOREM III: *In an isosceles triangle, the angles opposite equal sides are equal.*

Proof: Consider an isosceles triangle ABC with AB = AC and let $\widehat{ABC} = \hat{1}$, $\widehat{ACB} = \hat{2}$ (Fig. 9). Rotating the triangle ABC counterclockwise around its vertex A through an angle equal to $\widehat{BAC}$, we bring the side AB into coincidence with AC, while AC occupies a new position AD such that CD = CB, AD = AC, the angles $\widehat{DAC}$ and $\widehat{BAC}$ being equal. Angle $\hat{1}$ is now in the position $\widehat{ACD}$, and angle $\hat{2}$ is in the position $\widehat{ADC}$, so that $\widehat{ACD} = \hat{1}$ and $\widehat{ADC} = \hat{2}$. Triangle ACD is equal to triangle ABC because a rotation has no effect on a geometric configuration. Now we rotate the triangle ACD through 180° about the straight line EF as rotation axis. After this rotation,

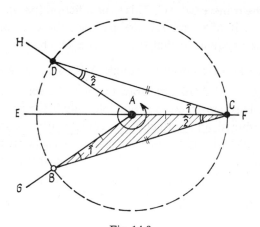

Fig. 14.9

the ray AH coincides with the ray AG since the angles HAC and GAC are equal: $\widehat{HAC} = \widehat{GAC}$. Moreover, the point D on AH coincides with B on AG since AD = AC = AB. Thus, since point C remains fixed, the straight line CD coincides with the CB and the angle $\widehat{CDA} = \hat{2}$ coincides with the angle $\widehat{CBA} = \hat{1}$. Therefore, the angles $\hat{1}$ and $\hat{2}$ as congruent are equal, and Theorem III is proved.

Playfair's Axiom deduced from Theorem II

Given a point B and a straight line DE non-incident with B (Fig. 10), the perpendicular BC to DE makes at C with DE a right angle $\widehat{BCE}$. Drawing through B a straight line PBQ perpendicular to BC, we obtain a parallel PQ to the line DE because the alternate interior angles made by the transversal BC are equal. To prove the uniqueness of this parallel to DE through B, that is, to deduce Playfair's Axiom, we have to show that any straight line passing through the point B and distinct from the line PQ intersects DE at a *finite* distance from the point C.

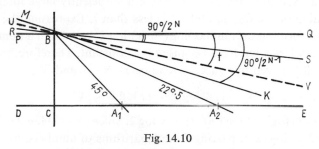

Fig. 14.10

We can simplify our problem by replacing in its enunciation the continuum of all straight lines through B and distinct from PQ by an infinite but denumerable set of straight lines whose angles at B with the ray BQ are aliquot parts of a right angle of a special kind, $90°/2^n$, where the integer n takes all positive values $n = 1, 2, 3, \ldots$ without reaching aleph-null, that is, remaining always an integer.

In other words, we begin by the proof of the following lemma (*lemma* means an auxiliary proposition needed in the proof of a theorem):

LEMMA: If a straight line through B, making with the ray BQ an angle equal to $90°/2^n$, intersects the ray CE whatever the value of the integer n, then *any* straight line through B and distinct from PQ intersects DE.

PROOF: Any straight line, UV, for example (Fig. 10), through B and distinct from PQ makes with this line PQ at B a fixed angle t. The positive number t, measure of this angle, may be as small as we please, but it is constant and different from zero for all straight lines through B and distinct from the line PQ. Since UV intersects PQ at B, one of its two rays must fall between the straight lines PQ and DE, while the other ray must lie above and outside of the strip bounded by PQ and DE. To fix our ideas, we suppose that the first ray, denoted by BV, which lies between PQ and DE, extends to the right of the perpendicular BC. If it were to the left, the reasoning which follows would apply without any change.

We have now to prove that the ray BV intersects the straight line DE no matter how small the angle t, provided that the rays which make with BQ angles equal to $90°/2^n$ intersect the line DE. Comparing the number t with the fractions $90°/2^n$, we observe that these fractions form an infinite sequence

$$90°/2, \ 90°/4, \ 90°/8, \ 90°/16, \ \ldots, \ 90°/2^n, \ 90°/2^{n+1}, \ \ldots$$

approaching zero when the integral exponent n increases without limit. Because t is a fixed number, we can choose a sufficiently large integer n such that the value of the fraction $90°/2^n$ is less than t. Expressing the angle t in degrees and forming the number $\log(90°/t)/\log 2$, we obtain a number which is maybe very large, but fixed because t is a constant. Therefore, this number is comprised between two successive integers $N-1$ and N:

$$N - 1 < \log(90°/t)/\log 2 < N,$$

that is, $(N-1) \log 2 < \log(90°/t) < N \log 2$. Since $(N-1) \log 2 = \log(2^{N-1})$ and $N \log 2 = \log(2^N)$, passing from logarithms to numbers, we have $2^{N-1} < 90°/t < 2^N$ and, therefore, $90°/2^{N-1} > t > 90°/2^N$.

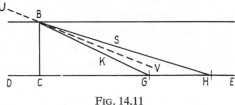

FIG. 14.11

This result shows that the ray BV is between the two rays BK and BS, which make with BQ angles equal to $90°/2^{N-1}$ and $90°/2^N$, respectively. By hypothesis, the rays BK and BS both intersect DE. Their points of intersection G and H together with the point B form a triangle BGH (Fig. 11). The straight line BV, penetrating inside this triangle BGH and distinct from its sides BG and BH, is infinite, while the triangle is a finite configuration.

Therefore, the infinite ray BV cannot terminate inside the triangle and must leave it, intersecting somewhere between G and H the side GH. The side GH is a segment of the line DE, and thus the line UV intersects DE, as is stated in the lemma.

In this first step of the deduction, we achieved an important simplification of our problem. We now know that it is sufficient to prove that a straight line through B making with BQ an angle equal to $90°/2^n$ intersects CE, to conclude, using the lemma, that *any* straight line through B and distinct from PQ intersects CE. It remains to prove that a straight line through B intersects CE, if it makes with BQ an angle equal to $90°/2^n$.

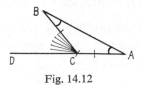

Fig. 14.12

At this point, we must use the fact that the sum of the angles of a triangle is equal to two right angles (Theorem II). More precisely, we will use a corollary of this fact, namely the following property of an isosceles triangle: interior angles opposite the equal sides of an isosceles triangle are equal to half the exterior angle adjacent to the interior angle included between the equal sides. To justify this, consider (Fig. 12) a triangle ABC with AC = BC, the angle included between the equal sides being $\widehat{ACB}$. The adjacent exterior angle $\widehat{DCB}$ is equal to $180° - \widehat{ACB}$. On the other hand, the angles $\widehat{CAB}$ and $\widehat{CBA}$ opposite the equal sides are equal, so that

$$\widehat{CAB} = \widehat{CBA} = \tfrac{1}{2}(\widehat{CAB} + \widehat{CBA}) = \tfrac{1}{2}(180° - \widehat{ACB}) = \widehat{DCB}/2$$

Choosing on CE a point A_1 (Fig. 10) such that $CA_1 = CB$ and joining it to B, we obtain an isosceles triangle BA_1C with a right angle at C. The adjacent exterior angle $\widehat{DCB}$ is also a right angle, and, therefore, $\widehat{CA_1B} = 90°/2$, which proves that a line through B and making with BQ an angle of $90°/2$ intersects CE. Repeating this construction, we choose on CE a second point A_2 such that the segment A_1A_2 is equal to BA_1 and join it to B. The second triangle thus formed, BA_2A_1, is also an isosceles one. For this triangle the angle $\widehat{CA_1B}$, which for the first triangle was an interior angle, is an exterior angle adjacent to the angle included between the equal sides. Therefore, the interior angle $\widehat{BA_2A_1}$ is equal to $\widehat{CA_1B}/2 = 90°/2^2$, and we see that a line through B and making with BQ an angle of $90°/2^2$ intersects CE at A_2.

The construction just described can now be repeated as many times as we want, and an infinite sequence of points on the line CE, $A_1 A_2, ..., A_n$, $A_{n+1}, ...$, is obtained such that $\overline{BA_n} = \overline{A_nA_{n+1}}$ for $n = 1, 2, 3, ...$ To this infinite sequence correspond other infinite sequences, namely, that of rays (R)

$$BA_1, BA_2, BA_3, ..., \quad BA_n, BA_{n+1}, ... \tag{R}$$

as well as that of angles (A)

$$\widehat{A_1BQ}, \widehat{A_2BQ}, \widehat{A_3BQ}, ..., \quad \widehat{A_nBQ}, \widehat{A_{n+1}BQ}, ... \tag{A}$$

these rays (R) make with the ray BQ. By construction, all the rays of the sequence (R) intersect the line CE, and we now set out to prove that the formula $\widehat{A_nBQ} = 90°/2^n$ holds for all the angles in (A).

For the first two rays, BA_1 and BA_2, this formula is true since $\widehat{A_1BQ}$ $= \widehat{CA_1B} = 90°/2^1$ and $\widehat{A_2BQ} = \widehat{BA_2A_1} = 90°/2^2$, as we just found. Applying the method of mathematical induction, we suppose that for some value m of the subscript n the general formula is already justified, so that $\widehat{A_mBQ}$ is known to be equal to $90°/2^m$. To study the next member, $\widehat{A_{m+1}BQ}$, of the sequence (A) we observe that $\widehat{A_mBQ} = \widehat{BA_mA_{m-1}}$ as well as $\widehat{A_{m+1}BQ}$ $= \widehat{BA_{m+1}A_m}$ because the lines CE and BQ are parallel. The triangle $BA_{m+1}A_m$ (Fig. 13) is isosceles since $BA_m = A_mA_{m+1}$. Therefore,

$$\widehat{A_{m+1}BQ} = \widehat{BA_{m+1}A_m} = \widehat{BA_mA_{m-1}}/2 = \widehat{A_mBQ}/2 = (90°/2^m)/2 = 90°/2^{m+1}$$

which proves that the general formula we are studying holds for $n = m + 1$, if it is true for $n = m$. Thus, this formula is a hereditary property of the sequence (A). Because it is known to be true for the first two members, it holds for all members of this sequence: $\widehat{A_nBQ} = 90°/2^n$ is true for all values of the integer n.

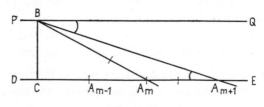

Fig. 14.13

We constructed an infinite sequence of straight lines through B making with BQ angles equal to $90°/2^n$ and intersecting CE no matter how large is the integer n. Therefore, using the lemma, we conclude the uniqueness of the parallel PQ, so that Playfair's Axiom is deduced from Theorem II. This result shows the complete equivalence of Theorem II and the Fifth Postulate.

Pasch's Axiom

In the first step of our deduction of Playfair's Axiom from Theorem II, we assumed that a straight line entering a triangle through its vertex necessarily leaves it and therefore intersects the opposite side. Our argument, namely, that the triangle is finite while the straight line is infinite, at closer analysis reveals itself as based on intuition. Therefore, as it was pointed out for the first time by Pasch, a special axiom is necessary to ensure that a straight line which cuts the perimeter of a triangle in a point intersects this perimeter again in a second point. This important assumption was implicitly made by Euclid since he uses it in his proofs, but it was neither formulated nor included in his system of axioms. The term *perimeter* of a triangle means the set of points consisting of three vertices A, B, C of a triangle ABC and of all the *interior* points of its three sides AB, BC, CA, the word *side* denoting here the finite segments AB, BC, CA of infinite straight lines AB, BC and CA. To avoid misunderstanding, it is advisable to use the terms *side-segment* and *side-line*, since the word side has a double meaning: it is used to denote a finite segment between two vertices as well as the whole straight line (infinite) of which it is a segment. In modern geometry, the important axiom we are discussing is enunciated as follows:

PASCH'S AXIOM: *If a straight line enters a triangle, cutting one of its side-segments, then it must also cut one of the other two side-segments or pass through the opposite vertex. If a straight line enters a triangle through one of its vertices, it must cut the opposite side-segment.*

The lack of this axiom in *Elements* constitutes an important omission. The meaning of Pasch's Axiom can be illustrated by stating that, according to it, a segment of straight line entering a triangle must leave it if extended. With the aid of this axiom, we can easily prove that the number of points which a straight line distinct from side-lines of a triangle can have in common with its perimeter cannot exceed two.

Suppose, to the contrary, that a straight line exists with more than two and, therefore, at least three points in common with the perimeter of a triangle. We have to disprove four different cases: (1) all three common points are vertices; (2) two of them are vertices, the third being the interior point of a side-segment; (3) one point is a vertex, the two others being interior points of side-segments; and (4) none of the three points is a vertex.

By definition of a triangle, its vertices are three non-collinear points, and this eliminates the first case. The second case is impossible because a straight line passing through two vertices cannot be distinct from a side-line. In the third case, the two points other than vertices must belong to two different side-segments, otherwise the given line would coincide with a side-line. If so, one of these two points will be collinear with the third point, which is a vertex, and again the given line would coincide with a side of the triangle. We come finally to the fourth case, in which all three common points are interior points on side-segments of the triangle. No two of them can be incident with one and the same side because then the given line would coincide with this side. Therefore, we have to discuss Fig. 14 and prove that no straight line can be incident with three points P, Q, R if the three relations (APC), (BQC), (ARB) are true.

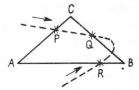

Fig. 14.14

Suppose, to the contrary, that such a straight line does exist, and denote the three points it has in common with the perimeter of a triangle ABC by P, Q, R in such a way that the relation (PQR) holds, the line entering the triangle at P and R. Applying Pasch's Axiom, we conclude the existence of a fourth common point the same line has with the perimeter and through which it leaves the triangle. This fourth point must belong to one side-segment or it is a vertex, so that again the given line would have two points in common with a side and thus would coincide with it. Thus, no straight line distinct from sides of a triangle can have more than two points in common with the perimeter of this triangle.

Dual Transform of Pasch's Axiom

It is of interest to study the form Pasch's Axiom takes when transformed by duality because its dual transform possesses an intuitive self-evidence which is lacking in Pasch's Axiom itself. Nobody can pretend, indeed, that for him it is intuitively clear what happens to a straight line inside an area it penetrates before the properties of a region are fixed with the aid of an axiom, and Pasch's Axiom is necessary to ensure that a straight line, if extended sufficiently, crosses a finite region and finally leaves it, intersecting its boundary for the second time.

In preparing the transformation of Pasch's Axiom by duality, we first must study how are transformed the various straight lines differently located with respect to a triangle ABC. They become points in the plane of the dual image of the triangle ABC, this dual image being itself another triangle DEF, and we have to characterize the location of these points with respect to the triangle DEF (Fig. 15).

The perimeter of a triangle divides its plane into two regions: the first one, which is finite, is bounded by the perimeter and is called the *interior* of the triangle; the second one, surrounding the triangle, is infinite and is called the *exterior*. From the point of view of their location relatively to a given triangle, the points in its plane belong to one of four classes, which together include all the points of the plane except the vertices of the triangle. These classes are defined as follows: (1) Class K—interior of the triangle; (2) Class L—perimeter, except the three vertices; (3) Class M—points exterior to the triangle and incident with its side-lines; (4) Class N—exterior points, non-incident with the side-lines, but incident with *two* lines belonging to *two* exterior angles.

Transforming these point-classes by duality, we obtain a classification of all straight lines of a plane from the point of view of their location relatively to a given triangle in this plane, *except* the three side-lines of the triangle. We have again four classes defined as follows: (1) Class k—straight lines having no common points with the perimeter of the triangle. (2) l—lines through a vertex and belonging to an exterior angle. (3) Class m—through a vertex and belonging to an interior angle. (4) Class n—lines incident with two points on the perimeter belonging to two side segments, none being a vertex.

Thus, a k-line is completely exterior to the triangle, an l-line belongs to an exterior angle, an m-line belongs to an interior angle of the triangle, and an

n-line cuts two side-segments. To justify the duality relating a point-class and a line-class denoted by the same letter, it is sufficient to study the dual transformation of three intersection points of a given line with the three sides of the reference triangle, using Fig. 15 and recalling that the dual image of a side-segment is the exterior angle of the triangle, while an interior angle is transformed dually into the side-line minus two vertices and minus the side-segment lying on this side-line. A table of classes just defined follows

Plane I (ABC) Straight Lines with points on the perimeter	Duality Class	Plane II (DEF) Points
none	k & K	interior
one (vertex)	l & L	on a side-segment
two (one vertex)	m & M	exterior, on a side-line
two (none of them a vertex)	n & N	exterior, non-incident with a side-line

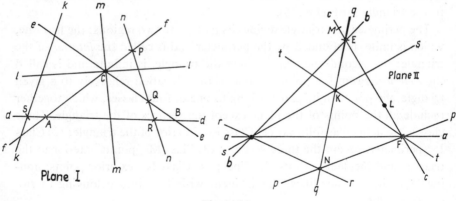

Fig. 14.15

To transform Pasch's Axiom, we first formulate it in terms of classes just defined. In fact, it can be expressed as follows: If a straight line is incident with a point of class L, then it is of class n or m; if a straight line is incident with a vertex and with a point of class K, then it is of class m.

This way of stating Pasch's Axiom allows an easy transformation by duality which reads as follows: If a point is incident with a straight line of class l, then it is of class N or M; if a point is incident with a side-line and with a line of class k, it is of class M.

But, substituting for classes their definitions, this dual companion of Pasch's Axiom takes the following self-evident form:

A point incident with a straight line passing through the vertex of a triangle and belonging to its exterior angle is exterior to the triangle; the intersection point of a side and of a line having no common points with the perimeter of a triangle is exterior to the triangle.

Beginning with this self-evident axiom and applying to it the transformation by duality, Pasch's Axiom is obtained because the duality is a reciprocal relationship.

Returning to Theorem II, we point out an easy corollary of this theorem, which is the following

THEOREM IV: *In any triangle, an exterior angle is greater than either of two non-adjacent interior angles.*

PROOF: In a triangle, the sum $\hat{A} + \hat{B} + \hat{C}$ of three interior angles is equal to 180°. On the other hand, denoting by $\hat{E}$ the exterior angle adjacent to the interior angle $\hat{C}$, we also have $\hat{E} + \hat{C} = 180°$. Thus, $\hat{A} + \hat{B} + \hat{C} = \hat{E} + \hat{C}$ and, therefore, $\hat{A} = \hat{E} - \hat{B} < \hat{E}$, as well as $\hat{B} = \hat{E} - \hat{A} < E$.

This proof of Theorem IV, that is of Proposition XVI, Book I of Euclid's *Elements,* is correct, but its defect consists in the use of Theorem II, which is a disguised form of the Fifth Postulate, and thus makes the validity of Theorem IV depend on the acceptance of the Fifth Postulate. This is not so, and therefore we also give here Euclid's proof of Theorem IV, which is independent of the Fifth Postulate.

To prove that the exterior angle $\overset{\frown}{ACD}$ (Fig. 16) is greater than the interior angle $\overset{\frown}{CAB}$, we draw a straight line BME through the vertex B and the midpoint M of the opposite side AC. We then take a point F on this line such that BM $=$ MF, the point M then being the midpoint of BF as well as of AC.

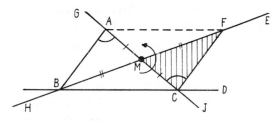

Fig. 14.16

Joining F to C, we form a triangle CMF which, if rotated counterclockwise through 180° around the point M, will coincide with triangle ABM: after the rotation, the rays MJ, ME coincide with rays MG, MH, respectively, and

5 Kogbetliantz

the points F and C coincide with B and A, respectively. The triangles CFM and ABM are equal as congruent and, in particular, $\widehat{ACF} = \widehat{CAB}$ as congruent angles. But the angle $\widehat{ACF}$ is a part of the angle $\widehat{ACD}$ because the ray BME always remains above the line BCD so that the straight line CF is between CA and CD no matter how large BM and BF = 2BM. A part is less than the whole (*Elements*, Common Notion III) and, therefore, $\widehat{CAB} = \widehat{ACF} < \widehat{ACD}$, which is Theorem IV.

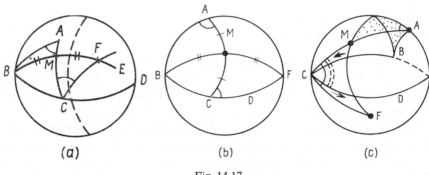

(a)   (b)   (c)

Fig. 14.17

It is necessary to emphasize in this proof the importance of the fact that the straight line BME remains always above BCD. In Riemannian geometry exemplified on the surface of a sphere, two straight lines behave as two great circles on the sphere, so that they recross each other for the second time if sufficiently extended. Therefore, it is of interest to see what happens with Theorem IV on the sphere. Repeating for spherical triangle ABC (Fig. 17) the same construction, we distinguish three cases. In the first case (Fig. 17a) when the arc of great circle BF is less than 180°, the proof and the conclusion of Theorem IV hold so that the interior angle $\widehat{CAB}$ is less than the exterior angle $\widehat{ACD}$. But, if the spherical distance of the vertex B from the midpoint M of the side AC is equal to 90° and thus BF is equal to 180° (Fig. 17b), the point F is no more above the side BCD since F is diametrically opposite to B and therefore all great circles which pass through B intersect also at the point F, so that F is on the side BCD and the interior angle $\widehat{CAB}$ is *equal* to the exterior angle $\widehat{ACD}$. Finally, in the third case (Fig. 17c) when BF is greater than 180° and the point F is *below* the side BCD, the interior angle is *greater* than the exterior angle, instead of being smaller.

Thus, Theorem IV holds for spherical triangles if they are sufficiently small but ceases to be true if half a great circle is reached or exceeded in the construction of a figure. The fact that Theorem IV holds for small spherical triangles is related to the peculiar relationship between Euclidean and Riemannian geometry, namely, that Euclidean geometry holds in the infinitesimal region of a Riemannian plane. In particular, when a spherical triangle decreases in such a way that all three sides tend to zero, at the limit its ultimate shape can be called an infinitesimal spherical triangle. Such a limiting case of a spherical triangle located at a point P of the sphere can be considered also as a plane triangle drawn in the tangent plane to the sphere whose contact point is P, where the infinitesimal triangle is located. Therefore, an infinitesimal spherical triangle ceases to be spherical and becomes a plane triangle which obeys the axioms and theorems of Euclidean geometry. If one prefers to avoid the use of infinitesimal triangles, the same conclusion can be reached by considering a spherical triangle with sides of fixed length and by increasing without limit the radius of the sphere to which this triangle belongs. At the limit when the radius becomes infinite, the sphere is transformed into a plane, and the spherical triangle becomes a plane Euclidean triangle. Its relative size, that is, its size compared to the size of the sphere, decreases when the radius increases, and, at the limit, our triangle, when compared to an infinite sphere, becomes relatively infinitesimal and at the same time remains a plane triangle of *finite* size.

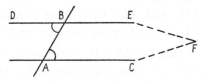

Fig. 14.18

Theorem IV can be used to prove the existence of parallel lines in the Euclidean plane. As we know, a transversal makes equal alternate interior angles with two parallel lines. To prove the converse, suppose that two lines are cut by a transversal AB in such a way that $\widehat{ABD} = \widehat{BAC}$ (Fig. 18). The lines AC and DE cannot intersect because the supposition of the existence of a common point F would entail for the triangle ABF thus formed the equality of its interior and exterior non-adjacent angles, since by hypothesis $\widehat{FAB} = \widehat{ABD}$, which would contradict Theorem IV. Therefore, two straight lines making equal alternate interior angles with a transversal are parallel.

Equality of Triangles

There are six metric elements in a triangle: three sides and three angles. Any three of them define the triangle and thus determine the other three elements which were not known, *except* the case in which the three given elements are three angles. The existence in Euclidean geometry of similar figures precludes the equality of two triangles which have the same angles.

Thus, we have three different sets of conditions for the equality of two triangles:

(1) All three sides of one are equal to three sides of another.

(2) Two sides and one angle of one are equal to two sides and one angle of another.

(3) One side and two angles of one are equal to one side and two angles of another triangle.

The proofs of the corresponding three theorems follow.

THEOREM V: *Two triangles are congruent if two sides and the included angle of one are equal, respectively, to two sides and the included angle of the other.*

We emphasize the condition imposed on the equal angles: they must be included between the equal sides. Let us first discuss the case when the equal angles are *not* included between the equal sides. Then the equal angles are opposite one pair of equal sides. Figure 19 shows the existence of two non-congruent triangles ABC and ABD which have two sides and the opposite angle of the one equal, respectively, to two sides and the opposite angle of the other. In these triangles, the side AB and the angle $\widehat{BAC}$ are common and BC = BD; the third sides are, however, unequal: AC ≠ AD. Thus, the condition imposed on equal angles in Theorem V is necessary, and the theorem fails if it is not fulfilled.

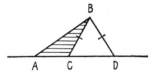

Fig. 14.19

Consider now two triangles $\widehat{ABC}$ and $\widehat{A'B'C'}$ (Fig. 20) with $\widehat{CAB} = \widehat{C'A'B'}$, AC = A'C' and AB = A'B'. Place the triangle A'B'C' in such a position that the sides AB and A'B' are on the same straight line SS without over-

lapping each other. Two cases are then possible: either the vertices C and C'
are on the same side of SS (Fig. 20a) or C and C' are separated by SS
(Fig. 20b). A rotation of the triangle A'B'C' through 180° about SS reduces
the second case to the first, so that it is sufficient to prove Theorem V considering the first case only.

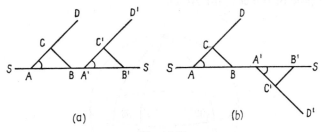

(a)   (b)

Fig. 14.20

PROOF: Shifting A'B'C' along SS, we place A'B' on AB, the points A', B'
coinciding with A, B, respectively. Since $\widehat{C'A'B'} = \widehat{CAB}$, the rays A'D' and
AD become superposed, and the points C' and C coincide because A'C'
= AC. The third sides B'C' and BC must then also be congruent because
their end points coincide, and two points define one and only one straight
line and have only one distance.

Thus, Theorem V is proved, and it follows that $\hat{B}' = \hat{B}, \hat{C}' = \hat{C}$, B'C' = BC.
Since the equality of interior angles in two triangles entails that of adjacent
exterior angles, the dual transformation of Theorem V gives the following
companion theorem:

THEOREM VI: *Two triangles are congruent if two angles and the included side
of one are equal to two angles and the included side of the other.*

The condition imposed in it on the equal sides, namely, that they must be
included between equal angles, is not necessary and can be omitted in the
case of Euclidean geometry because in this kind of geometry the sum of
angles of a triangle is the same for all triangles, and, therefore, if two angles
of one are equal to two angles of the other triangle, their third angles are also
equal, the equal sides being in this case always included between equal angles.

But this condition is essential because with it Theorem VI also holds in
both non-Euclidean geometries, and is no more true if the condition is not
fulfilled. On the sphere, for instance, two spherical triangles may have two
pairs of equal angles and one pair of equal sides without being equal, provided
the equal sides are opposite to equal angles instead of being included between

equal angles. In Fig. 21, ABC and ABD are two different triangles which nevertheless have in common their side AB and their angle $\hat{A}$ as well as equal angles at C and at D, $\overset{\frown}{ACB} = \overset{\frown}{ADB}$. The common vertex B, intersection point of two great circles $\overset{\frown}{CB}$ and $\overset{\frown}{DB}$ which make equal angles with $\overset{\frown}{AD}$, is the pole of the equator ACD,

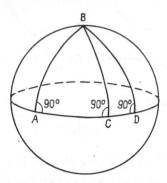

Fig. 14.21

Theorem V also holds in non-Euclidean geometries, provided that, in the case of Riemannian geometry, the triangles with a straight angle of 180° and the opposite side equal half the total length of Riemannian straight line are eliminated and considered as polygons with two sides only and not as triangles. On a sphere, two-sided polygon is called a *lune;* the two lunes in Fig. 22 illustrate the exception just mentioned.

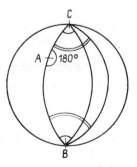

Fig. 14.22

Before studying the third case of equality of triangles, we must discuss the equality of two right triangles having two sides of one equal to two sides of the other. If the two legs of one are equal to those of the other, their right angles being included between equal sides, Theorem V applies, and the equality is established. But, if two right triangles have their hypotenuses and one pair of legs equal, then the equal right angles are opposite equal hypotenuses, and, in this case, Theorem V cannot be applied. Nevertheless, the triangles are equal, so that the following theorem holds:

THEOREM VII: *Two right triangles are congruent if the hypotenuse and a leg of one, are equal, respectively, to the hypotenuse and a leg of the other.*

PROOF: Let $A'C' = AC$ and $B'C' = BC$, $\widehat{ABC} = \widehat{A'B'C'}$ being right angles (Fig. 23). Place $A'B'C'$ in such a position DBC that points B', C' coincide with B, C, respectively, the point A' occupying the position D. Thus, DC $= A'C' = AC$, and, in the isosceles triangle ADC, the angles opposite equal sides are equal (Theorem III): $\widehat{BAC} = \widehat{BDC}$. Since $\widehat{ABC} = \widehat{A'B'C'} = \widehat{DBC}$ $= 90°$, the third angles in triangles ABC and BCD also are equal: $\widehat{ACB}$ $= 180° - \widehat{ABC} - \widehat{BAC} = 180° - \widehat{DBC} - \widehat{BDC} = \widehat{DCB}$. Now we see that the two triangles ABC and BCD have equal sides AC = DC included between equal angles and therefore (Theorem VI) they are equal. This proves Theorem VII since from ABC = BCD and BCD = A'B'C' we conclude A'B'C' = ABC.

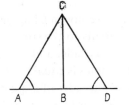

Fig. 14.23

Returning to conditions of equality of general triangles, we state now the third case of equality as follows:

THEOREM VIII: *Two triangles are congruent if three sides of one are equal, respectively, to three sides of the other.*

PROOF: Given two triangles ABC and DEF with AB = DE, BC = EF, and CA = FD (Fig. 24), we place DEF in the position ABG, where AG $= DF$ and BG = EF, and draw the segment CG. Consider now the two triangles ACG and BCG thus formed. Since in them AC = FD = AG and BC = EF = BG, both triangles are isosceles. Applying Theorem III, we find that $\overset{\frown}{ACG} = \overset{\frown}{AGC}$ and $\overset{\frown}{BCG} = \overset{\frown}{BGC}$ as angles opposite equal sides in an isosceles triangle. Therefore, the angles $\overset{\frown}{ACB}$ and $\overset{\frown}{AGB}$ are equal: $\overset{\frown}{ACB}$ $= \overset{\frown}{ACG} + \overset{\frown}{BCG} = \overset{\frown}{AGC} + \overset{\frown}{BGC} = \overset{\frown}{AGB}$. Thus, our reasoning proves that, in general, the angles opposite equal sides are equal, if all three sides of one triangle are equal, respectively, to three sides of the other. In other words, in two triangles with equal sides, the angles of one are equal, respectively, to the angles of the other, which proves Theorem VIII.

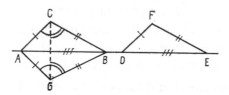

Fig. 14.24

Theorem VIII and its dual companion theorem hold in both non-Euclidean geometries, but the dual companion theorem, that is,

THEOREM VIII*: *Two triangles are congruent if three angles of one are equal, respectively, to three angles of the other*

does not hold in Euclidean geometry, as we saw in Chapter 13.
Quadrilateral. We apply now these theorems to the study of some quadrilaterals. The simplest, called a *square*, has equal sides and equal angles. The number n of sides being four, the sum of its angles is equal to $360° = 180° (4 - 2)$, so that a square has right angles. If now the sides of a quadrilateral are equal but its angles are not right angles, the quadrilateral is called a *rhombus* and has the following properties: its opposite sides are parallel, its opposite angles are equal, its diagonals are perpendicular and bisect each other, dividing it thus into four equal right triangles (which are not isosceles unless the rhombus is a square).

By Theorem III we know that in Fig. 25 we have $\overset{\frown}{ABD} = \overset{\frown}{ADB}$ and $\overset{\frown}{CBD}$ $= \overset{\frown}{CDB}$ because $AB = BC = CD = DA$, the quadrilateral ABCD being a rhombus. On the other hand, Theorem VIII shows that the triangles ABD and CBD are equal, so that $\overset{\frown}{ABD} = \overset{\frown}{DBC}$ and $\overset{\frown}{ADB} = \overset{\frown}{BDC}$. Combining these two results, we see that the alternate interior angles $\overset{\frown}{ABD}$ and $\overset{\frown}{BDC}$ as well as $\overset{\frown}{BDA}$ and $\overset{\frown}{DBC}$ are equal: $\overset{\frown}{ABD} = \overset{\frown}{DBC} = \overset{\frown}{BDC} = \overset{\frown}{BDA}$. Therefore, the opposite sides are parallel and, furthermore, $\overset{\frown}{ADC} = \overset{\frown}{ABC}$, that is, opposite angles are equal. Considering the two triangles ADC and ABC, we obtain the similar result $\widehat{BAC} = \widehat{BCA} = \widehat{DAC} = \widehat{DCA}$, so that $\widehat{BAD} = \widehat{BCD}$.

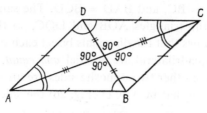

Fig. 14.25

Applying Theorem VI, we find that the triangles DOC and BOC are equal because DC = BC, $\widehat{ODC} = \widehat{OBC}$, and $\widehat{OCD} = \widehat{OCB}$. Therefore, $\widehat{DOC} = \widehat{BOC}$ as corresponding angles of congruent triangles, so that $2\widehat{DOC} = \widehat{DOC} + \widehat{BOC} = 180°$. This shows that $\widehat{DOC} = \widehat{BOC} = 90°$, and, thus, the diagonals are perpendicular. Moreover, BO = OD as corresponding sides of two equal triangles. Finally, we see that by Theorem V the triangles BOC and AOD are congruent and therefore AO = OC, so that the diagonals indeed bisect each other. We observe that they cannot be equal if the rhombus is not a square, because two equal and perpendicular segments bisecting each other are diagonals of a square, the proof of this last proposition being left to the reader.

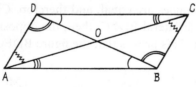

Fig. 14.26

A rhombus is a particular case of *parallelogram*, a parallelogram being defined as a quadrilateral whose opposite sides are parallel. As we will see, the opposite sides are then equal and this fact is often formulated as follows: *Parallel segments included between parallels are equal.* In general, the diagonals of a parallelogram are not perpendicular, but they always bisect each other. To prove these facts, consider the diagonal BD of a parallelogram ABCD (Fig. 26) as a transversal cutting the two pairs of parallel lines AB ∥ DC and AD ∥ BC. Then, $\widehat{ABD} = \widehat{CDB}$ and $\widehat{ADB} + \widehat{DBC}$

because they are pairs of alternate interior angles. But between these two pairs of equal angles is included the common side BD of the two triangles ABD and BDC. Therefore, by Theorem VI these triangles are congruent and AB = DC, AD = BC, and $\widehat{BAD} = \widehat{BCD}$. The same Theorem VI can now be applied to the triangles AOB and DOC, so that AO = OC and BO = OD, which shows that the diagonals bisect each other. Finally, if *two* opposite sides of a quadrilateral are parallel *and equal*, the figure is a parallelogram, that is, the other two opposite sides are also parallel and equal. To prove this, suppose that in ABCD (Fig. 26) the side AB is parallel and equal to DC. Therefore, $\widehat{BDC} = \widehat{DBA}$. But AB = DC and BD is common side in two triangles ABD and BDC. Applying to them Theorem V, we prove that they are equal, which entails AD = BC and $\widehat{ADB} = \widehat{DBC}$. Thus, the segments AD and BC are equal and parallel, which completes the proof.

The last property of parallelogram allows us to prove an important proposition concerning triangles:

THEOREM IX: *The segment joining the midpoints of two sides of a triangle is equal to half the third side and parallel to it.*

PROOF: Draw the straight line DEF through the midpoints D, E of AB and AC, respectively (Fig. 27), as well as the parallel CG to BA through C, defining thus the point F as their intersection point. In the two triangles DAE and CEF, we have $\widehat{DAE} = \widehat{ECF}$ because BA ∥ CG, $\widehat{DEA} = \widehat{CEF}$ because they are vertical angles, and AE = EC since E is the midpoint of AC. By Theorem VI, these triangles are equal, and therefore CF = AD = BD and EF = DE. In the quadrilateral BDFC, then, the opposite sides CF and BD are equal and parallel. This proves that the figure BDFC is a parallelogram,

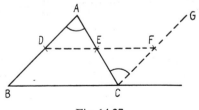

Fig. 14.27

and thus DF is equal and parallel to BC, so that DE is parallel to BC. To show that it is equal to one half the side BC, we observe that DF = BC and therefore DE = ½DF = ½BC, which completes the proof of Theorem IX.

We pass now to the study of properties of a general quadrilateral. A parallelogram is merely its particular case, but any quadrilateral possesses an *inscribed parallelogram* whose vertices are at the midpoints of sides of the quadrilateral. To prove that *the four segments joining the midpoints of adjacent sides of a quadrilateral form a parallelogram*, draw the diagonals AC,

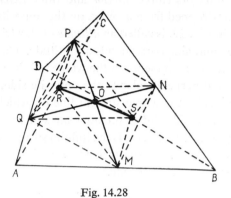

Fig. 14.28

BD (Fig. 28) and the four segments MN, NP, PQ, QM joining the midpoints M, N, P, Q of the sides of a quadrilateral ABCD. Applying Theorem IX to the four triangles ABC, BCD, CAD, DAB, we prove that the opposite sides of the quadrilateral MNPQ inscribed in ABCD are parallel and equal to one half the same diagonal, namely: MN $\overset{\shortparallel}{=}$ ½AC $\overset{\shortparallel}{=}$ PQ and NP $\overset{\shortparallel}{=}$ ½BD $\overset{\shortparallel}{=}$ QM. Therefore, MNPQ is a parallelogram since MN ∥ PQ and NP ∥ QM. Moreover, since the diagonals of a parallelogram bisect each other, the intersection point O of MP and NQ is the midpoint of both segments MP, NQ. But MP and NQ considered in relation to the quadrilateral ABCD connect the midpoints of opposite sides. Thus, *in any quadrilateral, the two segments joining the midpoints of opposite sides bisect each other*. Their intersection point O is also the midpoint of a third segment RS joining the midpoints R and S of the two diagonals AC and BD. To see this, consider the quadrilateral NRQS, in which SR and NQ are diagonals. Applying Theorem IX to triangles ABD and ABC, we conclude that NR is equal and parallel to QS because both of them are equal and parallel to ½AB. Hence, NRQS is a parallelogram, and its diagonals SR and NQ bisect each other at O, which is the midpoint of NQ. With the three segments SR, MP, and NQ bisecting each other are associated three parallelograms MNPQ, NRQS, and MSPR, whose vertices are six midpoints of four sides and two diagonals of the quadrilateral ABCD (Fig. 28).

Four Remarkable Points of a Triangle

We will now study four groups of concurrent lines related to a triangle: three *altitudes* (called also *heights*), three *medians*, three *perpendicular bisectors* of sides, and six *bisectors* (three *interior* and three *exterior*) of angles.

A perpendicular dropped from a vertex on the opposite side of a triangle, for instance, CD in Fig. 29, is called an *altitude* of this triangle. To each pair of opposite vertex and side corresponds an altitude. The term "altitude" is used also to denote not a segment but the whole infinite straight line passing through a vertex and perpendicular to the opposite side.

A segment (or, again, the whole straight line on which this segment lies) joining a vertex to the midpoint of the opposite side is called a *median* (CM in Fig. 29). A *perpendicular bisector* is the infinite straight line drawn through the midpoint of a side and perpendicular to this side (ME in Fig. 29). It is parallel to the corresponding altitude.

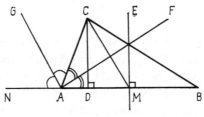

Fig. 14.29

A straight line passing through the vertex of an angle and dividing this angle into two equal parts is called the bisector of the angle. At every vertex of a triangle, there are two angles, interior and exterior, which supplement each other to 180°. In Fig. 29, for example, at the vertex A we have $\widehat{BAC}$ + $\widehat{NAC}$ = 180°. Therefore, through every vertex of a triangle pass two *bisectors:* the *interior* one, which bisects the interior angle, and the *exterior* one, which bisects the exterior angle (AF and AG in Fig. 29). They are perpendicular to each other because (Fig. 29):

$$\widehat{NAG} = \widehat{GAC} = \tfrac{1}{2}\widehat{NAC}; \ \widehat{BAF} = \widehat{FAC} = \tfrac{1}{2}\widehat{BAC}; \ \widehat{NAC} + \widehat{BAC} = 180°.$$

$$\widehat{GAF} = \widehat{GAC} + \widehat{CAF} = \tfrac{1}{2}\widehat{NAC} + \tfrac{1}{2}\widehat{BAC} = \tfrac{1}{2}(\widehat{NAC} + \widehat{BAC}) = 90°.$$

Altitudes and medians when considered as segments have a length, but perpendicular bisectors of sides and bisectors of angles cannot have a length since, by definition, they are not segments but whole straight lines. Four groups of concurrent straight lines related to a triangle define the four remarkable points of a triangle:

THEOREM X: *The three altitudes, three medians, three perpendicular bisectors of sides, and three bisectors of interior angles of a triangle form four groups of concurrent straight lines.*

The four points thus defined also have their special names: the altitudes intersect at the *orthocenter;* the intersection point of the three medians is the center of gravity of the triangle's area and is called the *centroid;* the perpendicular bisectors of three sides meet at the center of the circumscribed circle through three vertices of the triangle, and, by abbreviation, this point is called the *circumcenter;* finally, the center of the inscribed circle tangent to three sides of the triangle is the intersection point of the three bisectors of interior angles, and it is called the *incenter.* We shall prove Theorem X by considering separately each of these four groups of concurrent lines.

Circumcenter. A circle which passes through all these vertices of a triangle is said to be circumscribed about this triangle and the triangle is said to be inscribed in the circle. This circle is unique since through three given non-collinear points passes one and only one circle of finite radius. To prove this proposition, we need the following:

LEMMA: *The locus of points equidistant from two given points A and B is the perpendicular bisector of the segment AB.*

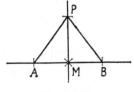

Fig. 14.30

Denote by M the midpoint of the segment AB (Fig. 30) and consider any point P on the perpendicular bisector of AB. Joining P to points A and B, two right triangles APM and BPM are formed in which AM = MB, MP = MP, and $\widehat{AMP} = \widehat{BMP} = 90°$. By Theorem V they are equal and therefore have equal hypotenuses, PA = PB, which proves that every point of the perpendicular bisector is equidistant from both ends of the segment. It remains to show that, conversely, any point P known to be equidistant from A and B lies on the perpendicular bisector of AB. Joining P to M, we have to show that the angles AMP and BMP are right angles. Since their sum is equal to 180°, it is sufficient to prove that $\widehat{AMP} = \widehat{BMP}$ to conclude that they are right angles. Now, AP = BP by hypothesis, AM = BM because M is the midpoint of AB, and MP = MP, so that by Theorem VIII the triangles AMP and BMP are equal. Thus, $\widehat{AMP} = \widehat{BMP}$, and MP is the perpendicular bisector of AB, which completes the proof of our lemma.

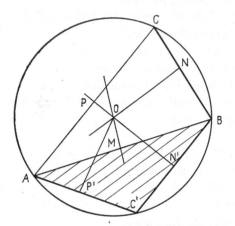

AM = MB , BN = NC, CP = PA , BN' = N'C', CP' = P'A

Fig. 14.31

Given two points A and B on a circle (Fig. 31), the segment AB joining them is called a *chord* of this circle. By definition of a circle, its center O is equidistant from points A and B, so that by applying the lemma just proved, we can state that the center of a circle is always incident with the perpendicular bisector of its chord. Conversely, every point of the perpendicular bisector of a segment AB can be taken as the center of a circle passing through A and B since this point is equidistant from A and B.

Therefore, there are an infinity of circles of various radii passing through two given points, and their centers fill out the whole perpendicular bisector of the segment defined by these two points. If a third point C is given, however, there is one and only one circle passing through all three given points A, B, C because its center O must be incident with the two perpendicular bisectors of the chords AB and BC, and two straight lines can interesect in only one point. Considering now the third chord AC, we see that its perpendicular bisector must also pass through O because AO = BO = CO, so that the points A and C are equidistant from O. Hence, we have proved that the perpendicular bisectors of the sides of a triangle are concurrent lines and meet at the circumcenter.

The position of the circumcenter with respect to the triangle depends on the shape of the triangle: it can be either interior or exterior to the triangle, coinciding in the intermediary case with the midpoint of the greatest side. It is exterior if the triangle has an obtuse angle and is interior if all three angles are acute. The intermediary case can occur only for a right triangle whose circumcenter is at the midpoint of the hypotenuse.

To prove this important property of right triangles, we have to show that (1) the center of a circle circumscribed about a right triangle is at the midpoint of the hypotenuse and (2) if the circumcenter of a triangle is at the midpoint of a side, the angle opposite to this side is a right angle.

Given a triangle ABC with a right angle at the vertex C, join the midpoint M of its hypotenuse AB to the vertex C as well as to the midpoints N and P of two legs (Fig. 32). The straight lines MN and MP are then parallel to AC and BC, respectively (Theorem IX), and, therefore, MN is perpendicular to BC and MP to AC. Thus, the lines MN and MP are perpendicular bisectors of segments BC and AC and their intersection point M, the midpoint of the hypotenuse, is the circumcenter of the given right triangle.

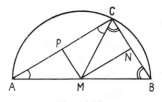

Fig. 14.32

Suppose now, conversely, that the midpoint M of AB is the circumcenter of a triangle ABC in which AB is the greatest side. Thus, the point M is equidistant from the vertices, that is, AM = BM = CM. To prove then that the angle $\overarc{ACB}$ is a right angle, we observe that the triangles AMC and BMC are isosceles, and therefore $\overarc{ACM} = \overarc{CAM}$ and $\overarc{BCM} = \overarc{CBM}$. The sum of angles being equal to 180°, we state that $\overarc{CAM} + \overarc{ACM} + \overarc{BCM} + \overarc{CBM}$ $= 2(\overarc{ACM} + \overarc{BCM}) = 2\,\overarc{ACB} = 180°$ and, finally, $\overarc{ACB} = 90°$.

Incenter. Continuing the proof of the Theorem X, we now study the bisectores of intrior angles. Given a triangle ABC (Fig. 33), the interior bisectors

AD and BE intersect in a point O whose distances from the sides are represented by perpendiculars OM, ON, and OP dropped from this point O on the
three sides of the triangle. We will prove that these distances are equal to each
other, so that O is equidistant from all three sides AB, BC, CA.

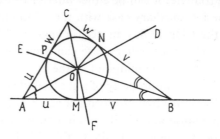

Fig. 14.33

Let us consider the right triangles AMO and APO on the one hand and
BMO and BNO on the other hand. Their angles at M, N, P are equal as right
angles and, moreover, $\widehat{MAO} = \widehat{PAO}$, $\widehat{MBO} = \widehat{NBO}$, by hypothesis. Therefore, in each pair of triangles, the third angles are equal also: $\widehat{AOM} = \widehat{AOP}$
as well as $\widehat{BOM} = \widehat{BON}$. The triangles AMO and APO have, therefore, a
common side AO included between equal angles, and the same is true for
the triangles BMO and BNO, which have in common the side BO. Applying
Theorem VI, we conclude the equality of the triangles AMO and APO on
the one hand and BMO and BNO on the other hand. Therefore, OM = OP
as well as OM = OP: OM = ON = OP.

Point O was defined as the intersection point of two bisectors AD and
BE of interior angles at A and B. Joining it to the third vertex C, we will
prove that the straight line COF bisects the third interior angle $\widehat{ACB}$. The
right triangles NOC and POC are equal because they have the common
hypotenuse OC and equal legs OP = ON (Theorem VII). Therefore, their an-
gles $\widehat{PCO}$ and $\widehat{NCO}$ are equal as opposite to equal sides in two equal triangles.
Thus, the line CF is the interior bisector of $\widehat{ACB}$ and the point O is incident
with all three interior bisectors.

A circle described about the point O as center with OM = ON = OP
as radii is said to be tangent to the sides of the triangle ABC at points M,
N, P and is referred to as the *inscribed* circle of triangle ABC. Each side has
with it only one point in common, namely, the contact point, since the distances from the center O of all the other points of this side exceed the radius

$R = $ OM, and the points at distances from O greater than R are exterior to the circle.

The contact points M, N, P cut each side into two segments, and we have seen that the segments adjacent to a vertex are equal because they are corresponding sides of two congruent right triangles. Therefore, we have AM $=$ AP $= u$, BM $=$ BN $= v$, and CN $=$ CP $= w$, where u, v, w denote three unknown lengths. To express these lengths in terms of the lengths of the three sides, we observe that AM $+$ MB $=$ AB, BN $+$ NC $=$ BC, and CP $+$ PA $=$ AC, so that denoting the lengths of sides by AB $= c$, BC $= a$, CA $= b$, we obtain the three equations $u + v = c$, $v + w = a$, $w + u = b$ with three unknowns u, v, w. Adding them and denoting the sum of the lengths of all three sides $a + b + c$ (called the *perimeter* of the triangle) by $2s$, we obtain $2u + 2v + 2w = a + b + c = 2s$, so that $u + v + w = s$. Subtracting from this equation the equation $u + v = c$ member by member, we obtain $w = s - c$. Likewise, subtracting the other two equations, the corresponding expressions $u = s - a$ and $v = s - b$ are obtained. We have incidentally proved, as an indirect result, the following proposition concerning two tangent lines drawn to a circle through an exterior point: *Two tangents to a circle from an external point are equal.* For example, in Fig. 33 we have AM $=$ AP. Here the term "tangent" means the length of the segment of tangent line between the contact point and the external point through which the two tangent lines are drawn. Another important property of straight lines tangent to a circle can be inferred from the same Fig. 33. *A straight line perpendicular to a radius at its extremity is tangent to the circle*: AB is perpendicular to the radius OM and passes through its endpoint.

Both constructions we just studied in the Euclidean plane hold also in spherical geometry: a spherical triangle has inscribed and circumscribed circles, and their centers are the common points of interior bisectors and of perpendicular bisectors, respectively. The only difference concerns the intermediary case when the center of the circumscribed circle coincides with the midpoint of the largest side. Here again, the two triangles AMC and MBC (Fig. 34) are isosceles, so that $\overset{\frown}{MAC} = \overset{\frown}{MCA}$ and $\overset{\frown}{MBC} = \overset{\frown}{MCB}$, and there-

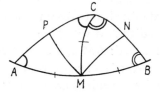

Fig. 14.34

fore $\widehat{ACB} = \widehat{CAB} + \widehat{CBA}$. But, as we will prove later, the sum of angles in a spherical triangle exceeds two right angles and the angle $\widehat{ACB}$, opposite to the side $\overline{AB}$, whose midpoint is the circumcenter of the triangle, is not a right but an obtuse angle. All that we can say for such a triangle is that the angle $\widehat{ACB}$ is equal to one half the sum of the three angles. Conversely, if in a spherical triangle one of its angles is equal to one half the sum of all three angles, the midpoint of the opposite side is then the center of the circumscribed circle. We add that the circumcenter of a spherical triangle is exterior to it if one of its angles is greater than the sum of the two other angles. It is interior to the triangle if the sum of any of its angles is greater than the third angle.

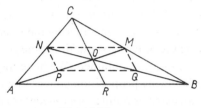

Fig. 14.35

Centroid. To prove that the medians of a triangle ABC are concurrent straight lines we draw two medians AM and BN joining the vertices A, B to midpoints M, N of opposite sides BC, AC (Fig. 35). Denoting their intersection point by O and the midpoints of segments AO, BO by P and Q, respectively, we draw the line PQ. This segment PQ is equal and parallel to $\frac{1}{2}$AB (Theorem IX). Likewise, the segment NM joining the midpoints N and M of sides AC and BC is equal and parallel to $\frac{1}{2}$AB. Therefore, in the quadrilateral MNPQ, the two sides PQ and MN are equal and parallel, which proves that MNPQ is a parallelogram. Since the diagonals of a parallelogram bisect each other, we conclude that QO = ON and PO = OM. But P and Q are midpoints of AO and BO, respectively, so that AP = PO = OM = AM/3 as well as BQ = QO = ON = BN/3.

In other words, two medians intersect each other at a point which, for each median, is one third of its length from the midpoint of the side. If now the intersection of the median AM with the third median CR is considered, the same conclusion is reached: AM and CR intersect at a point which on the median AM is one third of its length from the point M, that is, at the point O. Therefore, the three medians are concurrent at O, the centroid of the triangle ABC.

The three medians are also concurrent in non-Euclidean geometries (for the proof, see Appendix VIII), but the ratio of one third is no longer true. For every median, the ratio may be different, and it depends on the length of the corresponding side. The proof of the fact that the medians are concurrent is, of course, different from that just studied since our proof is based on the Fifth Postulate, which does not hold in non-Euclidean geometries.

Orthocenter. It remains now to study the intersection of altitudes (Fig. 36). We draw through vertices of a given triangle ABC straight lines parallel to opposite sides, thus forming a larger triangle DEF. The vertices of ABC are midpoints of sides of this larger triangle DEF because, considering, for example, the point C, the quadrilaterals ABDC and ABCE are parallelograms, and therefore EC = AB = CD, so that C is the midpoint of ED. The statement that ABDC and ABCE are parallelograms is justified by observing that parallel segments between parallels are equal. Likewise, A and B are midpoints of EF and FD, respectively. Thus, the three altitudes AG, BH, and CJ of the triangle ABC are perpendicular bisectors of the sides EF, FD, and DE, respectively, for the large triangle DEF. Therefore, these three straight lines are concurrent at the circumcenter O of the triangle DEF which, for the original given triangle ABC, is the orthocenter where the three altitudes of ABC intersect each other.

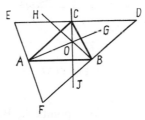

Fig. 14.36

This proof holds only for the Euclidean plane because it is based on the use of parallels (Fifth Postulate), but the fact that three altitudes of a triangle are concurrent lines is true also in non-Euclidean geometries (see Appendix VIII).

If all three angles of a triangle are acute, the orthocenter lies inside the triangle. If an angle is obtuse, it lies outside, and if the triangle is right, the orthocenter coincides with the vertex of the right angle.

The orthocenter and three vertices of a triangle form a remarkable configuration of four points called

Orthocentric System of Four Points. In such a system, each of the four points is the orthocenter of a triangle formed by three other points as vertices. Consider, for example, the triangle AOB in Fig. 36. Its three altitudes OJ ⊥ AB, AC ⊥ BO, and BC ⊥ AO meet at the point C, which, therefore, is the orthocenter of the triangle AOB.

The three midpoints R, S, T of the segments of altitudes OA, OB, OC joining the orthocenter O of ABC to the vertices of this triangle (Fig. 37) define a circle associated with the triangle ABC and called its *nine-point circle*. The reason for this name is the fact that this circle passes through the following nine points related to the triangle: the feet D, E, F of three altitudes, the midpoints L, M, N of three sides AB, BC, CA, and the midpoints of three segments OA, OB, OC. This circle was discovered by Euler and is often called *Euler's Circle*.

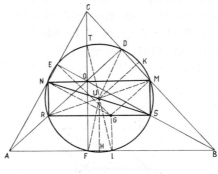

Fig. 14.37

The orthocentric system of four points A, B, C, O, which defines four triangles AOB, BOC, COA, and ABC, generates one and only one nine-point circle because all the four triangles of this system have the same circle as their common nine-point circle. To justify this fact, let us suppose, postponing the proof, that the circle defined by the three points R, S, T passes through the feet D, E, F of the altitudes and through the midpoints L, M, N of the sides of ABC. To prove that the nine-point circle of ABC is also that of the triangle AOB, we observe that, C being the orthocenter for AOB, this circle passes through the midpoints T, M, N of segments CO, CB, CA joining the orthocenter C to the vertices of AOB. Thus, by definition, it is the nine-point circle of AOB. The same reasoning applies to triangles BOC and COA with orthocenters A and B.

We shall now discuss and prove Euler's *nine-point circle theorem* which was unknown to Euclid:

THEOREM XI: *The feet of altitudes, the midpoints of sides of a triangle, and the midpoints of segments joining the vertices to the orthocenter lie upon a circle. The radius of this circle is one half the radius of the circumscribed circle, and its center lies midway between the orthocenter and the circumcenter of the triangle.*

Of the nine points involved in this theorem, we consider first the six midpoints L, M, N, R, S, T and draw fifteen segments joining them. Three of these fifteen segments, namely NS, MR, and LT, are diagonals of three quadrilaterals NRSM, NLST, LMTR, formed by the other twelve segments, each one of these three quadrilaterals having two midpoints of sides and two midpoints of altitude-segments as their vertices.

These quadrilaterals are not only parallelograms, but, more than that, they are rectangles. To show this, it is sufficient to consider one of them, for instance, NLST, since they are constructed similarly. Applying Theorem IX to segments NL, LS, ST, TN considered as drawn in triangles ABC, AOB, BOC, COA, respectively, we conclude that $NL \overset{\perp}{=} \frac{1}{2}BC$, $LS \overset{\perp}{=} \frac{1}{2}AO$, $ST \overset{\perp}{=} \frac{1}{2}BC$, and $TN \overset{\perp}{=} \frac{1}{2}AO$ since they join the midpoints of sides of triangles mentioned above. Thus, NL ∥ ST and LS ∥ TN, so that NLST is indeed a parallelogram. Furthermore, the sides of this parallelogram are parallel to AO and BC, which are perpendicular to each other. Thus, NLST is a rectangle, the same being true of NRSM and LMTR.

The diagonals of a rectangle bisect each other since this figure is a particular case of a parallelogram. Therefore, NS and MR bisect each other at their intersection point U. The same is true for the diagonals NS and LT of NLST, so that U is the common midpoint of all three diagonals NS, MR, and LT. Moreover, the diagonals of a rectangle are equal, which proves that NU = US = MU = UR = LU = UT. Thus, the six points L, M, N, R, S, T are equidistant from the point U, that is, they lie on a circle with center U and radius equal to NU = $\frac{1}{2}$NS, the three diagonals NS, MR, LT being diameters of this circle.

Consider now the right triangle RDM with the right angle $\overset{\frown}{RDM} = 90°$ at the vertex D. The midpoint U of its hypotenuse MR is also the circumcenter of the triangle RDM, so that UD = MU = UR, which proves that the point D lies on the circle in which are inscribed our three rectangles. Likewise, the right triangles ESN and FTL have their circumcenters at U, their vertices E and F lying on the same circle, and, thus, the proof of the existence of the nine-point circle is completed. It remains to show that the center of this circle lies midway between the orthocenter and the circumcenter of the triangle ABC and also that its radius is one half the radius R of the circumscribed circle. Here we must interrupt our study of the nine-point circle because we will need some properties of trapezoids which we now set out to deduce.

Trapezoid

A quadrilateral with two parallel sides (two other sides being non-parallel) is called a *trapezoid*. The non-parallel sides of a trapezoid are its *legs*, while the parallel sides are its *bases*. We shall now prove the following:

LEMMA: *The segment joining the midpoints of two legs of a trapezoid is parallel to its bases and equal to one half the sum of their lengths. Conversely, a line through the midpoint of one leg and parallel to the base bisects the other leg of a trapezoid.*

Consider a trapezoid ABCD (Fig. 38), and denote the midpoints of legs AD and BC by E and F. Join them and draw through F a line GH parallel to AD cutting AB and DC at G and H, respectively. The figure AGHD is then a parallelogram since AB ∥ DC and AD ∥ GH. Therefore, AG = DH and GH = AD.

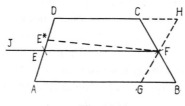

Fig. 14.38

The two triangles BFG and CFH have equal angles $\widehat{FCH} = \widehat{FBG}$ and $\widehat{CFH} = \widehat{GFB}$. Moreover, BF = FC by hypothesis, so that, applying Theorem VI, we prove the equality of these two triangles. Therefore, GB = CH and GF = FH = $\frac{1}{2}$GH = $\frac{1}{2}$AD = AE. We see that GF is not only parallel but also equal to AE, which proves that AGFE is a parallelogram. Thus, EF $\overset{\shortparallel}{=}$ AG. But AG = $\frac{1}{2}$(AB + DC) since 2AG = AG + DH = AB − GB + DC + CH = AB + DC − (GB − CH) = AB + DC, and, therefore, EF is parallel to the bases AB and DC and equal to one half the sum of their lengths.

Suppose now that in Fig. 38 F is again the midpoint of the leg BC but that the point E is now defined as the intersection point of the leg AD and the parallel FJ to the base drawn through the midpoint F of BC. We have to prove that E is the midpoint of AD. Suppose, to the contrary, it is not, and let E* be the midpoint of AD. The line E*F would then have to be a parallel to AB, and we would have two different parallels through F to the line AB, which is contrary to the Fifth Postulate. Thus, the points E* and E must coincide, and the lemma is established.

Returning now to our nine-point circle, we consider in Fig. 37 the trapezoids FLGO and DOGM, where point G is the circumcenter of ABC, so that AG = BG = CG as well as GL ⊥ AB, GM ⊥ BC and GN ⊥ CA, the lines GL, GM, GN being perpendicular bisectors of the sides of ABC. Denoting the midpoints of the chords FL and DM by H and K and drawing the perpendicular bisectors of both chords, we know that they must meet at the center U of the nine-point circle, since, as we saw, the center of a circle is always incident with the perpendicular bisector of its chord. Considered as parts of the trapezoids FLGO and DOGM, the segments HU and KU pass through the midpoint of one leg and are parallel to the base. Applying the lemma, we conclude that they must bisect the other leg of the corresponding trapezoid. But this other leg is the common leg OG, and, therefore, the straight lines HU and KU must meet at the midpoint of the segment OG. Since they intersect at the center U of the nine-point circle, we achieved the proof of the fact that this center U is midway between the orthocenter and the center G of the circumscribed circle.

It remains to be shown that the radius RU = NU is equal to one half the radius GA of the circumscribed circle. Indeed, RU joins the midpoints of sides AO, GO in the triangle AOG. Therefore, by Theorem IX, we have RU = $\frac{1}{2}$AG, and Theorem XI is proved.

The relation between the radii of the nine-point circle and the circumscribed circle entails an important corollary. Since the nine-point circle intersects all three sides of a triangle, while the inscribed circle lies entirely inside the triangle, the radius of the nine-point circle is, in general, greater than the radius of the inscribed circle. Since the radius of the nine-point circle is equal to one half the radius of the circumscribed circle, we come to the conclusion that the radius of the inscribed circle is less than one half the radius of the circumscribed circle. In other words, the diameter of the inscribed circle is less than the radius of the circumscribed circle.

There is an exceptional case when the nine-point circle and the inscribed circle coincide, and this can happen only, if the feet of all three altitudes are also midpoints of sides, so that the altitudes, medians, bisectors of interior angles, and perpendicular bisectors of sides are congruent. Such a triangle is necessarily an equilateral one, and, thus, the diameter of the inscribed circle is equal to the radius of the circumscribed circle only for equilateral triangles.

Eulerian Line of a Triangle

Three among the four remarkable points of a triangle are collinear in all triangles without exception. They are the orthocenter, the circumcenter, and, the centroid. This fact was discovered by Euler, and for this reason the straight line OG (Fig. 39) defined by the circumcenter G and the orthocenter O and on which lies also the centroid is called the *Eulerian line*.

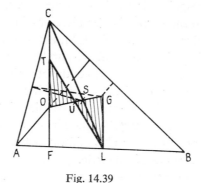

Fig. 14.39

To prove that the centroid is on OG, we use the fact that it is at one third of a median's length from the side of the triangle. Let us prove first that the distance LG of the circumcenter G from the side AB is equal to one half the distance OC of the orthocenter O from the opposite vertex C, LG $= \frac{1}{2}$OC. Considering the triangles OTU and GLU, we find, indeed, that they are equal because they have equal angles (since LG ∥ OC) and, moreover, OU $=$ UG, where U is the center of Euler's circle. Therefore, T being the midpoint of OC, we have LG $=$ OT $= \frac{1}{2}$OC. Consider now two other triangles OCS and LGS, the point S being, by definition, the intersection point of the median CL with the Eulerian line OG. They have equal angles because LG is parallel to OC, and, therefore, they are similar triangles. Anticipating the systematic study of similar triangles, we use here their fundamental property: *Corresponding sides of two similar triangles are proportional.* Here (as in equal triangles), the term "corresponding sides" means sides opposite to equal angles. Thus, we obtain

$$SL : SC = SG : SO = GL : OC = 1 : 2 = \tfrac{1}{2}$$

since, as we know, $GL = \tfrac{1}{2}OC$. Thus, $SL:SC = 1:2$, that is, the point S divides the median CL in the ratio $1:2$ and is therefore the centroid.

Furthermore, S also divides the Eulerian line in the same ratio, $SG:SO = 1:2$. We see, therefore, that the centroid S lies between the orthocenter O and the circumcenter G, twice as far from O as from G, as well as twice as far from G as from the center U of the nine-point circle: $SG = GO/3$ while $SU = (\tfrac{1}{2} - \tfrac{1}{3})GO = GO/6$.

Three Escribed Circles

Three interior bisectors of angles of a triangle intersect at the center of the inscribed circle, called the incenter, while three exterior bisectors form a triangle whose sides are perpendicular to the interior bisectors, so that the incenter of the given triangle is also the orthocenter of the triangle formed by the three exterior bisectors. What can be said now about the intersections of exterior and interior bisectors?

We will show that there are three groups of three concurrent bisectors, each composed of one interior and two exterior bisectors of all three angles of a triangle. Thus, to four remarkable points of a triangle, three other points may be added, and, besides the inscribed circle which we already studied and which has its contact points on the side-segments of the triangle, there are three more tangent circles associated with a triangle since the intersection points of bisectors are equidistant from all three sides of a triangle. But these externally tangent circles (they are called *escribed circles*) are exterior to the triangle's area, and two of their contact points lie on the extensions of side-segments, only one contact point lying on the side-segment itself.

To justify our assertions, we need the following lemma:

LEMMA: *The locus of points equidistant from two given intersecting straight lines is composed of two bisectors of angles formed by these two straight lines.*

PROOF: If (Fig. 40) MN $\perp$ CD and MP $\perp$ CE are equal, MN = MP, so that the point is. equidistant from CD and CE, then by Theorem VII, the two right triangles CNM and CPM are equal because the hypotenuse and one leg of the one are equal, respectively to the hypotenuse and a leg of the other. Therefore, $\widehat{NCM} = \widehat{PCM}$, which proves that a point equidistant from two intersecting lines lies necessarily on a bisector of their angle.

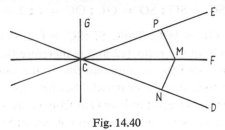

Fig. 14.40

Conversely, suppose that CF bisects the angle $\widehat{DCE}$ and consider any point M on CF. Again, two right triangles CNM and CPM are equal, but this time because they have equal angles and a common hypotenuse. Therefore, their legs MN and MP are equal as opposite to equal angles, so that the point M is shown to be equidistant from CD and CE. The same reasoning applies to the bisector CG of the second angle formed by these two lines. Thus, the lemma is proved.

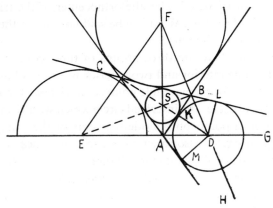

Fig. 14.41

Let us consider the intersection-point D (Fig. 41) of two exterior bisectors AG and BH of a triangle ABC. Joining this point D to the vertex C and dropping from D the perpendiculars DK, DL, DM on the sides of ABC, we wish to prove that CD bisects the interior angle ACB. Since D is a point of the bisector BH, by the lemma we have DK = DL. But D lies also on the bisector

AG, so that DK = DM. Therefore, DL = DM, and this proves, again according to the lemma, that CD indeed bisects the angle ACB.

Thus, we conclude that the bisectors of two exterior angles and of the remaining interior angle are always concurrent lines and, consequently, that circles exist which are externally tangent ot the sides of a triangle and which have the common points of two exterior and one interior bisectors for their centers. To each of three interior bisectors corresponds one such circle, called an *escribed* circle. Hence, for any triangle, there exist three escribed circles and, in all, the inscribed circle included, four circles, each of which is tangent to all three sides.

We observed above that the incenter S of a given triangle ABC (Fig. 41) is at the same time the orthocenter of another triangle DEF formed by three exterior bisectors of the given triangle ABC. Since the three vertices and the orthocenter of a triangle form an orthocentric system of four points, we conclude that, for any triangle ABC, the three centers D,E,F of escribed circles and the incenter S form an orthocentric system of four points.

Infinite Sequence of Triangles with a Common Nine-Point Circle

We can now construct an infinite sequence of triangles all having the same nine-point circle. The midpoints of the sides of any triangle, member of this sequence, become feet of altitudes in the next triangle of the chain of triangles. During the construction of the next triangle, an auxiliary triangle (not included in the sequence) with vertices at the midpoints of the sides of the previous triangle is used.

Given a triangle ABC (Fig. 42), denote the midpoints of its sides by D, E, F and draw the auxiliary triangle DEF. Its six bisectors define an orthocentric system of four points G, H, I, J, which are, for the triangle DEF, centers of three escribed and one inscribed circles. The triangle GHI formed by the three exterior bisectors GH, HI, and IG has as its altitudes the three interior bisectors DI, EG, and FH, and the midpoints of the sides of ABC are the feet of these altitudes of GHI.

The two triangles ABC and GHI have the same nine-point circle which passes through three points D, E, F because three points are sufficient to define a circle, and, on the other hand, a circle which passes through the midpoints of sides or through the feet of altitudes of a triangle is the nine-point circle of this triangle. We wish now to show that the construction just described when endlessly continued, tends to equalize the angles of the triangle.

To prove this, we will compute the expressions of angles $\hat{G}$, $\hat{H}$, $\hat{I}$ of the triangle GHI in terms of angles $\hat{A}$, $\hat{B}$, $\hat{C}$ of the original triangle ABC.

In Fig. 42, the quadrilateral BDFE is a parallelogram since (Theorem IX) $DF \overset{\shortparallel}{=} BE$, so that $\widehat{EFD} = \hat{B}$. By construction, the straight line FH bisects the angle $\widehat{DFE}$, and therefore $\widehat{HFE} = \frac{1}{2}\widehat{DFE} = \frac{1}{2}\hat{B}$. Since the altitude FH of the triangle HGI is perpendicular to its side GI, we have $\widehat{EFI} = \widehat{HFI} - \widehat{HFE}$ $= 90° - \frac{1}{2}\hat{B}$. A similar reasoning applied to the angle $\widehat{FEI}$ yields the result $\widehat{FEI} = 90° - \frac{1}{2}\hat{A}$ because the figure ADEF is a parallelogram, and, thus,

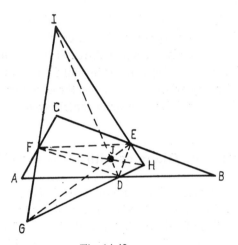

Fig. 14.42

$\widehat{FEG} = \frac{1}{2}\widehat{FED} = \frac{1}{2}\hat{A}$. Now the angle $\hat{I}$, when considered as an angle of the triangle EFI, is equal to.

$$\hat{I} = 180° - \widehat{EFI} - \widehat{FEI} = 180° - [90° - \frac{1}{2}\hat{B}] - [90° - \frac{1}{2}\hat{A}] = \frac{1}{2}(\hat{A} + \hat{B}).$$

Applying this result to the two other angles $\hat{G}$ and $\hat{H}$, we find the similar expressions $\hat{G} = \frac{1}{2}(\hat{B} + \hat{C})$ and $\hat{H} = \frac{1}{2}(\hat{C} + \hat{A})$, so that we have

$$\hat{I} = \frac{1}{2}(\hat{A} + \hat{B}); \quad \hat{G} = \frac{1}{2}(\hat{B} + \hat{C}); \quad \hat{H} = \frac{1}{2}(\hat{C} + \hat{A}). \tag{1}$$

We can now repeat this construction, drawing through the midpoints of the sides GH, HI, IG of the triangle GHI the six bisectors of angles of the triangle whose vertices are the midpoints of the sides of the triangle GHI. The new triangle formed by three exterior bisectors will have the midpoints of sides of the triangle GHI as the feet of its altitudes and therefore will have the same nine-point circle as GHI and as ABC. Repeating this construction endlessly, we build up an infinite chain of triangles with the same nine-point circle as the original triangle ABC, which is the first member of this infinite sequence of triangles.

Since at every step of the construction of this infinite sequence of triangles the angles are transformed according to equations (1) it can be proved that the infinite sequence tends to an *equilateral* triangle, so that, at the limit, the three angles become equal. In other words, we will prove that the infinite sequence of triangles just defined converges to an *equilateral* triangle as its limit.

To prove this, let us denote the angles $\hat{A}$, $\hat{B}$, $\hat{C}$ of the first triangle by $\hat{A}_1$, $\hat{B}_1$, $\hat{C}_1$; those $\hat{G}$, $\hat{H}$, $\hat{I}$ of the second triangle by $\hat{A}_2$, $\hat{B}_2$, $\hat{C}_2$, respectively, and so on, so that the angles of the nth triangle are $\hat{A}_n$, $\hat{B}_n$, $\hat{C}_n$, of the $(n + 1)$th triangle, $\hat{A}_{n+1}$, $\hat{B}_{n+1}$, $\hat{C}_{n+1}$, etc. for $n = 1, 2, 3, \ldots$ *ad infinitum*. Therefore, we will have, applying the result (1), an infinite sequence of recurrent relations

$$\hat{A}_{n+1} = \tfrac{1}{2}(\hat{B}_n + \hat{C}_n), \quad \hat{B}_{n+1} = \tfrac{1}{2}(\hat{C}_n + \hat{A}_n), \quad \hat{C}_{n+1} = \tfrac{1}{2}(\hat{A}_n + \hat{B}_n)$$

which hold for all values of the integer n.

Computing now the differences $\hat{B}_{n+1} - \hat{A}_{n+1}$ and $\hat{C}_{n+1} - \hat{A}_{n+1}$, we find

$$\hat{B}_{n+1} - \hat{A}_{n+1} = -(\hat{B}_n - \hat{A}_n)/2, \quad \hat{C}_{n+1} - \hat{A}_{n+1} = -(\hat{C}_n - \hat{A}_n)/2$$

Therefore, each difference of this type is equal to the previous one multiplied by $(-\tfrac{1}{2})$. In other words, increasing the subscript by one, we must multiply the difference by $(-\tfrac{1}{2})$. Repeating this operation n times, we express our differences in terms of the first ones with the subscript 1:

$$\hat{B}_{n+1} - \hat{A}_{n+1} = (-1)^n(\hat{B}_1 - \hat{A}_1)/2^n, \quad \hat{C}_{n+1} - \hat{A}_{n+1} = (-1)^n(\hat{C}_1 - \hat{A}_1)/2^n$$

The righthand members in these expressions are fractions with finite numerators and with the denominator 2^n, which increases without limit with increasing n. Passing to the limit for $n = \infty$, we find that the righthand members vanish, so that the limit for both differences $\hat{B}_n - \hat{A}_n$ and $\hat{C}_n - \hat{A}_n$ is equal to zero:

$$\lim_{n=\infty} (\hat{B}_n - \hat{A}_n) = \lim_{n=\infty} (\hat{C}_n - \hat{A}_n) = 0 \qquad (2)$$

We can now find the limit of $\hat{A}_n$ for $n = \infty$, using Theorem II, that is, the numerical value of the sum of three angles of a triangle, $\hat{A}_n + \hat{B}_n + \hat{C}_n = 180°$. Since for all values of the integer n the sum $\hat{A}_n + \hat{B}_n + \hat{C}_n$ remains

equal to 180° its limit is also equal to 180° and we will use this fact in computing the limit of $3\hat{A}_n$:

$$3\hat{A}_n = \hat{A}_n + \hat{B}_n + \hat{C}_n - (\hat{B}_n - \hat{A}_n) - (\hat{C}_n - \hat{A}_n)$$

$$= 180° - (\hat{B}_n - \hat{A}_n) - (\hat{C}_n - \hat{A}_n)$$

With the aid of (2) we conclude that the limit of $3\hat{A}_n$ is equal to 180°, and
therefore, $\lim_{n=\infty} \hat{A}_n = 60°$ does exist. The limits of $\hat{B}_n$ and $\hat{C}_n$ are also equal to
60° since by (2) they are equal to the limit of $\hat{A}_n$. Thus, the limit of the in-
finite sequence of triangles, all of them having the same nine-point circle, is
indeed an equilateral triangle.

But, in an equilateral triangle, the midpoints of its sides are at the same
time the feet of its altitudes, since the perpendicular bisector of a side of
an equilateral triangle is also the median, the altitude, and the interior bisector of the opposite angle. Therefore, the nine-point circle of an equilateral
triangle is its inscribed circle, and it turns out that the limit of our infinite
sequence of triangles having the same circle as their common nine-point
circle is an equilateral triangle circumscribed about this circle.

And, indeed, the construction we have used to build up our infinite chain
of triangles does not change an equilateral triangle into another since the
sides of an equilateral triangle are bisectors of the exterior angles of the
auxiliary triangle with its vertices at the midpoints fo the sides of the equilateral triangle.

The convergent sequence of triangles approaching indefinitely the equilateral triangle as its limit is a vivid illustration of the concept of absolute infinity in its aspect of aleph-null. There is no last member in the infinite chain
of triangles if we proceed step-by-step, constructing successively each next
triangle from the previous one with the aid of the same standard transformation. Therefore, we will never reach the final equilateral triangle by continuing the procedure and applying the transformation again and again.
There nevertheless exists the final ultimate triangle such that our standard
transformation has no effect on it and does not transform it into another
triangle, and this final triangle can be reached by a passage to the limit,
which is based on the existence of aleph-null, that is, on the use of *absolute
infinity*.

Terminating the discussion of the nine-point circle, we add without proof
that the nine-point circle of a triangle is tangent to the three escribed circles
as well as to the inscribed circle of this triangle.

Extremum Problems Related to Triangles

Many examples of the importance of extreme values (that is, maxima and minima) for a better understanding and practical applications of physical laws can be found in our environment. In studying the quadratic equation, we already saw that the laws of nature find their best expression in terms of a minimum principle.

Here we wish to discuss some simple problems on extreme values related to triangles. Their solution may take purely geometric form or may use algebraic methods. Thus, the first problem which follows is solved with the aid of algebra, while the solution of the second one uses geometric methods.

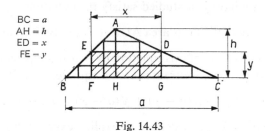

$$BC = a$$
$$AH = h$$
$$ED = x$$
$$FE - y$$

Fig. 14.43

Given a triangle ABC to the base $BC = a$ and the height $AH = h$, we call a rectangle DEFG (Fig. 43) *inscribed* in it if the rectangle's base FG lies on that, BC, of the triangle, while the two vertices D and E are incident with two sides AB and AC of the triangle. The base $FG = x$ and the height $FE = y$ can vary, and there are an infinite number of different rectangles inscribed in the same triangle ABC. If the base x of an inscribed rectangle increases, its height y decreases, and *vice versa*. When y reaches its maximum, which is equal to h, the base x of the inscribed rectangle shrinks to nothing, and its area vanishes. When x reaches its maximum, which is equal to a, the height y shrinks to zero and, its area again vanishes.

Thus, we come to the conclusion that as the base $x = FG$ of the inscribed rectangle varies from zero to its maximum $BC = a$, its area increases from zero to a certain maximum and then decreases and ultimately vanishes.

We now ask what are the dimensions x and y of the inscribed rectangle of *maximum area* and what is the ratio of this maximum area to the area of the triangle in which the rectangle is inscribed?

The solution of this maximum problem is based on the well known expressions for triangular and rectangular areas discussed and proved in

Chapter 16. Here we formulate and use these expressions, anticipating their deduction. The area of a rectangle is equal to the product of its base times its height, so that the area A of the rectangle DEFG is expressed by the product xy : $A = xy$. The area of a triangle is equal to one half the product of its base times its height, so that, for example, the area of the triangle ABC is equal to $\frac{1}{2}ah$. Computing by the same rule the areas of three triangles BFE, CDG, and DAE, we have: area BFE $= yBF/2$, area CDG $= yGC/2$, and area DAE $= x(h - y)/2$ because the height of the triangle ADE is equal to the difference $h - y$ of heights of ABC and of DEFG. Adding the areas of the two triangles BFE and CDG, we obtain: area BFE + area CDG $= y(BF + GC)/2$. But BF + GC = BC − FG $= a - x$, so that, finally, area BFE + area CDG $= y(a - x)/2$.

The five areas we have just studied satisfy the equation

area ABC = area DEFG + area ADE + (area BFE + area CDG).

Multiplying both members of this equation by two and replacing the doubled areas by their expressions, we transcribe the equation as follows:

$$ah = 2xy + x(h - y) + y(a - x) = hx + ay.$$

Solving this equation for y, we deduce its explicit expression $y = h(a - x)/a$ in terms of the given and fixed quantities a, h and of the variable x. With the aid of this expression, we can now find the value of the area A of the inscribed rectangle in terms of the variable x alone, eliminating the height y of the rectangle. Thus,

$$A = xy = xh(a - x)/a = (h/a)(ax - x^2) = (h/a)(a^2/4 - a^2/4 + ax - x^2)$$

The reason for adding and subtracting $a^2/4$ in the second factor is to reduce the second factor to a difference of two squares:

$$a^2/4 - a^2/4 + ax - x^2 = a^2/4 - [a^2/4 - ax + x^2] = a^2/4 - (a/2 - x)^2$$

Therefore, the variable area of an inscribed rectangle is equal to

$$A = (h/a)[a^2/4 - (a/2 - x)^2]. \tag{3}$$

The second term of the second factor in the righthand member of (3) is negative, and its value depends on the value of the variable x, while the first term $a^2/4$ is constant and positive. Therefore, the value of the righthand member, that is, the value of the area A, increases when the magnitude of the term $(a/2 - x)^2$ decreases, and the area A reaches its maximum value if this term vanishes. Now the term $(a/2 - x)^2$ vanishes if $x = a/2$, and, therefore, the rectangle of maximum area has a base $x = a/2$ equal to one half the base $BC = a$ of the triangle in which it is inscribed. The corresponding value of the height y is obtained with the aid of the expression $y = h (a - x)/a$, which, for $x = a/2$, yields $y = h (a - a/2)/a = h/2$. Thus, the vertices E and D of the inscribed rectangle of maximum area are midpoints of sides AB and AC of the triangle.

The value of the maximum area, as obtained from (3) for $x = a/2$, is

$$\text{Maximum } A = ah/4 = \tfrac{1}{2} (\text{area ABC})$$

so that it is equal to one half the area of the triangle ABC. This proves, incidentally, that the three rectangles of maximum area inscribed in the same triangle and, having their bases respectively on the three sides of triangle, have the same area, namely, one half of the triangle's area.

Our next example of an extremum problem is related to the so-called *altitude triangle* of a given acute-angled triangle (a triangle is *acute-angled* if all its three angles are acute). The altitude triangle of a given triangle ABC is, by definition, triangle DEF, whose vertices are the feet of altitudes AD, BE, CF of the given triangle (Fig. 45). A triangle is said to be *inscribed* in another triangle if it has one vertex on each side-segment of the other triangle. Therefore, the altitude triangle is one of the inscribed triangles. The total length of the sides of an inscribed triangle, that is, its *perimeter*, depends on the position of its vertices. The maximum of the perimeter is attained clearly when the vertices of the inscribed triangle coincide with those of the triangle in which it is inscribed, so that the perimeter of the given triangle represents the maximum perimeter of triangles inscribed in the given triangle.

We shall prove that the altitude triangle is obtained as the solution of the following minimum problem: Inscribe in a given acute-angled triangle a triangle of *minimum perimeter*. In other words, the perimeter of an inscribed triangle reaches its minimum if the vertices of the inscribed triangle coincide with the feet of the altitudes of the triangle in which it is inscribed. Thus, among all triangles inscribed in a given acute-angled triangle, its altitude triangle has the least perimeter. Moreover, the altitudes of the given triangle are interior bisectors of the angles of its altitude triangle, so that the incenter of the altitude triangle coincides with the orthocenter of the given triangle.

To prove all these properties of altitude triangles, we need the following:

LEMMA: *An angle inscribed in a circle is equal to one half the central angle which is subtended by the same arc of the circle as the inscribed angle.*

An angle formed by two chords of a circle is said to be *inscribed* in this circle if its vertex lies on the circumference of the circle. An angle formed by two diameters of a circle has its vertex at the center of the circle and is called a *central angle*. Let us first consider an inscribed angle formed by a diameter and a chord, such as the angle ABC in Fig. 44a. Drawing the radius AO, an isosceles triangle ABO is constructed because AO = BO. To the inscribed angle $\widehat{ABC}$ corresponds the central angle $\widehat{AOC}$ because both angles are subtended by the same arc AC. To prove that $\widehat{ABC} = \frac{1}{2}\widehat{AOC}$, we observe first that $\widehat{AOC} = \widehat{OAB} + \widehat{ABO}$ since $\widehat{AOC}$, as exterior angle for the triangle AOB, is equal to the sum of two non-adjacent angles of this triangle. But $\widehat{OAB} = \widehat{ABO} = \widehat{ABC}$ and therefore $\widehat{AOC} = 2\widehat{ABC}$, which proves the lemma in the particular case when one side of the inscribed angle is a diameter.

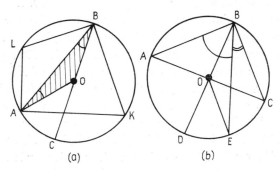

(a)   (b)

Fig. 14.44

In the general case when an inscribed angle is formed by two chords, this angle is the sum or difference of two angles of the particular type just studied (Fig. 44b): $\widehat{ABC} = \widehat{ABD} + \widehat{DBC}$ or $\widehat{EBC} = \widehat{DBC} - \widehat{DBE}$. Drawing the radii AO, EO, CO, we state that $\widehat{ABD} = \frac{1}{2}\widehat{AOD}$ and $\widehat{DBC} = \frac{1}{2}\widehat{DOC}$, so that $\widehat{ABC} = \frac{1}{2}(\widehat{AOD} + \widehat{DOC}) = \frac{1}{2}\widehat{AOC}$. Likewise, $\widehat{DBE} = \frac{1}{2}\widehat{DOE}$ and $\widehat{DBC} = \frac{1}{2}\widehat{DOC}$, which entails $\widehat{EBC} = \widehat{DBC} - \widehat{DBE} = \frac{1}{2}(\widehat{DOC} - \widehat{DOE})$ $= \frac{1}{2}\widehat{EOC}$. The lemma is thus proved in the general case too.

An important corollary of this lemma is the fact that the value of an inscribed angle subtended by an arc of a circle does not depend on the *position* of its vertex on the circle's circumference, provided that the vertex remains exterior to the arc subtending the inscribed angle. In other words, the locus of points from which a given segment AB (chord of an arc $\overset{\smile}{AB}$) is seen under a given angle is the arc of a circle $\overset{\smile}{AB}$. If the given angle is a right angle, the segment AB is a diameter, and then the locus is the whole circle of diameter AB. If AB is a proper chord, that is, not a diameter, it is seen under two different angles from the points of two unequal arcs into which the straight line AB divides the whole circle. From the points of the smaller arc, the chord AB is seen under an obtuse angle; from those of the larger arc it is seen under an acute angle, and the sum of these two angles is always equal to 180°: $\overset{\frown}{AKB} + \overset{\frown}{ALB} = 180°$ (Fig. 44a) because the sum of the corresponding central angles is 360°.

Thus, for a quadrilateral inscribed in a circle, such as, for example, ALBK, the sum of its opposite angles is equal to 180°. Conversely, if the sum of opposite angles in a quadrilateral is equal to 180°, this quadrilateral is inscribable in a circle, that is, its four vertices are on the circumference of a circle. In general, a quadrilateral does not have a circumscribed circle, and its four vertices define four different circles, each passing through three of the vertices while the fourth vertex does not belong to this circle.

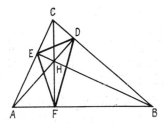

Fig. 14.45

Returning to the altitude triangle (Fig. 45), we consider three quadrilaterals BCEF, ABDE, and AFDC. Each of them has two vertices of the fundamental triangle ABC and the feet of the altitudes dropped from these vertices on the opposite sides as its four vertices, so that one of its sides is the side of the triangle ABC. These quadrilaterals do have circumscribed circles, and for each of them the side it has in common with the triangle ABC is the diameter of the circumscribed circle. Consider, for instance, the side BC. A circle having BC as its diameter passes through the points E and F since the angles $\overset{\frown}{BEC}$ and $\overset{\frown}{BFC}$ are right angles, $\overset{\frown}{BEC} = \overset{\frown}{BFC} = 90°$. Therefore the quadrilateral BCEF is inscribed in a circle, and the same is true for two other quadrilaterals ABDE, AFDC. To prove that the altitudes AD, BE, CF bisect the angles of the altitude triangle DEF, we observe that the opposite angles of a quadrilateral insribed in a circle have a sum equal to 180°. Therefore,

$\overset{\frown}{AED} + \overset{\frown}{ABD} = 180°$ as opposite angles of ABDE, and, on the other hand, $\overset{\frown}{CEF} + \overset{\frown}{ABD} = 180°$ as opposite angles of BCEF. Thus, the angles $\overset{\frown}{AED}$ and $\overset{\frown}{CEF}$ are equal, $\overset{\frown}{AED} = \overset{\frown}{CEF}$. But $\overset{\frown}{AED} = \overset{\frown}{AEB} + \overset{\frown}{BED} = 90° + \overset{\frown}{BED}$ as well as $\overset{\frown}{CEF} = \overset{\frown}{CEB} + \overset{\frown}{BEF} = 90° + \overset{\frown}{BEF}$, so that $90° + \overset{\frown}{BED} = 90° + \overset{\frown}{BEF}$, that is, $\overset{\frown}{BED} = \overset{\frown}{BEF}$. Thus, the altitude BE bisects the angle $\overset{\frown}{DEF}$, which proves our assertion in general: the altitudes are interior bisectors of angles of the altitude triangle, and the orthocenter H of ABC is the incenter for the altitude triangle DEF. Furthermore, the sides of ABC are exterior bisectors for the triangle DEF because they are perpendicular to the altitudes of ABC, that is, to interior bisectors of DEF.

We have shown that two exterior bisectors and one interior bisector meet at the center of an escribed circle tangent externally to the triangle. Therefore, the vertices A, B, C of the fundamental triangle are centers of escribed circles for the altitude triangle DEF. This fact can also be stated as follows: The three straight lines joining the feet of altitudes of a triangle are equidistant from each vertex as well as from the orthocenter of this triangle.

The figure 45 and the statements deduced from it concern an acute-angled triangle. The altitude triangle of a right triangle degenerates into a double segment, namely, the double altitude perpendicular to the hypotenuse because the orthocenter H coincides with the vertex of the right angle. But of more interest is the case of a triangle with an obtuse angle. Let $\overset{\frown}{ACB}$ be an obtuse angle (Fig. 46). Then the orthocenter H and the vertices A and B are outside the altitude triangle DEF, while the vertex C is within. The straight lines DE, EF, FD are equidistant from each of the four points A, B, C, H so that now, for the altitude triangle DEF, it is the vertex C of the obtuse angle which is the incenter, while the orthocenter H becomes the center of an escribed circle. The minimum property of an altitude triangle which characterizes it in the case of an acute-angled fundamental triangle, namely, the least perimeter, is lost when the fundamental triangle has an obtuse angle, but it is valid in the case of a right triangle.

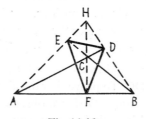

Fig. 14.46

The proof of this minimum property which follows was devised, as was the problem itself, by the German mathematician H. Schwarz. Reflecting the triangle ABC (Fig. 47) in one of its sides, for instance, AB, as in a mirror, we observe that the sides DF and EF of the altitude triangle DEF are extended into the reflections FE′ and FD′ of each other. This is a corollary of the fact that the altitude CF bisects the angle $\widehat{DFE}$: a reflection does not change the angles and, therefore, $\widehat{C'FD'} = \widehat{CFD} = \widehat{CFE}$. On the other hand, the altitudes FC and FC′ lie on the same straight line since both are perpendicular to AB. Thus, the segments EF and FD′ are a continuation of each other because they form equal vertical angles with the line CFC′, and the same holds for the segments DF and FE′.

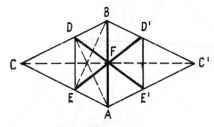

Fig. 14.47

Repeating the reflections five times (Fig. 48), we build up a chain of six equal triangles. The sides EF, FD_1, D_1E_2, E_2F_2, F_2D_3 and D_3E_4 of their altitude triangles inscribed in these six triangles then form a straight line segment EE_4 whose length is double the perimeter of the altitude triangle EDF since each side of this triangle is represented twice in this segment EE_4. Any other triangle, for instance, PQR, inscribed in the fundamental triangle ABC is also reflected so that the broken line $PQR_1P_2Q_2R_3P_4$ represents its doubled perimeter, each side being repeated twice.

The side AC is reflected four times (since in the third reflection it plays the role of a mirror and does not therefore change its position), and in its final position A_2C_2 it is parallel to its initial position AC because the alternate interior angles $\widehat{E_4EC}$ and $\widehat{EE_4A_2}$ are equal: we have, indeed, $\widehat{E_4EC} = \widehat{FEB}$ $+ 90° = \widehat{BED} + 90° = \widehat{B_1E_4D_3} + 90° = \widehat{EE_4A_2}$. Thus, the quadrilateral P_4PEE_4 is a parallelogram because PE is equal and parallel to P_4E_4. Therefore, the straight line segment PP_4 is equal to EE_4, while the broken line $PQR_1P_2Q_2R_3P_4$, which has the same end points as the segment PP_4, is longer than this segment.

We conclude that the doubled perimeter of the triangle PQR, whose length is equal to that of the broken line, exceeds the doubled perimeter of the altitude triangle DEF, so that the minimum property of the altitude triangle is proved. We add that the straight line segment CC_2 is also equal to EE_4 so that the broken line CC_1C_2, consisting of two segments CC_1 and C_1C_2, is longer than EE_4. This proves that, if the double altitude CF is considered as an inscribed triangle with two vertices coinciding at C, the doubled perimeter of such a degenerated inscribed triangle is also longer than that of the altitude triangle DEF.

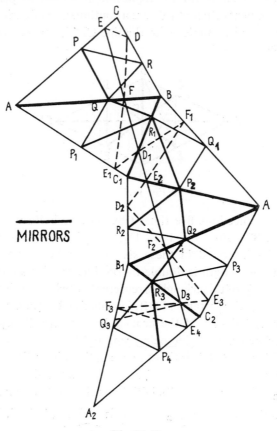

Fig. 14.48

The line CC_1C_2 is a straight line only if the triangle ABC has a right angle at the vertex C, and, in this case, the double altitude FC is indeed the degenerated altitude triangle of the right triangle ABC. In this case, the perimeter of any inscribed triangle is greater than 2FC.

Returning to the measurement of angles related to a circle, we note that the lemma concerning the angles inscribed in a circle is but a particular case of the following more general proposition:

THEOREM XII: *An angle formed by two tangents to a circle or by a secant line and a tangent or by two secants intersecting within, on, or inside a circle, is measured by one half the sum of the oriented arcs of the circle intercepted by the two sides and directed from the initial to the terminal side of the angle.*

The measure of a circular arc is the central angle which intercepts the arc being subtended by it. Measuring angles in *radians* (see Chapter 10), we ascribe to the circumference, that is, to four right angles, the measure of 2π radians, where the number π denotes the ratio of the length of the circumference to that of its diameter. Thus, the value of a right angle expressed in radians is equal to $\frac{1}{2}\pi$. The arcs considered in Theorem XII are *oriented*, that is, they are considered as positive if directed counterclockwise and as negative if directed clockwise. To define an oriented arc, it is not sufficient to give the central angle subtended by it. It is necessary to add in what direction the central angle is to be read, that is, to specify which of its two sides is the initial side, the other side being then the terminal side. If O denotes the center of a circle, a central angle $\overparen{AOB}$ has, by definition of the notation $\overparen{AOB}$, the side AO as its initial side, so that $\overparen{AOB}$ is positive if the point A precedes the point B moving on the circumference in the counterclockwise direction, provived the radius OA sweeps the angle $\overparen{AOB}$ when it moves towards OB. Thus, reading the same central angle in two opposite directions as $\overparen{AOB}$ and as $\overparen{BOA}$, we have always $\overparen{AOB} + \overparen{BOA} = O$. Therefore, the two arcs intercepted by two secants, or by two tangents, or by a secant and a tangent are both to be measured from the same initial straight line towards the other considered as a terminal line.

Since, by definition, a straight line tangent to a circle is the ultimate limiting position of a secant when two intersection points of the secant with the circle coincide, it is sufficient to prove the theorem for two secants and then deduce the results for the two other cases by moving the secant into the position of a tangent. Moreover, it is sufficient to consider only the two cases when the intersection point of the two secants lies inside or outside the circle because, if it is on the circumference, then the angle is inscribed, and the lemma proves that Theorem XII holds for this case. The proofs of these two cases are themselves based on the same lemma.

Suppose that the intersection point M of two secants AMD and BMC is within the circle (Fig. 49a), and consider the triangle AMC obtained by drawing the chord AC. For this triangle, the angle $\overset{\frown}{AMB}$ is an exterior angle which supplements the interior angle $\overset{\frown}{AMC}$ to 180°. Therefore, $\overset{\frown}{AMB} = \overset{\frown}{ACB} + \overset{\frown}{DAC} = \frac{1}{2}\overset{\frown}{AOB} + \frac{1}{2}\overset{\frown}{DOC} = \frac{1}{2}\overset{\smile}{AB} + \frac{1}{2}\overset{\smile}{DC} = \frac{1}{2}(\overset{\smile}{AB} + \overset{\smile}{DC})$, the arcs $\overset{\smile}{AB}$ and $\overset{\smile}{DC}$ being measured from the first secant AD towards the second secant BC and therefore being both positive. The result $\overset{\frown}{AMB} = \frac{1}{2}(\overset{\smile}{AB} + \overset{\smile}{DC})$ is obtained by applying the lemma and replacing the central angles $\overset{\frown}{AOB}$, $\overset{\frown}{DOC}$ by the arcs $\overset{\smile}{AB}$, $\overset{\smile}{DC}$ which they intercept.

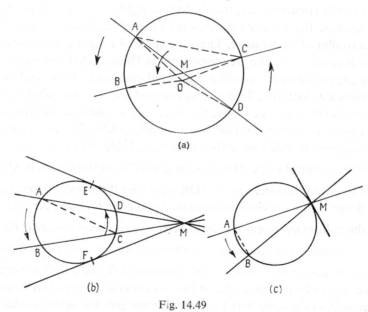

(a)

(b)   (c)

Fig. 14.49

What about the other angle BMD formed by the same two secants? On the one hand, we have $\overset{\frown}{BMD} = 180° - \overset{\frown}{AMB} = \pi - \overset{\frown}{AMB}$, while, on the other hand, $\overset{\smile}{AB} + \overset{\smile}{DC} = 360° - (\overset{\smile}{BD} + \overset{\smile}{CA}) = 2\pi - (\overset{\smile}{BD} + \overset{\smile}{CA})$, so that $\overset{\frown}{AMB} = \frac{1}{2}(\overset{\smile}{AB} + \overset{\smile}{DC}) = \pi - \frac{1}{2}(\overset{\smile}{BD} + \overset{\smile}{CA})$, and, thus,

$$\overset{\frown}{BMD} = \pi - \overset{\frown}{AMB} = \pi - [\pi - \tfrac{1}{2}(\overset{\smile}{BD} + \overset{\smile}{CA})] = \tfrac{1}{2}(\overset{\smile}{BD} + \overset{\smile}{CA}),$$

which, of course, could be deduced directly by observing that $\overset{\frown}{BMD}$ is an exterior angle for the triangle CMD and applying the same proof as for $\overset{\frown}{AMB}$.

We pass now to the case when the intersection point M is outside the circle (Fig. 49b) and consider the positive angle $\overset{\frown}{AMB}$ as interior to the triangle AMC. Therefore it is equal to the difference of the exterior angle $\overset{\frown}{ACB}$ $= \frac{1}{2}AB$ and the other interior non-adjacent angle $\overset{\frown}{CAD} = \frac{1}{2}CD$, so that $\overset{\frown}{AMB} = \frac{1}{2}(\overset{\smile}{AB} - \overset{\smile}{CD})$. Both arcs $\overset{\smile}{AB}$ and $\overset{\smile}{CD}$ are positive; the first is measured from the secant ADM as initial side, but the second, $\overset{\smile}{CD}$, is measured from the other secant BCM towards the first secant ADM. But $-\overset{\smile}{CD} = \overset{\smile}{DC}$, and, therefore, we have also another expression for $\overset{\frown}{AMB}$, namely, $\overset{\frown}{AMB} = \frac{1}{2}(\overset{\smile}{AB} + \overset{\smile}{DC})$, which conforms to Theorem XII. Thus, this theorem is proved for angles formed by two secants.

If one or both secants are rotated about M (Fig. 49b), the theorem remains true, and at the limit, when a secant becomes tangent to the circle, we obtain for the angle $\overset{\frown}{AMF}$ the expression $\overset{\frown}{AMF} = \frac{1}{2}(\overset{\smile}{ABF} + \overset{\smile}{DCF})$. If both secants become tangent to the circle, an angle of two tangents is obtained and again we obtain

$$\overset{\frown}{EMF} = \lim_{\substack{A \to E \\ B \to F}} \overset{\frown}{AMB} = \lim_{\substack{A \to E \\ B \to F}} \tfrac{1}{2}(\overset{\smile}{AB} + \overset{\smile}{DC}) = \tfrac{1}{2}(\overset{\frown}{EABF} + \overset{\frown}{EDCF}).$$

Finally, we must consider a special case when a secant passes through the contact point of a tangent (Fig. 49c). In this case, $\overset{\frown}{AMC} = \lim_{B \to M} \overset{\frown}{AMB}$ $= \lim_{B \to M} \tfrac{1}{2} \overset{\smile}{AB} = \tfrac{1}{2} \overset{\frown}{ABM}$, which completes the proof Theorem XII.

Duality

We end this chapter with examples of dual theorems related to triangles. In many cases, the dual companion of a very simple and easy to prove theorem happens to be much more difficult to prove by direct methods. Since two dually related theorems represent the same logical deduction chain, the validity of the one entails that of the other. Therefore, the direct proof of a theorem can be replaced by the dual transformation and the proof of its companion theorem, except, of course, the cases when the restricted duality fails, the Fifth Postulate being involved.

Let us first consider the dual transformation of a configuration (A, M, B, P_∞, c) of four collinear points A, M, B, P_∞ incident with a straight line c, where M denotes the midpoint of the segment AB, P_∞ being the point at infinity of the line c.

Denoting the dual transform of an element (point, straight line) by the same letter, capital for a point and small for a line, we construct another configuration $(a, m, b, p;\ C)$ which is the dual transform of the given configuration $(A, M, B, P_\infty;\ c)$ and consists therefore of four concurrent straight lines a, m, b, p incident with the point C (Fig. 50b).

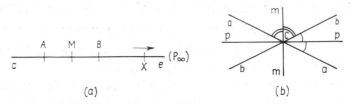

(a)   (b)

Fig. 14.50

The segments $P_\infty A, AM, MB, BP_\infty$ are transformed into angles $\overset{\frown}{pCa},\ \overset{\frown}{aCm},$ $\overset{\frown}{mCb},\ \overset{\frown}{bCp}$, and we have by symmetry $\overset{\frown}{aCm} = \overset{\frown}{mCb}$ because AM $=$ MB, so that the *midpoint* M of the segment AB becomes the *bisector* of the angle $\overset{\frown}{aCb}$. But the point at infinity P_∞ can also be considered as a midpoint, namely, as the midpoint of infinite segment $BP_\infty A$ joining the points A and B through the point at infinity P_∞. To justify this, we consider a variable point X which moves away and reaches at the limit the point P_∞. The ratio AX/BX of its distances from A and B approaches one and, at the limit, when X coincides with P_∞, becomes equal to one. We have, indeed, AX $=$ AB $+$ BX so that AX/BX $=$ AB/BX $+ 1$ and at the limit AB/BX vanishes because AB is a fixed length, while the length of BX tends to infinity. Since $\lim_{X \to P_\infty} (AX/BX)$ $= 1$, our assertion that P_∞ is the midpoint of the infinite segment $BP_\infty A$ is justified. Thus, the straight line $\underline{p}$, the dual image of the point P_∞, is the second bisector of angles formed by the lines $\underline{a}$ and $\underline{b}$. Therefore, the lines $\underline{m}$ and $\underline{p}$ are perpendicular, and the following lemma is established:

LEMMA: *To the midpoint of a straight line segment and to the point at infinity on the same line correspond as their dual transforms two perpendicular straight lines bisecting the angles formed by two other straight lines which are the dual transforms of the segment's end points.*

It is important to observe that the lemma just proved does not correlate any two perpendicular lines with a pair of points, one of which is at infinity;

it states, rather, the dual correlation between two configurations of *five* elements, one point and four straight lines on the one hand and four points and one line on the other hand.

If we want now to study the group of theorems related to the bisectors of angles of a triangle, we may approach this question by studying the dual transformation which involves the midpoints of sides and the points at infinity on lines forming the dual triangle. Consider, for example, a triangle ABC with midpoints G, H, I of its sides (Fig. 51). The points at infinity D_∞, E_∞, F_∞ on the straight lines $\underline{k}$, $\underline{l}$, $\underline{m}$ on which lie the sides BC, CA, AB, respectively, are incident with the points at infinity on the lines $\underline{p}$, $\underline{q}$, $\underline{r}$ drawn through the midpoints of these sides, for we know by Theorem IX that they are parallel: $\underline{p} \parallel \underline{k}$, $\underline{q} \parallel \underline{l}$, and $\underline{r} \parallel \underline{m}$.

Configuration I

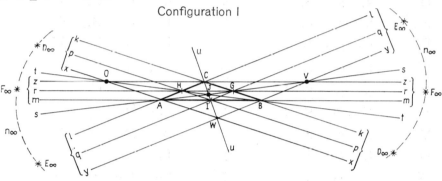

Fig. 14.51

By Theorem X, the three medians $\underline{s}$, $\underline{t}$, $\underline{u}$ corresponding to the vertices A, B, C, respectively, are concurrent and meet at the centroid J of the triangle ABC. Furthermore, we draw through A, B, C the three parallels to opposite sides $\underline{k}$, $\underline{l}$, $\underline{m}$, denoting these parallels by $\underline{x}$, $\underline{y}$, $\underline{z}$: $\underline{x} \parallel \underline{k} \parallel p$, $\underline{y} \parallel \underline{l} \parallel q$, $\underline{z} \parallel \underline{m} \parallel r$, and add to configuration (I) (Fig. 51) their intersection points V $(\underline{y}, \underline{z})$, O $(\underline{z}, \underline{x})$, and W $(\underline{x}, \underline{y})$ through which pass the medians $\underline{s}$, $\underline{t}$, $\underline{u}$, respectively. Finally, we complete the configuration (I) by adjoining to elements previously described the straight line at infinity incident with the points D_∞, E_∞, F_∞. The subscript ∞ being used for the elements at infinity, we denote this last line by $\underline{n}_\infty$.

Thus, configuration (I), represented in Fig. 51, consists in all of thirteen straight lines and as many points. It is constructed with the aid of only two very simple theorems, namely, Theorem IX and the fact that three medians of a triangle are concurrent lines. Among the twenty-six elements of configuration (I), one line, $\underline{n}_\infty$, and three points, D_∞, E_∞, F_∞, are elements at infinity, and without them we could not deduce the theorems which follow, using such a simple method of proof as the dual transformation of the companion theorem.

The various incidence relations between points and lines of configuration (I) are tabulated below, the incident elements being listed in the same row:

Point	Lines				Line	Points			
A	$\underline{l}$,	$\underline{m}$,	$\underline{s}$,	$\underline{x}$	$\underline{k}$	B,	C,	D_∞,	G
B	$\underline{m}$,	$\underline{k}$,	$\underline{t}$,	$\underline{y}$	$\underline{l}$	C,	A,	E_∞,	H
C	$\underline{k}$,	$\underline{l}$,	$\underline{u}$,	$\underline{z}$	$\underline{m}$	A,	B,	F_∞,	I
D_∞	$\underline{k}$,	$\underline{n}_\infty$,	$\underline{p}$,	$\underline{x}$	$\underline{s}$	J,	A,	G,	V
E_∞	$\underline{l}$,	$\underline{n}_\infty$,	$\underline{q}$,	$\underline{y}$	$\underline{t}$	J,	B,	H,	O
F_∞	$\underline{m}$,	$\underline{n}_\infty$,	$\underline{r}$,	$\underline{z}$	$\underline{u}$	J,	C,	I,	W
G	$\underline{k}$,	$\underline{q}$,	$\underline{r}$,	$\underline{s}$	$\underline{p}$	D_∞,	H,	I	
H	$\underline{l}$,	$\underline{r}$,	$\underline{p}$,	$\underline{t}$	$\underline{q}$	E_∞,	I,	G	
I	$\underline{m}$,	$\underline{p}$,	$\underline{q}$,	$\underline{u}$	$\underline{r}$	F_∞,	G,	H	
V	$\underline{s}$,	$\underline{y}$,	$\underline{z}$		$\underline{x}$	A,	D_∞,	O,	W
O	$\underline{t}$,	$\underline{z}$,	$\underline{x}$		$\underline{y}$	B,	E_∞,	W,	V
W	$\underline{u}$,	$\underline{x}$,	$\underline{y}$		$\underline{z}$	C,	F_∞,	V,	O
J	$\underline{s}$,	$\underline{t}$,	$\underline{u}$		$\underline{n}_\infty$	D_∞,	E_∞,	F_∞	

Transforming configuration (I) by duality, we obtain another configuration (II), also involving thirteen points and thirteen straight lines (Fig. 52). To the triangle with the vertices A, B, C and sides $\underline{k}$, $\underline{l}$, $\underline{m}$ in (I) corresponds another triangle with the vertices K, L, M and sides $\underline{a}$, $\underline{b}$, $\underline{c}$ in (II). The three points at infinity D_∞, E_∞, F_∞, and the midpoints G, H, I become exterior and interior bisectors of angles of the triangle KLM. If a point at infinity becomes the interior bisector, the two other points at infinity, by reason of logical symmetry, must also be transformed into interior bisectors, and the same holds for the three midpoints.

But into which kind of bisectors are the points at infinity transformed? We know that the midpoints of sides of a triangle form another triangle, that is, they are not collinear, while the points at infinity are collinear. On the other hand, the exterior bisectors of a triangle form another triangle, that is, they are not concurrent lines, while the interior bisectors are concurrent.

Since concurrent straight lines and collinear points are dual transforms of each other, the collinear points at infinity cannot be dually related to non-concurrent exterior bisectors. We see, therefore, that the points at infinity D_∞, E_∞, F_∞ become interior bisectors $\underline{d}$, $\underline{e}$, $\underline{f}$, while the midpoints G, H, I are transformed into exterior bisectors $\underline{g}$, $\underline{h}$, $\underline{i}$. The centroid J is transformed into a straight line $\overline{j}$ with which the dual images S, T, U of three medians $\underline{s}$, $\underline{t}$, $\underline{u}$ are incident.

To indicate the economy of proofs, when duality is used, we shall first repeat the deduction of some of the facts already studied and will also apply the dual transformation to present a few new theorems.

Configuration II

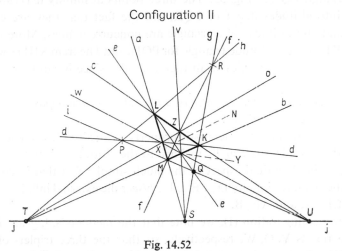

Fig. 14.52

Since the three interior bisectors $\underline{d}$, $\underline{e}$, $\underline{f}$ are dual transforms of collinear points D_∞, E_∞, F_∞, we conclude immediately the existence of a point (incenter) N, dual image of the line at infinity $\underline{n}_\infty$, where three interior bisectors meet because they must be concurrent lines.

Two exterior bisectors such as $\underline{g}$ and $\underline{h}$, for instance, intersect at the point R, but the dual image of this point R, namely, the straight line $\underline{r}$, passes not only through the points G and H but also through the point at infinity F_∞ to which corresponds in (II) an interior bisector $\underline{f}$. Therefore, the dual transformation proves that an interior and two exterior bisectors of a triangle are concurrent lines.

A median is defined by two points: it is incident with a vertex and with the midpoint of a side which is opposite this vertex. Therefore, the dual image of a median is the intersection point of a side (dual companion to a vertex) and of an exterior bisector opposite to this side (dual companion to a mid-point). The medians $\underline{s}, \underline{t}, \underline{u}$ in (I) pass through the centroid J. Therefore, their dual images, the points S, T, U in (II), are collinear and incident with a straight line $\underline{j}$. This is a theorem which is new for us:

THEOREM XIII: *The three intersection points of sides of a triangle with their opposite exterior bisectors are collinear.*

So far we have considered the dual image of the triangle ABC, but now let us concentrate our attention on the dual image of the triangle GHI, that is, on the triangle PQR in Fig. 52. The three points at infinity in (I) are transformed into altitudes $\underline{d}, \underline{e}, \underline{f}$ of PQR, and the fact that they are collinear proves that the altitudes of a triangle are concurrent lines. Moreover, the triangle KLM is the altitude triangle for PQR, and Theorem XIII now throws a new light on the properties of altitude triangles since it can be restated as follows:

Three intersection points of sides of a triangle with the opposite sides of its altitude triangle are collinear.

We find also that the characteristic property of an altitude triangle, namely the fact that its sides are equally inclined to the altitudes of the fundamental triangle, is simply a dual aspect of the much simpler fact that in configuration (I) the points at infinity D_∞, E_∞, F_∞ *bisect* the external infinite segments $BD_\infty C$, $CE_\infty A$, and $AF_\infty B$.

Studying configuration (I), we note that the medians $\underline{s}, \underline{t}, \underline{u}$ are incident with the points V, O, W, respectively, so that the three triplets of points (A, G, V), (B, H, O) and (C, I, W) are collinear. Transforming them by duality, we obtain in configuration (II) three triplets of concurrent lines ($\underline{a}, \underline{g}, \underline{v}$), ($\underline{b}, \underline{h}, \underline{o}$) and ($\underline{c}, \underline{i}, \underline{w}$). We thus find a complement to Theorem XIII:

The side of a triangle, the exterior bisector through the opposite vertex, and the straight line joining the intersection points of the two other sides with the interior bisectors of the two other angles are concurrent lines.

For example, in the triangle KLM, the side LM, the exterior bisector KQ, and the straight line YZ meet at the point S.

Another important feature of the dual transformation is expressed in the fact that, in configuration (I), the triangle ABC is inscribed in that [$\underline{x}$ $\underline{y}$ $\underline{z}$] and circumscribed about the triangle GHI, while in configuration (II) their duals show the reversed situation, the triangle KLM being circumscribed about XYZ and inscribed in the triangle [$\underline{g}$ $\underline{h}$ $\underline{i}$]. Considering the dual triangles ABC and KLM as fundamental, we are led to the conclusion that in a dual transformation the interior of a triangle is transformed into the exterior of its dual triangle and *vice versa*. This is why, for instance, the points at infinity on the sides of a triangle are transformed into interior rather than exterior bisectors of angles of its dual triangle.

There are many geometric constructions which perform the dual transformation of a given configuration. We describe here only the simplest one, which is based on an arbitrary choice of a fundamental circle remaining invariant by this special dual transformation, defined with respect to the fundamental circle in such a way that this circle is *self-dual*.

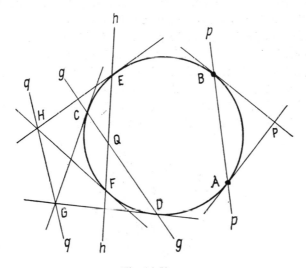

Fig. 14.53

Given a point P outside the fundamental circle, there are two tangents through it, PA and PB (Fig. 53), the points A and B being their contact points with the circle. We associate with the point P as its dual the straight line AB incident with the contact points of tangent lines through P.

To find the dual transform of a point Q within the circle, draw through Q two secants g (CQD) and h (EQF), the points C, D, E, F being on the circumference. The tangents to the circle at C and D intersect at a point G and this point G is the dual image of the secant CD. Likewise, the point H, defined as the intersection point of the tangents at E and F, is the dual image of the secant EF. Since Q is incident with CD and EF, its dual transform is a straight line incident with the points G and H, which solves the question.

When a variable point P approaches from the outside a fixed point M on the circumference of the fundamental circle, the two tangents through P, as well as the dual transform of the point P, that is, the secant AB passing through the contact points of two tangents, tend to coincide, and, at the limit, when P reaches M, their ultimate common position is the tangent to the circle at M. Thus, point M and the tangent line at M, as ultimate positions of dual companions P and the secant AB, are dually related: the dual transformation as defined by an invariant circle transforms a point on the circumference of this circle into the tangent to the circle at this point and *vice versa*. Thus, the fundamental circle, as the locus of points equidistant from the center, is transformed into itself and appears as a curve tangent to all the straight lines equidistant from the same center. It is now defined by the set of all its tangents instead of being defined by the set of all its points.

Every curve in fact can be considered as defined by the set of all its tangents and, if so, it is called the *envelope* of this set of straight lines. Thus, duality leads to the conclusion that a circle is not only the locus of points equidistant from a given point, but also the envelope of straight lines equidistant from the same point. In both definitions, the distance is the same, and it is called the radius of the circle.

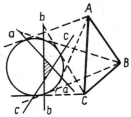

Fig. 14.54

A triangle exterior to the fundamental circle, that is, having its vertices outside the circle, has as its dual companion another triangle whose vertices are inside the circle because it is formed by straight lines which cut the circle. Thus, a triangle ABC exterior to the circle is the dual image of an interior triangle formed by the straight lines a, b, c, which are dual images of points A, B, C (Fig. 54). In general, just as the exterior of the fundamental triangle in our previous discussion was transformed dually into the interior of the dual triangle, the exterior of the fundamental circle, which is its own dual image, is transformed into its interior.

As our last example of dual theorems, we choose Pascal's and Brianchon's Theorems considered for the particular case of a circle only, although actually they hold for more general curves, namely, for conics (ellipse, hyperbola, parabola, or two straight lines). Pascal discovered his theorem in 1640, while the dual companion, Brianchon's Theorem, was found 166 years later. We give here their particular cases for a circle, omitting the proof:

PASCAL'S THEOREM: *For a hexagon inscribed in a circle, the three intersection points of opposite sides are collinear.*

BRIANCHON'S THEOREM: *For a hexagon circumscribed about a circle, the three diagonals joining the opposite vertices are concurrent.*

Given a hexagon inscribed in a circle, we shall transform it dually, considering the circle as the fundamental invariant circle of the dual transformation. The six vertices of the inscribed hexagon become six straight lines tangent at the same points to the circle, while its sides are transformed into the vertices of the circumscribed hexagon having these six tangents as its sides.

Therefore, the dual image of the inscribed hexagon is the circumscribed hexagon whose sides are tangent to the circle at the vertices of the inscribed hexagon. Moreover, the dual images of the intersection points of opposite sides of the inscribed hexagon are diagonals of the circumscribed hexagon joining its opposite vertices, so that Pascal's and Brianchon's Theorems are indeed two dual companion theorems (Fig. 55 and 56). The intersection point of the three diagonals is called Brianchon's Point, and its dual image in Pascal's Theorem is the so-called Pascal's Line.

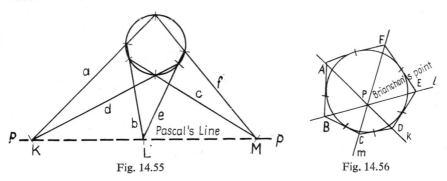

Fig. 14.55   Fig. 14.56

From these theorems we can deduce analogous propositions about inscribed and circumscribed pentagons, quadrilaterals, and triangles. As a matter of fact, if one side of an inscribed polygon shrinks to nothing and ultimately vanishes, the relation of incidence involving its line remains valid because the side is replaced by the tangent to the circle at the new vertex formed by the fusion of the two end points (vertices) of the vanishing side.

Likewise, if one of the angles of a circumscribed polygon becomes equal to

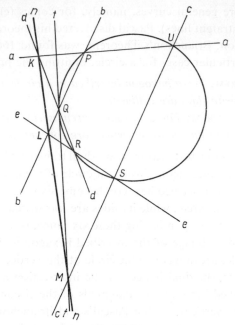

Fig. 14.57

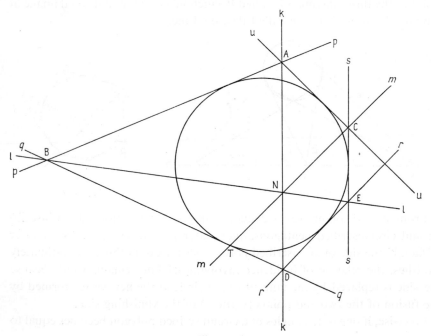

Fig. 14.58

two right angles, its vertex is transformed into a contact point of a new side formed by the fusion of two sides incident with the lost vertex, the relation of incidence involving the vanishing vertex remains valid because this vertex is replaced by the contact point of the newly formed side.

Thus, applying the two passages to the limit just described, we obtain for the pentagons the following particular cases of Pascal's and Brianchon's Theorems (Fig. 57 and 58):

In an inscribed pentagon the intersection point of any side and of the tangent to the circle at the opposite vertex is collinear with the two intersection points of pairs of the other four sides.

The straight line joining the contact point of any side of a circumscribed pentagon to the opposite vertex is concurrent with the two diagonals joining the other four vertices.

We observe that an inscribed pentagon has five distinct Pascal's lines which form another pentagon associated with the inscribed pentagon. Likewise, a circumscribed pentagon has five distinct Brianchon's points which also form another pentagon associated with the circumscribed pentagon.

Reducing again a side of the inscribed pentagon to a point and increasing an angle of the circumscribed pentagon to 180°, we transform them into quadrilaterals and obtain the corresponding particular cases of Pascal's and Brianchon's Theorems (Fig. 59 and 60):

The four intersection points of two pairs of opposite sides and of two pairs of tangents at opposite vertices of an inscribed quadrilateral are collinear.

Four straight lines, namely, the two diagonals and the two lines joining the contact points of opposite sides of a circumscribed quadrilateral are concurrent.

Finally, for triangles, we have the following results (Fig. 61 and 62):

The three intersection points of sides of a triangle with the tangents to the circumscribed circle at opposite vertices are collinear.

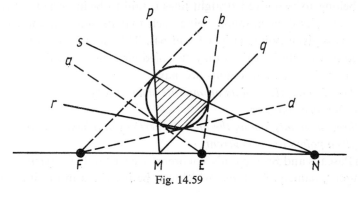

Fig. 14.59

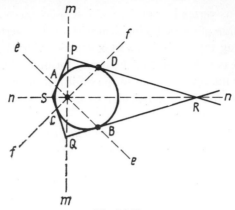

Fig. 14.60

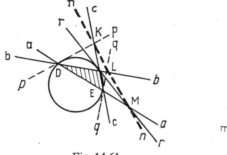

Fig. 14.61

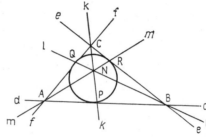

Fig. 14.62

The three straight lines joining the contact points of sides of a triangle with the inscribed circle to the opposite vertices are concurrent.

It is also of interest to mention the form Pascal's and Brianchon's Theorems take when two straight lines and two points (their duals) are substituted for the selfdual fundamental circle. A hexagon whose vertices alternately belong to two given straight lines is said to be inscribed in these two straight lines, its dual hexagon being such that its sides alternatively pass through two given points (Fig. 63 and 64). This dual image of a hexagon inscribed in two straight lines may be called circumscribed about two given points. For these two hexagons we have

The three intersection points of opposite sides of a hexagon inscribed in two straight lines are collinear.

The three diagonals joining the opposite vertices of a hexagon circumscribed to two given points are concurrent.

Both Pascal's and Brianchon's Theorems are true only for particular kinds of hexagons, namely, for those which can be inscribed in or circumscribed

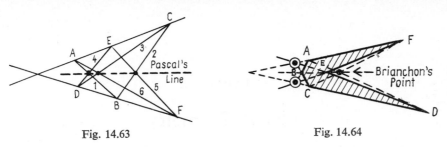

Fig. 14.63   Fig. 14.64

about a conic. A conic is defined completely if five of its points or five of its tangents are given. Therefore, in general, a hexagon can neither be inscribed in nor circumscribed about a conic. But a pentagon with its five sides and five vertices can, and, therefore, a given pentagon defines two conics associated with it, namely, a circumscribed and an inscribed conic. Thus, for *any* pentagon we have the dual theorems:

The intersection point of a side of a pentagon and of the tangent at the opposite vertex to the circumscribed conic is collinear with the two intersection points of pairs of the four sides.

The line joining the contact point of a side of a pentagon to the inscribed conic and the opposite vertex passes through the intersection point of the two diagonals joining the other four vertices.

The cases represented in Fig. 57 and 58 do not hold for all pentagons but only for those that can be inscribed in or circumscribed about a circle. The same is true for the quadrilaterals which in general are not inscribable in or circumscribable about a circle. However, a given quadrilateral can always be considered at inscribed in or circumscribed about a parabola because a parabola is completely determined by any four of its tangents.

Therefore, for *any* quadrilateral, the following dual theorems are valid:

The four intersection points of two pairs of opposite sides and of two pairs of straight lines through opposite vertices and tangent to the circumscribed parabola are collinear.

Four straight lines, namely, the two diagonals and the two lines joining the contact points of opposite sides with the inscribed parabola, are concurrent.

Now a triangle always has an inscribed and a circumscribed circle. Therefore, the theorems represented in Figs. 61 and 62 hold for all triangles without exception.

Finally, the configurations in Figs. 63 and 64, as well as the theorems they illustrate, are true only for hexagons of the particular kind represented there. The vertices of a hexagon in general are not alternatively incident with two straight lines, neither do its sides belong to two triplets of concurrent straight lines.

CHAPTER 15

Metric Geometry

In Chapters 13 and 14 geometric configurations were studied mainly from the point of view of the relative position of their elements. This chapter deals with so-called metric geometry, which studies the interdependence between the magnitudes of elements of geometric configurations such as angles, segments, areas, *etc.* Again the triangle appears as the fundamental figure, and its metric properties are the most important because the metric characteristics of all other configurations can be deduced from those of a triangle.

Before studying the metric relations in a triangle (this study bears the name of *trigonometry*), we will discuss the similar triangles whose existence is a special feature of Euclidean geometry as well as the Pythagorean Theorem, which, without any exaggeration, may be called the cornerstone of science.

Arithmetic, Geometric and Harmonic Means

Four positive quantities a, b, c, d form a *proportion* $a:b = c:d$, if and only if the two ratios a/b and c/d are equal, that is, the products ad and bc are equal. The quantities a and c are said to be proportional to b and d, respectively. The first and fourth terms a and d of a proportion $a:b = c:d$ are called the *extremes*, while the second and third terms b and c are the *means* of a proportion. Thus, in any proportion, the product of the extremes is equal to the product of the means. Therefore, the means or the extremes can be exchanged without destroying the proportion, so that if $a:b = c:d$ then also $a:c = b:d$ as well as $d:b = c:a$. Furthermore, inverting the ratios, we obtain $b:a = d:c$, so that the means can be exchanged with the extremes.

If now three quantities a, b, c form a proportion with two equal mean terms, $a:b = b:c$, we have $b^2 = ac$, so that $b = (ac)^{1/2}$. The square root $(ac)^{1/2}$ of the product ac is called the *geometric* mean (or the *mean proportional*) of two numbers a and c.

EXAMPLE: 10 is the mean proportional between 2 and 50 because $2:10 = 10:50$. The geometric mean of two numbers is always less than their *arithmetic* mean, which, by definition, is equal to one half the sum of two numbers. Thus, the arithmetic mean $\frac{1}{2}(2 + 50) = 26$ of 2 and 50 is greater than their geometric mean 10. This fact is easy to prove by observing that the square of the difference $a^{1/2} - b^{1/2}$ is always positive (as are the squares of all real numbers), so that $(a^{1/2} - b^{1/2})^2 = a - 2(ab)^{1/2} + b > 0$, and, therefore, dividing by two and transposing the square root to the right, $\frac{1}{2}(a + b) > (ab)^{1/2}$.

A third mean of two quantities, called the *harmonic* mean, is defined as follows: The reciprocal $1/H$ of the harmonic mean H of two numbers a and b is equal by definition to the arithmetic mean $\frac{1}{2}(1/a + 1/b)$ of the reciprocals $1/a$ and $1/b$ of these two numbers, that is, $1/H = \frac{1}{2}(1/a + 1/b)$. Solving this equation for H, we find the relation $ab = \frac{1}{2}(a + b)H = [(ab)^{1/2}]^2$, so that the square ab of the geometric mean $(ab)^{1/2}$ is equal to the product of the harmonic and arithmetic means. Denoting the arithmetic, geometric, and harmonic means of any two positive numbers by M, G, and H, respectively, we have the proportion $M:G = G:H$ because $G^2 = MH$. We see, therefore, that the geometric mean G is also the mean proportional between the arithmetic and harmonic means of the same numbers. Since $M > G$, we have also $G > H$, so that the three different means M, G, H always verify the inequality $M > G > H$. We saw that the arithmetic and geometric means of 2 and 50 are equal to 26 and 10, respectively. Their harmonic mean H is therefore equal to G^2/M, that is, to $10^2/26 = 50/13$, and we have, indeed, the inequality $H = 50/13 < G = 10$.

Proportional Segments

We will now prove that to construct four proportional segments it is sufficient to cut two intersecting straight lines by two parallel transversals, thus forming a triangle ABC with sides AC, BC cut by a parallel DE to the base AB (Figs. 1 and 2). In other words, we will prove the following theorem:

THEOREM XIV: *A line parallel to one side of a triangle divides the two other sides proportionally*: DA/CD = EB/CE.

PROOF: If the segments CD and DA (Fig. 1) have a common measure so that they are both multiples of a third length and are thus commensurable, then the proof is simple and easy. Suppose this common measure to be contained m times in DA and n times in DC, m and n being integers, so that it is contained $m + n$ times in AC. Dividing AC into $m + n$ equal parts, we are sure that the point D will be one of division points. Now drawing parallels to AB through all these division points (one of these parallels is DE), we divide the side BC also into $m + n$ parts. To prove that these parts are equal,

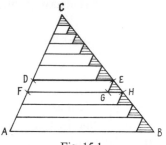

Fig. 15.1

we draw parallels to AC through all the points of division on BC, forming parallelograms such as FGED and triangles (shaded) such as GHE. All these triangles then have their sides parallel to AC *equal*, because opposite sides of a parallelogram are equal, and all our parallelograms have equal sides on AC. Furthermore, all these triangles have equal angles because their sides are parallel to the sides of the triangle ABC, which proves that their angles are equal to those of ABC. Hence, all our triangles are equal, and this proves that the $m + n$ parts on BC are equal to each other.

Therefore, we can state that the side BC of the large triangle ABC is divided into $m + n$ equal parts, whose common length is the common measure of EB and CE. There are m equal parts in EB and n in CE, so that EB/CE $= m/n$. On the other hand, we had also DA/CD $= m/n$ by hypothesis. Thus, EB/CE $=$ DA/CD, *q.e.d.*

The proof of Theorem XIV is, however, more complicated when the segments DA and CD are incommensurable and have no common measure which is contained an integral number of times in both of them. As we saw in Chapter 6 (Volume 1), the ratio of two incommensurable segments is an irrational number. On the other hand, an irrational number is an infinite aperiodic decimal fraction and can be defined only with the aid of a passage to the limit, thus using the concept of absolute infinity. Hence, the proof of our theorem in the general case when the segments DA and CA are incommensurable necessitates a passage to the limit, and we introduce this passage to the limit as follows: We try to measure the segment DA with the aid of an N-th part of the segment CD, and naturally we fail for all possible choices of the integer N because, by hypothesis, DA and CD are incommensurable. In other words, the length DA, being incommensurable with CD and therefore also with CD/N, is always, for any integer N, between two consecutive multiples of CD/N. Let us now apply, beginning at the point D, the segment of length $s = $ CD/N to DA as many times as possible without exceeding DA. If the largest multiple of s contained in DA is denoted by ms, then the length $(m + 1) s$, by definition of m, is greater than DA, and $ms < $ DA $< (m + 1)s$. We mark on AC two points A′ and A* such that DA′ $= ms$, while DA* $= (m + 1) s$. The point A is between A′ and A* because DA′ $<$ DA $<$ DA* and A′A* $= s$, (Fig. 2).

Notice that the length $s = $ CD/N and the integer $m = $ DA′/$s = ($DA′/CD$)N$ depend on the choice of N: if N increases, s decreases and therefore m increases. Moreover, when N increases without limit, s tends to zero, while $m = $ DA′/s tends to infinity. At the limit, for $N = \infty$, s vanishes and m becomes infinite.

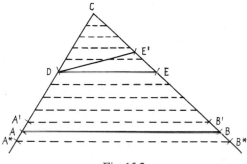

Fig. 15.2

Applying the length $s = $ CD/N to the segment CA* (we know that by construction CA* is a multiple of s), we divide CA* $= (N + m + 1) s$ into $N + m + 1$ equal parts, N parts being contained in CD, m parts in DA′, and the last, $(N + m + 1)$-th, part being the segment A′A* $= s$. Then, as in the previous case of commensurable segments, we draw parallels to AB through the $N + m$ division points on CA*. They intersect the side CB in $N + m$ points, B′ included, and the parallel through A* intersects CB in B*. Thus, the segment CB* is divided into $N + m + 1$ equal parts. Using the same reasoning as in the previous case, we have

EB′/CE = DA′/CD = m/N,   EB*/CE = DA*/CD = $(m + 1)/N$

To prove that the difference DA/CD − EB/CE is equal to zero, we evaluate upper and lower bounds for it by replacing the terms DA/CD and EB/CE by their upper and lower bounds. Thus, increasing the first and decreasing the second term, we find as an upper bound the fraction $1/N$:

$$DA/CD - EB/CE < DA^*/CD - EB'/CE$$

$$= (m+1)/N - m/N = (m + 1 - m)/N = 1/N$$

On the other hand, decreasing the first term and increasing the second term, we obtain the fraction $-1/N$ as the lower bound:

$$DA/CD - EB/CE > DA'/CD - EB^*/CE$$

$$= m/N - (m+1)/N = (m - m - 1)/N = -1/N.$$

Thus, we have the double inequality

$$-1/N < DA/CD - EB/CE < 1/N$$

which holds for all possible choices of the positive integer N.

If we now increase N without limit, both bounds $1/N$ and $-1/N$ tend to zero, and, at the limit, for $N = \infty$, they vanish. Therefore, the *constant* difference $DA/CD - EB/CE$ can have the only value zero, which proves that $DA/CD = EB/CE$.

The converse of Theorem XIV is manifestly true: a straight line which divides two sides of a triangle proportionally is parallel to the third side. Suppose (Fig. 2) that a straight line DE' cutting AC and CB in D and E' is such that $CE'/E'B = CD/DA$. If it were not parallel to AB, another line passing through D and parallel to AB would cut BC in a point E distinct from E'. Therefore, by Theorem XIV, $CE/EB = DC/DA$ and, combining this proportion with $CE'/E'B = CD/DA$, we would have $CE'/E'B = CE/EB$. Adding both sides one, we obtain $CE'/E'B + E'B/E'B = CE/EB + EB/EB$, that is, $(CE' + E'B)/E'B = (CE + EB)/EB$. But $CE' + E'B = CE + EB = CB$ and the proportion $CB/E'B = CB/EB$ proves that $E'B = EB$, which is possible only when the points E' and E coincide. The contradiction thus obtained shows that our assumption of non-parallelism to the base AB of a straight line dividing the two other sides of the triangle ABC proportionally is impossible, and this proves the converse of Theorem XIV.

In Theorem XIV and its converse, we considered only the proportion $DA/CD = EB/CE$ or its inverse $CD/DA = CE/EB$. It is important to mention that any proportion can assume many different aspects. Given any four *arbitrary* numbers r, s, t, u, and a proportion $A/B = C/D$, where A, B, C, D are known and fixed numbers, the proportion $(rA + sB)/(tA + uB)$

$= (rC + sD)/(tC + uD)$ is also true, and it is equivalent to the given proportion $A/B = C/D$. To prove this we have to show that the equation

$$(rA + sB)(tC + uD) = (rC + sD)(tA + uB)$$

is a corollary of $AD = BC$, the factors r, s, t, u being completely arbitrary. In other words, we have to prove that the difference

$$\Delta = (rA + sB)(tC + uD) - (rC + sD)(tA + sB)$$

vanishes if $AD - BC = 0$. Computing this difference Δ, we obtain

$$\Delta = (ru - st)\,AD + (st - ru)\,BC = (ru - st)(AD - BC),$$

so that, indeed, the difference Δ is zero, if $A/B = C/D$. Applying this general result to the proportion $CD/DA = CE/EB$, we state that in Theorem XIV this proportion can be replaced by the equivalent proportion $(rCD + sDA)/(tCD + uDA) = (rCE + sEB)/(tCE + uEB)$ with arbitrary coefficients r, s, t, u.

Similar Figures

We know that any geometric configuration of Euclidean geometry can undergo a dilatation or contraction without distortion, so that its shape remains the same but its size varies. This means that, for any figure in Euclidean geometry, there exist an infinite number of other figures in which the angles are the same while all distances and lengths are proportional to those of the original figure. The original figure and the figure obtained by its contraction or dilatation are called *similar*. The definition of similar figures can be formulated also as follows: *Two figures with equal corresponding angles and with proportional corresponding segments are similar.* The ratio of lengths of corresponding segments is their *ratio of similitude*. It is the same for all pairs of corresponding segments.

In particular, two triangles which are similar must have equal angles and their sides must be proportional. The sufficient conditions of similarity for two triangles are stated in the following theorem:

THEOREM XV: *Two triangles are similar if one of three following conditions is fulfilled:*

(1) The angles of the one are equal respectively to the angles of the other triangle.

(2) An angle of the one is equal to an angle of the other, the equal angles being included between proportional sides.

(3) The sides of the one are proportional to the sides of the other triangle.

CASE (1): Given two triangles ABC and KLM (Fig. 3) with $\hat{A} = \hat{K}$, $\hat{B} = \hat{L}$, $\hat{C} = \hat{M}$, apply ABC to KLM so that the vertex A and the sides AB, AC coincide with the vertex K and the lines KL, KM, respectively, and mark off the points D, E on KL, KM such that KD = AB and KE = AC, forming thus the triangle KDE equal to that ABC. The straight line DE is parallel to LM because $\overset{\frown}{KDE} = \overset{\frown}{ABC} = \overset{\frown}{KLM}$. Therefore, by Theorem XIV,

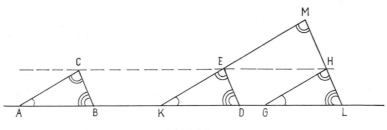

Fig. 15.3

we have KD/KL = KE/KM. Applying ABC to KLM again, this time let coincide the vertices B and L, so that LG = BA and LH = BC. Repeating the previous reasoning, we now obtain the proportion LG/LK = LH/LM. Combining these two results and replacing the segments KD = LG, KE, LH by equal segments AB, AC, BC, we conclude that AB/KL = AC/KM = BC/LM, which shows that the corresponding sides of two triangles are proportional, and, therefore, the triangles are indeed similar.

CASE (2): This case can be reduced to the first as follows: Suppose that in Fig. 3 the angles $\overset{\frown}{BAC}$ and $\overset{\frown}{LKM}$ are equal, while the sides including them are proportional, that is, AB/KL = AC/KM. Drawing the straight line DE in the triangle KLM in such a way that KD = AB, KE = AC and, therefore, the triangle KDE is equal to that ABC, we can substitute KD and KE for AB and AC in the proportion AB/KL = AC/KM, obtaining thus the proportion KD/KL = KE/KM. By the converse of Theorem XIV, it follows that DE is parallel to LM, so that $\overset{\frown}{KED} = \overset{\frown}{KML}$ and $\overset{\frown}{KDE} = \overset{\frown}{KLM}$. But $\overset{\frown}{KED} = \overset{\frown}{ACB}$ and $\overset{\frown}{KDE} = \overset{\frown}{ABC}$, so that $\overset{\frown}{ACB} = \overset{\frown}{KML}$ and $\overset{\frown}{ABC} = \overset{\frown}{KLM}$, which achieves the reduction to Case (1) and proves, therefore, the similarity of two triangles.

Case (3): In this third case, the sides of two triangles are proportional by hypothesis, $AB/KL = BC/LM = CA/KM$, and we have to prove that their corresponding angles are equal. Marking off the points G and H on LK and LM so that $LG = AB$ and $LH = BC$, we draw GH (Fig. 3). By the converse to Theorem XIV, the line GH is parallel to KM since $AB/LK = BC/LM$ gives also $LG/LK = LH/LM$. From GH ∥ KM we conclude that $\widehat{LGH} = \widehat{LKM}$ and $\widehat{LHG} = \widehat{LMK}$, so that the triangles GHL and MKL have equal angles. It remains to prove the equality of triangles GHL and ABC. By construction, they have two pairs of equal sides, $LG = AB$ and $LH = BC$. Therefore, it will be sufficient to prove that $GH = AC$. Applying Case (1), we conclude that the two triangles LGH and LMK are similar, and this entails the proportion $GH/KM = LG/LK$. But $LG = AB$, so that $GH/KM = AB/KL = CA/KM$, which proves that $GH = AC$, thus completing the proof of Theorem XV.

In general, the simplest way of constructing a polygon similar to a given arbitrary polygon consists in drawing straight lines which join the vertices of the given figure to an arbitrarily chosen point *(center of similitude)* and marking off on every line a point corresponding to the vertex through which this line passes. Denoting the center of similitude by C, the vertices of the given polygon by V_k and their corresponding points by H_k (Fig. 4), the point H_1

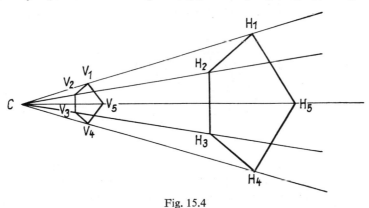

Fig. 15.4

can be chosen *at will*, but all the other points H_k for $k = 2, 3, 4, \ldots, n$, must be chosen in such a way that the ratios CV_k/CH_k are equal, all of them, to the first ratio $CV_1/CH_1 = r$. Thus, the segments CH_k are proportional to those CV_k, the common ratio r being the ratio of similitude. Joining now each point H_k to the next H_{k+1}, we construct a polygon with vertices H_k, $k = 1$, $2, 3, \ldots, n$, which is similar to the given polygon. Consider indeed two corresponding triangles V_kCV_{k+1} and H_kCH_{k+1}. They are similar because their common angle at C is included between proportional sides: $CV_k/CH_k = CV_{k+1}/CH_{k+1} = r$ (Theorem XV-2). Therefore, they have equal angles, so that $V_kV_{k+1} \parallel H_kH_{k+1}$ and, moreover, $V_kV_{k+1}/H_kH_{k+1} = r$. Thus, the sides of two polygons are proportional and their angles are equal because their sides are parallel, which means that they are similar.

Theorem XV, apart from being important for the construction of similar figures, constitutes the foundation of the method of similar triangles which we now apply to the study of metric relations in general and first of all in a right triangle.

Right Triangle

In a triangle ABC with the right angle at the vertex C (Fig. 5), the side AB opposite the right angle is called the *hypotenuse*, the two other sides being the two *legs* of the right triangle. Drawing the perpendicular CD to the hypotenuse through the vertex C, we divide AB into two segments AD and DB. The three right triangles ABC, BCD, and CDA are similar because they have equal angles: ABC and BCD have in common their acute angle $\hat{B}$, so that $\widehat{DCB} = 90° - \hat{B} = \widehat{CAD}$ and $\widehat{DCA} = 90° - \hat{A} = \widehat{ABC}$. Therefore,

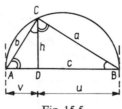

Fig. 15.5

the corresponding sides in these three similar triangles are proportional (in writing down the proportions it is important to remember that corresponding sides of two similar triangles lie opposite to equal angles). Denoting the lengths of the six segments just considered by $a = BC$, $b = CA$, $c = AB$, $h = CD$, $u = DB$, and $v = AD$, we write down the following proportions:

$$h/u = v/h = b/a, \quad h/a = v/b = b/c, \quad u/a = h/b = a/c$$

To find the expressions of u, v, h in terms of the side lengths a, b, c, we solve these formulas for u, v, h and obtain $h = ab/c$, $u = a^2/c$, $v = b^2/c$, so that $h^2 = uv$. Therefore, the following result is established:

THEOREM XVI: *In a right triangle, the altitude upon the hypotenuse is the mean proportional between the two segments determined by it on the hypotenuse, and either side is the mean proportional between the hypotenuse and the adjacent segment of the hypotenuse.*

We know that the center of a circle circumscribed about a right triangle is the midpoint of the hypotenuse of this triangle, so that an angle inscribed in a circle is a right angle if it is subtended by a diameter. This fact justifies the following corollary of Theorem XVI:

A perpendicular drawn from any point of a circle to its diameter is a mean proportional between the segments of the diameter, and a chord joining that point to an extremity of the diameter is a mean proportional between the diameter and the segment of the diameter which is the projection of the chord on the diameter.

This corollary gives a simple construction of a mean proportional between two given segments: Draw half a circle on the sum of two given segments as the diameter and cut it by a line perpendicular to the diameter and passing through the point common to both segments; the segment intercepted on this line by the diameter and the circumference is the mean proportional. If, for instance, the given segments are AD and DB (Fig. 5), joining them at the common point D, we consider their sum AB as the diameter of a circle. A perpendicular to AB through the point D then cuts the upper half-circle at the point C, and the segment DC is the mean proportional between AD and DB.

Thus, any square root can be constructed by this method. To construct an incommensurable length such as $\sqrt{7}$, for instance, it is sufficient to draw a circle of radius 4 and cut it by a perpendicular to the diameter through a point which divides the diameter into two segments of lengths 7 and 1. The length of the segment of this perpendicular between the diameter and the circumference is equal to $\sqrt{7}$, while the lengths of two chords are $2\sqrt{14}$ and $2\sqrt{2}$.

Returning to the right triangle with legs a, b and hypotenuse c, we deduce from the expressions of the two segments $AD = v = b^2/c$ and $DB = u = a^2/c$ the most important metric relation, discovered some twenty-five centuries ago by Pythagoras and known as the *Pythagorean Theorem*:

THEOREM XVII: *The area of a square constructed on the hypotenuse of a right triangle is equal to the sum of the areas of squares on its two legs.*

Since the area of a square is expressed in units of area by the square of the number which measures the length of its side in units of length, Theorem XVII asserts that $c^2 = a^2 + b^2$, where a, b, c denote the lengths of the legs and hypotenuse of a right triangle. The proof is simple: by the definition of segments AD $= v$ and DB $= u$, we have AD + DB = AB, that is, $u + v = c$. But $a^2 = cu$ and $b^2 = cv$, so that $a^2 + b^2 = cu + cv = c(u + v) = c \cdot c = c^2$.

The importance of this metric relation, characteristic of right triangles in Euclidean geometry, cannot be emphasized too strongly.

To understand and study the environment and the laws of Nature we must first of all learn how to measure all possible distances, the inaccessible ones included. To achieve the mastery of distances, we must know the geometric law which governs the combination of distances and thus expresses the intrinsic structure of space. Since all combinations of distances are reducible to the particular combination of two mutually perpendicular distances and because the Pythagorean Theorem formulates the law obeyed by this important combination, we see, indeed, that this theorem may be considered the keystone of our scientific knowledge.

In particular, suppose that we want to measure the distance AB (Fig. 6) between two points A and B separated by an obstacle which precludes direct measurement along the straight line AB. It is sufficient to choose on any line AD through A a point C such that the segment CB makes a right angle with the line AD and then measure the accessible distances AC $= b$ and BC $= a$. Applying Theorem XVII to the right triangle ABC, we find the measure c of the distance AB by computing the square root $(a^2 + b^2)^{1/2} = c$.

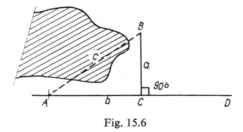

Fig. 15.6

The concept of distance is so fundamental that the Pythagorean Theorem is basic to all sciences. For instance, analytic geometry, without which mathematical physics could not exist, is based on the expression of the distance d between two points A (x, y) and B (a, b), (Fig. 7), given by their coordinates x, y and a, b: AB$^2 = d^2 = (x - a)^2 + (y - b)^2$. And this again is nothing more than the Pythagorean Theorem. Drawing through A and B parallels to the coordinate axes OX and OY which intersect in the point C, we build up a right triangle ABC in which AB $= d$ is the hypotenuse and BC $= x - a$ and CA $= y - b$ are the two legs. Therefore, the above expression of d^2 is due to Theorem XVII.

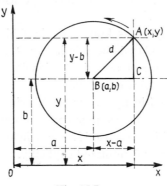

Fig. 15.7

In Fig. 7 the point A can also be considered as a variable point which in its motion remains at a fixed distance d from the fixed point B, describing thus the circumference of a circle with center B and radius d. In such an interpretation of the Pythagorean relation $(x - a)^2 + (y - b)^2 = d^2$, the last three among the five symbols x, y, a, b, d are to be considered as known and constant numbers, while x and y are variable since they are coordinates of a variable point A (x, y). Despite their variation, the relation $(x - a)^2 + (y - b)^2 = d^2$ holds because its lefthand member expresses the square of the distance between A and B, and this distance remains constant and equal to d for all possible positions of the variable point A on the circumference of our circle. Therefore, this relation is the algebraic equivalent and representation of the circle's circumference, and this is why it is called the *equation of a circle*. Thus, for example, a circle with center at $a = 3, b = 4$ and radius $d = 5$ is represented by the equation $(x - 3)^2 + (y - 4)^2 = 25$, that is, $x^2 + y^2 - 6x - 8y = 0$. We see that, in analytic geometry, the Pythagorean Theorem yields the equation of a circle.

In trigonometry, the fundamental relations which hold for the squares of trigonometric functions, $\cos^2 t + \sin^2 t = 1$, $\cot^2 t + 1 = \csc^2 t$, and $1 + \tan^2 t = \sec^2 t$, are also paraphrases of the same theorem, as is, in calculus, the expression of the square $ds^2 = dx^2 + dy^2$ of the infinitesimal element (differential) ds of arc of a plane curve on which is based the computation of lengths of curves, areas of surfaces of revolution, etc.

The Special (or Restricted) Theory of Relativity uses the invariant ds^2

$= dx^2 + dy^2 + dz^2 + (i\,dt)^2$, which expresses the Pythagorean Theorem for the four-dimensional universe, and the General Theory of Relativity is based on its generalization. All these examples show clearly that the Pythagorean Theorem permeats all the sciences and therefore also all the industry which is based on applied science.

A special right triangle was known to the Chinese and Egyptians long before Pythagoras formulated the relation $a^2 + b^2 = c^2$ and achieved its proof in the general case of any right triangle. Thus, in the writings of Tschao Pi (*circa* 1100 B.C.), we find mentioned the same right triangle with sides 3, 4, 5 which served in Egypt for tracing right angles. In remote antiquity, the Hindus used for the same purpose another right triangle, namely, that with legs 5, 12 and hypotenuse 13. Nevertheless, before Pythagoras the general relation was never formulated explicitly.

Cosine Law

The Pythagorean Theorem expresses the square of a side opposite a right angle in terms of the legs of a right triangle, but what about the square of a side opposite an acute or an obtuse angle in any triangle?

The corresponding generalization of the Pythagorean Theorem is the so-called *Cosine Law*, which gives the expression of the square of a side in terms of the two other sides and included angle. This expression is the same in all three cases, when the included angle is acute, right, or obtuse, and its generality is due to the use in it of the trigonometric function cosine of the included angle. This function was defined and studied in Chapter 7, and here we will use its properties without repeating the proofs.

Any triangle can be considered as a sum or as a difference of two right triangles, obtained by drawing an altitude (Fig. 8). Consequently, the expression of the square of a side can be derived with the aid of Theorem XVII applied to these two right triangles.

In proving the Cosine Law, we must study separately the square of a side opposite an acute angle and that of a side opposite an obtuse angle. In the first case, we will discuss separately the two subcases of (a) an acute-angled triangle (Fig. 8a) and (b) a triangle with an obtuse angle (Fig. 8b). Considering in both cases the segment BC opposite the acute angle A as the side whose square we wish to express, we observe that in Figure 8a the altitude CD is inside the triangle ABC, while in Fig. 8b it is outside. In both cases, however, the segment AD is the projection of the side AC on the base AB. Thus, by definition of the function cosine (Chapter 7, Volume I), we have always $AD = AC \cos \hat{A}$.

Applying Theorem XVII to the right triangle BCD, we have $BC^2 = BD^2 + CD^2$, where CD can also be considered as a leg of a second right triangle ACD. Therefore, by Theorem XVII again, $AD^2 + CD^2 = AC^2$, which gives $CD^2 = AC^2 - AD^2$. Replacing in the expression of BC^2 the term CD^2 by the difference $AC^2 - AD^2$, we obtain for BC^2 the following expression: $BC^2 = BD^2 + AC^2 - AD^2$. Now in Fig. 8a, $BD^2 = (AB - AD)^2$,

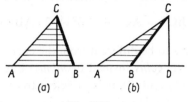

Fig. 15.8

while in Figure 8b $BD^2 = (AD - AB)^2$, but the squares of $AB - AD$ and $AD - AB$ are equal, so that in both cases we have $BD^2 = AD^2 - 2 \cdot AD \cdot AB + AB^2$. Using this value of BD^2 in the expression of BC^2, we obtain the following formula:

$$BC^2 = AB^2 - 2 \cdot AB \cdot AD + AD^2 + AC^2 - AD^2$$

$$= AB^2 + AC^2 - 2 \cdot AB \cdot AD \qquad (1)$$

which holds in both cases and which we formulate as follows:

In any triangle, the square of a side opposite an acute angle is equal to the sum of the squares of the two other sides *minus* the doubled product of the one of those sides times the projection of the other upon that side.

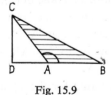

Fig. 15.9

This solves the question for a side opposite an acute angle, and we pass now to the case of a side opposite an obtuse angle. The square of the side BC of a triangle ABC with an obtuse angle at the vertex A (Fig. 9) can be computed applying Theorem XVII to the right triangles BCD and ACD as follows:

since $CD^2 = AC^2 - DA^2$, we have

$$BC^2 = CD^2 + DB^2 = AC^2 - DA^2 + (DA + AB)^2$$
$$= AC^2 - DA^2 + DA^2 + AB^2 + 2 \cdot AB \cdot DA$$
$$= AC^2 + AB^2 + 2 \cdot AB \cdot DA.$$

Therefore, in any triangle, the square of a side opposite an obtuse angle is equal to the sum of the squares of the two other sides *plus* the doubled product of the one of those sides times the projection of the other upon that side:

$$BC^2 = AC^2 + AB^2 + 2 \cdot AB \cdot DA \qquad (2)$$

This statement seems to be different from the corresponding statement for an acute included angle (*plus* instead of *minus*) but actually, it is not. To unify both equations (1) and (2), it is sufficient to observe that the length of a projection is equal to the length of the projected segment times the cosine of the angle between the two lines if this angle is an acute angle since a length is always expressed by a positive number and the cosine of an acute angle is also a positive number. Therefore, the projection AD of the side AC involved in equation (1) is equal to the product $AC \cos \hat{A}$, the angle $\hat{A}$ being acute. We can thus rewrite (1) as follows:

$$BC^2 = AB^2 + AC^2 - 2 \cdot AB \cdot AC \cos \hat{A}.$$

On the other hand, in Fig. 9 we also have $DA = AC \cos \widehat{CAD}$ because the angle $\widehat{CAD}$ is acute. But this time the angle $\hat{A}$, included between the two sides AB and AC of the triangle ABC, is the complement to $180°$ of the acute angle $\widehat{CAD}$, that is, $\widehat{CAD} = 180° - \hat{A}$. Therefore, computing $\cos \widehat{CAD}$, we obtain $\cos(180° - \hat{A}) = -\cos \hat{A}$, as it must be because $\cos \hat{A}$ is a negative number, the angle $\hat{A}$ being obtuse. Thus, in (2), the segment DA is equal to $DA = -AC \cos \hat{A}$, and, using this value of DA in the term $+2 \cdot AB \cdot DA$, we find that this term is equal to $-2 \cdot AB \cdot AC \cdot \cos \hat{A}$, which yields again the same expression for BC^2, namely, $BC^2 = AB^2 + AC^2 - 2 \cdot AB \cdot AC. \cos \hat{A}$ as for an acute included angle $\hat{A}$.

Thus, the trigonometric formula for the square of a side

$$BC^2 = AB^2 + AC^2 - 2 \cdot AB \cdot AC \cdot \cos \hat{A} \qquad (3)$$

holds in both cases of an acute and obtuse angle $\hat{A}$. Finally, the same expression (3) remains true if $\hat{A}$ is a right angle because the cosine of a right angle vanishes, and, therefore, for a right triangle, equation (3), reduces to Theorem XVII and gives $BC^2 = AB^2 + AC^2$. The result (3) is known in trigonometry as the Cosine Law, and we formulate it as the following

THEOREM XVIII: *In any triangle, the square of a side is equal to the sum of the squares of the two other sides minus their doubled product times the cosine of the included angle.*

Using the notations $a = BC$, $b = AC$, and $c = AB$ for the lengths of sides, so that an opposite side and angle are denoted by the same letter (capital for an angle and small for a side) we express Theorem XVIII as follows:

$$a^2 = b^2 + c^2 - 2bc \cos A; \quad b^2 = c^2 + a^2 - 2ca \cos B;$$

$$c^2 = a^2 + b^2 - 2ab \cos C \tag{4}$$

With the aid of Theorem XVIII, it is possible to find the angles of a triangle whose sides are given. Considering their lengths a, b, c as known and solving the equations (4) with respect to $\cos A$, $\cos B$, and $\cos C$, we obtain formulas of the type $\cos A = (b^2 + c^2 - a^2)/2bc$, and the table of values for the function cosine yields the angles A, B, C when their cosines are known.

But this simple method does not give small angles with precision since the variation of the function cosine is very slow for small angles, and more sensitive formulae are needed if high precision is desired. These formulae express the tangents of half-angles, such as $\tan (A/2)$, for instance, in terms of side-lengths a, b, c, and they result from the transformation of equations (4).

To deduce the expression of $\tan (A/2)$, we begin by rewriting the first of equations (4) as follows:

$$2bc \cos A = b^2 + c^2 - a^2.$$

Adding $2bc$ to both sides and replacing $b^2 + c^2 + 2bc$ by $(b + c)^2$, we have

$$2bc (1 + \cos A) = (b + c)^2 - a^2 = (a + b + c)(b + c - a).$$

Subtracting $2bc$ from both sides and changing the sign of all terms, we have also

$$2bc (1 - \cos A) = a^2 - (b^2 + c^2 - 2bc) = a^2 - (b - c)^2$$

$$= (a - b + c)(a + b - c).$$

Using the notation $2s$ for the sum of three sides (perimeter) $a + b + c$, the expressions standing in the righthand members can be written in a more condensed form. If, indeed, $a + b + c = 2s$, then $a + b - c = 2s - 2c = 2(s - c)$, and, likewise $a - b + c = 2(s - b)$ and $b + c - a = 2(2-a)$.

Therefore,

$$2bc\,(1 + \cos A) = 4s\,(s - a); \quad 2bc\,(1 - \cos A) = 4\,(s - b)\,(s - c).$$

On the other hand, the expressions $1 + \cos A$ and $1 - \cos A$ are related to the functions sine and cosine of the half-angle $A/2$ because

$$1 + \cos A = 2\cos^2(A/2); \quad 1 - \cos A = 2\sin^2(A/2)$$

(see Chapter 6, form. 30). Therefore, we have

$$bc\cos^2(A/2) = s\,(s - a); \quad bc\sin^2(A/2) = (s - b)\,(s - c)$$

and, thus, dividing the second relation by the first, member by member, and extracting the square root,

$$\tan(A/2) = [(s - b)\,(s - c)/s\,(s - a)]^{1/2}. \tag{5}$$

We have transformed the first relation in (4). The same transformation applied to the two other relations (4) yields the analogous formulas for $\tan(B/2)$ and $\tan(C/2)$:

$$\tan(B/2) = [(s - c)\,(s - a)/s\,(s - b)]^{1/2},$$

$$\tan(C/2) = [(s - a)\,(s - b)/s\,(s - c)]^{1/2}. \tag{6}$$

Moreover, we obtain also the expressions for the sine and cosine of the half-angle $A/2$, namely, $\cos(A/2) = [s\,(s - a)/bc]^{1/2}$ and $\sin(A/2) = [(s - b)\,(s - c)/bc]^{1/2}$, as well as the analogous expressions for the sine and cosine of $B/2$ and $C/2$.

They can be written down transforming those for $A/2$ by so-called circular substitution which consists in the replacement of a, b, c by b, c, a, respectively, when in the lefthand member A is replaced by B, B by C, C by A. In general, any formula related to metric properties of a triangle and involving a combination of symbols A, B, C (angles) and a, b, c (sides) remains true if B, C, A, b, c, a are substituted in it for A, B, C, a, b, c, respectively. This substitution is called *circular* because it is performed in a cyclic order, the three angles A, B, C, on the one hand, and the three sides a, b, c, on the other, forming cycles: A → B → C → A and $a → b → c → a$. The fact that circular substitution does not destroy the validity of a formula is explained by the logical identity of the roles played in the structure of a triangle by its three angles on the one hand and by its three sides on the other.

EXAMPLE: To illustrate the application of equation (5), we will compute the acute angle A of the Chinese-Egyptian right triangle ABC with C = 90°, the hypotenuse $c = 5$, and the legs AC = $b = 3$, BC = $a = 4$. Its perimeter $2s$

is equal to $3 + 4 + 5 = 12 = 2s$, so that $s = 6$ and thus $s - a = 2$, $s - b = 3$, and $s - c = 1$. By equation (5), we have $\tan(A/2) = (\frac{1}{4})^{1/2} = \frac{1}{2}$. With the aid of the table of values for the tangent, we find that $A/2$ is equal to $0.46364761...$ radians, which corresponds to $26° 33' 54''$, so that $A = 53° 07' 48''$.

Stewart's Relation

Joining a vertex, say vertex C, of a triangle ABC to a point D on the opposite side AB by a segment DC (Fig. 10), there must be a relation between the length $CD = d$ of this segment and the distance $AD = u$ of the point D from the vertex A since the length d is determined by the choice of the point D, that is, by the value of u. This relation must involve also the three side lengths $a = BC$, $b = CA$, $c = AB$ of the triangle ABC because the length d of the segment CD depends naturally on the shape and size of the triangle ABC.

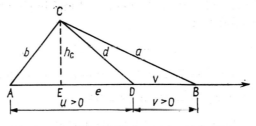

Fig. 15.10

The five quantities a, b, c, u, and d satisfy indeed a relation, called *Stewart's Relation*, and this relation is an important corollary of Theorem XVIII. We write it down in a symmetrical form, using also a sixth quantity $v = DB$ since the position of the point D on AB can be equally well characterized by the value of DB. The two segments AD and DB form together the side $AB = c$, so that we have $u + v = c$, where u and v can have any real values, positive, negative, or zero. The point D indeed is not necessarily between A and B as illustrated on Fig. 10, which corresponds to the case when both u and v are positive. It can be chosen anywhere on the straight line AB, provided AD and DB are considered as *directed* segments, the positive sense on AB being by definition that from A towards B. Therefore, if D is to the left of A, v is positive and u is negative, while if D is to the right of B, u is positive and v is negative.

To prove Stewart's Relation

$$cd^2 = ua^2 + vb^2 - uvc \tag{7}$$

apply Theorem XVIII to triangles ADC and BCD with the common side $CD = d$, expressing in both cases the square of a side opposite the vertex D:

$$a^2 = d^2 + v^2 + 2dv \cos \widehat{ADC}$$

$$b^2 = d^2 + u^2 - 2du \cos \widehat{ADC},$$

where in the first relation the factor $\cos \widehat{BDC}$ is replaced by $-\cos \widehat{ADC}$ since $\widehat{BDC} = 180° - \widehat{ADC}$ entails $\cos \widehat{BDC} = \cos (180° - \widehat{ADC}) = -\cos \widehat{ADC}$.

Multiplying the first relation by u, the second by v, and adding them, we eliminate $\cos ADC$ and obtain equation (7) because $u + v = c$.

This relation can be used for the computation of the altitude $CE = h_c$ in terms of sides a, b, c, this computation being based on the fact that the altitude represents the minimum of the segment CD: $h_c = \min CD = \min d$. Replacing in (7) v by its value $c - u$ and multiplying both sides by $4c$, we rewrite (7) as follows:

$$4c^2d^2 = 4cua^2 + 4c (c - u) b^2 - 4c^2u (c - u)$$

$$= 4c^2u^2 - 2 \cdot 2cu (b^2 + c^2 - a^2) + (b^2 + c^2 - a^2)^2$$

$$+ 4c^2b^2 - (b^2 + c^2 - a^2)^2$$

$$4c^2d^2 = [2cu - (b^2 + c^2 - a_2)]^2 + (2cb)^2 - (b^2 + c^2 - a^2)^2. \tag{8}$$

In this expression of $4c^2d^2$, the first term $[2cu - (b^2 + c^2 - a^2)]^2$ is variable since it involves u, which can be chosen arbitrarily, while the last two terms are constants, the sides a, b, c of a given triangle being fixed lengths. Moreover, the sum of these two last terms is positive and this can be shown by transforming it into a product of positive factors as follows:

$$(2cb)^2 - (b^2 + c^2 - a^2)^2 = [2cb + (b^2 + c^2 - a^2)] [2cb - (b^2 + c^2 - a^2)]$$

$$= [(b + c)^2 - a^2] [a^2 - (b - c)^2]$$

$$= (b + c + a) (b + c - a) (a - b + c) (a + b - c)$$

$$= 16s (s - a) (s - b) (s - c)$$

Therefore, the variation of the length $CD = d$ is due merely to the first term which is positive because it is a square of a real number. To obtain the minimum value of the product $4c^2d^2$, it is sufficient to give to the variable u

such a value that the first term vanishes, that is, $u = \frac{1}{2}(b^2 + c^2 - a^2)/c$. Thus, the minimum value of $4c^2d^2$, which is equal to $4c^2h_c^2$, is represented by the sum of the two last terms in (8), and we obtain for the altitude h_c the following result:

$$4c^2h_c^2 = 16s\,(s - a)\,(s - b)\,(s - c)$$

Dividing both sides by 16, extracting the square root and observing that half the product ch_c is the measure of the triangle's area, we have

$$\text{Area ABC} = \tfrac{1}{2}ch_c = [s\,(s - a)\,(s - b)\,(s - c)]^{1/2}.$$

This result yields an important formula for the area of a triangle in terms of its sides a, b, c and also an expression for the altitude h_c related to the side c, namely,

$$h_c = 2\,[s\,(s - a)\,(s - b)\,(s - c)]^{1/2}/c.$$

Similarly, we have

$$h_a = 2\,[s\,(s - a)\,(s - b)\,(s - c)]^{1/2}/a$$

and

$$h_b = 2\,[s\,(s - a)\,(s - b)\,(s - c)]^{1/2}/b,$$

where h_a and h_b denote the altitudes related to sides a and b, respectively.

Thus, combining these expressions in one formula, we have

$$ah_a/2 = bh_b/2 = ch_c/2 = [s\,(s - a)\,(s - b)\,(s - c)]^{1/2} = \text{Area ABC}. \qquad (9)$$

We could without any computation say that the area of the triangle ABC is equal to one half the product of the base and the altitude, that is, $\tfrac{1}{2}ah_a$ or $\tfrac{1}{2}bh_b$, or $\tfrac{1}{2}ch_c$, so that the equality of the three products $\tfrac{1}{2}ah_a = \tfrac{1}{2}bh_b = \tfrac{1}{2}ch_c$ is easily established. But what is important in our result is the expression $[s\,(s - a)\,(s - b)\,(s - c)]^{1/2}$ of the area in terms of three sides a, b, c of the triangle.

Thus, if three sides of a triangle are known, we can immediately compute the area without knowing the altitudes, and if we wish to find the altitudes,

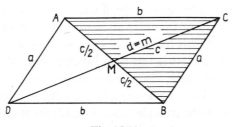

Fig. 15.11

we have merely to divide the value of the area by one half the side length opposite the vertex through which the altitude passes.

Another particular case of (7), when the point D is the midpoint of the side AB, so that CD is the *median* related to the side c, is especially interesting for it yields the proof of the most characteristic feature of a parallelogram as well as the evaluation of a median's length m_c in terms of sides of a triangle.

Considering (Fig. 11) the triangle ABC as half the parallelogram ADBC, we observe that the median MC $= m_c$ of the triangle ABC is half the diagonal DC. Applying (7) with $u =$ AM $= v =$ MB $= \frac{1}{2}c$, we obtain for $d = m_c$

$$cm_c^2 = \tfrac{1}{2}c\,(a^2 + b^2) - (\tfrac{1}{2}c)^2\,c.$$

Dividing by $\frac{1}{4}c$ and solving for $DC^2 + AB^2 = 4m_c^2 + c^2$, we have

$$DC^2 + AB^2 = 4m_c^2 + c^2 = 2\,(a^2 + b^2)$$

that is,

$$DC^2 + AB^2 = AD^2 + DB^2 + BC^2 + CA^2$$

which proves the following theorem:

THEOREM XIX: *The sum of squares of four sides of a parallelogram is equal to the sum of squares of its two diagonals.*

On the other hand, we find that the three medians m_a, m_b, m_c of a triangle, related to the sides a, b, c respectively, are expressed as follows

$$m_a^2 = \tfrac{1}{2}(b^2 + c^2 - \tfrac{1}{2}a^2); \quad m_b^2 = \tfrac{1}{2}(c^2 + a^2 - \tfrac{1}{2}b^2);$$

$$m_c^2 = \tfrac{1}{2}(a^2 + b^2 - \tfrac{1}{2}c^2). \tag{10}$$

Adding these expressions, a curious result is obtained: The sum of the squares of three medians is equal to three quarters of the sum of the squares of the sides, that is,

$$m_a^2 + m_b^2 + m_c^2 = \tfrac{3}{4}(a^2 + b^2 + c^2).$$

We saw that CD (Fig. 10) coincides with the altitude CE $= h_c$, when $u = \frac{1}{2}(b^2 + c^2 - a^2)/c$, while $u = \frac{1}{2}c$, if CD is the median m_c. We now ask in what particular kind of triangles an altitude h_c coincides with the corresponding median m_c? This happens if $\frac{1}{2}(b^2 + c^2 - a^2)/c = \frac{1}{2}c$, that is, if $b^2 = a^2$, and therefore the triangle is an isosceles one. Moreover, in an isosceles triangle the altitude is also the interior bisector, so that the altitude, median and interior bisector are one and the same segment.

Suppose now that in the triangle ABC (Fig. 12) the length and the position of the base BC $= a$ are fixed, while for the median AM $= m_a$ only its length

$m_a = R$ remains fixed, its inclination being variable, so that the vertex A describes a circle of radius $AM = R$ with the center at the midpoint M of the base BC.

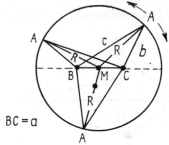

BC = a

Fig. 15.12

When A moves on the circle, the distances $AB = c$ and $AC = b$ vary, but the sum of their squares remains always equal to a constant, namely, $2R^2 + \frac{1}{2}a^2$; we have indeed $b^2 + c^2 = 2m^2 + \frac{1}{2}a^2 = 2R^2 + \frac{1}{2}a^2$. Denoting this constant by k^2, where k is a fixed length, we obtain for the radius R of the circle the expression $R = \frac{1}{2}(2k^2 - a^2)^{1/2}$. This discussion leads to the following proposition:

The locus of points A such that the sum of the squares of their distances AB, AC from two fixed points B and C is equal to a constant k^2, $AB^2 + AC^2 = k^2$, is a circle with radius $R = \frac{1}{2}(2k^2 - a^2)^{1/2}$ and center at the midpoint of the segment $BC = a$, provided k^2 is greater than $\frac{1}{2}a^2$.

If $k^2 = \frac{1}{2}a^2$, then $R = 0$ and the circle degenerates into a single point, namely its center M, midpoint of BC. For all other choices of an initial point A the condition of reality for R, $k^2 > \frac{1}{2}a^2$, is satisfied. Thus, the midpoint M of the segment BC appears as the solution of the following problem: Find a point such that the sum of the squares of its distances from two given points B and C is a minimum.

Having established that the locus of points with a constant sum of squares of distances from two fixed points is a circle, we now ask whether this result can be generalized by increasing the number of fixed points? For three fixed points the affirmative answer is given in the following theorem:

THEOREM XX (LEIBNIZ'S THEOREM): *Given a fixed triangle ABC, the locus of points P with a constant sum of squares of distances from the vertices, $PA^2 + PB^2 + PC^2 = k^2$, is a circle with center at the centroid G of the triangle and its radius R is given by the expression $3R^2 = k^2 - (GA^2 + GB^2 + GC^2)$.*

The condition of reality for R, namely, $k^2 \geqslant GA^2 + GB^2 + GC^2$, proves that the centroid G of the triangle ABC is the solution of the following problem: Find a point such that the sum of squares of its distances from the vertices of a given triangle is a minimum. To compute this minimum of k^2,

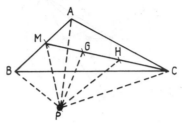

Fig. 15.13

that is, to compute the sum $GA^2 + GB^2 + GC^2 = k_0^2 = \min k^2$, we observe that the distance of the centroid G from a vertex is equal to two thirds of the corresponding median, so that $GA = 2m_a/3$, $GB = 2m_b/3$, $GC = 2\,m_c/3$. Therefore,

$$k_0^2 = GA^2 + GB^2 + GC^2 = 4\,(m_a^2 + m_b^2 + m_c^2)/9 = (a^2 + b^2 + c^2)/3.$$

Thus, in Leibniz's Theorem the radius R of the circle is given by the relation $3R^2 = k^2 - k_0^2 = k^2 - (a^2 + b^2 + c^2)/3$.

PROOF OF THEOREM XX. The points G (centroid) and H divide the median MC (Fig. 13) into three equal parts $MG = GH = HC$. Joining any point P, non-incident with G, to the six points A, B, C, H, G, M, consider the four triangles ABP, MHP, GCP, and ABG with their medians PM, PG, PH, GM and apply (10):

$$PA^2 + PB^2 - \tfrac{1}{2}AB^2 = 2PM^2; \quad 2PM^2 + 2PH^2 - MH^2 = 4PG^2;$$

$$PG^2 + PC^2 - \tfrac{1}{2}GC^2 = 2PH^2; \quad GA^2 + GB^2 - \tfrac{1}{2}AB^2 = 2GM^2.$$

Adding member by member the first three relations, subtracting from the resulting relation the last of our four relations, using the equalities MH $= GC$ and $2MG^2 = \tfrac{1}{2}GC^2$, transposing and simplifying, we deduce the theorem XX:

$$PA^2 + PB^2 + PC^2 = 3PG^2 + GA^2 + GB^2 + GC^2.$$

For any point P non-incident with G, so that $PG > 0$, we have $PA^2 + PB^2 + PC^2 > GA^2 + GB^2 + GC^2$ which proves the minimum property of the centroid G stated above. Moreover, if $PA^2 + PB^2 + PC^2 = k^2$ is a constant, then PG^2 is also constant which completes the proof of Leibniz's Theorem.

Returning to Fig. 12 and rotating it about the straight line BC, we obtain a sphere of same center M and radius $R = \frac{1}{2}(2k^2 - a^2)^{1/2}$ as the circle and therefore in the three-dimensional space the locus of points with a constant sum of squares of distances from two given points is a sphere. Thus, the circle—solution of the corresponding two-dimensional problem—is a section of this sphere by a plane through the diameter BC of the sphere.

From this point of view, Theorem XX* below is a complete generalization of the previous result since the relation $PA^2 + PB^2 + PC^2 = 3PG^2 + GA^2 + GB^2 + GC^2$ remains true even if the point P does not lie in the plane of the triangle ABC. A three-dimensional configuration formed by four non-coplanar points and consisting of four vertices, four triangular faces and six edges is called a *tetrahedron*. Thus, in other words, Fig. 13 can be looked upon as a representation of a tetrahedron PABC. The proof given above does not depend on the location of the point P in the plane ABC, and it holds for the tetrahedron PABC. Therefore, the complete proposition may be formulated as follows (Leibniz's Theorem in *space*):

THEOREM XX*: *Given a fixed triangle ABC, the locus of points with a constant sum k^2 of squares of distances from the vertices of the triangle is a sphere with center at the centroid G and radius R given by*

$$3R^2 = k^2 - (AB^2 + BC^2 + CA^2)/3.$$

The circle of Theorem XX appears now as a section of the sphere of Theorem XX* by the plane of the triangle ABC, so that Theorem XX is included in Theorem XX*.

What happens now with this theorem if *four* fixed points A, B, C, D are given in space, forming a tetrahedron ABCD? Can it be said that the locus of points P (Fig. 14) such that the sum of the four squares $PA^2 + PB^2 + PC^2 + PD^2 = k^2$, where k^2 is a constant, is a sphere? As we will see in Solid Geometry, the answer is *yes*: a tretrahedron possesses a centroid G, and Leibniz's relation for it becomes

$$PA^2 + PB^2 + PC^2 + PD^2 = 4PG^2 + GA^2 + GB^2 + GC^2 + GD^2. \quad (11)$$

Therefore, if the sum of the four squares in the lefthand member of (11) is equal to a constant k^2, the radius $R = PG$ of the sphere is given by the relation $4R^2 = k^2 - (GA^2 + GB^2 + GC^2 + GD^2)$ and its center is at the point G.

It is of interest to add that again the point P can leave the three-dimensional space S_3, in which the given tetrahedron ABCD is located, and nevertheless the relation (11) remains true. In other words, Figure 14 can be interpreted as a representation of a *four-dimensional configuration* in which the point P does not belong to the three-dimensional space S_3 defined by the four fixed points A, B, C, D. The locus of points P in S_4 with a constant sum of squares $PA^2 + PB^2 + PC^2 + PD^2$ is a three-dimensional solid called a hypersphere. It is almost entirely located in S_4, having in common with S_3 only a spherical surface of radius $PG = R$ and the center G, this surface being a section of the solid by the space S_3. The best definition of the solid hypersphere is the locus of points in S_4 equidistant from a given point G. Their common distance $PG = R$ from G is the radius.

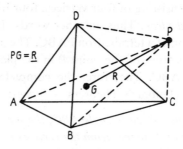

Fig. 15.14

On the other hand, the same Fig. 14 can be looked upon as a *two-dimensional* configuration, all of its points belonging to the same plane ABC. In this case the point G can be defined as the center of gravity of four unit-masses concentrated at the four vertices of the plane quadrilateral ABCD. Thus, a theorem of plane geometry is obtained:

The locus of points P with a constant sum k^2 of squares of distances from four vertices of a given quadrilateral ABCD is a circle, having its center at G and a radius R given by the relation $4R^2 = k^2 - (GA^2 = GB^2 + GC^2 + GD^2)$.

We state that the same theorem holds in plane geometry for two, three and four fixed points with similar formulas for the radius R of the circle-locus, namely,

$$2R^2 = 2PG^2 = k^2 - (GA^2 + GB^2)$$

$$3R^2 = 3PG^2 = k^2 - (GA^2 + GB^2 + GC^2)$$

$$4R^2 = 4PG^2 = k^2 - (GA^2 + GB^2 + GC^2 + GD^2).$$

It now seems highly probable that the number of fixed points does not matter and that the theorem must be true for any number n of fixed points. To prove this we consider n points A_1, A_2, ... A_n, given in a plane π. Denoting by G the center of gravity of n unit-masses located at these n points $A_s, s = 1, 2, 3, \ldots, n - 1, n$, and considering in the plane π those points P for which the sum of squares of distances from n points A_s is a constant k^2

$$\sum_{s=1}^{n} PA_s^2 = PA_1^2 + PA_2^2 + PA_3^2 + \cdots + PA_n^2 = k^2$$

(the symbol $\sum$ denotes a summation from $s = 1$ up to $s = n$ with respect to the subscript s, the result being a sum of n terms), we will prove that their locus is a circle with center G and radius PG $= R$ defined by the relation

$$nR^2 = k^2 - \sum_{s=1}^{n} GA_s^2 = k^2 - (GA_1^2 + GA_2^2 + \cdots + GA_n^2).$$

Our proof of this general theorem uses mathematical induction and Stewart's Relation (7). Supposing that this theorem is true for n fixed points, so that the validity of the relation

$$n PG^2 = \sum_{s=1}^{n} PA_s^2 - \sum_{s=1}^{n} GA_s^2 \tag{12}$$

is already established, we have to verify that then the same relation holds for $n + 1$ fixed points.

Introducing the $(n + 1)$-th fixed point A and denoting by H the new center of gravity of the $n + 1$ unit-masses located at the n points A_s, $1 \leqslant s \leqslant n$, and at the $(n + 1)$-th point A, we must first of all find the location of the point H. In locating H, we note that the effect of n unit-masses, one at each of the n points A_s, is, by definition, the same as the action of a *single* mass of n units concentrated at the point G because G is their center of gravity. Therefore, H can be considered as the center of gravity of two unequal masses located at G and at A, the mass at G being n times greater than that at A. Thus, H belongs to the segment GA and divides it in the ratio HA/HG $= n$ (Fig. 15).

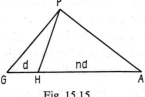

Fig. 15.15

If the distance GH is denoted by d, we have GA $= (n + 1) d$ and HA $= nd$. Applying (7) to the triangle GPA and the point H, we obtain

$$\text{GH} \cdot \text{PA}^2 + \text{HA} \cdot \text{PG}^2 - \text{GH} \cdot \text{HA} \cdot \text{GA} = \text{PH}^2 \cdot \text{GA}.$$

Replacing in this relation GH, HA, GA by their values d, nd, $(n + 1) d$, dividing by the common factor d and transposing, we rewrite it as follows:

$$\text{PA}^2 + n\text{PG}^2 = (n + 1) \text{PH}^2 + n (n + 1) d^2. \tag{13}$$

By hypothesis, Leibniz's relation (12) holds for n fixed points. Therefore, applying it first to the point H and then to the point P, we have

$$\Sigma \, \text{HA}_s^2 = n\text{GH}^2 + \Sigma \, \text{GA}_s^2; \quad \Sigma \, \text{PA}_s^2 = n\text{PG}^2 + \Sigma \, \text{GA}_s^2.$$

Eliminating $\Sigma \, \text{GA}_s^2$ and observing that GH $= d$, we deduce from these

$$\Sigma \, \text{PA}_s^2 - n\text{PG}^2 = \Sigma \, \text{HA}_s^2 - nd^2.$$

Adding this relation and the relation (13) member by member, we find finally Leibniz's relation for $n + 1$ fixed points, that is,

$$\text{PA}^2 + \Sigma \, \text{PA}_s^2 = (n + 1) \text{PH}^2 + \text{HA}^2 + \Sigma \, \text{HA}_s^2$$

because $n (n + 1) d^2 - nd^2 = (nd)^2 = \text{HA}^2$.

The hereditary property of Leibniz's relation being proved, it is justified for any number of fixed points since it is true for two, three, and four fixed points. Thus, it is proved that the locus of points with a constant sum of squares of distances from n fixed coplanar points is a circle.

What now about the locus of points P such that the sum of multiples of squares PA_s^2 is constant, that is,

$$\Sigma \, x_s \text{PA}_s^2 = x_1 \text{PA}_1^2 + x_2 \text{PA}_2^2 + \cdots + x_n \text{PA}_n^2 = k^2.$$

Leibniz's Relation can be extended to this case also and the locus is again a circle, the coefficients x_s being any real numbers, positive or negative, rational or irrational. We will prove it only for the case of positive x_s.

Given n positive integers m_s, $1 \leqslant s \leqslant n$, we consider a distribution of masses m_s at points A_s. A point A_s, where the mass m_s is located, can be considered as a limiting case of m_s distinct points of unit-mass, these m_s points approaching A_s and coinciding with each other at the limit in the point A_s. Therefore, stating the relation (12) for $n = \Sigma \, m_s = m_1 + m_2 + \cdots + m_n$ unit-masses at n points and then passing to the limit, we obtain for our mass distribution the corresponding generalization of the relation (12), namely,

$$\Sigma \, m_s \cdot \text{PA}_s^2 = \text{PG}^2 \cdot (\Sigma m_s) + \sum m_s \cdot \text{GA}_s^2, \tag{14}$$

where again G denotes the center of gravity of our n masses m_s at the n fixed points A_s, $1 \leqslant s \leqslant n$.

But, if we wish to generalize from integral multiples m_s to any positive real coefficients x_s, we can go still further. Given a finite set of any real positive numbers $x_1, x_2, \ldots x_n$, we can assume without any loss of generality that their sum is equal to one since Leibniz's Relation is homogeneous with respect to the coefficients x_s. In general, the numbers x_s are irrational and therefore n infinite convergent sequences of rational numbers $m_s^{(i)}/N_i$, $1 \leqslant i \to \infty$, can be constructed with $N \to \infty$ for $i \to \infty$ and for which

$$\lim_{i = \infty} [m_s^{(i)}/N_i] = x_s \qquad (1 \leqslant s \leqslant n)$$

for $s = 1, 2, \ldots n$. Replacing in (14) the numbers m_s by $m_s^{(i)}$, dividing both sides by N_I, and passing to the limit for $i = \infty$, we deduce the relation

$$\Sigma \, x_s \cdot PA_s^2 = PG^2 + \Sigma \, x_s \cdot GA_s^2 . \qquad (\Sigma \, x_s = 1)$$

Thus, the locus of points P verifying the condition

$$\Sigma \, x_s \cdot PA_s^2 = x_1 \cdot PA_1^2 + x_2 \cdot PA_2^2 + \cdots + x_n \cdot PA_n^2 = k^2$$

is a circle having its center at G and whose radius $PG = R$ is given by

$$R^2 = k^2 - \Sigma \, x_s \cdot GA_s^2 .$$

Metric Relations in a Quadrilateral

A parallelogram is merely a particular case of a quadrilateral and Theorem XIX which states that the sum of the squares of diagonals in a parallelogram is equal to the sum of the squares of its four sides is also a particular case of a more general metric relation which is true for any quadrilateral.

As we know the diagonals of a parallelogram bisect each other, so that the distance between their midpoints vanishes. The more a quadrilateral deviates from the parallelogram the greater becomes the distance between the midpoints of its diagonals. The general metric relation, of which Theorem XIX is a particular case, involves the square of this distance as well as those of the distances between the midpoints of opposite sides. We formulate it as

THEOREM XXI: *The sum of the six squares of four sides and two diagonals of a quadrilateral is equal to four times the sum of the squares of the three segments joining the midpoints of opposite sides and the midpoints of two diagonals.*

In Fig. 16 are drawn not only the nine segments directly involved in Theorem XXI, namely, four sides and two diagonals of the quadrilateral ABCD and three segments EF, GH, KL, but also the twelve auxiliary segments, sides of three parallelograms EGFH, EKFL and GKHL, which are used in the proof. Let E, G, F, H, K, L denote the midpoints of sides and diagonals of ABCD.

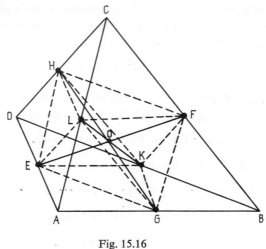

Fig. 15.16

The theorem asserts the validity of the following relation.

$$AB^2 + BC^2 + CD^2 + DA^2 + AC^2 + BD^2 = 4(EF^2 + GH^2 + KL^2). \quad (15)$$

To justify it, we apply Theorem XIX to the three parallelograms EGFH, EKFL, GKHL:

$$EF^2 + GH^2 = 2(EG^2 + EH^2);$$

$$GH^2 + KL^2 = 2(GK^2 + HK^2);$$

$$EF^2 + KL^2 = 2(EK^2 + FK^2).$$

Adding these relations member by member, multiplying both sides of the resulting relation by two, and observing that 2EG = BD, 2EH = AC, 2GK = AD, 2HK = BC, 2EK = AB and 2FK = CD, we obtain the proof of Theorem XXI. Noticing that in (15)

$$4(EF^2 + GH^2) = 4(EG^2 + GF^2 + FH^2 + HE^2) = 2(AC^2 + BD^2),$$

we have another, equivalent formulation of Theroem XXI, namely.

THEOREM XXI*: *The sum of the squares of the sides of a quadrilateral is equal to the sum of the squares of its diagonals plus four times the square of the segment joining the midpoints of the diagonals:*

$$AB^2 + BC^2 + CD^2 + DA^2 = AC^2 + BD^2 + 4KL^2.$$

For a parallelogram the segment KL vanishes and Theorem XXI* reduces to Theorem XIX.

Theorem XXI itself is a particular case of a more general metric relation which holds for any tetrahedron and belongs to solid geometry. Figure 16, indeed, when looked upon as a three-dimensional configuration, defines a tetrahedron ABCD with the vertex C above the plane of its base ABD, six edges AB, BC, CD, DA, AC, BD and the three plane lateral faces ABC, BCD, CDA. The segments EF, GH, KL are now joining the midpoints of opposite edges of the tetrahedron ABCD. They are no more coplanar and define three distinct planes passing through their common midpoint 0, namely, those of the three parallelograms EGFH, EKFL, GKHL.

We wish to prove that Theorem XXI as formulated in the relation (15) remains true also for the three-dimensional interpretation of Fig. 16, so that:

THEOREM XXII: *In a tetrahedron ABCD, the sum of squares of the six edges is equal to four times the sum of the squares of the three segments joining the midpoints of opposite edges.*

The proof of this theorem is based on the fact that HE and GF, being parallel and equal to $\frac{1}{2}$AC, define a plane, so that the four coplanar points E, H, G, F form a parallelogram. The same holds for the quadruplets of points H, L, G, K and E, K, F, L. The remaining part of the proof is the same as for Theorem XXI.

To deduce Theorem XXI from Theorem XXII as its particular case, we must transform gradually and continuously the tetrahedron ABCD into a flat quadrilateral bringing the vertex C into the plane of the base ABD. During this continuous transformation, the shape, angles and lengths change but relation (15) remains true. It holds, therefore, also at the limit when, C reaching the plane ABD the tetrahedron degenerates into a plane quadrilateral, the edges AC and BD becoming diagonals of this quadrilateral.

If the variable point C approaching the plane ABD coincides at the limit with the point D, the tetrahedron ABCD degenerates into a triangle, the edge CD vanishes, while those CA and CB coincide with DA and DB respectively. Of the three segments joining the midpoints of opposite sides, GH becomes a median GD, while KL and EF coincide with the segment EK.

Therefore, the relation (15) is transformed into $2AD^2 + 2BD^2 + AB^2 = 4(2EK^2 + DG^2)$. But, $EK = \frac{1}{2}AB$, so that $8EK^2 = 2AB^2$. Thus, transposing this term to the left, we obtain for the square of the median DG of our triangle the already known result $DG^2 = \frac{1}{2}(AD^2 + BD^2) - \frac{1}{4}AB^2$. The relation (10) is deduced this time as a limiting case of Theorem XXI.

Sine Law

Returning to triangles, we now study a second group of important metric relations in a triangle known as the *Sine Law*. This law gives the expressions of sides a, b, c in terms of the radius R of the circumscribed circle and the opposite angles:

$$a = 2R \sin A; \quad b = 2R \sin B; \quad c = 2R \sin C, \tag{16}$$

where A, B, C denote the angles of a triangle ABC opposite, respectively, to the sides $a = BC$, $b = CA$ and $c = AB$ (Fig. 17).

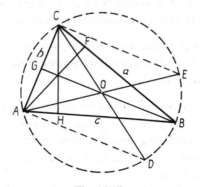

Fig. 15.17

To prove (16) we draw the diameters AE and CD of the circumscribed circle and join their endpoints D and E to other vertices of the triangle. The three angles $\widehat{ADC}$, $\widehat{ABC}$ and $\widehat{AEC}$ subtended by the same arc $\widehat{AC}$, are equal: $\widehat{ADC} = \widehat{AEC} = \hat{B}$. Likewise we find that $\widehat{BDC} = \hat{A}$, both angles being subtended by the arc $\widehat{BEC}$. Consider now the right triangles ADC and BDC, with right angles at A and B.

Applying the definition of the function sine to $\widehat{BDC}$, $\widehat{ADC}$, $\widehat{AEB}$ and substituting $2R$ for CD and AE, we obtain: $\sin \widehat{BDC} = \sin \hat{A} = BC/CD = a/2R$, $\sin \widehat{ADC} = \sin \hat{B} = AC/CD = b/2R$ and $\sin \widehat{AEB} = \sin \hat{C} =$

AB/AE $= c/2R$. Multiplying by $2R$, we deduce (16), which can also be written down as follows

$$a/\sin A = b/\sin B = c/\sin C = 2R. \qquad (17)$$

Dropping from the vertices of ABC the perpendiculars AF $= h_a$, BG $= h_b$, CH $= h_c$ to the sides a, b, c respectively, and considering the right triangles ACH, BCH for h_c and the corresponding pairs of triangles for h_a and for h_b, we have also

$$h_a = b \sin C = c \sin B: \quad h_b = c \sin A = a \sin C: \quad h_c = a \sin B = b \sin A.$$

Substituting in these the expressions of the sines of three angles given by the Sine Law, namely, $\sin A = a/2R$ etc., the following expressions for the altitudes are found

$$h_a = bc/2R; \quad h_b = ca/2R; \quad h_c = ab/2R.$$

Combining this result with (9), we obtain an important relation between the area $[s\,(s-a)\,(s-b)\,(s-c)]^{1/2}$ of a triangle and the radius R of its circumscribed circle:

$$[s\,(s-a)\,(s-b)\,(s-c)]^{1/2} = abc/4R.$$

This relation allows the computation of the radius R if the sides of a triangle are known.

EXAMPLE: Given the sides $a = 5$, $b = 12$ and $c = 13$, find R. First of all we compute the perimeter $2s = 5 + 12 + 13 = 30$ which gives $s = 15$, $s - a = 10$, $s - b = 3$, $s - c = 2$. Thus, $[s\,(s-a)\,(s-b)\,(s-c)]^{1/2} = 30$, while $abc = 780$. Finally, $R = 780/120 = 6.5$. This value of R is easy to check: Our triangle is a right triangle since in it $a^2 + b^2 = 25 + 144 = 169 = c^2$. Therefore, the hypotenuse $c = 13$ is at the same time a diameter of the circumscribed circle, so that $2R = c = 13$.

The area of a triangle ABC (Fig. 18) can also be expressed as the product rs, where r denotes the radius of the inscribed circle, while $s = \frac{1}{2}(a + b + c)$,

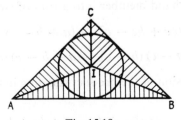

Fig. 15.18

as usual. The area of ABC is a sum of three areas obtained by joining the incenter I to the vertices of the triangle, area ABC = area AIB + area BIC + area CIA = $\frac{1}{2}cr + \frac{1}{2}ar + \frac{1}{2}br = \frac{1}{2}(a+b+c)r = \frac{1}{2}(2s)r = sr$, that is,

$$\text{area ABC} = [s(s-a)(s-b)(s-c)]^{1/2} = rs.$$

EXAMPLE: The radius r of an inscribed circle is easily computed with the aid of the previous relation, which gives $r = \text{area}/s$. Thus, in our previous example, we had $s = 15$ and $[s(s-a)(s-b)(s-c)]^{1/2} = 30$. Therefore, for the right triangle $a = 5$, $b = 12$, $c = 13$, the radius r is equal to $\frac{30}{15} = 2$.

In Chapter 14 we proved that the radius of the nine-point circle related to a triangle is equal to one half the radius R of the circumscribed circle and from this fact we concluded that the radius r of the inscribed circle is always less than $\frac{1}{2}R$, unless the triangle is equilateral, in which case $r = \frac{1}{2}R$. Here we now give another purely algebraic proof of the same inequality $r \leqslant \frac{1}{2}R$ based on the explicit expression of the difference $1 - 2r/R$ in terms of a, b, c.

To fix our ideas, let us denote by c the smallest side of the triangle, so that both differences $a - c$ and $b - c$ are positive, unless the triangle is equilateral with $a = b = c$. Thus, we have $a - c > 0$ and $b - c > 0$. Forming the expression $2abcr/R$, we find that it is equal to $8(s-a)(s-b)(s-c)$. We have, indeed, denoting the area $[s(s-a)(s-b)(s-c)]^{1/2}$ of ABC by Δ, $2r = 2\Delta/s$ and $abc/R = 4\Delta$, so that $2abcr/R = 8\Delta^2/s$, which is equal to $8(s-a)(s-b)(s-c)$. Thus, recalling that $2s = a + b + c$,

$$abc(1 - 2r/R) = abc - 2abcr/R = abc - (2s-2a)(2s-2b)(2s-2c)$$

$$= abc - (-a+b+c)(a-b+c)(a+b-c)$$

$$= abc - [c-(a-b)][c+(a-b)](a+b-c)$$

$$= abc - [c^2 - (a-b)^2](a+b-c).$$

Observing that the second term of the righthand member can be written as $[c^2 - (a-b)^2](a+b-c) = c(ac + bc - c^2) - (a+b-c)(a-b)^2$, we transform the righthand member into a sum of two positive terms:

$$abc - c(ac + bc - c^2) + (a+b-c)(a-b)^2$$

$$= c(a-c)(b-c) + (a+b-c)(a-b)^2$$

so that the final expression of the product standing in the lefthand member becomes

$$abc(1 - 2r/R) = c(a-c)(b-c) + (a+b-c)(a-b)^2.$$

In this expression, the righthand member is positive because $a - c > 0$ and $b - c > 0$, and this proves that the factor $1 - 2r/R$ in the lefthand member must be positive too, which means that the ration r/R is less than one half: $r/R < \frac{1}{2}$. The maximum value $\frac{1}{2}$ of this ratio ($r = \frac{1}{2}R$) can be attained only when the righthand member vanishes. This can happen only when both terms in the righthand member vanish separately because neither term is negative. The first factor $a + b - c$ of the second term cannot vanish because it exceeds a. Therefore, the second term vanishes only when $a = b$, its second factor being zero. But if $b = a$, then the first term becomes equal to $c(a - c)^2$, and this can vanish only when $a = c$. Thus, $r = \frac{1}{2}R$ only for a equilateral triangle with $a = b = c$.

The reciprocal $1/r$ of the radius r of the inscribed circle is related to the reciprocals of three altitudes of a triangle by the following curios formula:

$$1/h_a + 1/h_b + 1/h_c = 1/r. \tag{18}$$

To justify (18), we recall that $ah_a = bh_b = ch_c = 2\Delta$, where Δ denotes the triangle's area. Therefore, solving for the reciprocals of altitudes, we obtain

$$1/h_a + 1/h_b + 1/h_c = a/2\Delta + b/2\Delta + c/2\Delta = (a + b + c)/2\Delta$$
$$= 2s/2\Delta = s/\Delta = 1/r$$

EXAMPLE: Returning again to the right triangle with $a = 5, b = 12, c = 13$, we see that $a = h_b = 5$ and $b = h_a = 12$, while $h_c = 2\,(\text{area})/c = \frac{60}{13}$. Therefore, the sum of the reciprocals of altitudes is equal to $\frac{1}{5} + \frac{1}{12} + \frac{13}{60} = (5 + 12 + 13)/60 = \frac{1}{2}$ and $r = 2$, as we already know.

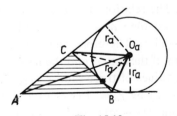

Fig. 15.19

The radii r_a, r_b, r_c of the three excribed (externally tangent) circles of a triangle are also related to the area Δ of the triangle. Consider, for instance, the escribed circle tangent externally to the side-segment $BC = a$ in an interior point of this segment (Fig. 19). Joining its center O_a to the vertices of ABC, we form three triangles ABO_a, BCO_a, and CAO_a, whose areas are equal respectively to $cr_a/2$, $ar_a/2$, and $br_a/2$, where the radius r_a of the escribed circle is the common altitude of these three triangles. These areas, together with the area Δ of the triangle ABC, satisfy the following relation

$$\text{area ABC} + \text{area BCO}_a = \Delta + \tfrac{1}{2}ar_a = \text{area CAO}_a + \text{area BAO}_a$$

$$= \tfrac{1}{2}br_a + \tfrac{1}{2}cr_a = \tfrac{1}{2}(b+c)r_a$$

which yields for r_a the equation: $\Delta = \tfrac{1}{2}(b+c)r_a - \tfrac{1}{2}ar_a = (s-a)r_a$.

Therefore, we obtain for the area Δ of the triangle ABC a new expression, namely, $\Delta = r_a(s-a)$. Applying the same reasoning to the escribed circles with radii r_b and r_c, we deduce the similar expressions $\Delta = r_b(s-b)$ and $\Delta = r_c(s-c)$. Thus, solving for the radii of escribed circles, we have a group of three formulas to which we add the known relation $r = \Delta/s$:

$$r = \Delta/s, \quad r_a = \Delta/(s-a), \quad r_b = \Delta/(s-b), \quad r_c = \Delta/(s-c).$$

Inverting them and adding the resulting expressions of the three recipro-cals $1/r_a$, $1/r_b$, and $1/r_c$, we prove that their sum is equal to $1/r$:

$$1/r_a + 1/r_b + 1/r_c = 1/r$$

because $(s-a) + (s-b) + (s-c) = 3s - (a+b+c) = 3s - 2s = s$.

We have also $rr_ar_br_c = s(s-a)(s-b)(s-c)$, so that the area Δ is equal to the square root $(rr_ar_br_c)^{1/2}$ of the product of four radii of tangent circles.

We conclude the study of metric relations in a triangle, solving the follow-ing problem:

PROBLEM: Knowing the radii r_a, r_b, r_c of escribed circles, find the three sides a, b, c of a triangle. The relation $\Delta = r_a(s-a)$, solved for the side a, gives first $s - a = \Delta/r_a$ and then $a = s - \Delta/r_a$. Likewise, we prove that $b = s - \Delta/r_b$ and $c = s - \Delta/r_c$. Therefore, the sides can be computed with the aid of these expressions, if the area Δ and the half-perimeter s are already deduced from the known values of three radii r_a, r_b, r_c.

Multiplying $r_a = \Delta/(s-a)$ by $r_b = \Delta/(s-b)$ and replacing the square Δ^2 of the area by its value $s(s-a)(s-b)(s-c)$, we deduce that $r_ar_b = s(s-c)$. Similarly, we find that $r_br_c = s(s-a)$ and $r_cr_a = s(s-b)$. Adding these three products, we obtain the square of the half-perimeter s^2:

$$r_br_c + r_cr_a + r_ar_b = s(s-a) + s(s-b) + s(s-c)$$

$$= s(3s - a - b - c) = s(3s - 2s) = s^2.$$

Therefore, the half-perimeter s is computed with the aid of the relation $s = (r_ar_b + r_br_c + r_cr_a)^{1/2}$. On the other hand, forming the product of all three radii, we find $r_a r_b r_c = \Delta^3/(s-a)(s-b)(s-c) = s\Delta$, so that the area Δ is equal to $r_a r_b r_c/s : \Delta = r_a r_b r_c/s$, which completes the solution of the problem.

EXAMPLE: Find the triangle for which the radii of three escribed circles are equal to $\sqrt{11}$, $2\sqrt{11}$, and $3\sqrt{11}$. The formula for the half-perimeter s gives $s = 11$. On the other hand, the product of all three radii is equal to $66\sqrt{11}$, so that the area Δ is equal to $66\sqrt{11}/11 = 6\sqrt{11}$. Therefore, $\Delta/r_a = 6$, $\Delta/r_b = 3$, and $\Delta/r_c = 2$, and this yields $a = 11 - 6 = 5$, $b = 11 - 3 = 8$, $c = 11 - 2 = 9$.

Metric Relations in a Circle

The simplest configuration involving a circle consists of a circle and a point. It is completely characterized by two given lengths, the radius R of the circle, and the distance d of the given point from the circle's center. If $d > R$, the point is outside the circle. It is inside the circle if $d < R$ and on its circumference if $d = R$.

If $d < R$, the point P being inside the circle, any straight line through P intersects the circle in two points A and B (Fig. 20), while for $d > R$ (that is, P outside the circle) the straight lines through P belong to two different classes: some intersect the circle in two distinct points (they are called *secants*),

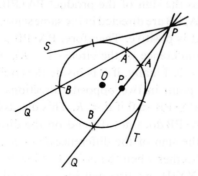

Fig. 15.20

but the other do not meet the circle at all. The lines of these two classes are separated by two tangents PS and PT to the circle.

Drawing through P a secant PQ, we consider on it the two directed segments PA and PB, where A and B are the intersection-points of the secant with the circle, the positive sense on the secant PQ being by definition that from P towards Q.

Their lengths depend on the direction of the secant PQ, and when the secant rotates about the fixed point P, the segments PA and PB vary in opposite sense: if PA increases, PB decreases and *vice versa*. If $d = OP > R$, the point P being outside the circle, the segment PB remains greater than PA, so that the maximum of PB corresponds to the minimum of PA, and these extreme values of PA and PB are attained for a special position of the secant PQ, namely, when it passes through the center O and $AB = 2R$ is a diameter. The same happens for a secant through a point P interior to the circle.

It is important to emphasize that, despite the variation of PA and PB, their product PA·PB does not depend on the direction of the secant and remains constant for all secants passing through P. The value of this product PA·PB is related to the location of the point P with respect to the circle and characterizes therefore the configuration formed by the point P and the circle. This is why this value can be expressed in terms of the two parameters R and d of the configuration:

THEOREM XXIII: *The product of two segments determined by a circle and a point on a secant through this point does not depend on the particular secant and it is equal to $d^2 - R^2$, d and R being the distance of the point from the circle's center and the radius of the circle, respectively.*

We must first discuss the sign of the product PA·PB. If P is outside the circle, both segments PA, PB are directed in the same sense. They have the same sign, and their product is positive. Therefore, $PA \cdot PB > 0$ if $d > R$. If P is incident with the circumference of the circle ($d = R$), one of the segments vanishes and $PA \cdot PB = 0$. Finally, if P is inside the circle, then the directed segments PA and PB point in two opposite directions and have therefore opposite signs. Thus, $PA \cdot PB < 0$ if $d < R$. This discussion proves that the sign of the product PA·PB does not depend on the direction of the secant and agrees well with the sign of the difference $d^2 - R^2$. Moreover, PA·PB and $d^2 - R^2$ vanish together when the point P is incident with the circle.

To prove Theorem XXIII, we first consider a special case when AB is a diameter, the secant PQ passing through the center. We must study separately the two cases (1) $d > R$ and (2) $d < R$.

CASE (1): Since P is outside the circle, both $PA = PO - AO = d - R$ and $PB = PO + OB = d + R$ are positive and $PA \cdot PB = (d - R)(d + R) = d^2 - R^2$.

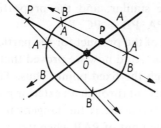

Fig. 15.21

CASE (2): Now P is inside the circle, so that PA is negative: PA = PO + OA = PO − AO = $d − R$, while PB is positive and equal again to $d + R$. Therefore, PA·PB = $d^2 − R^2$ as in the previous case (1) (Fig. 21). To complete the proof of the theorem, it remains to show that the value of the product PA·PB is the same for any two secants, and to do this we apply the method of similar triangles.

Taking first two secants AD, BC intersecting within the circle at Q and joining the points A and C to those B and D, respectively (Fig. 22), we form two similar triangles ABQ and CDQ: $\overparen{BAD} = \overparen{BCD}$ and $\overparen{CBA} = \overparen{CDA}$ because they are subtended by the same arcs; hence, all the angles are equal, and the triangles are similar (Theorem XV, case 1). Corresponding sides of similar triangles are proportional, and the proportion QA/QC = QB/QD gives QA·QD = QB·QC, which proves the theorem for an interior point Q.

Consider now two secants PB and PD intersecting at an exterior point P (Fig. 22), draw the chords AD, BC, and form thus two triangles BCP and DAP. They have a common angle at their common vertex P and $\overparen{CBP} = \overparen{ADP}$, as subtended by the same arc AC. Therefore, by Theorem XV,

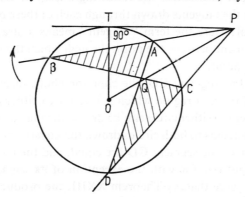

Fig. 15.22

case 1, these triangles are similar, and the proportion PA/PC = PD/PB yields the desired result: PA·PB = PC·PD.

We know that the value of the product for the particular secant which is a diameter is equal to $d^2 - R^2$, and now we proved that it is the same for any two secants passing through the fixed point. Thus, Theorem XXIII is true. The limiting position of a secant through an exterior point when its two intersection points at the limit coincide is the tangent to the circle. In Fig. 22 therefore, PT appears as the limit of PAB when this secant rotates clockwise about P, the two intersection points A and B approaching the point T. At the limit, both segments PA and PB coincide with the tangent's segment PT, and the product PA·PB becomes equal to PT^2. Since its value does not depend on the direction of the secant, we obtain $PT^2 = d^2 - R^2$, where $d = OP$. Transposing R^2 in the lefthand member and replacing it by OT^2, we have $OP^2 = PT^2 + OT^2$, which proves that the triangle OTP is a right triangle with OP as its hypotenuse. Thus, the radius of the contact point is perpendicular to the tangent to a circle.

Radical Axis of Two Circles

Given two intersecting circles (Fig. 23), the points of the plane fall in two regions: the region composed of points interior to either one of the two circles and the region composed of points exterior to both circles. These regions are separated from each other by the two circumferences and, from any point of the second, exterior region tangents can be drawn to both circles, while no point of the first region has this property.

Theorem XXIII now solves the following question: What is the locus of points such that the tangents drawn through each of these points to two given circles are equal? Here the term "tangent" means a straight line segment, namely, the segment between the point through which the tangent line passes and its contact point.

The straight line segment CD, the common chord of two circles, belongs to that part of the first region which is interior to either of two circles. Although no tangent to either circle can be drawn through any point of this segment CD, the tangents to both circles drawn through the points of the straight line PR exterior to the segment CD are equal, and the locus we are looking for is this straight line PR with the exception of its segment CD. To prove this, we first observe that, by Theorem XXIII, the product PC·PD is equal on the one hand to the square PA^2 of the tangent to the circle ACSDNA and, on the other hand, to the square PB^2 of the tangent to the circle BCDTMB. Thus, since the point P is any point on PR exterior to the segment CD, the locus comprises indeed the line PR minus its segment CD.

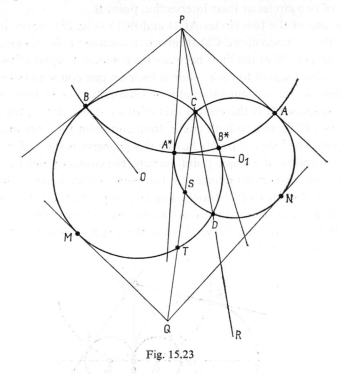

Fig. 15.23

But it may be that there are other points having the same property and which do not belong to the line PR. To prove that this is not the case, let us consider a point Q off the line PR and the two tangents QM and QN through it. Drawing through Q and C a secant QTSC and applying Theorem XXIII, we obtain QM^2 = QC·QT and QN^2 = QC·QS, so that QN^2 − QM^2 = QC(QS − QT) = QC·TS > 0 because TS can vanish only if Q lies on the line PR. Therefore, the segments QM and QN cannot be equal if the point Q is off the line PR, and this achieves the proof of our proposition. The straight line PR is called the *radical axis* of two circles.

Any point P on PR exterior to CD can be considered as the center of a circle perpendicular to either of our two circles, the radius R of this *orthogonal* circle being equal to the length of tangents from P, that is, R = PA = PA* = PB = PB*. To prove that the circle BA*B*A is perpendicular to both given circles, it is sufficient to recall that the radius of the contact point is perpendicular to the tangent. Therefore, at the intersection point B, for in-stance, the tangent to the circle BA* is perpendicular to the radius PB, that is, perpendicular to the tangent to the circle BCD, and this proves the ortho-gonality of two circles at their intersection point B.

If now one of the two circles ACD and BCD (Fig. 23) moves in such a way that the common chord CD shrinks to a common point C (Fig. 24), the common secant PR at the limit becomes the common tangent of two circles which are also tangent to each other at their unique common point C. The two circles can be tangent internally or externally, but in both cases the common tangent PR is the radical axis of two tangent circles, the tangents PA, PB, PC, PE drawn to both circles from any point P of this straight line being equal. The locus of points having this property is the radical axis PR with the exception of a single point, namely, the contact point C.

Whether the two circles intersect in two points or are tangent, the radical axis is perpendicular to the straight line joining their centers because, both circles being symmetric with respect to the line of their centers, to each point with equal tangents above this line there is a symmetrical point with equal tangents below it.

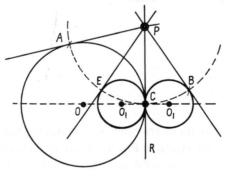

Fig. 15.24

We consider now the case of two non-incident circles which corresponds either to circles exterior to each other or to the inclusion of the smaller circle inside the larger one. In both cases, by the reason of symmetry, radical axis is again perpendicular to the line of centers OO_1. It is defined as locus of points such that the tangents from these points to both non-incident circles are equal. To prove that the radical axis of two non-incident circles is a straight line perpendicular to the line of centers and to locate its point M where this line is cut by the radical axis, we will use the Pythagorean Theorem and the algebraical method.

Choosing the center O of the large circle as the origin of distances on the line of centers, we distinguish two cases:

(1) when the small circle is interior to the large one and

(2) when the two circles are exterior to each other (Fig. 25). In case (1), let A and r denote the center and the radius of the included circle, while in case (2), the center of the second circle will be denoted by B, the radius being again r.

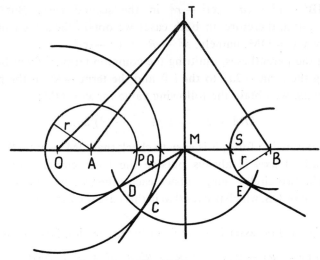

Fig. 15.25

The configuration formed by two non-incident circles is completely characterized by the three parameters R (radius of the large circle), r, and the distance OA or OB of their centers. In both cases, we denote this distance by a, so that either OA $= a$ or OB $= a$. The five different arrangements the two circles can exhibit are characterized by relations of equality and inequality between the three parameters R, r and a. Thus, if the distance of two centers a verifies the double inequality $R - r < a < R + r$, the circles intersect each other. They are tangent internally or externally, if $a = R - r$ or $a = R + r$, respectively. Finally, returning to the case we are now discussing, the two circles are non-incident when either $a < R - r$ or $a > R + r$. In case (1), when the small circle is inside the large one, we have, indeed, OP $=$ OA $+$ AP $= a + r < $ OQ $= R$, so that $a < R - r$. But in case (2) when the circles are exterior to each other, we find that OB $= a > $ OQ $+$ SB $= R + r$, and, therefore, $a > R + r$. Thus, the configuration formed by two non-incident circles is characterized by one of the two mutually exclusive inequalities, $a < R - r$ and $a > R + r$, which correspond to the cases (1) and (2), respectively.

To locate now the point M, where the radical axis intersects the centers' line OB, we will compute the unknnwn distance OM $= x$ of this point M from the origin O, using either the condition $MC^2 = MD^2$, if $a < R - r$, or the condition $MC^2 = ME^2$, if $a > R + r$. Thus, $MC^2 = x^2 - R^2$ (by Theorem XXIII) is equal to $AM^2 - r^2 = (x - a)^2 - r^2$ in the first case and to $ME^2 = MB^2 - r^2 = (a - x)^2 - r^2$ in the second case. But $(x - a)^2 = (a - x)^2$, and, therefore, in both cases we obtain the same equation for the unknown $x = OM$, namely, $x^2 - R^2 = (a - x)^2 - r^2$.

Opening the parentheses, omitting the common term x^2 from both sides, transposing the term $-2ax$ to the left and the term $-R^2$ to the right, and dividing by $2a$, we obtain the following value for $x = OM$:

$$OM = x = (R^2 + a^2 - r^2)/2a. \tag{19}$$

Using this expression for x, it is easy to check that $OM = x > R = OQ$, so that the radical axis is always outside the large circle. Moreover, if $a > R + r$, the two circles being outside each other, we will find out that $OM = x < a - r = OS$, which proves that in this case the radical axis is between the circles.

To justify our first assertion, we form the expression $2a(x - R)$:

$$2a(x - R) = 2ax - 2aR = R^2 + a^2 - r^2 - 2aR$$
$$= (R - a)^2 - r^2 = (R + r - a)(R - r - a).$$

Each factor of the righthand member is positive in both cases $a > R + r$ and $a < R - r$, so that the product $2a(x - R)$ is also positive, and this means $x > R$.

To prove that in the case $a > R + r$ the radical axis is between the two circles, we must show that the expression $2a(a - x - r)$ is positive, which is equivalent to $x < a - r$. Forming this expression

$$2a(a - x - r) = 2a^2 - (R^2 + a^2 - r^2) - 2ar$$
$$= a^2 - 2ar + r^2 - R^2 = (a - r)^2 - R^2$$
$$= (a + R - r)(a - R - r)$$

and taking into consideration that $a > R + r$, we state that $2a(a - x - r)$ is positive, so that, indeed, $x < a - r$.

We now set out to prove that the perpendicular MT to the center line OB through the point M is the locus of points with equal tangents to both circles. Let T be any point of this perpendicular (Fig. 25). Joining T to centers O, A, B and applying the Pythagorean Theorem, we state the three relations

$$OT^2 = OM^2 + MT^2; \quad AT^2 = AM^2 + MT^2; \quad BT^2 = BM^2 + MT^2 \quad (20)$$

On the other hand, the point M is characterized by either of the two relations:

$$OM^2 - R^2 = AM^2 - r^2; \quad OM^2 - R^2 = BM^2 - r^2.$$

Adding to both members of these relations the square MT^2 and using (20), we obtain $OT^2 - R^2 = AT^2 - r^2$, as well as $OT^2 - R^2 = BT^2 - r^2$, which proves that the straight line MT is the radical axis of the two circles.

It is important to add that the expression (19) for $OM = x$ holds also when the circles intersect each other or are tangent. With the aid of (19), it can be proved that the minimum value of x is positive and equal to $(R^2 - r^2)^{1/2}$, which means that the radical axis does not pass through the center of the larger circle. This minimum value is attained in the case of two intersecting circles when the center of the smaller one is on the radical axis.

To prove this we will apply the principle of extremum in quadratic equations (Chapter 7). Suppose that the radii R and r are given as well as the position of the radical axis of two circles, so that $OM = x$ is also a known quantity. We now ask where is the center of the second circle, that is, what is the value of the distance a between the two centers which corresponds to the given data R, r, and x?

Equation (19) shows that the unknown a verifies a quadratic equation, namely, the equation $2ax = R^2 + a^2 - r^2$, which we rewrite as $a^2 - 2ax + (R^2 - r^2) = 0$. Solving it with the aid of the general formula (16), Chapter 7, we find for a the following expression

$$a = x \pm [x^2 - (R^2 - r^2)]^{1/2}.$$

The discriminant (the quantity under the square root sign) cannot be negative since a as a distance must be a real number. This limitation imposes on our data R, r, and x a very essential condition $x^2 \geqslant R^2 - r^2$, thus proving that the segment $OM = x$ cannot be less than $(R^2 - r^2)^{1/2}$. Moreover, when $OM = x$ reaches its minimum value $(R^2 - r^2)^{1/2}$, then the discriminant vanishes and a becomes equal to x: $a = x = (R^2 - r^2)^{1/2}$. Therefore, for two given circles with radii R and r their radical axis is nearest to the center of the larger circle when the circles intersect, the radical axis being then incident with the center of the small circle.

11 Kogbetliantz

Three Circles

The configuration formed by three circles involves three radical axes since three circles form three different pairs. It can be proved that these three radical axes meet in a point, called the *radical center* of the three circles. In the particular case when the centers of three circles are collinear points, their radical axes are parallel, and, therefore, their radical center is the point at infinity in the direction of radical axes. If the three circles intersect one another, their radical center is the intersection point of the three common chords and is therefore interior to every one of three circles. In such a case, no tangents can be drawn to either of the three circles through their radical center.

Omitting these two cases, we state that the six tangents drawn to three given circles from their radical center are equal (Fig. 26). Their six contact points, two on every circle, lie on a circle with center at the radical center of three given circles. This fourth circle (dotted line on Fig. 26) is perpendicular to the three given circles because the tangents to the given circles are radii of this fourth circle.

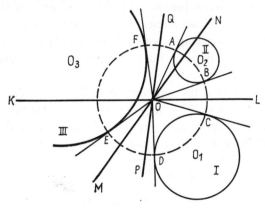

Fig. 15.26

To prove that three radical axes of three circles I, II, and III are actually concurrent lines, we define the point O as the intersection point of two radical axes KL and MN of circles pairs I, II and I, III, respectively. By definition of the point O, we then have on the one hand $OA = OB = OC = OD$ and also, on the other hand, $OC = OD = OE = OF$. We conclude that $OE = OF = OA = OB$, which means that the point O lies on the radical axis PQ of the two circles II and III. Thus, this point O is the common point of all three radical axes defined by the three given circles.

The dual transformation of this proposition yields, as a particular case, another interesting property of the configuration formed by any three circles exterior to each other. This property is related to the tangent line common to these circles taken two at a time, and it can be formulated as follows:

The intersection points of pairs of tangents common to two circles are collinear by groups of three, provided these three points are related to different pairs of circles.

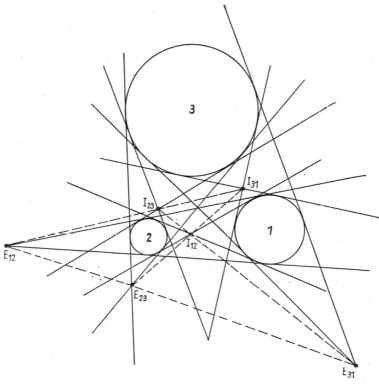

Fig. 15.27

Thus, denoting the three given circles by numbers 1, 2, 3 (Fig. 27) and drawing their twelve common tangents, four (two exterior and two interior) per pair of circles, we obtain in all six intersection points E_{12}, E_{23}, E_{31}, I_{12}, I_{23}, and I_{31}, where E and I denote, respectively, intersection points of two exterior (E) and two interior (I) common tangents to a pair of circles, while the subscripts denote the circles. For instance, E_{12} and I_{12} are respectively intersection points of two exterior and two interior common tangents to circles 1 and 2.

These six points form four collinear triplets of points, namely, $E_{12}E_{23}E_{31}$, $E_{12}I_{23}I_{31}$, $E_{23}I_{31}I_{12}$, $E_{31}I_{12}I_{23}$. The first triplet consists of points defined by exterior common tangents of three pairs of circles (1–2), (2–3), and (3–1). The three others involve only one such point, while the two other points are defined by interior common tangents.

We omit the proof of this property of three circles exterior to each other and wish here only to describe how the duality transforms a property of radical axes into that of common tangents.

In general, the dual transform of a circle is a conic section (ellipse, hyperbola, or parabola), and a point of the circle's circumference is transformed into a tangent line to this conic section, which is the dual image of the given circle. Thus, if we consider two intersecting circles with their radical axis which is their common chord and therefore passes through their two common points, the dual transform of this configuration consists of two conics, two common tangents, and the intersection point of these two common tangents, so that the dual transform of the radical axis is the intersection point of two common tangents.

We see therefore that, transforming dually the three concurrent radical axes of three mutually intersecting circles, we obtain the three collinear intersection points of pairs of common tangents to three conics. Now what is true for conics in general holds also for circles since a circle, as a particular case of an ellipse, is a conic of a special kind. The foregoing description cannot be considered as a proof because the question is more complicated: any two circles always have in common two imaginary points at infinity, so-called cyclic points, so that two intersecting circles have not only their radical axis but also the line at infinity as their common chords. This explains the existence of four triplets of collinear intersection points, while there is only one triplet of concurrent radical axes: the first triplet $E_{12}E_{23}E_{31}$ is the dual image of the three radical axes, the exterior common tangents corresponding to real intersection points of circles, while their common cyclic points are transformed into interior tangents.

We cannot discuss this question more fully, and wish only to consider the particular case of Fig. 27 when the three circles are tangent to each other (Fig. 28). The points I_{12}, I_{23}, I_{31} then become contact points C_{12}, C_{23}, C_{31}, so that this time the four triplets of collinear points are

$$E_{12}E_{23}E_{31}; \quad E_{12}C_{23}C_{31}; \quad E_{23}C_{31}C_{12}; \quad E_{31}C_{12}C_{23}.$$

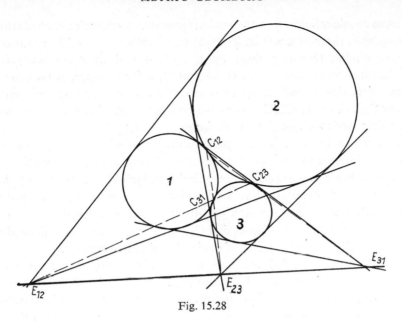

Fig. 15.28

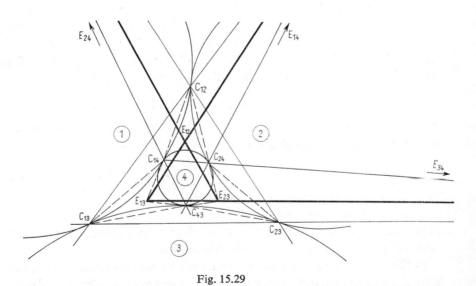

Fig. 15.29

Let us consider finally a configuration formed by four circles, each of which is tangent to three others (Fig. 29), that is, a configuration of four mutually tangent circles. Denoting them by 1, 2, 3, 4 and their contact points by C_{mn} ($m \neq n$; $m, n = 1, 2, 3, 4$), so that C_{12}, for instance, is the contact point of circles 1 and 2, let us consider the chords joining the contact points C_{mn}. A chord $C_{mk}C_{mj}$ joins the contact point of the circle m with two other circles k and j, so that, for example, $C_{12}C_{13}$ is the chord of the circle 1 which joins its contact points with the circles 2 and 3. We define finally the intersection points of chords, considering only the intersections of two chords belonging to two different circles and joining their contact points with the two other circles. Thus, such an intersection point J_{mn} is defined by chords of circles m and n which join their contact points with the circles k and j, that is, by chords $C_{mk}C_{mj}$ and $C_{nk}C_{nj}$. For instance, J_{12} is defined by the chords $C_{13}C_{14}$ and $C_{23}C_{24}$ of circles 1 and 2, respectively.

In Fig. 29, where all four circles are tangent to each other externally so that $I_{ij} = C_{ij}$, every point J_{kj} is also E_{mn}, where the four letters $kjmn$ represent any permutation of four numbers 1, 2, 3, 4 since it is the intersection point of the exterior common tangents to the circles m and n. To justify this assertion, let us consider, for example, the point E_{14}. In the configuration of three circles 1, 2, 4, we have the triplet of collinear points $E_{41}C_{12}C_{24}$, while the configuration of three circles 1, 3, 4 has another triplet $E_{41}C_{13}C_{34}$. Therefore, the point E_{41} is the intersection point of two chords $C_{12}C_{24}$ and $C_{13}C_{34}$, that is, E_{41} is also J_{23}, Considering now four different groups of three circles contained in the configuration of four circles, we write down for each of these four groups the triplet of collinear points E_{mn}:

$$E_{12}E_{23}E_{31}; \quad E_{23}E_{34}E_{42}; \quad E_{13}E_{34}E_{41}; \quad E_{12}E_{24}E_{41}$$

Replacing E_{mn} by J_{kj} ($j, k, m, n = 1, 2, 3, 4$, no two being equal), we obtain the four triplets of collinear points J_{kj}:

$$J_{41}J_{42}J_{43}; \quad J_{12}J_{13}J_{14}; \quad J_{21}J_{23}J_{24}; \quad J_{31}J_{32}J_{34} \tag{21}$$

so that the following proposition is deduced:

Given four mutually tangent circles 1, 2, 3, 4, the six intersection points J_{mn} ($m \neq n$; $m, n = 1, 2, 3, 4$) of their chords through the contact points C_{kj} form four triplets (21) of collinear points.

In this proposition, no mention is made of common tangents, and it holds also in the case when three of four circles are tangent internally to the fourth circle, as is illustrated in Fig. 30. In Fig. 30, three of six points J_{mn}, namely, the points J_{12}, J_{13}, J_{14} are also points E_{34}, E_{24}, E_{23}, respectively, while

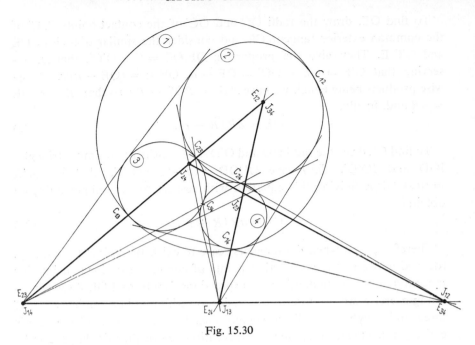

Fig. 15.30

the three others are *not* intersection points of common tangents. Nevertheless, the proposition remains valid.

The intersection points E and I of two exterior and two interior common tangents to two given circles lie on the straight line through their centers (Fig. 31), and their locations can be characterized by their distances OE and OI from the center O of the larger circle. Denoting the distance of centers O and O′ by $a = OO′$ and the radii by R and r, we will compute these distances for the case $a > R + r$ when, the circles being exterior to each other, the common tangents which intersect at E and at I are real. But the expressions obtained for OE and OI continue to exist and therefore to define the points E and I even when the interior or exterior and interior tangents cease to exist because a is less than $R + r$ or less than $R - r$.

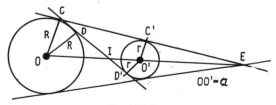

Fig. 15.31

To find OE, draw the radii OC and OC′ of the contact points C, C′ of the common exterior tangent CE and consider the similar triangles OCE and O′C′E. They give the proportion OE/OC = O′E/O′C′, that is, observing that O′E = OE − OO′ = OE − a, OE/R = (OE − a)/r. Crosswise products being equal, we have rOE = ROE − Ra, so that $(R − r)$OE = aR and, finally,

$$OE = aR/(R − r). \tag{22}$$

To find OI, draw the radii OD and O′D′ and consider two similar triangles IOD and IO′D′. They give OI/OD = $(a − OI)/O′D′$, that is, OI/R = $(a − OI)/r$. Solving this equation with respect to the unknown OI, we obtain

$$OI = aR/(R + r). \tag{23}$$

Therefore, even when the tangents cease to exist, the points E_{mn} and I_{mn} (defined above as the intersection points of common exterior and interior tangents) can be plotted, using the expressions for OE and OI. As an interesting exercise, we propose to the reader to verify that in a configuration of three circles with non-collinear centers such that the first smallest circle is entirely inside the second, which itself is entirely inside the third largest circle, the six points $E_{12}, E_{23}, E_{31}, I_{12}, I_{23}$, and I_{31} plotted with the aid of the two formulas (22) and (23) form four triplets of collinear points. They are six distinct points if no two circles are concentric. Thus, the formulae (22) and (23) allow us to plot the points E_{mn} and I_{mn} in any case, and these points form triplets of collinear points when there are no common tangents at all.

Four Harmonic Points

We recall that a directed straight line segment has not only a length but also a sign. Choosing on a given straight line a positive sense, we ascribe to a segment of this straight line a plus sign if this segment points in the positive direction and a minus sign to a segment pointing in the opposite direction.

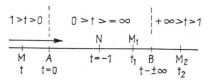

Fig. 15.32

Considering a fixed given positive segment AB and a point M on the same straight line, we form the ratio $t = $ MA/MB of two directed segments MA and MB into which the point M divides the segment AB (Fig. 32). This ratio t is negative if M divides AB internally, that is, if M is between A and B, because then the segments MA and MB point in opposite directions and have opposite signs. But if M is to the left of A or to the right of B, then the segments MA, MB point in the same direction, the segment AB is said to be divided externally, and the ratio $t = $ MA/MB is positive.

We can express MA and MB in terms of the length $d = $ AB of the segment AB and the pure number t, the value of the ratio MA/MB, the length d being constant and t variable with the position of the point M. Since AM $= -$MA, we have

$$d = \text{AB} = \text{AM} + \text{MB} = \text{MB} - \text{MA} = \text{MB} - t\text{MB} = \text{MB}\,(1 - t)$$

and, therefore, dividing through by $1 - t$, MB $= d/(1 - t)$ and MA $= t$MB $= dt/(1 - t)$.

To each value of the variable t corresponds, therefore, a definite position of the point M and *vice versa*. When t is negative, the difference $1 - t$ is greater than one and MB $= d/(1 - t)$ is positive (as is by definition AB $= d$) and less than AB $= d$. Therefore, when t decreases from zero (point A, since MA $= 0$ for $t = 0$) to minus infinity (point B, since MB $= 0$ for $t = \pm \infty$), the point M remains in the interior of the segment AB moving from A towards B. When t is infinite, M is at B and if t decreases from plus infinity to plus one, the difference $1 - t$ is negative and with it the segment MB is also negative, which proves that M moves away from B to the right and disappears at infinity when t reaches the value one. If now t, continuing to decrease, takes positive values less than one, $1 - t$ is positive and less than one, so that MB $= d/(1 - t)$ is positive and greater than AM. This shows that when t decreases from one to zero, the point M reappears at the left of A, emerging from infinity, and approaches A. Finally, when t vanishes, reassuming its initial value of zero, the point M returns again to its initial position A.

Thus, the variable point M describes once the whole infinite straight line AB, when the ratio t in which this point divides the fundamental segment AB varies from minus to plus infinity. In the above description of this continuous motion of M on the closed infinite straight line AB, the point M moves in the positive sense, from the left to the right, because t decreases from plus to minus infinity. To increasing t corresponds the motion of M in the opposite direction, from the right to the left. The uniqueness of the point at infinity on the straight line AB is emphasized by the fact that t is equal to the unique value $t = 1$ when M is at infinity, all the other values of t being correlated to points on the straight line AB at a finite distance from the observer. Inversely, to positively and negatively infinite values of t corresponds one and only one point on AB namely, the point B, which emphasizes the uniqueness of the absolute infinity which can be reached in both ways, increasing without limit a positive variable (in this case it is denoted by $+ \infty$) or decreasing without limit a negative variable (it is denoted by $- \infty$).

The midpoint N of the interval AB corresponds to MB $= \frac{1}{2}$AB, that is, to $d/(1 - t) = \frac{1}{2}d$, which yields $1 - t = 2$ and, finally, $t = -1$. Abstracting from the directions and considering only the ratio of lengths, we say that N divides AB into two equal parts internally. The same can be said when M is at infinity because the finite length d of AB becomes completely negligible when compared to infinite distances of the point at infinity from A and from B. Denoting the point at infinity by P_∞, we have, indeed, $t = 1$ when M is at P_∞, so that $\lim_{M \to P_\infty} (MA/MB) = 1$, which proves that when M is at infinity its distances (infinite distances) from A and from B must be considered as equal, so that AB is divided into two equal parts externally by the point at infinity.

Two points M_1 and M_2 (Fig. 32) which divide a given segment in the same ratio of lengths externally and internally and which therefore are correlated to two numerical values t_1 and t_2 of the ratio t equal in magnitude and opposite in sign, form together with the fundamental points A and B an important configuration of four collinear points A, B; M_1, M_2. Such a configuration of four collinear points is called four *harmonic* points, the two points M_1 and M_2 such that $t_1 = -t_2$ being *harmonic conjugates* of each other with respect to A and B. The segment AB is said to be *divided harmonically* by the two harmonic conjugates M_1 and M_2, and the four segments M_1A, M_1B, M_2A, M_2B verify the condition $M_1A/M_1B = -M_2A/M_2B$.

DEFINITION: *Four collinear points* A, B; C, D *are harmonic if* CA$\cdot$DB/CB$\cdot$DA $= -1$.

Thus, to every interior point of a given segment corresponds an exterior point which is the harmonic conjugate of the interior point with respect to the end points of the given segment and *vice versa*. In particular, the harmonic conjugate of the midpoint N, Fig. 32, is the point at infinity P_∞.

If the condition of harmonic division CA$\cdot$DB/CB$\cdot$DA $= -1$ is fulfilled, the segments AB and CD must overlap. Consequently, if the pairing of four harmonic points changes, they cease to be four harmonic points. For instance, if two overlapping pairs A, B and C, D (Fig. 33) form a harmonic configuration of four collinear points, the pairs A, C and B, D or A, D and B, C do not because the corresponding segments AC, BD are exterior to each other, while BC is interior to AD.

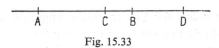

Fig. 15.33

In the definition of four harmonic points as we gave it, the pairing of points is indicated by the omission of segments AB and CD in the condition $CA \cdot DB/CB \cdot DA = -1$. Moreover, the endpoints A and B of the fundamental segment AB are recognizable as heads of four directed segments CA, DA, CB, DB while the harmonic conjugates C and D are tails of these four directed segments. Therefore, the roles played by the two pairs A, B and C, D seem to be different. This impression is not true because if C and D are harmonic conjugates with respect to A and B then, conversely, the points A and B are also harmonic conjugates with respect to the points C and D. In other words, if the segment AB is divided harmonically by C and D, then the segment CD is also divided harmonically by A and B. To prove this, it is sufficient to observe that the fulfillment of the condition $CA \cdot DB/CB \cdot DA = -1$ entails also $AC \cdot BD/BC \cdot AD = -1$ since, reversing the directions of all four segments, we change their signs, that is, we multiply each of them by the factor minus one, which does not change the value of the lefthand member. Thus, from $CA \cdot DB/CB \cdot DA = -1$, we deduce $AC \cdot BD/BC \cdot AD = -1$, and this proves that A and B are harmonic conjugates with respect to the segment CD: if A, B; C, D are four harmonic points, then C, D; A, B also form a harmonic configuration of four collinear points.

A harmonic group of four points involves a harmonic mean: the segment AB is the harmonic mean between the two segments AC and AD and the segment CD is the harmonic mean between AD and BD. To justify this, we have to show that twice the reciprocal $1/AB$ of AB (or the reciprocal $1/CD$ of CD) is equal to the sum of the reciprocals $1/AC$, $1/AD$ of AC and AD (or of $1/AD$ and $1/BD$). The condition of harmonic division $AC \cdot BD/BC \cdot AD = -1$ can be rewritten $AC \cdot BD = -AD \cdot BC = AD \cdot CB$ so that it becomes $AC \cdot BD - AD \cdot CB = 0$. But, $BD = AD - AB$ and $CB = AB - AC$ (Fig. 33). Therefore, opening the parentheses in $AC (AD - AB) - (AB - AC) AD = 0$, changing the signs of all terms, and dividing through by $AB \cdot AC \cdot AD$, we prove that

$$1/AC - 2/AB + 1/AD = 0.$$

Likewise, replacing in $AC \cdot BD - AD \cdot CB = 0$, the segments AC and CB by $AD - CD$ and $CD - BD$, respectively, changing the signs and dividing through by $AD \cdot BD \cdot CD$, we find that

$$1/AD - 2/CD + 1/BD = 0.$$

The term *harmonic points* for this special configuration of four collinear points stems from the fact that if A, B; C, D are four harmonic points, then AB and CD are the harmonic means between AC, AD and AD, BD, respectively.

Metric Properties of Bisectors

Returning to metric relations in a triangle, we now consider the segments into which the bisectors of angles of a triangle divide its sides. It happens that the intersection points of a side and of the exterior and interior bisectors of the opposite angles divide this side harmonically, as it is stated in the following theorem:

THEOREM XXIV: *The bisectors of an interior and the adjacent exterior angle divide the opposite side of a triangle harmonically and also in the ratio of the adjacent sides.*

The intersection points C, D (Fig. 34) of two bisectors VG, VH of the angle at vertex V of the triangle ABV divide the segment AB internally and externally, so that we have only to prove the equality of the three ratios AC/CB, AD/BD, and AV/BV, the equality of the first two ratios establishing the harmonic division of AB by C and D and the last ratio being the ratio of the two adjacent sides AV (adjacent to AC) and BV (adjacent to CB).

Theorem XXIV can be proved with the aid of the method of similar triangles and to form them we draw through the vertex A a parallel GAE to the side BVF, G and E being the intersection points of this parallel with the two bisectors VG and VH. Triangle ADE is then similar to that BDV ($\widehat{AED} = \widehat{BVD}$, while the angle at D is common) and triangle AGC is similar to that BCV ($\widehat{AGC} = \widehat{CVB}$, $\widehat{ACG} = \widehat{BCV}$). Therefore, we have, on the one hand, $AD/BD = AE/BV$ and, on the other hand, $AC/CB = AG/BV$. But the triangles AEV and AGV are isosceles: the first because $\widehat{AEV} = \widehat{BVD}$ $= \widehat{EVF} = \widehat{AEV}$ (the line VH bisecting $\widehat{AVF}$) and the second because $\widehat{AGC}$ $= \widehat{CVB} = \widehat{AVC}$ (the line VG bisecting $\widehat{AVB}$). Therefore, $AE = AV = AG$, and this fact, used in the proportions AD/BD = AE/BV, AC/CB = AG/BV, transforms them into AD/BD = AV/BV and AC/CB = AV/BV, so that AD/BD = AC/CB, that is, AC·BD/BC·AD = −1, which completes the proof of Theorem XXIV. This theorem can also be formulated as follows:

THEOREM XXIV*: *If two perpendicular straight lines c and d bisect the angles formed by two other straight lines a and b, the intersection points A, B, C, D of these four concurrent straight lines a, b, c, d with any straight line f form a harmonic configuration of four collinear points.*

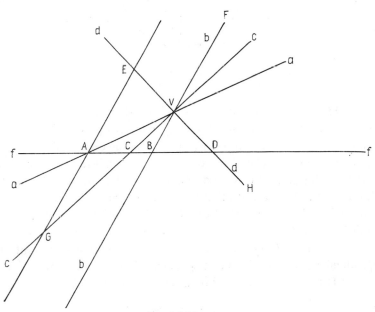

Fig. 15.34

We will apply Theorem XXIV to the solution of the following problem:

PROBLEM: Given three collinear points, find the fourth harmonic point.

Denoting the given points by A, B, C (Fig. 35), where C is between A and B, we describe a circle on AB as a diameter and draw through the center O (midpoint of AB) a diameter DOE perpendicular to AB. Joining the points C and D, we denote by F the intersection point of the line CD with the circle and, joining it to A and B, consider the triangle ABF thus formed. In this triangle, FD is the interior bisector of the angle $\overset{\frown}{AFB}$ since $\overset{\frown}{AFD} = \overset{\frown}{DFB}$, as inscribed angles subtended by equal arcs $\overset{\frown}{AD} = \overset{\frown}{DB}$. Therefore, joining the point E to the point F by a perpendicular EG to the line DF, we obtain the exterior bisector whose intersection point H with the side AB of the triangle ABF is the fourth harmonic point to A, B, C, as is stated in Theorem XXIV.

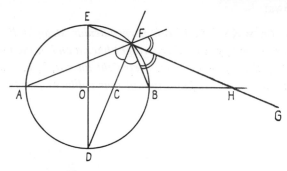

Fig. 15.35

We add that this construction of the fourth harmonic can be generalized: draw through the midpoint M of the segment AB a perpendicular MO to AB and take any point O of this perpendicular as the center of a circle through the points A and B. If D and E are two endpoints of the diameter DE defined by the line MO, join D to C and denote by F the intersection point of DC with the circle. Draw the straight line EF. The fourth harmonic is the intersection point of EF with AB. If the three given points A, B, H are such that the third, H, is exterior to the interval AB, the fourth harmonic can be found with the aid of the same construction (Fig. 36): taking any point O of the perpendicular bisector of AB as the center of a circle through A and B, join the point D to H and draw on DH as on a diameter a circle of radius $\frac{1}{2}$DH.

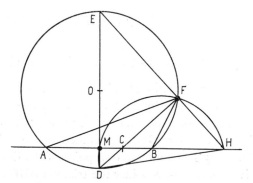

Fig. 15.36

The two circles intersect at a point F, and, joining F to D, the fourth harmonic C is found as the intersection point of AB and FD.

Finally, we describe without proof another construction of the fourth harmonic in which no circle is used. Denoting the three given points by E, F, L (Fig. 37), where L is between E and F, we draw through L an arbitrary straight line AL and choose an arbitrary point C on the segment AL between A and L. Then we draw four straight lines EA, EC, FA, FC joining the points E and F to A and C. These four lines intersect at four points, two of which, namely, A and C, were already defined, so that only two new points B and D are thus constructed. The fourth harmonic S will then be found by drawing the seventh straight line BD, and it will be the intersection point of DB and EF.

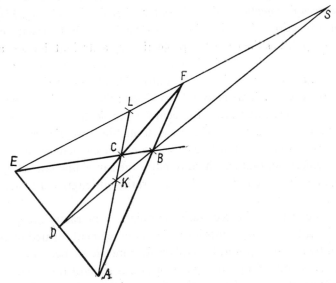

Fig. 15.37

If now the points E, F, S are given and the harmonic conjugate to S is asked, then we draw an arbitrary straight line DS through S and choose any point B between D and S. Joining E and F to B and D, we define A and C and the intersection of the line AC with the given line EF yields the fourth harmonic L between E and F. Thus, in both cases the construction is the same.

The configuration constructed in Fig. 37 is called a *complete quadrilateral*. It has four sides AB, BC, CD, and DA. The intersection points of any two sides is a vertex of the complete quadrilateral, so that there are six vertices A, B, C, D, E, and F. Any two vertices which do not belong to the same side are called opposite. There are three pairs of such opposite vertices, and they define three diagonals AC, BD, EF. On every diagonal the intersection points with the two other diagonals are harmonic conjugates with respect to the two vertices. Thus, (A, C; K, L), (D, B; K,S), and (E, F; L, S) are quadruplets of harmonic points.

Cross-Ratio of Four Points

To define the operation of projection, it is necessary to choose a fixed point as a *center of projection*. Given a center of projection C (Fig. 37), the operation of projection of a point K onto a straight line ED consists in joining the projected point to the center of projection by a straight line KC and defining the intersection point A of this line with the line ED onto which the point is projected, as the projection of K onto ED. The operation of projection is important because it corresponds to vision: the rays of light being approximately rectilinear, our eye is the center of projection and the image formed on our retina is the result of a projection. Since we can recognize different objects by vision there must be some geometric element which is not affected by the projection, that is, which remains the same, unchanged by the projection, while all the lengths, angles, and ratios of lengths are altered in a projection.

A configuration of three collinear points is characterized by the value of the ratio of the two segments into which the segment formed by two points is divided by the third point. It involves four metric elements: the three lengths of segments defined by three pairs of points (one of three lengths being the sum of two others) and the ratio of two of them. None of these metric elements, however, are invariant under projection, and they all vary when a given group of three collinear points is projected into another triplet of collinear points on some other straight line.

Any three collinear points P, Q, R can, indeed, be projected onto any other three collinear points S, T, U by two successive operations of projection (Fig. 38). Drawing the line PS and an arbitrary straight line SN through the point S, we choose any point O on PS as center of the first projection onto the line SN. Projecting P, Q, R from the center O onto SN, we obtain the points S, K, L, respectively. Joining now the point K to T and the point L to U, we draw the two straight lines KT and LU and choose their intersection point O* as the center of the second projection. Thus, the set of points P, Q, R is finally projected into S, T, U. The ratios QR/QP and TU/TS in general will not be equal because the two sets of three points P, Q, R and S, T, U were chosen arbitrarily. Therefore, a configuration of three collinear points is not invariant under projection.

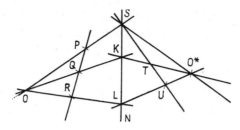

Fig. 15.38

Now in Fig. 37 we met with an invariant under projection: four harmonic points (D, B; K, S), if projected from the center of projection A onto the straight line ES, are transformed into (E, F; L, S), and their property of being a harmonic configuration is transmitted to their projections because the configuration (E, F; L, S) is also harmonic. In other words, the harmonic division is invariant under projection: the ratio of two ratios of lengths (KD/KB)/(SD/SB), that is, KD · SB/KB · SD remains unchanged and equal to minus one when each point in it is replaced by its projection because LE · SF/LF · SE is also equal to minus one and therefore KD · SB/KB · SD = LE · SF/LF · SE = −1.

However, we have not yet proved the fact that a diagonal of the complete quadrilateral is divided harmonically by its intersection points with the two other diagonals. To prove this, we introduce a more general concept of the cross-ratio of four collinear points which characterizes a configuration formed on a straight line by any four of its points. This concept is important precisely because, as we will show, the value of a cross-ratio is invariant under projection.

Any four collinear points considered together as forming a geometric figure may be characterized by various metric properties such as the lengths of segments they form or the ratios of these lengths, but these numerical characteristics do not retain their values unchanged when the configuration is projected onto another straight line. Nevertheless, there are invariant metric properties which are not altered by projection, and these are obtained as the quotients of two ratios of lengths.

Such a quotient of two ratios of lengths is called the *cross-ratio* of four collinear points. The value of a cross-ratio depends on the order in which we associate the four given points when forming the quotient of two ratios. This order may be chosen at will, and it is independent of the geometric order in which they follow each other on the straight line. The definition of the cross-ratio of four collinear points A, B, C, D is based on the tacit assumption that the order in which we want to consider these four points is that of the four letters in the symbol (ABCD) we now adopt for the cross-ratio of four points taken in the order A, B, C, D. Under this assumption, we have the following definition:

DEFINITION: The symbol (ABCD) will always mean the cross-ratio of four collinear points A, B, C, D defined by the quotient of the two ratios CA/CB and DA/DB, so that

$$(ABCD) = (CA/CB) : (DA/DB) = CA \cdot DB/CB \cdot DA \qquad (24)$$

We recognize here the same expression which, when set equal to minus one, characterizes a harmonic configuration.

In (24), the symbols CA, CB, DA, DB represent the directed segments CA, CB, DA, DB in length and in direction. The are positive or negative according to the direction of the segment. Their signs depend also on the choice of the positive sense on the straight line itself because a segment pointing in the positive direction of the line is, by definition, positive, while a segment having the opposite direction is negative. We recall that the direction of a segment is expressed in its notation, the first letter standing for the tail and the second for the head of a directed segment. Thus, for instance, CA is directed from the point C towards the point A. But the value (ABCD) of a cross-ratio does not depend on the orientation of the straight line because the reversal of the direction considered as positive changes the signs of all four segments involved in the definition (24) and thus has no effect at all on the numerical value of the symbol (ABCD).

Now there are twenty-four (the number of permutations of four elements) ways of ordering four letters, and to each one of these twenty-four ways corresponds a formally different cross-ration for a given set of four points. But there can be only six distinct numerical values of the cross-ratio, each of which is obtained four times, because four different ways of ordering lead to the same numerical value of the cross-ratio: it is easy to check with the aid of (24) that (ABCD) = (BADC) = (CDAB) = (DCBA). The six distinct values are not independent, and this could be expected because all six correspond to the same geometric figure formed by four collinear points on their straight line. Denoting the numerical value of the cross-ratio (ABCD) by r, (ABCD) $= r$, we can express the five other cross-ratios which can be formed with the same set of four points A, B, C, D as follows:

$$(ABCD) = r, \quad (ABDC) = 1/r, \quad (ACBD) = 1 - r,$$

$$(ACDB) = 1/(1 - r), \quad (ADBC) = 1 - (1/r),$$

$$(ADCB) = r/(r - 1) = 1 - [1/(1 - r)].$$

When r varies between minus one and zero, $-1 < r < 0$, the six distinct values of various cross-ratios corresponding to different arrangements of a given and fixed set of four collinear points cover in their variation the whole infinite interval from minus infinity to plus infinity.

We can now state that four harmonic points have their cross-ratio equal to minus one. In this particular case, the two segments AB and CD formed by the first two points A, B and by the last ones C, D overlap. In general, to overlapping segments AB, CD corresponds a negative cross-ratio (ABCD) and *vice versa*, if (ABCD) is negative, then AB and CD overlap. A positive sign of the cross-ratio (ABCD) indicates that the segments AB and CD do not overlap, and in this case they can be exterior to each other, or one of them may be completely inside the other.

To prove this, we observe that CA $=$ CB $+$ BA and DA $=$ DB $+$ BA, so that $r =$ (ABCD) can be written as follows:

$$r = (ABCD) = CA \cdot DB/CB \cdot DA = [1 + (BA/CB)] : [1 + (BA/DB)]$$

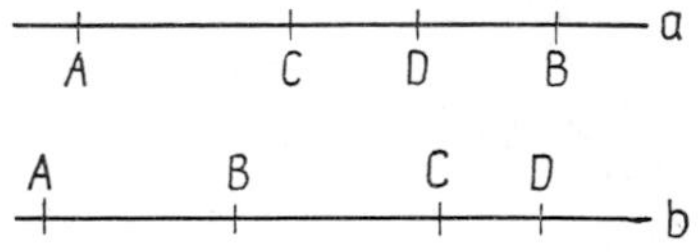

Fig. 15.39

Applying this expression of (ABCD) to the case when the segments AB and CD are exterior to each other (Fig. 39b), and comparing the two positive ratios BA/CB and BA/DB, we conclude that the denominator $1 + (BA/DB)$ is less than the numerator $1 + (BA/CB)$ because DB is greater than CB. Therefore, the cross-ratio $r =$ (ABCD) is greater than one when AB and CD are exterior to each other.

Now, when the segment CD is interior to AB (Fig. 39a), we rewrite the cross-ratio $r =$ (CA/CB):(DA/DB) as $r =$ (AC/CB):(AD/DB) so that both ratios AC/CB and AD/DB are positive. Since AC is less than AD and DB is less than CB, the first ratio AC/CB is less than the second AD/DB and r = (ABCD) is therefore less than one.

We see, thus, that to a positive cross-ratio greater than one correspond the segments AB and CD exterior to each other, while one of them is interior to the other, if the positive value of the cross-ratio is less than one.

If $r = 1$, then $1 - r = 0$ and $1/(1 - r)$ is infinite. Thus, zero, one, and infinity are three particular and special values of the cross-ratio which we have to discuss. If r = (ABCD) = CA · DB/CB · DA vanishes, then the product CA · DB must be zero and therefore CA = 0 or DB = 0, which means that either A and C or B and D coincide. If (ABCD) is infinite, then 1/(ABCD) = CB · DA/CA · DB = 0, so that either B and C or A and D coincide. Finally, if r = (ABCD) = 1, then (ABCD) = 1 − (ABCD) = 0, that is, BA · DC/BC · DA = 0 and therefore either A and B or C and D coincide.

Thus we come to the conclusion that, if any two of the given four points coincide, their cross-ratio takes one of three special values, which are zero, plus one, and infinity. Therefore, the cross-ratio of four distinct points is never equal to zero, plus one, or infinity.

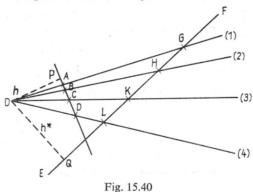

Fig. 15.40

We prove now the fundamental property of the cross-ratio, namely, its invariance under projection. In Fig. 40, four collinear points A, B, C, D are projected from the center O onto the straight line EF, their projections being G, H, K, L, respectively. Denoting the projecting straight lines OA, OB, OC, OD by the numbers 1, 2, 3, 4, respectively, we consider the various angles they form at the projection's center O. We will denote these angles by two numbers which correspond to the sides of the angle. Thus, for instance, the angle KOG formed by the two straight lines OK, OG and counted from the straight line (3) towards the line (1) counterclockwise around the vertex O is denoted by (3, 1), and it is positive. Moreover, we introduce the areas of various triangles with the common vertex at O, bases on the line AD or EF, and two other sides formed by lines (1), (2), (3), or (4). Therefore, we will need their altitudes $h =$ OP and $h^* =$ OQ.

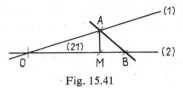

· Fig. 15.41

Studying one of these areas, for example, the area of the triangle ABO, we first express it as one half the product of the base AB times the altitude $h =$ OP. Applying the sine law, we note that the same area ABO $= \frac{1}{2}ABh$ can be expressed as one half the product of two sides OA · OB times the sine of the included angle $\widehat{AOB} = (2, 1)$: area ABO $= \frac{1}{2}$OA · OB sin (2, 1). We have, indeed (Fig. 41), for the altitude AM perpendicular to the side OB, the expression AM = OA sin (2, 1), so that the area $\frac{1}{2}$OB · AM of the triangle AOB is also expressed as $\frac{1}{2}$OB · OA sin (2, 1). Thus, for any triangle with the vertex at O, its area is equal to one half the product of the two sides interrecting at O times the sine of the included angle.

We now transform the expression of the cross-ratio (ABCD) = CA · DB/ CB · DA as follows:

$$(ABCD) = (\tfrac{1}{2}CAh)\,(\tfrac{1}{2}DBh)/(\tfrac{1}{2}CBh)\,(\tfrac{1}{2}DAh)$$

$$= (\text{area OCA})\,(\text{area ODB})/(\text{area OCB})\,(\text{area ODA})$$

$$= \frac{[\tfrac{1}{2}OC \cdot OA \sin (3,1)]\,[\tfrac{1}{2}OD \cdot OB \sin (4,2)]}{[\tfrac{1}{2}OC \cdot OB \sin (3,2)]\,[\tfrac{1}{2}OD \cdot OA \sin (4,1)]}$$

The product OA · OB · OC · OD/4 is a common factor in both terms of the fraction standing in the righthand member. Omitting this common factor, we obtain a new expression for the cross-ratio (ABCD) of our four points which involves only the sines of the four angles at O formed by the straight lines (1), (2), (3), and (4):

$$(ABCD) = \sin (3, 1) \sin (4, 2)/\sin (3, 2) \sin (4, 1).$$

Applying the same reasoning to the cross-ratio (GHKL) of the four points on the line EF, we obtain again the same result:

$$(GHKL) = \sin (3, 1) \sin (4, 2)/\sin (3, 2) \sin (4, 1), \qquad (25)$$

which proves the equality of the two cross-ratios: (ABCD) = (GHKL).

Therefore, the cross-ratio of the four projections G, H, K, L is the same as that of the projected points A, B, C, D, and this proves the invariance property of the cross-ratio under projection.

Moreover, the expression (25) proves that a cross-ratio characterizes not only a configuration of four collinear points but also a configuration formed by four concurrent straight lines. If the four concurrent straight lines are kept fixed, their four intersection points with a variable transversal form an infinite number of different configurations of four collinear points, one for each instantaneous position of the variable transversal, and all these sets of four collinear points have the same cross-ratio, namely, the cross-ratio of four fixed straight lines (1), (2), (3), (4):

$$(1234) = [\sin(3,1)/\sin(3,2)] : [\sin(4,1)/\sin(4,2)]. \tag{26}$$

Thus, this cross-ratio is defined independently from four points by the quotient of two ratios of sines of angles the third and fourth lines make with the first and second. We have denoted this cross-ratio by (1234) to emphasize that it is now considered as the cross-ratio of four given concurrent straight lines, but its numerical value clearly is the same as that of (ABCD).

Not only are the numerical values of cross-ratios (1234) and (ABCD) the same, but the configurations they represent are also dual transforms of each other, so that there is only one concept of the cross-ratio of four fundamental elements, points or lines, provided the directed segments between two points are made correspond to the sines of oriented angles between the lines, which are dual transforms of points.

Let us, indeed, keep fixed the four collinear points A, B, C, D and the straight line f(AD) incident with them and join these points by straight lines to a fifth and variable point E, Fig. 15.42. This configuration of the fixed set of four points together with the straight line f incident with them plus the variable set of four concurrent straight lines g(EA), h(EB), k(EC), l(ED) together with the variable point E is then the dual transform of another configuration consisting of the fixed set of four concurrent straight lines a, b, c, d together with a point F incident with them plus the variable set of four collinear points G, H, K, L together with the variable straight line e incident with them.

When now the point E of the first configuration moves freely in the plane, the four straight lines g, h, k, l vary and with them vary also the angles they form. But the variation of every one of the four sines involved in the definition (26) of the cross-ratio (1234) of four lines does not change the numerical value of this cross-ratio (1234). This cross-ratio remains the same for all possible positions of the variable point E in the plane. Therefore, the cross-ratio (1234) does express rather the invariant configuration of the fixed four points A, B, C, D, which is the unique invariant element of the first configuration.

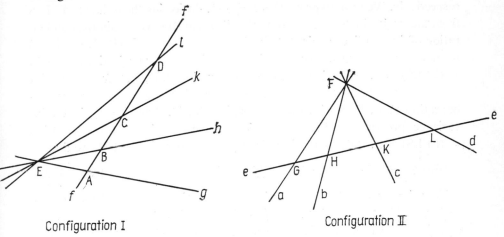

Configuration I   Configuration II

Fig. 15.42

In the same way, of course, when the variable transversal *e* of the second configuration moves freely in the plane, the intersection points of this transversal with the four fixed straight lines move on the transversal, so that every one of the four segments involved in the expression of the cross-ratio $(GHKL) = KG \cdot LH / KH \cdot LG$ varies. But their variation does not change the value of the cross-ratio $(GHKL)$ and this cross-ratio remains the same for all possible positions of the transversal in the plane. Therefore, the cross-ratio $(GHKL)$ does express rather the invariant configuration of the fixed four concurrent straight lines *a, b, c, d,* which is the unique invariant element of the second configuration.

Having proved the invariance of the cross-ratio under projection, we can deduce from it the fact that the cross-ratio of four points on the diagonal of a complete quadrilateral is equal to minus one and thus justify our statement as well as the method of constructing the fourth harmonic point with the aid of a complete quadrilateral.

THEOREM XXV: *On a diagonal of the complete quadrilateral its intersection points with the two other diagonals are harmonic conjugates with respect to the two vertices joined by this diagonal.*

PROOF: Returning to Fig. 37 and considering the diagonal EF of the complete quadrilateral ABCDEF, let us denote by x the unknown numerical value of the cross-ratio (EFLS) $= x$ of the four points E, F, L, S, where L and S are the intersection points of the diagonal EF with those AC and BD, respectively. We have to prove that $x = -1$. Projecting the points E, F, L, S from the projection's center C onto the diagonal BD, we obtain the configuration of four collinear points B, D, K, S whose cross-ratio (BDKS) is equal to that (EFLS) because a cross-ratio is invariant under projection: (BDKS) $=$ (EFLS) $= x$. Projecting now the configuration B, D, K, S from the point A back onto the diagonal EF, we obtain on this diagonal EF another configuration F, E, L, S with the cross-ratio (FELS). Applying again the invariance property of the cross-ratio, we have again (FELS) $=$ (BDKS) $=$ (EFLS) $= x$. But, computing directly the cross-ratio (FELS), we find

$$(FELS) = LF \cdot SE/LE \cdot SF = 1/(LE \cdot SF/LF \cdot SE) = 1/(EFLS) = 1/x.$$

Therefore, our unknown x verifies the equation $x =$ (EFLS) $=$ (FELS) $= 1/x$, that is, the equation $x = 1/x$ which is equivalent to $x^2 = 1$. This last equation has two solutions, $x = 1$ and $x = -1$, and the first one is extraneous to our problem because a cross-ratio of four distinct points cannot be equal to plus one. Thus, we find that $x = -1$, that is, (EFLS) $= -1$, which proves that the four points E, F, L, S form a harmonic configuration.

In three-dimensional space, the concept of cross-ratio can be applied also to the configuration formed by four coaxial planes: the cross-ratio of four planes passing through a straight line is equal to the cross-ratio of four collinear points which are the intersection points of these four planes with any straight line distinct from their axis.

CHAPTER 16

Metric Geometry (Continuation). Surface Measurements

In Euclidean geometry the measurement of areas is based on the existence of parallel straight lines which are at the same time equidistant lines, as well as on the existence of similar figures. In this geometry a surface measurement consists essentially in the comparison of an area with the square of unit side whose area by definition is considered as the unit of area. The term "square" means here a figure with four equal rectilinear sides and four right angles, opposite sides being thus parallel.

However, squares do not exist in non-Euclidean geometries. A Riemannian plane has no straight parallel lines at all, so that a trirectangular quadrilateral ABCD (Fig. 1) with two equal sides AB = BC and three right angles $\hat{A} = \hat{B} = \hat{C} = 90°$ is not a square because its fourth angle $\hat{D}$ is obtuse. The value of this angle $\hat{D}$ depends on the area of ABCD and it increases when the area increases. The two other sides CD and DA, although equal to each other, CD = DA, are unequal to AB = BC: BC ≠ CD. Four such quadrilaterals around the point B form a quadrilateral DEFG with four equal sides and four equal angles, but this quadrilateral DEFG is not a square because it has obtuse angles.

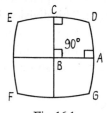

Fig. 16.1

The same holds for Lobatchevsky's plane (hyperbolic geometry) with the essential difference that in this case the fourth angle $\hat{M}$ (Fig. 2) is acute instead of being obtuse. The figure formed by four trirectangular quadri-

733

laterals juxtaposed around K (Fig. 2) will have four equal angles as well as four equal sides, but its angles are all acute, so that again MNPQ is not a square.

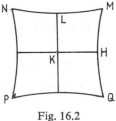

Fig. 16.2

On the other hand, it is important to emphasize from the beginning that the size of our unit of area, the unit-square, can be chosen arbitrarily which again is a feature particular to the Euclidean plane. There are squares of any size and therefore of any area in Euclidean geometry because of the existence of similar figures. But in non-Euclidean geometries there are no similar figures and figures with proportional sides have their corresponding angles unequal and dependent upon the size of the figure. In Riemannian geometry the angles increase when all the sides are increased in the same ratio, while in hyperbolic geometry the angles decrease when the sides increase.

The existence of squares of any size similar to the unit-square is essential to the measurement of Euclidean areas. It is not sufficient to compare a given area to the unit square and count the number of units of area contained in it. However small we may choose this unit-square, in general there will always remain a part of the measured area which cannot be evaluated with the aid of the unit-square because it is smaller than this unit of area. We use then instead of the unit square its $1/n^2$ part, dividing the unit area into n^2 equal parts each of which is also a square and which has a side of length equal to $1/n$ of the unit of length. This division is performed by drawing parallels to the sides of the unit square at a distance of $1/n$ from each other. Without the similarity of squares there could be no fractions of the unit area which are squares also and therefore can be used exactly as the unit square.

Area of a Rectangle

First of all we will justify the formula $A = bh$ which expresses the area A of a rectangle with the base $BC = b$ and altitude $CD = h$ (Fig. 3). In general the base and the altitude of a rectangle are incommensurable; that is, have no common measure. The proof of the formula A = *bh* necessitates in this case the use of the passage to the limit. We begin by studying the particular case when the base and altitude are two commensurable segments, so that there is a third segment of finite length *c* which is contained an integral number of times in both BC and CD. Then we can express these two segments as multiples of *c*: BC = *b* = *mc* and CD = *h* = *nc*, *m* and *n* being integers. Dividing BC and CD in *m* and *n* equal parts, each of length *c*, and drawing through the division points the parallels to BC and CD, we see that the area BCDE contains exactly *mn* small squares of area c^2 each. Therefore, the rectangle's area A is equal to A = mnc^2 = (*mc*) (*nc*) = *bh*.

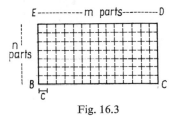

Fig. 16.3

This proof of the rule A = *bh* for commensurable base and altitude uses the expression c^2 for the area of a square of side *c*. We could choose as a unit of length the segment *c* and thus consider the *mn* squares into which the rectangle's area was subdivided as unit squares, so that *b* = *m*, *h* = *n* and A = *mn* = *bh*. Or, we could choose an aliquote part of the segment *c* as the unit of length and thus consider *c* as an integer which indicates the number of units of length contained in *c* and, then, subdividing the area of the square with side *c* into units of area, conclude that this square's area is c^2.

The study of the particular case allows us to discuss the general case, when BC = *b* and CD = *h* are incommensurable. Therefore, if by chance one of these two segments is commensurable with the unit of length, the other is not. We suppose that they are both incommensurable with our unit of length. In applying to BC and CD the 1/*N*th part of the unit of length, we then find that BC is greater than *n* such parts, but less than *n* + 1 *N*th parts of the unit, while CD contains *m* such parts, but is contained in *m* + 1 *N*th parts of the unit of length, so that

$$n/N < b = BC < (n + 1)/N; \quad m/N < h = CD < (m + 1)/N. \quad (1)$$

The integers *m* and *n* thus found depend on the choice of the integer *N*. They increase if *N* increases, because the smaller the segment 1/*N* becomes the greater is the number of times it is contained in a given fixed length. If N becomes infinite m and n must also become infinite because then $1/N$ vanishes and a vanishing segment is contained an infinite number of times in a finite length.

We discuss the variation of N because its choice is at our disposal and therefore in our reasoning we can consider an infinite sequence of steps, each step being related to a definite choice of a fixed N and the values of N which correspond to various steps forming an infinite sequence increasing without limit.

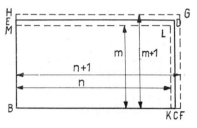

Fig. 16.4

Plotting the points K, F on BC and the points M, H on BE (Fig. 4) such that $BK = n/N$, $BF = (n+1)/N$ and $BM = m/N$, $BH = (m+1)/N$ and drawing the parallels KL, FG, ML, HG, we find that the rectangle BCDE is inside the rectangle BFGH, but contains the third rectangle BKLM. The two auxiliary rectangles BFGH and BKLM have their bases and altitudes commensurable by construction. Therefore, applying to these areas the rule $A = bh$, we have

$$\text{area BFGH} = (m + 1)(n + 1)/N^2; \qquad \text{area BKLM} = mn/N^2.$$

Since the area of our rectangle BCDE with incommensurable sides is greater the area BKLM it contains and smaller than the area BFGH, we obtain

$$mn/N^2 < \text{area BCDE} < (m + 1)(n + 1)/N^2. \tag{2}$$

On the other hand, forming the product $BC \cdot CD = bh$ and using the inequalities (1), we derive a second set of inequalities

$$mn/N^2 < BC \cdot CD = bh < (m + 1)(n + 1)/N^2. \tag{3}$$

We compare now the area $A = \text{area BCDE}$ to the product base times altitude bh, forming the difference $A - bh$. Using the inequalities (2) and (3), we can find the upper and lower bounds for this difference $A - bh$.

To find the upper bound we subtract the lower bound of bh from the upper bound of the area A:

$$A - bh < (m + 1)(n + 1)/N^2 - mn/N^2$$

$$= (m + n + 1)/N^2 < (m + n + N)/N^2.$$

We know that $m/N < h$ and $n/N < b$, so that $m < Nh$ and $n < Nb$. Therefore $m + n + N < Nh + Nb + N = N(h + b + 1)$ which gives $(m + n + N)/N^2 < (h + b + 1)/N$ and finally

$$A - bh < (h + b + 1)/N.$$

We now obtain the lower bound of $A - bh$ by subtracting the upper bound of bh from the lower bound of A:

$$A - bh > mn/N^2 - (m + 1)(n + 1)/N^2$$

$$= -(m + n + 1)/N^2 > -(m + n + N)/N^2 = -(h + b + 1)/N$$

which proves that the lower bound is equal to the upper bound with changed sign. Thus, we have

$$-(b + h + 1)/N < A - bh < (b + h + 1)/N,$$

and the absolute value of the difference $A - bh$ is less than the expression $(b + h + 1)/N$ whose numerator $b + h + 1$ has a fixed value, while the denominator N can be chosen as large as we want. In other words, the difference $A - bh$ in absolute value is less than an infinitely small number.

To justify the rule $A = bh$ for incommensurable b and h, it is sufficient to prove that the difference $A - bh$ vanishes. But how could a fixed number $A - bh$ be different from zero, if it is known to be less in absolute value than an infinitely small number $(b + h + 1)/N$ which approaches zero as near as we want for $N \to \infty$? This is impossible and therefore the difference $A - bh$ must vanish and the rule $A = bh$ holds in the general case. In other words, the number N being at our disposal, we can increase it without limits and at the limit $N = \infty$, the inequality $|A - bh| < (b + h + 1)/N$ is transformed into the equality $|A - bh| \leqslant 0$ since $\lim_{N \to \infty} [(b + h + 1)/N] = 0$ and in the ultimate inequality $|A - bh| \leqslant 0$ the sign $<$ must be discarded since $|A - bh|$ cannot be negative.

Thus, at the very beginning of the theory of areas we are obliged to use the passage to the limit and invoke the ultimate vanishing of an infinitely small quantity to prove such a simple, but fundamental theorem that the area of a rectangle is the product of its base and altitude. Here, again, the concept of absolute infinity appears as the very foundation of the measurement of areas.

Area of a Triangle

Two equal right triangles with legs a, b and hypotenuse c have equal areas because they coincide, if superposed. If juxtaposed along the common hypotenuse with parallel equal legs, they form a rectangle with sides a and b (Fig. 5a). The area of this rectangle is equal to the product ab as well as to the double of the right triangle's area. Thus, the area of a right triangle with legs a and b is measured by half the product $\frac{1}{2}ab$ of its two legs, one of which may be considered as the base with the other leg as the altitude.

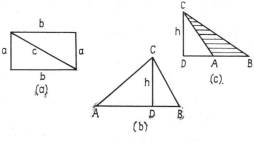

Fig. 16.5

We consider now any triangle ABC (Fig. 5). If both angles at the base $\hat{A}$ and $\hat{B}$ are acute, the triangle ABC is the sum of two right triangles ADC and BDC (Fig. 5b), having the same altitude CD $= h$ ar the triangle ABC and the bases AD and DB. Therefore, we have (denoting the base AB by c):

$$\text{area ABC} = \text{area ADC} + \text{area DBC} = (\text{AD} + \text{DB})\,h/2 = ch/2;$$

thus the area is equal to half the product base times altitude.

If one of the base-angles is obtuse (Fig. 5c), the area of such a triangle can be expressed as a difference of areas of two right triangles and the rule is again justified. Denoting the sides of a triangle by a, b, c and the corresponding altitudes by h_a, h_b, h_c, we have three equivalent expressions for its area:

$$\text{area ABC} = \tfrac{1}{2}ah_a = \tfrac{1}{2}bh_b = \tfrac{1}{2}ch_c.$$

Area of a parallelogram. Given a parallelogram ABCE (Fig. 6) with the base AB = b and altitude CD = h, we divide its area into two equal triangles ABC and BCE by the diagonal BC. These triangles have the same base

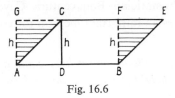

Fig. 16.6

and the same altitude as the parallelogram ABCE, and their areas are equal to $\frac{1}{2}bh$. Therefore, the parallelogram's area, which is equal to the sum of triangles' areas, is expressed by the product bh. The expression A = bh of the parallelogram's area can also be obtained by comparing the areas of the parallelogram ABCE and of the rectangle ABFG with the same base and altitude (Fig. 6). The triangles AGC and BFE being congruent, these areas are equal and thus the rule A = bh is justified.

This rule is a particular case of a more general rule A = $\frac{1}{2}(a + b)\,h$ which gives the area of a *trapezoid* ABCD (Fig. 7) with bases AB = a, CD = b and altitude CE = DF = h. A trapezoid, by definition, is a quadrilateral with two sides parallel. In general, the parallel sides of a trapezoid, called *bases*, are unequal; thus parallelogram is a particular case of trapezoid, namely, when the parallel sides of a trapezoid become equal. The two obtuse angles of a parallelogram are opposite and equal. The two obtuse angles of a trapezoid may be opposite or adjacent and in general they are unequal. A trapezoid with two adjacent obtuse angles is called an *isosceles* trapezoid if its adjacent obtuse angles are equal.

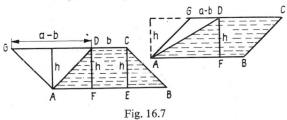

Fig. 16.7

The trapezoid's area is equal to the difference of two areas and it is obtained by subtracting a triangle from a parallelogram:

$$\text{area ABCD} = \text{area ABCG} - \text{area ADG} = ah - \tfrac{1}{2}(a - b)\,h$$
$$= \tfrac{1}{2}(2a - a + b)\,h = \tfrac{1}{2}(a + b)\,h.$$

Thus, the area of a trapezoid is equal to the arithmetic mean of two bases multiplied by the altitude. If in particular $a = b$, the trapezoid becomes a parallelogram and the formula $A = \frac{1}{2}(a + b)h$ reduces to $A = bh$.

To the Italian mathematician Bonaventura Cavalieri (1598–1647) the science of geometry owes an important method for computing areas, known under his name as

CAVALIERI'S PRINCIPLE: *Plane figures have equal areas if their linear sections drawn at the same height from the common base have equal lengths.*

He formulated this principle for volumes also, equality of areas of plane sections replacing that of lengths of linear sections, but we will discuss this later.

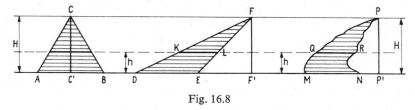

Fig. 16.8

To illustrate how this principle is applied we consider two triangles ABC and GHC on the one hand, and DEF and KLF on the other (Fig. 8) with equal bases AB = DE and equal altitudes CC′ = FF′ = H. The linear sections GH and KL of large triangles ABC and DEF are parallel to AE and equidistant from their bases, the distance being denoted by h. The triangles ABC, GHC on the one hand, and DEF, KLF on the other hand are similar, so that we have GH/AB = $(H - h)/H$ as well as KL/DE = $(H - h)/H$. In the proportion GH/AB = KL/DE the terms AB and DE are equal, AB = DE, and therefore the linear sections GH and KL must be equal too: GH = KL. Applying Cavalieri's Principle, we can immediately deduce the equality of areas ABC and DEF without resorting to the formulas Area ABC = $\frac{1}{2}$AB · H and Area DEF = $\frac{1}{2}$DE · H which presuppose the use of the passage to the limit with the aid of which these formulas were deduced.

But the principle gives much more than this. According to it any curvilinear figure such as MNRPQM, whatever its shape may be, having the same base MN = AB = b and the same altitude PP′ = CC′ = H as the triangle ABC, will have the same area $bH/2$, provided its linear sections QR are equal to those of the triangle at the same height h from the base-line AN, QR = GH, this condition being fulfilled for all values of h from zero to H, $0 \leqslant h \leqslant H$.

To prove this proposition without using Cavalieri's Principle necessitates the use of integral calculus. Therefore, this principle incarnates an idea which is at least as profound and powerful as the fundamental idea of calculus. It is known that the calculus, with its two principal operations of differentiation and integration, is based on the passage to the limit; that is, on the concept of absolute infinity in its aspect of aleph-null.

Cavalieri's Principle also embodies the idea of absolute infinity. In substance it asserts that an area is simply the sum of its linear and parallel sections; that is, a sum of lengths. But how could a sum of elements, each of which has no area and only length, possess an area? What is the reason explaining the sudden appearance in a sum of a new dimension lacking in the terms of that sum?

To answer these questions we must study more closely Cavalieri's concept of area as a sum of segments. We observe that there are as many linear sections of an area as there are distinct straight lines parallel to the base and cutting the area. Considering the intersection points of these straight lines with the altitude of the area, we can state more precisely that there are as many sectional segments of the area parallel to the base as there are points in the altitude. Indeed, through each point of the altitude a distinct parallel to the base can be drawn and, *vice versa*, each parallel determines a distinct point on the altitude. Therefore, a one-to-one correspondence exists between the set of points on the altitude and the set of linear segments, sections of the area parallel to the base.

On the other hand, we saw (Chapter 5) that there are a continuum of points in every segment of non-vanishing length. Thus, Cavalieri's Principle defines an area as a continuum of lengths, so that the absolute infinity embodied in Cavalieri's concept of area appears in it under the aspect of the continuum.

Studying the concept of segment as a continuum of points (Chapter 5), we emphasized the appearance in a sum of points of a new quality which is lacking in the elements constituting the sum, namely, length. It was proved that to form a length it is not sufficient to juxtapose aleph-null points on an empty straight line (here the word empty means devoid of points): the sum of aleph-null dimensionless points is itself dimensionless and does not form a segment because it has no length, while a segment always does have a length.

Thus, the sum of an infinity of points has the properties of its elements, if the infinity involved is the first transfinite number aleph-null. However, if the sum of a continuum C of points is used, a segment is formed and a length is obtained. Therefore, the appearance in a sum of an infinity of points of a new quality of which the points are devoid, is due to the *use of a continuum* of points and, thus, this new quality (length) is a manifestation of the continuum itself. In other words, the formation in our mind of the concept of length is due essentially to our mode of perceiving the kind of absolute infinity which is called the continuum. It is the continuum which is responsible for the appearance of a new property in a sum the terms of which are devoid of this property.

The same phenomenon reappears when we, with Cavalieri, dare to understand areas as continua of parallel segments piled upon one another. Segments have no area. They have only one dimension-length, but their sum possesses a new property: it appears to us as an area, provided the number of terms in a sum of segments is a continuum. Aleph-null of parallel segments piled upon one another do not form an area because the points these segments determine on the altitude (perpendicular to them) do not form a segment and appear to us as merely a point. It is the continuum involved implicitly in the formulation of Cavalieri's Principle which creates an area from arealess segments. Likewise in solid geometry volumes are obtained by piling volumeless plane and parallel areas upon one another in sufficient quantity, namely a continuum of them.

Cavalieri's Principle is a very powerful tool and admits of important applications. Let us consider again a rectangle of base b and altitude h. All its linear sections by parallels to the base are segments of equal length b and therefore the area A of the rectangle, considered as the sum of linear sections, is represented by $A = b \cdot C^{(h)}$, where $C^{(h)}$ stands for the continuum of linear sections, the same continuum which—as a continuum of points—is responsible for the length h of the altitude. The symbol $C^{(h)}$ is used here to represent the number of terms in the sum A, each of which is equal to the same length b.

Now we overturn the rectangle so that the previous altitude h becomes the new base and the new altitude is b. Repeating our argument, we find for the same area A another expression, namely $A = h \cdot C^{(b)}$, where $C^{(b)}$ denotes the continuum of points forming the length of the new altitude b. Thus, we must have

$$b \cdot C^{(h)} = h \cdot C^{(b)}.$$

From this equality we conclude that $C^{(h)} = h$ as well as $C^{(b)} = b$, which is simply a symbolic expression of the fact that we perceive the continuum of points $C^{(h)}$ forming a segment of length h, as the length of this segment.

Thus, the old formula $A = bh$ is justified. But, at the same time, its content is enormously enriched. It is deduced without an arbitrary choice of unit of area and without an elaborate discussion of two cases, that of commensurable segments b and h and that of imcommensurable segments. This is a much simpler and direct approach to the final result $A = bh$ and the simplification of the proof is due to the use of a more powerful tool. While in our first proof, applying the passage to the limit, we used the idea of absolute infinity in the aspect of aleph-null, Cavalieri's Principle works with a stronger aspect of absolute infinity, the continuum.

To illustrate the meaning of the expression "stronger aspect of absolute infinity" and throw some light on the mutual relation of the two aspects of absolute infinity, namely, aleph-null and continuum, let us consider the effects of various changes of the scale of magnitudes. We distinguish between finite and transfinite numbers, the order of magnitude of a finite number being that of the unit of scale, which means that the ratio R of its magnitude to that of the number chosen as the unit of magnitude is finite. Among transfinite numbers for which the ratio R is infinite, there are numbers whose order of magnitude is that of aleph-null as well as numbers of order of magnitude of continuum and so on. But, all transfinite numbers of various orders of magnitude appear as infinite, when compared to (or measured with the aid of) our unit of magnitude.

If we change the scale of magnitudes and replace the old unit by another whose ratio to the old unit is finite, the only effect of the choice of a new unit is a change in the notation of numbers, their order of magnitude remaining the same: numbers which were finite remain finite, those transfinite remain infinite and of the same order, whatever their class.

We now consider a more radical change of scale and choose the aleph-null of the old scale of magnitudes as our new unit: we call henceforth the aleph-null of the old scale *one* in the new scale. The effect of such a change of scale on the numbers which were finite in the old scale is catastrophic: they all simply vanish and are absorbed by the zero of the new scale. The beam of light of our thought we call attention is shifted from the domain of our familiar numbers on that of transfinite numbers which before the change of scale were of the order of magnitude of aleph-null, but now, in the new scale of magnitude, are finite because comparable to our new unit.

But the choice of aleph-null as the new unit of magnitude has no effect at all on the infinitude of continuum. The continuum of the old scale remains infinite also in the new scale and is as inaccessible for arithmetic operations with the new unit as it was with the old one before the change of scale. Moreover, if we change the scale again, bringing this time in the focus of our attention the continuum as a new unit of magnitude, then in their turn aleph-null and all the numbers of its order of magnitude sink, drowned in the new zero, and vanish.

Returning to Cavalieri's Principle, we emphasize that its usefulness is based not only on the possibility of shifting the one-dimensional sections of an area without changing the measure of this area, but also on the possibility of changing their shape without altering their length. To illustrate this point we turn now to the area of a circle.

Area of a Circle

By a very elegant application of Cavalieri's Principle we can deduce the expression πR^2 for the area of a circle of radius R from the expression $2\pi R$ of the length of its circumference. Taking for granted that a circle's circumference has a length (which must be proved because a length has been defined for rectilinear segments only), the value of the ratio of this length to the length $2R$ of the diameter is equal to the number π *by definition* of this number. Thus, assuming the existence of a perfectly determined length of the circumference of a circle of radius R, we can state without any proof that the measure of this length is $2\pi R$.

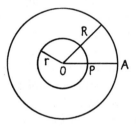

Fig. 16.9

Drawing a radius OA $= R$ (Fig. 9) and a concentric circle of radius OP $= r$, we see that to each point P of the segment OA there corresponds a circle with center at O and radius $r =$ OP, passing through this point. Conversely, each concentric interior circle of radius r $(r < R)$ intersects the segment OA in just one point P. When $r =$ OP increases from zero to R, the point P travels on the segment OA gliding from the center O to the point A. We consider now a continuum of concentric circles having their common center at O and passing through all the points of the segment OA, so that their radii have all the values of r between zero and R: $0 \leqslant r \leqslant R$.

Applying the concept of area as a continuum of lengths, we state that the circle's area is the sum of lengths $2\pi r$ of all the concentric circumferences which for $0 \leqslant r \leqslant R$ completely fill out the circle of radius R. To evaluate this sum we plot all these lengths in another figure.

Straightening a circumference of radius r, we give to it the form of a rectilinear segment of length $2\pi r$ and plot this segment PQ as a section of a right triangle ABO with legs AB $= 2\pi R$ and AO $= R$ by a parallel to the base AB at a distance r from the vertex O (Fig. 10). The triangles ABO and PQO being similar, we have indeed PQ/AB $=$ OP/OA, so that

$$PQ = AB \cdot OP/OA = 2\pi R \cdot r/R = 2\pi r, \qquad (0 \leqslant r \leqslant R)$$

for every value of r between 0 and R.

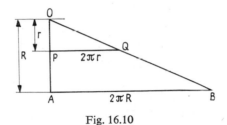

Fig. 16.10

Therefore, the area of the triangle ABO is the sum of the same terms as those which compose the circle's area: the leg OA of length R represents the radius OA of the circle and for each one of its points at the distance r from O the section of the right triangle ABO is equal to the length of the circumference of radius r passing through the corresponding point of the radius OA in Fig. 9. Applying now the Principle of Cavalieri, we conclude that the circle of radius R and the right triangle with the legs R and $2\pi R$ have equal areas. Thus, the triangle's area being equal to $\frac{1}{2}R \cdot 2\pi R = \pi R^2$, the formula for the circle's area is justified.

Projection of Areas

As another example of the importance of Cavalieri's Principle we consider the proof of the following theorem:

The area of the perpendicular projection of any plane figure onto a plane making an angle t with the plane of the original figure is equal to the area of the projected figure multiplied by the cosine of the angle t.

A projection is called perpendicular if its center is at infinity so that the projecting straight lines are parallel, and if moreover these projecting lines are perpendicular to the plane onto which the figure is projected. The perpendicular projection of a plane figure located in a given plane BCDE (Fig. 11) yields in the projection plane BCFG another figure whose area S depends on the value A of the area which is projected as well as on the angle t of the two planes. By definition, this angle t is equal to the angle $\overparen{KHL}$ formed at the point H by any two intersecting segments HK and HL lying in the planes BCDE and BCFG and perpendicular to the common intersection-line BC of these two planes.

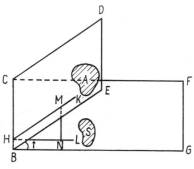

Fig. 16.11

The rule $S = A\cos t$ stated in the theorem is the same as the rule for the length of the perpendicular projection of a segment. Take, for instance, the segment HM on the line HK. It is projected onto the line HL making the angle t with the segment HM, and its projection is the segment HN, the line MN being perpendicular to HL. Thus, in the right triangle HMN the projected segment HM is the hypotenuse, while its projection HN is a leg adjacent to the angle t. By definition, $\cos \overparen{MHN} = \cos t = HN/HM$ and therefore

$$HN = \text{projection of } HM = HM \cos t.$$

Any segment lying in the plane BCDE and perpendicular to the straight line BC makes with its projection the same angle t which is the angle of the two planes. Therefore, the projection on the plane BCFG of a segment perpendicular to BC is equal to the product of the length of this segment times the cosine of the angle t. Moreover, if we consider two such segments, lying in the plane BCDE both perpendicular to BC and consequently parallel, the distance between their projections (which also are parallel to each other) is the same as the distance between the original segments in their plane BCDE. Therefore, considering the projected area A as a sum of segments perpendicular to the straight line BC and observing that each term of this sum shrinks under the projection in the same ratio cos t, we conclude that their sum, that is, the area A also shrinks under the projection in the ratio cos t, so that the area S of its projection is equal to the product A cos t.

We emphasize that the shape of the projected area has no relation to our proof and therefore the theorem holds true for areas of any shape. Here again the use of Cavalieri's Principle eliminates the need for using the calculus.

As an example of the theorem just proved let us consider the area of the projection of a circle of radius a (Fig. 12). This projection is bounded by a closed curve which is symmetrical with respect to the projection O* of the circle's center O and the projections of the circle's diameters all pass through O*, their lengths oscillating between the maximum length GH = $2a$ = CD of the diameter CD parallel to the intersection-line KL of the two planes and the minimum length EF = AB cos t = $2a$ cos t of the projection EF of the diameter AB which is perpendicular to KL. The segments GH and EF are major and minor axes of the curve EGFH which is called an *ellipse*.

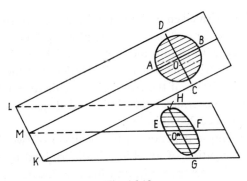

Fig. 16.12

Thus, the major axis is equal to the diameter $2a$ of the projected circle, while the minor axis EF, denoted by $2b$, is equal to $2a \cos t$: GH = $2a$, EF = $2b$ = $2a \cos t$.

By Cavalieri's Principle we know that the area of the ellipse is equal to the circle's area πa^2 multiplied by cos t and thus it is expressed by the product $\pi a^2 \cos t$. But $a \cos t = b$ and therefore the area of an ellipse with axes $2a$ and $2b$ is equal to πab.

An ellipse can be drawn, using the characteristic property of this curve, namely, that it is the locus of points P (Fig. 13) such that the sum of their distances PF_1 and PF_2 to two given points F_1, F_2 called *foci* is constant. The constant value of this sum is the length $2a$ of the major axis AB, so that $PF_1 + PF_2 = 2a$. The minor axis CD $= 2b$ is found by plotting the intersection points C, D of two circles of radius a (half the major axis) with centers at the foci of the ellipse F_1, F_2. Thus, denoting the distance F_1F_2 between the two foci (focal distance) by $2c$, we have $a^2 = b^2 + c^2$ and $b = (a^2 - c^2)^{1/2}$.

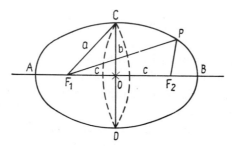

Fig. 16.13

To draw an ellipse with given major and minor axes $2a$, $2b$ we compute the focal distance $F_1F_2 = 2c = 2(a^2 - b^2)^{1/2}$, plot the foci F_1 and F_2, fasten a string of length $2a$ with thumb tacks at F_1 and F_2 and trace the ellipse, pulling the string taut with the pencil at P. Notice that the same procedure will give a circle of radius a, if the two foci coincide ($c = 0$ because $a = b$). Therefore, an ellipse generalizes the circle and degenerate into a circle if $a = b$, the focal distance $2c$ vanishing.

The shape of an ellipse depends on the position of two foci inside it. In other words, the elongation of an ellipse is determined by the ratio of the focal distance $2c$ to the major axis $2a$ on which are located the two foci. This ratio is denoted by e, so that $e = c/a$, and it is called the *eccentricity* of an ellipse. If e is small the foci are near the center and the ellipse resembles to a circle. If e approaches one (the eccentricity of an ellipse is always less than one because $c < a$), the foci are near the ends of the major axis, the minor axis is small and the ellipse is a very elongated and narrow curve close to the segment F_1F_2.

An ellipse is one of the three conic sections which, by definition, are intersections of a circular cone with various inclined planes. Together with the two others (parabola and hyperbola), it was studied by Greek mathematicians nineteen centuries before Kepler proved, in 1609, that the planets in their motion around the sun describe ellipses. The sun always occupies one of two foci of the elliptical orbit. The same holds for our moon and the satellites of other planets: they move in elliptical orbits around their planets at the focus. The path of a comet which returns periodically is also an ellipse with the sun at its focus, but the elliptical orbits of comets are very elongated, while those of planets are nearly circular.

Proof of the Pythagorean Theorem with the Aid of Areas

Originally Theorem XVII (Pythagorean) was proved with the aid if areas. Squares were constructed on the legs and on the hypotenuse of a right triangle and the area of the largest one, built on the hypotenuse, was shown to be equal to the sum of the areas of the two other squares.

We will now study some interesting versions of proof by areas of this important theorem. The most simple and ingenious is the Chinese proof which runs as follows (Fig. 14): consider a square ABCD with sides of length $a + b$ and plot on the sides the points E, F, G, H such that AE = BF = CG =DH = a, while EB = FC = GD = HA = b; join these points by lines EF, FG, GH, HE forming four equal right triangles AHE, BEF, CFG and DGH.

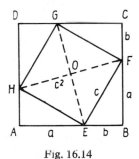

Fig. 16.14

Denoting the length of their hypotenuses by c, so that EF = FG = GH = HE = c, we observe that the quadrilateral EFGH is a square because all its angles and sides are equal.

To prove this point, rotate through a right angle the figure ABCD around its center of symmetry O. After the rotation it will be exactly the same figure, and the self-congruence by rotation proves that EFGH is a square. We express now the fact that the sum of the five areas into which we have subdivided the area ABCD is equal to this total area ABCD:

$$ABCD = AEH + BEF + CFG + DGH + EFGH = 4 \cdot AEH + EFGH$$

$$= 4 \cdot (ab/2) + c^2 = 2ab + c^2.$$

On the other hand, the area ABCD is equal to $(a+b)^2 = a^2 + 2ab + b^2$. Therefore, $a^2 + 2ab + b^2 = 2ab + c^2$ and thus $c^2 = a^2 + b^2$, which proves the theorem.

In a version of the Chinese proof one half of the large square ABCD, that is, the trapezoid ABFH, is used, which does not change the fundamental idea of this proof. The critics of the thousand of years old Chinese proof object that the mixture of geometry and algebra it represents is devoid of mathematical beauty. It is not difficult to eliminate this objection and give to the Chinese proof a purely geometrical form.

The square ABCD in Fig. 14 can be cut also into six parts by parallels KL, MN to its sides and diagonals DI, BI, where I is the intersection point of the two parallels KL, MN (Fig. 15). We have AM = AK = a, CL = CN = b,

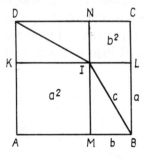

Fig. 16.15

so that the four equal right triangles BLI, BMI, DKI, DNI are exactly identical to the four right triangles AEH, BEF, CFG, DGH. Therefore, comparing the two divisions (Fig. 14 and 15) of the same square, we come to the conclusion that the area of the square EFGH constructed on the hypotenuse EF = c of the right triangle BEF is equal to the sum of the areas of two squares AMIK and CNIL (Fig. 15) constructed on its legs AM = a and IL = b, which achieves the proof of the Pythagorean Theorem.

Greek Proof

In the original Greek proof the area of the square AEBG built on the hypotenuse AB of a right triangle ABC (Fig. 16) is divided by the altitude CFND parallel to AE into two rectangular areas AEDF and BFDG, which are then shown to be equal to the square areas ACHK and BLMC respectively.

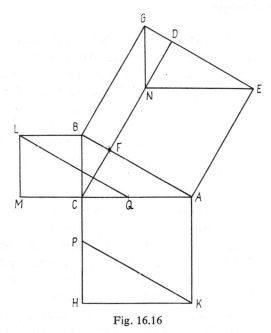

Fig. 16.16

To prove this, three points N, P, Q are defined on CD, CH, CA respectively, such that CN = AB, BP = MQ = AC. Drawing the segments NG, NE, PK, LQ, three right triangles EGN, QLM and KPH are formed equal to the given right triangle ABC. The four quadrilaterals AENC, ABPK, BCNG, ABLQ are parallelograms, because in each one of them one pair of opposite sides are equal and parallel: CN $\overset{\shortparallel}{=}$ AE, AK $\overset{\shortparallel}{=}$ BP, CN $\overset{\shortparallel}{=}$ BG, AQ $\overset{\shortparallel}{=}$ BL.

Moreover, comparing the parallelograms AENC and ABPK, we see that they are equal, and the same holds for the parallelograms ABLQ and BCNG. Now we can prove the equivalence of the areas AEDF and ACHK as follows. Adding the triangle CAF to AEDF and subtracting the equal triangle DNE, we transform AEDF into AENC which is equal to ABPK, so that AEDF = ABPK. On the other hand, adding to ABPK the triangle KPH and then subtracting the equal triangle ABC, we prove that ABPK is equivalent to ACHK and, therefore, the rectangular area AEDF is equal to the square area ACHK. By the same reasoning, we can prove that the area BFDG is equal to that BLMC, and thus the theorem is proved. The perfection of Chinese proof when compared with Greek proof is striking.

Pythagorean Triplets

The question now arises as to whether it is possible to determine explicitly all right triangles with commensurable sides. We know that the sides of such a triangle can be expressed as integral numbers since they contain their common measure an integral number of times. Such are, for instance, the Egyptian triangle, whose sides are proportional to integers 3, 4, 5 (with $3^2 + 4^2 = 5^2$) and the Chinese triangle, with sides 5, 12 and 13 ($5^2 + 12^2 = 13^2$). Thus the question raised above is identical to the algebraic problem of finding all the solutions in integral numbers of the equation $a^2 + b^2 = c^2$, where a, b, c are considered as three unknowns.

To each set of three integers a, b, c verifying the condition $a^2 + b^2 = c^2$ corresponds a right triangle with commensurable sides, and *vice versa*. It is possible now to characterize the structure of all such triplets of integers a, b, c called *Pythagorean triplets*. Replacing this term by an abbreviation PT, we observe that, if (a, b, c) is a PT, then for any integer k the triplet (ka, kb, kc) is also a PT. We have indeed $(ka)^2 + (kb)^2 = k^2(a^2 + b^2) = k^2c^2 = (kc)^2$, if $a^2 + b^2 = c^2$. Thus, an infinite sequence of PT's can be built from a given PT, multiplying its elements by $k = 2, 3, 4, \ldots$, etc.

On the other hand, if in a PT (a, b, c) the integers a, b, c have a common factor k, so that $a = kg$, $b = kh$, $c = kj$, the triplet (g, h, j) is also a PT. We have indeed $a^2 + b^2 - c^2 = 0$, that is, $k^2g^2 + k^2h^2 - k^2j^2 = k^2(g^2 + h^2 - j^2) = 0$, where k^2 does not vanish. Therefore, $g^2 + h^2 - j^2 = 0$ and (g, h, j) is a PT.

Thus it is sufficient to consider only such PT's the elements of which are relatively prime integers, that is, have no common divisor. Such relatively prime solutions of the equation $a^2 + b^2 = c^2$ and the corresponding PT's are called primitive solutions and *primitive Pythagorean triplets*, or PPT by abbreviation. The structure of a PPT is described in the following theorem:—
Given two relatively prime integers m and n $\neq$ m, one of which is even while the other is odd, the set of three integers

$$a = 2mn, \quad b = n^2 - m^2, \quad c = n^2 + m^2 \tag{4}$$

is a primitive Pythagorean triplet. Conversely, if three relatively prime integers a, b, c verify the equation $a^2 + b^2 = c^2$, then there are two relatively prime integers m and $n \neq m$ one of which is even while the other is odd, such that a, b, c are expressible in terms of m and n by the formulas (4).

The three integers a, b, c given by (4) form indeed a PT because

$$a^2 + b^2 = 4m^2n^2 + n^4 - 2n^2m^2 + m^4$$

$$= n^4 + 2n^2m^2 + m^4 = (n^2 + m^2)^2 = c^2$$

and to prove the first part of the theorem it remains to show that they are relatively prime numbers. Since the square of an even number is even and that of an odd number is odd, one of the two squares m^2, n^2 is even while the other is odd. Thus, both integers $b = n^2 - m^2$ and $c = n^2 + m^2$ are odd. To prove that (a, b, c) in (4) is a PPT let us suppose to the contrary that the integers a, b, c have a common odd factor, which is then a common factor of two squares $n^2 = \frac{1}{2}(b + c)$ and $m^2 = \frac{1}{2}(c - b)$. Since the squares of two relatively prime numbers cannot have a common factor we obtain thus a contradiction because m and n by hypothesis are relatively prime. This contradiction is a corollary of our assumption that b and c have a common factor, so that it proves that b and c in (4) are necessarily relatively prime. Now a and b also must be relatively prime because otherwise their common factor would be also a factor of c, so that b and c would have a common factor. Thus, (a, b, c) given by the formulas (4) is a PPT and thus the first part of the theorem is proved.

To prove the second part we have to study the structure of a primitive solution (a, b, c) of the equation $a^2 + b^2 = c^2$ for which no two of the three integers a, b, c can have a common factor. Therefore, a and b cannot both be even. But they cannot either both be odd. To prove this we suppose to the contrary that $a = 2u + 1$ and $b = 2v + 1$, both a and b being odd. Then

$$c^2 = (2u + 1)^2 + (2v + 1)^2 = 4u^2 + 4u + 1 + 4v^2 + 4v + 1$$

$$= 4(u^2 + u + v^2 + v) + 2 = 4M + 2$$

and $c = (4M + 2)^{1/2}$, where $M = u^2 + u + v^2 + v$ is an integer. But the value $(4M + 2)^{1/2}$ for c is impossible because c must be an integer, while $(4M + 2)^{1/2}$ is an irrational number since no perfect square of an integer can be of the form $4M + 2$; the square of an even integer $2k$ is equal to $4k^2$ which is of the form $4M$, and the square of an odd integer $2k + 1$ is $4k^2 + 4k + 1 = 4(k^2 + k) + 1$ which is of the form $4M + 1$. Therefore, a and b cannot *both* be neither odd nor even. Denoting the even number by a and the odd by b, we have $a = 2K$ and $b = 2M + 1$. The sum of their squares $4(K^2 + M^2 + M) + 1 = c^2$ being odd, the third number c is odd and we denote its value by $c = 2N + 1$. Thus, substituting $2K$, $2M + 1$, $2N + 1$ for a, b, c respectively, we transform the equation $a^2 + b^2 = c^2$ into

$$4K^2 + (4M + 1)^2 = (2N + 1)^2.$$

Opening the parentheses, subtracting both sides the term 1 and dividing through by 4, we obtain $K^2 + M^2 + M = N^2 + N$. This equation for our three unknown integers K, M, N is equivalent to $K^2 = N^2 - M^2 + N - M = (N - M)(N + M) + (N - M)$ and, finally, to

$$K^2 = (N - M)(N + M + 1). \tag{5}$$

It is easy to prove that $N - M$ and $N + M + 1$ cannot have a common factor. They are equal to $\frac{1}{2}(c - b)$ and $\frac{1}{2}(c + b)$ respectively and these two numbers must be relatively prime otherwise their sum c and difference b would have a common factor, too, which is impossible, because, by hypothesis formulated in the theorem, no two elements of the PPT (a, b, c) can have a common factor. Hence, we see that $N - M$ and $N + M + 1$ cannot have a common factor.

On the other hand, equation (5) proves that their product is a perfect square. Therefore, the prime factors in the factoring of $N - M$ and $N + M + 1$ must all have *even* exponents, which means that $N - M$ and $N + M + 1$ are perfect squares themselves: $N + M + 1 = n^2$ and $N - M = m^2$, where the integers m and $n > m$ (because $N + M + 1 > N - M$) are relatively prime. Our equation (5) becomes now $K^2 = m^2n^2$, so that $K = mn$ and $a = 2K = 2mn$. We have also $b = 2M + 1 = (N + M + 1) - (N - M) = n^2 - m^2$, as well as $c = 2N + 1 = (N + M + 1) + (N - M) = n^2 + m^2$. Thus, the proof of the theorem is achieved.

The integers m and n must be relatively prime, one being even and the other odd, but otherwise they are arbitrary and can be chosen freely. They cannot both be even, being relatively prime. Furthermore, they cannot both be odd because the sum of their squares $n^2 + m^2 = c = 2N + 1$ must be odd, while the sum of squares of two odd numbers is even.

To every PPT (a, b, c) generated by a choice of m and n corresponds a right triangle with commensurable sides expressed by integral numbers a, b, c as well as an infinite number of similar right triangles obtainable by amplifying its sides an integral number of times. Conversely, to any right triangle with commensurable sides corresponds a Pythagorean triplet which is a primitive one, if the unit of length is chosen so that the sides are expressed by relatively prime integers.

EXAMPLE: Taking $n = 8$, $m = 3$, one finds $a = 48$, $b = 55$ and $c = 73$. Check: $c^2 - b^2 = (c + b)(c - b) = 128 \cdot 18 = 64 \cdot 36 = 8^2 \cdot 6^2 = 48^2 = a^2$. Conversely: to the right triangle $a = 12$, $b = 5$, $c = 13$ correspond $n^2 = \frac{1}{2}(c + b) = 9$, $m^2 = \frac{1}{2}(c - b) = 4$, so that $n = 3$ and $m = 2$.

It is of interest to study another proof of the same theorem, a proof in which are used three branches of mathematics, namely, algebra, geometry and so-called analytic geometry, which is a combination of algebra and geometry. This proof well illustrates the fundamental unity of mathematics and shows at the same time how two different geometrical questions can be solved with the aid of the same algebraic apparatus.

We saw that the solution of the question—What right triangles have commensurable sides?—was found by determining all the integral solutions of the algebraic equation $x^2 + y^2 = z^2$. We will now formulate another geometric question which has nothing in common with right triangles, but whose solution again will be obtained with the aid of the integral solutions of the same equation $x^2 + y^2 = z^2$.

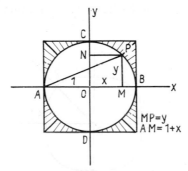

Fig. 16.17

The location of a point in a plane can be characterized by two numbers x and y called the cartesian coordinates of this point. They represent the distances $NP = OM = x$ and $MP = ON = y$ of the point P from the axes of coordinates OX, OY (Fig. 17). The numbers x and y can be rational or irrational and three cases are possible: (1) both are rational, (2) one is rational, while the other is irrational and (3) both are irrational. In the first case, when both x and y are rational, the corresponding point will be called a *rational* point, while in the cases (2) and (3) it will be called *irrational*. Thus, the continuum of points forming the plane OXY is composed of two sets of points: the set of rational points of the plane and the set of irrational points.

We know that the set of rational points, though infinite and everywhere dense in the plane, is not a continuum (Chapter 4). There are only aleph-null rational points in the plane and therefore, if all the irrational points lying amongst the rational points are dropped and the remaining rational points are condensed, no area nor even a length can be formed.

Consider now all the points at the distance one from the origin. They form a circle of radius one with the center at the origin O. Applying the Pythagorean Theorem to the triangle OPM (Fig. 17), where P is any point on our circle, we obtain the condition $x^2 + y^2 = 1$ imposed on the coordinates x, y of the circle's points. Conversely, if the coordinates x, y of a point are known to verify the condition $x^2 + y^2 = 1$, then this point belongs to the circle because it is at the distance one from the origin O. For this reason the condition $x^2 + y^2 = 1$ is called the equation of the circle with center at the origin O and radius one. Such a circle is often called the unit-circle.

We now concern ourselves with the question of how the unit-circle threads its way through the continuum of points forming the plane XOY? Are all of its points irrational or are some of them rational? If there are rational points on the circumference of the unit-circle, which are they and how can we find them?

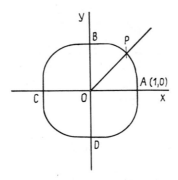

Fig. 16.18

This question is rendered meaningful by the fact that there exist continuous curves which thread through the everywhere dense set of rational points without passing through more than a finite number of them. Consider, for example, the locus of points whose coordinates x, y verify the condition $x^4 + y^4 = 1$. It can be proved that this curve (Fig. 18) has only four rational points, namely, the four intersection-points A, B, C, D with the axes OX, OY so that the four arcs $\overarc{AB}$, $\overarc{BC}$, $\overarc{CD}$, $\overarc{DA}$ between the rational points A, B, C, D have not a single rational point on them.

The unit-circle, as we will now prove it, has an infinite number of rational points on its circumference and these are distributed so that they are everywhere dense on the circle. To prove this we establish a one-to-one correspondence between the points of the circle and the rays (half-straight lines) of a pencil of rays with the vertex at the point A $(-1, 0)$ of the circle whose coordinates are $x = -1$ and $y = 0$ (Fig. 17). To each point P of the circle we let correspond the ray APA' which passes through this point and, conversely, to each ray AA' corresponds its intersection point P with the circle. Let us now consider the slopes s of these rays. By definition the slope of a straight line is the value of the ratio of a vertical displacement to the corresponding horizontal displacement when a point travels on this straight line. Supposing that a point moves from A to P, for example, we see that to the horizontal displacement $AM = AO + OM = 1 + x$ corresponds the vertical displacement $MP = y$. Thus, the slope s of the ray AP is equal to the ratio $y/(1 + x): s = y/(1 + x)$.

Here again we distinguish two cases: the number s measuring the slope can be rational and then the ray is called a *rational* ray, or s is irrational and then the corresponding ray is called an *irrational* ray. Every ray corresponds to a point on the circumference of the circle and it is easy to show that to a rational point P (x, y) corresponds a rational ray. If the point is rational, the numbers x and y are rational and so is also $1 + x$. Thus, the slope $s = y/(1 + x)$ of the corresponding ray also has a rational value because the quotient of two rational numbers y and $1 + x$ is a rational number. Thus, to a rational point of the circle corresponds a rational ray.

Conversely, we shall prove that to a rational ray corresponds a rational point of the circle. In other words, we shall prove that the coordinates x and y of a point P on the circle are rational numbers, if the slope s of the corresponding ray AP is a rational number. These two coordinates can be considered as two unknowns verifying the two equations $x^2 + y^2 = 1$ (equation of the circle) and $s = y/(1 + x)$, where s is a given and known *rational* number. Writing the second equation as $y = s(1 + x)$ and substituting $s^2(1 + x)^2$ for y^2 in the first equation, we eliminate the unknown y and obtain an equivalent equation containing only the one unknown x: $x^2 + s^2(x + 1)^2 = 1$.

Transposing the term 1 to the left and factoring the difference $x^2 - 1$ into the product of two factors $(x + 1)(x - 1)$, we have $(x + 1)(x - 1) + s^2(x + 1)^2 = 0$. Factoring out the common factor $x + 1$, we write this quadratic equation as a product of two linear factors

$$(x + 1)(x - 1 + s^2x + s^2) = 0,$$

so that its two roots may be obtained by equating each of the two factors separately to zero. Equating to zero the first factor, $x + 1 = 0$, we obtain the first root $x = -1$ and this root corresponds to the point A, vertex of the pencil of rays, which is one of two intersection-points of the straight line APA' with the circle. Equating to zero the second factor, we obtain the equation

$$x - 1 + s^2 x + s^2 = 0,$$

whose solution yields the coordinate x of the point P expressed in terms of the slope s. This solution is

$$x = (1 - s^2)/(1 + s^2)$$

and the expression of x in terms of s proves that x is rational, if s has a rational value. Since $y = s(1 + x)$ we see that then y is also rational and this achieves the proof of the fact that to a rational ray corresponds a rational point of the circle. The coordinate y can be expressed in terms of s alone because $1 + x = (1 + s^2)/(1 + s^2) + (1 - s^2)/(1 + s^2) = 2/(1 + s^2)$, so that

$$x = (1 - s^2)/(1 + s^2), \quad y = 2s/(1 + s^2). \tag{6}$$

Since to every real number s corresponds a value of the slope of a ray through A, there are an infinite number of rational rays and they are everywhere dense in the continuum of rays issued from the point A. But, to every rational ray corresponds a rational point and therefore there are an infinite number of rational points on the circumference of the circle and they are everywhere dense on it.

Furthermore, because to every rational point on the circle corresponds a rational ray with its rational slope s, we conclude that all the rational points of the circle are represented by the two expressions (6). Replacing in (6) the rational number s by its expression $s = m/n$, where n and m are two integers, and multiplying the fractions x and y upstairs and downstairs by the square of the integer n, we write the formulas (6) as follows:

$$x = (n^2 - m^2)/(n^2 + m^2), \quad y = 2mn/(n^2 + m^2). \tag{7}$$

Remembering that these two coordinates are those of a point P on the circumference of the circle $x^2 + y^2 = 1$, we state that the expressions (7) give all rational solutions of the equation $x^2 + y^2 = 1$. But to a rational solution $x = b/c, y = a/c$ of this equation corresponds a solution in integral numbers of the equation $x^2 + y^2 = z^2$ because $(b/c)^2 + (a/c)^2 = 1$ is equivalent to the relation $b^2 + a^2 = c^2$, where a, b, c are three integers. Thus (7) is equivalent to (4) and we find again, this time with the aid of a geometric proof, the general form of a primitive Pythagorean triplet (a, b, c).

Thus, between the rational points on the circumference of the unit-circle and the right triangles with commensurable sides there is a one-to-one correspondence. On the other hand, the totality of all right triangles is represented by all points of the same unit-circle, so that there are a continuum of various right triangles, whereas the set of right triangles with commensurable sides is denumerable, their number being only aleph-null.

The Great Fermat Theorem

The equation $x^4 + y^4 = z^4$ has no solution in integers and this fact can be stated also by saying that the equation $x^4 + y^4 = 1$ has no rational solutions, except the four trivial ones, namely, $x = 0$, $y = \pm 1$ and $y = 0$, $x = \pm 1$. In other words, the unique rational points of the curve in Fig. 18 whose equation is $x^4 + y^4 = 1$, are the four points A, B, C, D. Nevertheless, the slope $s = y/x$ of the line OP varies continuously and passes through all real values rational and irrational, when the point P describes the curve. The explanation of this is simple: a quotient of two irrational numbers can have rational values since the product of an irrational and of a rational number is irrational. Thus, all the interior points of the arc $\overset{\frown}{AB}$ (Fig. 18) being irrational, rational rays issued from the origin can pass through some of them since $s = y/x$ may be rational, when both x and y are irrational.

The general question as to whether or not the equation $x^n + y^n = z^n$ can have integral solutions, the exponent n being an arbitrary integer greater than two, is not yet solved. It is known under the name of the Great Fermat Theorem, because in 1637 a French mathematician Fermat (1601–1665) wrote a short marginal note on one of his books in which he formulated a negative answer to this question, asserting that he had found "a truly marvellous demonstration which this margin is too narrow to contain".

Fermat's Great Theorem, which says that for $n > 2$ no equation $x^n + y^n = z^n$ can be solved in integers, is a problem child of mathematics. All efforts to prove it in its general form, that is, for any integer $n > 2$, have failed. But Fermat's assertion is now known to be true for all numbers n less than 14,000. The geometrical form of this result is the following fact: for $2 < n < 14,000$ all the curves defined by the equation $x^n + y^n = 1$ pass through only four rational points A, B, C, D (Fig. 18) which are the same for all of them. For even exponent $n = 2m$ these curves lie between the unit-circle and the square circumscribed about the unit-square (that is, in the region shaded in Fig. 17). No two of them are incident in points other than A, B, C, D because a curve C_m of equation $x^{2m} + y^{2m} = 1$ lies between the unit-circle and the curve C_k of equation $x^{2k} + y^{2k} = 1$, if $k > m > 1$.

Length and Area of a Circle

The computation of the length of a circle of radius R reduces to the computation of the famous number π. By definition, this number expresses the ratio of the length of a circumference to that of its diameter $2R$. Therefore the formula for the length C of a circumference of radius R is simply $C = 2\pi R$ because $C/2R = \pi$ by definition.

But the computation of the numerical value of π is based on the tacit assumption that the circumference of a circle does possess a perfectly defined and determined length and, therefore, before computing π we must prove the existence of this length C. This proof is necessary because all what we know about length until now is that a segment of a straight line has a length, the existence of the length of an arc of a curve being not yet discussed.

One could argue that to prove the existence of the length C of a circle, it is sufficient to cut the circumference at a point and then straighten it out, thus transforming this curve into a segment of a straight line. The objection that such a physical operation cannot be used in a geometrical proof could be easily dismissed by defining the straightening of curves as a purely abstract geometrical operation.

But then a logical difficulty arises. We cannot suppose that a curved arc has no length because, if this were so, the length created by the operation of straightening could not be considered as the length of the circumference, but only as the length of the rectilinear segment into which the circumference was transformed by the straightening. Thus, the operation of straightening presupposes the existence of length and therefore can serve only for measuring it, if by definition the straightening is performed without stretching or compressing.

The logical basis necessary for the proof of existence and for the definition of the length and area of a circle was discovered by Archimedes of Syracuse (287–212 B.C.), a famous mathematician of antiquity, who was also the first to compute the surface area and the volume of a sphere. His work on circle and his reasoning are so important that we reproduce them here.

Almost two centuries before Archimedes, another Greek mathematician,

Antiphon of Athens (480–411 B.C.), invented the basic construction applied by Archimedes. Antiphon inscribed a sequence of regular polygons in a circle, beginning with a square and duplicating at each step the number of sides. Thus, at the second step an octagon, that is, a polygon with 2^3 sides was inscribed, at the third step a polygon with 2^4 sides and, in general, at the nth step a regular polygon with 2^{n+1} sides were inscribed.

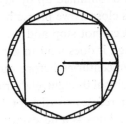

Fig. 16.19

Antiphon stated that the inscribed polygons approach the circumference of the circle when the number of sides increases. Moreover, he says explicitly that when the number n of steps already performed increases without limit the area (shaded on Fig. 19) between the perimeter of the nth inscribed polygon with 2^{n+1} sides and the circumference approaches zero and can be made as small as we want by choosing a sufficiently large n.

In other words, twenty-four centuries ago Antiphon described the behavior of an infinitely small quantity which approaches zero as close as we please. From this discovery there was only one step to the definition of the length of a circumference as the limit of perimeters of inscribed regular polygons when the number of sides becomes infinite. This step was discussed by Antiphon because he studied the question of what happens to an inscribed regular polygon when the number of its sides becomes infinite. Is it transformed into the circle's circumference or not?

The answer given by Antiphon was negative. Justifying this negative answer, Antiphon says that the shaded area separating the perimeter of an inscribed regular polygon from the circumference cannot vanish. At every step of the reasoning, that is, at each duplication of the number of sides, this area decreases. It can be made as small as we want, repeating indefinitely the geometric construction which doubles the number of sides, but—says Antiphon—after any given number of duplications this area remains and is thus always present as a small, may be exceedingly small, but finite and non-vanishing area. The number of steps of thought used in the reasoning can be made as large as we want, but this number is always an integer and remains therefore finite. There is no last integer so that the construction continues necessarily for ever. It cannot have an end and while it is continuing the residual area is always present. Therefore—concludes Antiphon—the sequence of inscribed regular polygons does not reach the circle and circle's properties cannot be deduced from those of inscribed polygons.

Antiphon's argument can be summed up by saying that an infinitely small quantity approaches zero as close as we please but does not reach it, that is, cannot vanish: its variation cannot stop and there is no fixed limit zero for this variable quantity, though it does tend to zero.

Thus, already twenty-four centuries before our time, Greek culture had achieved a remarkable maturity of thought, elaborating a strong, logically continuous thinking. Antiphon refuses to disrupt the continuity of a logical chain of arguments. He postulates as a necessary foundation of his thinking process the possibility of checking the logical validity of the passage from each previous link to the next link of a logical chain, and this possibility is for him a condition *sine qua non* of truth. From a logical point of view there is a striking similarity between the Arguments of Zeno of Elea and Antiphon's discussion of the sequence of inscribed regular polygons. Both Zeno and Antiphon belonged to the same generation (Zeno was only ten years older than Antiphon), and they can be considered as typical representatives of Greek thought.

A contemporary of Antiphon, Bryson of Heraclea, added circumscribed regular polygons to Antiphon's inscribed polygons and applied to them the same process of duplication of the number of sides, preparing thus the work of Archimedes. He proved that the circumscribed polygons also approach indefinitely the circle's circumference when the number of their sides increases without limit. But Bryson shared the point of view of Antiphon and Zeno and did not attempt to define the length of a circumference comprized between inscribed and circumscribed polygons as the limit of their perimeters.

This audacious break with the Greek tradition of logically continuous thinking was reserved for Archimedes. Reexamining the constructions of Antiphon and Bryson and repeating them without any alteration, he boldy considered the circle as the limit of an infinite sequence of inscribed regular polygons, as well as the limit of an infinite sequence of circumscribed polygons. This definition of circle as a limit of regular inscribed and circumscribed polygons, when the number of their sides becomes infinite, is equivalent to the assertion that the process of exhaustion of the infinitely small area shaded in Fig. 19 can be considered as completely performed and terminated.

This can mean only one thing, namely, that the infinite chain of duplications of the number of sides finally stops and the ultimate shape of polygons which is attained at the end of this infinite chain of arguments is a circle.

In our modern language we say that by definition an infinitely small quantity ultimated reaches zero as its limit, so that its variation stops. In other words, to the potential infinity of Antiphon and Bryson (infinite sequences of inscribed and circumscribed polygons) Archimedes added the actual, absolute infinity (limit of sequences), establishing thus a new principle of thinking, namely, the possibility of reaching a definite conclusion at the end of an infinite chain of steps of thinking.

"There is no such thing as a last integer, but after and beyond the infinite sequence of integers there is a first transfinite number aleph-null greater than all the integers", said Georg Cantor, two thousand years after Archimedes, reviving the fundamental idea of this Greek genius. There is no doubt that Archimedes' definition of the circle as a regular polygon with aleph-null equal sides helped prepare Cantor's analysis of absolute infinity.

Thus Archimedes ascribes a length to a circumference, this length being by definition the limit, when n becomes infinite, of the perimeter's length P_n of an inscribed regular polygon with 2^{n+1} sides as well as the limit of the perimeter Q_n of a circumscribed regular polygon with the same number 2^{n+1} of sides:

$$C = 2\pi R = \lim_{n=\infty} P_n = \lim_{n=\infty} Q_n. \tag{8}$$

Denoting the circle's area by A and those of the inscribed and circumscribed polygons with 2^{n+1} sides by S_n and T_n respectively, we conclude also that

$$A = \lim_{n=\infty} S_n = \lim_{n=\infty} T_n, \tag{9}$$

if the circle is the ultimate shape of both polygons for $n = \infty$.

Definitions (8) and (9) become possible and can be used in computing the length C and the area A of a circle only if our thinking does not follow step by step the potentially endless geometrical operation of duplicating the number of sides, thus remaining slavishly tied to the sequence of successive logical links of a potentially infinite chain of arguments. They result from a new act of thinking which does away with the Greek tradition of a continuous logical chain and jumps over the infinite sequence of its links to the final conclusion reached by our thought in the same way as aleph-null is reached beyond the sequence of all the integers. This logical jump to the final conclusion is possible only when the existence of aleph-null beyond the integers is accepted, which entails the introduction of the passage to the limit as a legitimate mathematical operation.

We pass now to the existence proof of the limits of P_n, Q_n, S_n and T_n, when n becomes infinite. Denoting by s_n the side of a regular inscribed polygon with 2^{n+1} sides, so that the side of a polygon 2^{n+2} sides, obtained by duplicating the number of sides of the 2^{n+1}-gon, will be s_{n+1}, we introduce also the so-called *apothem* $a_n = OE$ (Fig. 20), which is defined as the perpendicular drawn from the center O to the side $s_n = CF$ of the 2^{n+1}-gon.

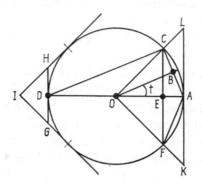

Fig. 16.20.

$AO = R$; $OE = a_n$; $OB = a_{n+1}$; $FC = s_n$; $FA = AC = s_{n+1}$

Thus, $AC = AF = s_{n+1}$ being the sides of the 2^{n+2}-gon, we have also $OB = a_{n+1}$ as the apothem of the regular inscribed polygon with 2^{n+2} sides. We wish now prove the two relations

$$R \cdot s_n = 2a_{n+1} \cdot s_{n+1}; \qquad 2a_{n+1}^2 = R^2 + R \cdot a_n \qquad (10)$$

between the sides s_n, s_{n+1} and apothems a_n, a_{n+1} of two successive polygons with 2^{n+1} and 2^{n+2} sides, where R denotes the radius of the circle in which these polygons are inscribed.

Evaluating the area of the triangle OAC (Fig. 20) in two ways as $OA \cdot EC/2$ and $AC \cdot OB/2$ and equating these expressions, we obtain after a multiplication by four $OA \cdot FC = 2OB \cdot AC$ which is the first relation (10). To deduce the second, we observe that the right triangles ACD and AEC are similar because they have a common acute angle at the vertex A. Therefore, we have the proportion $AC/AE = AD/AC$, that is, $s_{n+1}/(R - a_n) = 2R/s_{n+1}$.

Crossmultiplication yields $s_{n+1}^2 = 2R(R - a_n)$. On the other hand, the Pythagorean Theorem applied to the triangle OAB gives $AB^2 = OA^2 - OB^2$, that is, $s_{n+1}^2/4 = R^2 - a_{n+1}^2$, so that the square s_{n+1}^2 can also be expressed as $s_{n+1}^2 = 4R^2 - 4a_{n+1}^2$. Comparing the two expressions of s_{n+1}^2, we obtain $2R^2 - 2Ra_n = 4R^2 - 4a_{n+1}^2$, which proves the second relation (10).

The relations (10) can easily be established also with the aid of complex numbers. Denoting the angle $\widehat{AOB}$ by t, so that the angle $\widehat{AOC} = 2 \cdot \widehat{AOB} = 2t$, we consider two complex numbers $z_n = a_n + is_n/2 = Re^{2it}$ and $z_{n+1} = a_{n+1} + is_{n+1}/2 = Re^{it}$ which are related since $z_{n+1}^2 = R^2 e^{2it} = Rz_n$. Thus, replacing them by their expressions, we have $(a_{n+1} + is_n/2)^2 = R(a_n + is_n/2)$. Squaring out, substituting $R^2 - a_{n+1}^2$ for $s_{n+1}^2/4$ and separating the real and imaginary components, we obtain precisely the relations (10).

The operation of duplicating the number of sides increases the perimeter P_n and the area S_n of the regular inscribed 2^{n+1}-gon, so that the inequalities $P_{n+1} > P_n$ and $S_{n+1} > S_n$ do not need further justification. It is of interest to observe that the area S_{n+1} of the 2^{n+2}-gon and the perimeter P_n of the 2^{n+1}-gon verify the relation

$$S_{n+1} = R \cdot P_n/2.$$

We have, indeed,

$$S_{n+1} = 2^{n+2} \cdot s_{n+1} \cdot a_{n+1}/2 = 2^n \cdot 2a_{n+1} \cdot s_{n+1} = 2^n \cdot R \cdot s_n = R \cdot P_n/2$$

because $2a_{n+1} \cdot s_{n+1} = R \cdot s_n$ and $P_n = 2^{n+1} \cdot s_n$.

The infinite sequences $P_1, P_2, P_3, \ldots, P_n, \ldots$ and $S_1, S_2, \ldots, S_n, \ldots$ are increasing sequences. If they are bounded from above, their terms all remaining less than a fixed number, they cannot increase without limit and tend therefore to a unique finite limit. To prove the existence of their limits it is sufficient to find the upper bounds for all P_n and S_n. These bounds are easily found by considering the circumscribed regular polygons with 2^{n+1} sides. The apothem for all sides of a circumscribed polygon is the radius R of the contact point because it is perpendicular to the tangent line (side). To find the expression of the side b_n of a circumscribed polygon with 2^{n+1} sides consider (Fig. 20) two similar triangles OCF and OLK, where KL $= b_n$, FC $= s_n$, OE $= a_n$ and OA $= R$. The proportion KL/FC $=$ OA/OE, that is, $b_n/s_n = R/a_n$ yields the expression $b_n = Rs_n/a_n$, so that $Q_n = 2^{n+1}b_n = 2^{n+1}s_n \cdot R/a_n = P_n \cdot (R/a_n) > P_n$ because $a_n < R$. Thus, we have the inequality $P_n < Q_n$.

Moreover, we observe that the duplication of sides decreases the perimeter of a circumscribed regular polygon. This operation indeed replaces two sides of an equilateral triangle GHI (Fig. 20) by its base GH, thus decreasing the perimeter. Therefore, the sequence $Q_1, Q_2, Q_3, \ldots, Q_n, \ldots$ is a decreasing sequence, $Q_{n+1} < Q_n$, and combining the inequalities $P_n < Q_n$

and $Q_n < Q_1$, we find that $P_n < Q_1$ for all values of n. Thus, the upper bound for all terms of the increasing sequence (P_n) is a finite number Q_1. From $P_n < Q_1$ we conclude the existence of a limit P for the increasing and bounded sequence of general term P_n:

$$\lim_{n=\infty} P_n = P.$$

On the other hand, the decreasing sequence of general term Q_n is also a bounded sequence because $Q_n > P_n > P_1$, so that for all values of n we have the inequality $Q_n > P_1$. Therefore, this sequence also converges to a limit Q:

$$\lim_{n=\infty} Q_n = Q.$$

Since for every n we have $Q_n > P_n$, at the limit we must have $\lim_{n=\infty} Q_n \geqslant \lim_{n=\infty} P_n$, the sign of equality holds only if at the limit the difference $Q_n - P_n$ vanishes. We will prove now that this is precisely the case: the perimeters of the circumscribed and inscribed regular polygons tend to the same limit, when the number of their sides increases without limit. The proof of this important fact is based on the properties of the infinite sequence of apothems $a_1, a_2, \ldots, a_n, \ldots$.

We first prove that this increasing sequence converges to the limit R. We have $a_n < R$, so that it is a bounded sequence. Therefore its convergence follows from the fact that it is an increasing sequence. To prove this fact we observe that the second relation (10), namely, $2a_{n+1}^2 = R^2 + Ra_n$ gives the inequality $2a_{n+1}^2 > 2a_n^2$ since $R > a_n$. Thus, $a_{n+1}^2 > a_n^2$ and $a_{n+1} > a_n$. We conclude from $a_n < a_{n+1} < R$ the existence of the limit $\lim_{n=\infty} a_n$ which is at most equal to R. The same second relation (36) allows us to prove that this limit is equal to R. We form the difference $2R^2 - 2a_{n+1}^2$, using the relation $2a_{n+1}^2 = R^2 + Ra_n$: $2R^2 - 2a_{n+1}^2 = R^2 - Ra_n = R(R - a_n)$. On the other hand, $2(R^2 - a_{n+1}^2)$ can be factored as follows: $2(R + a_{n+1})(R - a_{n+1})$, so that, dropping a_{n+1} in the sum $R + a_{n+1}$, we obtain the inequality $2R^2 - 2a_{n+1}^2 = R(R - a_n) > 2R(R - a_{n+1})$ which we write as follows

$$R - a_{n+1} < \tfrac{1}{2}(R - a_n). \tag{11}$$

If $n = 1$, we have the apothem a_1 of the inscribed square which is equal to $a_1 = R\sqrt{2}/2$, so that $R - a_1 = R(2 - \sqrt{2})/2 < \tfrac{1}{2}R$. Therefore, the inequality (11) gives for $n = 1$: $R - a_2 < \tfrac{1}{2}(R - a_1) < \tfrac{1}{2} \cdot \tfrac{1}{2}R = \tfrac{1}{4}R$. Writing down (11) for successive integral values of the subscript n from $n = 1$

up to $n = k - 1$, we have

$$R - a_2 < \tfrac{1}{2}R$$

$$R - a_3 < \tfrac{1}{2}(R - a_2)$$

$$R - a_4 < \tfrac{1}{2}(R - a_3)$$

$$\cdots \cdots \cdots \cdots$$

$$R - a_k < \tfrac{1}{2}(R - a_{k-1}).$$

Multiplying all these $k - 1$ inequalities member by member and observing that the differences $R - a_m$ with $2 \leqslant m \leqslant k - 1$ are common factors of both left and righthand members, we can divide both sides by these common factors, so that the final result takes the following form

$$0 < R - a_k < (\tfrac{1}{2})^k \cdot R.$$

When now the parameter k increases by integral values without limit, the first factor of the righthand member, $(\tfrac{1}{2})^k$, approaches zero and vanishes at the limit for $k = \infty$. Thus, we obtain at the limit

$$0 \leqslant \lim_{k=\infty} (R - a_k) \leqslant \lim_{k=\infty} [(\tfrac{1}{2})^k R] = 0,$$

which proves that $\lim_{k=\infty} (R - a_k) = 0$, that is, $\lim_{k=\infty} a_k = R$.

Having proved that the limit of the infinite sequence of apothems is the radius, we can now deduce from this fact the equality of the two limits $\lim_{n=\infty} P_n$ and $\lim_{n=\infty} Q_n$. It is sufficient to show that the difference $Q_n - P_n$ tends to zero when n increases without limit. We recall that $Q_n = P_n (R/a_n)$, which allows us to rewrite the difference $Q_n - P_n$ as follows:

$$0 < Q_n - P_n = P_n(R - a_n)/a_n < Q_1 (R - a_n)/a_n$$

$$= 8 \cdot (R - a_n) \sqrt{2} < 12 (R - a_n).$$

We have indeed $P_n < Q_1 = 8R$ and $a_n > a_1 = R/\sqrt{2}$, so that $P_n/a_n < Q_1/a_1 = 8\sqrt{2}$.

The inequality

$$0 < Q_n - P_n < 12 (R - a_n)$$

proves that at the limit, for $n = \infty$, the difference $Q_n - P_n$ vanishes because $\lim_{n=\infty} (R - a_n) = 0$. Therefore, the perimeters P_n and Q_n of the inscribed and circumscribed regular polygons with 2^{n+1} sides tend to their common limit $C = \lim_{n=\infty} P_n = \lim_{n=\infty} Q_n$ when the parameter n becomes infinite.

Now for each value of n the inscribed polygon is completely interior to the circumscribed polygon with the same number of sides (their sides can be made parallel), so that the two broken and closed lines P_n and Q_n do not intersect and do not meet at all, being separated by the circle's circumference. Therefore, when at the limit for $n = \infty$ their length become equal it can mean only that ultimately these two closed and non-intersecting lines coincide.

On the other hand, the circumference of the circle remains for all values of n between the two polygons P_n and Q_n and moreover it is a fixed curve which does not vary when n increases without limit. Therefore, when at the limit for $n = \infty$, the perimeters P_n and Q_n of inscribed and circumscribed polygons coincide, they necessarily coincide on the circumference of the circle. This proves that the common limit $C = \lim\limits_{n=\infty} P_n = \lim\limits_{n=\infty} Q_n$ of their lengths is the length of the circumference. The existence of the length of a circumference is thus established since the limit of a length can be only a length.

The same reasoning proves the existence of circle's area A which is the limit of the areas S_n and T_n of regular inscribed and circumscribed polygons for $n = \infty$. The relation $S_{n+1} = R \cdot P_n/2$ and the formula $C = 2\pi R$ entail

$$A = \lim_{n=\infty} S_{n+1} = R \cdot \lim_{n=\infty} P_n/2 = R \cdot C/2 = R \cdot \pi R = \pi R^2 \, .$$

It is easy to prove that the difference $T_n - S_n$ at the limit for $n = \infty$ vanishes:

$$T_n - S_{n+1} = 2^{n+1} \cdot b_n R/2 - S_{n+1} = Q_n R/2 - P_n R/2 = R(Q_n - P_n)/2,$$

so that

$$\lim_{n=\infty} (T_n - S_n) = \lim_{n=\infty} (T_n - S_{n+1}) = R \cdot \lim_{n=\infty} (Q_n - P_n)/2 = 0 \, .$$

Thus, the circle's area A, which by definition is the limit of the areas of regular inscribed and circumscribed polygons when the number of their sides becomes infinite, is equal to the product πR^2.

The results $C = \lim\limits_{n=\infty} P_n = \lim\limits_{n=\infty} Q_n$ and $A = \lim\limits_{n=\infty} S_n = \lim\limits_{n=\infty} T_n$ can be generalized replacing the perimeters and areas of 2^{n+1}-gons by those of regular inscribed and circumscribed polygons with N sides, where N is any integer (not necessarily of the form 2^{n+1}) increasing without limit. We will show it only for the length of the circumference C. Let us denote the perimeters of regular inscribed and circumscribed N-gons by p_N and q_N respectively. The numbers p_N form an increasing sequence, while the sequence of general term q_N is a decreasing sequence:

$$p_3 < p_4 < \cdots < p_N < \cdots, \quad q_3 > q_4 > \cdots > q_N > \cdots \qquad (12)$$

The numbers P_n and Q_n are among the terms of these sequences since 2^{n+1} is an integer. Moreover, any given integer N is comprized between two successive powers of the number 2, so that $2^k \leqslant N < 2^{k+1}$, where the integer k depends on N. Therefore, we have the inequalities

$$P_{k-1} \leqslant p_N < P_k; \quad Q_k \leqslant q_N \leqslant Q_{k-1} \qquad (13)$$

where k increases without limit, when N tends to infinity. Passing in (13) to the limit for $N = \infty$, and observing that $\lim\limits_{k=\infty} P_{k-1} = \lim\limits_{k=\infty} P_k = \lim\limits_{k=\infty} Q_{k-1} = \lim\limits_{k=\infty} Q_k = C$, we prove that $\lim\limits_{N=\infty} p_N = \lim\limits_{N=\infty} q_N = C$.

Computation of π

Since $C = 2\pi R$ is between P_n and Q_n, $P_n < 2\pi R < Q_n$, we have for each value of n the following inequalities for π:

$$P_n/2R = 2^n s_n/R < \pi < 2^n s_n/a_n = Q_n/2R,$$

which yield two approximate values for the number, namely, $2^n s_n/R$ and $2^n s_n/a_n$. The difference between them can be made as small as we please by choosing a sufficiently large value for n. Therefore, the irrational number π can be computed with a prescribed accuracy, the error being as small as we want.

Using the unit-circle ($R = 1$), the lower and upper bounds for π are simply equal to $2^n s_n$ and $2^n s_n/a_n$, where $s_n = 2(1 - a_n^2)^{1/2}$, the sequence of apothems a_n being defined by $a_1 = R/\sqrt{2} = 1/\sqrt{2}$ and the recurrent relation $2a_{n+1}^2 = 1 + a_n$. Computing the first terms of this sequence, we have $2a_2^2 = 1 + a_1 = 1 + 2^{1/2}/2$, so that $4a_2^2 = (2a_2)^2 = 2 + 2^{1/2}$ and therefore $2a_2 = (2 + 2^{1/2})^{1/2}$. Further, $4a_3^2 = 2 + 2a_2 = 2 + (2 + 2^{1/2})^{1/2}$ and thus $2a_3 = [2 + (2 + 2^{1/2})^{1/2}]^{1/2}$. These results

$$2a_1 = 2^{1/2}, \quad 2a_2 = (2 + 2^{1/2})^{1/2}, \quad 2a_3 = [2 + (2 + 2^{1/2})^{1/2}]^{1/2}$$

suggest the following expression for $2a_n$, involving n extractions of square root:

$$2a_n = \{2 + \{2 + [2 + \cdots (2 + 2^{1/2})^{1/2} \ldots]^{1/2}\}^{1/2}\}^{1/2}. \qquad (14)$$

With the aid of mathematical induction it is easy indeed to prove that (14) holds for any integer n. Since (14) is true for $n = 1, 2, 3$, it is sufficient to prove its hereditary character, that is, justify it for $n = k + 1$, if it holds for $n = k$. The recurrent relation $4a_{k+1}^2 = 2 + 2a_k$ can be written $2a_{k+1} = (2 + 2a_k)^{1/2}$, and this proves the point. Therefore, a_n can be computed for any given n with the aid of (14).

Incidentally, it is of interest to observe that, passing in (14) to the limit for $n = \infty$ and using the fact that in our case $\lim\limits_{n=\infty} a_n = R = 1$, we obtain a curious representation of the number 2 by the following infinite expression involving an infinite number of successive extractions of square root:

$$2 = \{2 + \{2 + [2 + (2 + \cdots)^{1/2}]^{1/2}\}^{1/2}\}^{1/2}. \tag{15}$$

The numerical value 2 of the infinite expression (15) is easy to deduce directly without using geometry, that is, without using (14). Denoting the unknown value of the righthand member in (15) by x, we see immediately that x is a solution of the equation $x = (2 + x)^{1/2}$ since the value of an infinite periodic expression is not changed by dropping the first period. Squaring, we obtain for x a quadratic equation $x^2 - x - 2 = 0$ whose solution yields the two roots $x_1 = 2$ and $x_2 = -1$. The second root $x_2 = -1$ must be rejected because the infinite expression (15) can represent only a positive number. Therefore, its value is 2. As always with infinite expressions, it is the question of the existence of a value represented by (15) which is important and must be solved in the affirmative before proceeding to the computation of the number it represents and this question was solved only because we had the result (14).

Having computed the apothems a_n we deduce from them the sides with the aide of the relation $s_n = 2 (1 - a_n^2)^{1/2}$ and then compute the expressions $2^n s_n$ and $2^n s_n / a_n$ between which is comprized π. The results obtained for the first seven values of n are tabulated in the following short table:

n	2^{n+1}	a_n	s_n	$2^n s_n$	$2^n s_n / a_n$
1	4	0.7071	1.4142	2.8284	4.0000
2	8	0.9238	0.7655	3.0620	3.3142
3	16	0.9808	0.3896	3.1169	3.1780
4	32	0.9952	0.1957	3.1317	3.1469
5	64	0.9988	0.0981	3.1403	3.1440
6	128	0.9997	0.0491	3.1413	3.1422
7	256	0.9999	0.0245	3.1415	3.1417

The arithmetic mean $\frac{1}{2}$ (3.1415... + 3.1417...) = 3.1416... of the last two approximate values is already near to π = 3.14159..., but in general, if a great accuracy is asked, the method of Archimedes becomes difficult because it necessitates too many numerical computations. Archimedes himself was satisfied with the inequalities

$$3 + 10/71 < \pi < 3 + 10/70,$$

the relative error being less than 0.04%.

Nevertheless, until the end of the sixteenth century no other method was known, and in 1579 Vietá was obliged to consider the perimeter of a regular polygon with 393,216 sides, that is, to apply sixteen times the duplication process to the regular inscribed hexagon (393,216 = $6 \cdot 2^{16}$), to compute π to only nine decimal places after the dot, namely, π = 3.141 592 653... He did not know that in 1430, a hundred and fifty years before he laboured painfully to obtain his nine figures, in Asia Al-Kashi had already found sixteen correct decimal places. Al-Kashi was surpassed by a Dutchman named Van Ceulen, who died in 1610, probably from physical exhaustion, because he sacrificed his whole life to the computation of π by Archimedes' method. He was able to compute only thirty-six correct decimal places and the corresponding approximate value of π is engraved on his tombstone at Leyden. *Tempora mutantur et nos mutamur in illis:* Van Ceulen was the last mathematician to apply inscribed and circumscribed regular polygons to the computation of π. New methods were devised and with their aid Abraham Sharp found (in 1699) seventy-one and Machin (in 1706) a hundred exact decimal places. The long list of laborious computers of π, who extended further and further the knowledge of decimals in the expression of π, ends with the name of William Shanks, to whom we owe the expression of 707 known decimal places, a result obtained in 1873.

Modern methods are based on the use of infinite series. Thus, for instance, Rutherford (in 1853) observed that $\pi/4$ is equal to $4A - B + C$, where the three acute angles A, B, C expressed in radians, are defined by their tangents: tan A = 1/5, tan B = 1/70, tan C = 1/99. Therefore

$$\pi/4 = 4 \cdot \text{Arctan} (1/5) - \text{Arctan} (1/70) + \text{Arctan} (1/99).$$

Using Gregory's series (Chapter 11) for the computation of angles A, B, C

$$\text{Arctan } z = z/1 - z^3/3 + z^5/5 - z^7/7 + \cdots, \tag{16}$$

Rutherford easily found 440 decimals after the dot. The series (16) converges rapidly, if z is small, and the error in the value obtained for the lefthand member by computing a certain number of terms is less in absolute value than the first neglected term.

This series was discovered by J. Gregory in 1671 and was used by many mathematicians for computing π. The representation of $\pi/4$ found by Rutherford is not unique. So, for example, Escott proposed to use

$$\pi/4 = 22 \cdot \text{Arctan} \, (1/28) + 2 \cdot \text{Arctan} \, (1/443) - 5 \cdot \text{Arctan} \, (1/1393)$$

$$- 10 \cdot \text{Arctan} \, (1/11018)$$

which allows much more rapid computation of π. Machin and Clausen used the formulas

$$\pi/4 = 4 \cdot \text{Arctan} \, (1/5) - \text{Arctan} \, (1/239),$$

$$\pi/4 = 2 \cdot \text{Arctan} \, (1/3) + \text{Arctan} \, (1/7).$$

Working with inscribed regular polygons, Vietá discovered in 1646 the first representation of the number π with the aid of an infinite product:

$$2/\pi = (\tfrac{1}{2})^{1/2} \cdot [\tfrac{1}{2} + \tfrac{1}{2}(\tfrac{1}{2})^{1/2}]^{1/2} \cdot \{\tfrac{1}{2} + \tfrac{1}{2}[\tfrac{1}{2} + \tfrac{1}{2}(\tfrac{1}{2})^{1/2}]^{1/2}\}^{1/2} \ldots,$$

which in our notation becomes an infinite product of apothems

$$2/\pi = a_1 \cdot a_2 \cdot a_3 \cdot a_4 \cdots a_n \cdot a_{n+1} \ldots, \qquad (17)$$

because the expression (14) for $2a_n$ gives, dividing both sides by 2:

$$a_n = \{\{\tfrac{1}{2} + \tfrac{1}{2}\{\tfrac{1}{2} + \tfrac{1}{2}[\tfrac{1}{2} + (\tfrac{1}{2} + \cdots \tfrac{1}{2}[\tfrac{1}{2} + \tfrac{1}{2}(\tfrac{1}{2})^{1/2}])^{1/2} \cdots {}^{1/2}]^{1/2}\}^{1/2}\}^{1/2}.$$

To prove that the product (17) of all the apothems a_n is equal to $2/\pi$, we observe that the relation (10) for $R = 1$ reduces to $s_n = 2s_{n+1} \cdot a_{n+1}$, which after the multiplication on both sides by 2^{n+1} becomes

$$2^{n+1} \cdot s_n = P_n = 2^{n+2} \cdot s_{n+1} \cdot a_{n+1} = P_{n+1} \cdot a_{n+1}.$$

Thus, for all the values of n we have

$$a_{n+1} = P_n/P_{n+1}. \qquad (18)$$

Writing down the relations (18) for $n = 1, 2, 3, \ldots, N$ and multiplying them out member by member, we obtain

$$a_2 \cdot a_3 \cdot a_4 \cdots a_{N+1} = (P_1/P_2) \cdot (P_2/P_3) \cdot (P_3/P_z) \cdots (P_N/P_{N+1})$$

$$= P_1/P_{N+1}.$$

At the limit, for $N = \infty$, we obtain in the lefthand member the infinite product of all the apothems except the first a_1, while the limit of the righthand member is equal to P_1/C, where C is the length of the circumference of the unit-circle, that is, $C = 2\pi$. Thus, the passage to the limit yields the relation

$$a_1 \cdot a_2 \cdot a_3 \cdots a_n \cdots = a_1 \cdot P_1/2\pi = 4/2\pi = 2/\pi,$$

because $a_1 P_1 = (2^{1/2}/2) \cdot 4 \cdot 2^{1/2} = 4$. Thus, Vietá's relation (17) is justified.

Ten years later, in 1656, the English mathematician Wallis found another infinite product representing the same number $2/\pi$:

$$2/\pi = (1 - 1/2^2)(1 - 1/4^2)(1 - 1/6^2) \cdots (1 - 1/4n^2) \ldots$$

which can also, be written as

$$\pi/2 = (4/3) \cdot (16/15) \cdot (36/35) \cdot (64/63) \cdots [4n^2/(4n^2 - 1)] \ldots$$

Length of an Arc and Area of a Circular Sector

The part of a circle bounded by two radii OA, OB and the arc $\overset{\smile}{AB}$ (Fig. 21) is called a circular sector. Its area is proportional to the central angle $\widehat{AOB}$, whose measure in radians we denote by w, as well as to the square R^2 of the circle's radius R. Therefore, this area AOB is proportional to the product $w \cdot R^2$ and can be expressed as $k \cdot wR^2$, where the factor of proportionality k is a constant to be determined. To find k we observe that the area of the whole circle, that is, πR^2 can be considered as that of a circular sector with

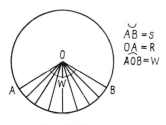

$$\overset{\smile}{AB} = s$$
$$O\!A = R$$
$$\widehat{AOB} = W$$

Fig. 16.21

a central angle w equal to 2π. Thus, we must have $k \cdot 2\pi R^2 = \pi \cdot R^2$ which yields for k the value $\frac{1}{2}$. Therefore, $k = \frac{1}{2}$ and the expression of a circular sector's area is $\frac{1}{2}wR^2$:

$$\text{area OAB} = \tfrac{1}{2}wR^2.$$

The length s of the circular arc AB is proportional to the central angle w and also to the radius R, so that $s = c \cdot wR$, where again c is unknown. When

$w = 2\pi$, the arc $\overgroup{\text{AB}}$ covers the whole circumference and $s = 2\pi R$. There-fore, the coefficient of proportionality c is equal to one and the formula for the length of a circular arc is

$$s = \text{arc } \overgroup{\text{AB}} = wR.$$

Replacing in the expression of the area $\frac{1}{2}wR^2$ the product wR by s, we find the following relation between the arc s and the area OAB of a circular sec-tor

$$\text{area OAB} = \tfrac{1}{2}sR,$$

so that the area is equal to the length s of the sector's base AB times half its altitude R. The expression $s \cdot (\frac{1}{2}R)$ is of the same type as the formula $b \cdot (\frac{1}{2}h)$ for the area of a triangle with base b and altitude h. This fact suggests that expression $\frac{1}{2}sR$ for the area of a circular sector can be deduced with the aid of the expression $\frac{1}{2}bh$ for a triangle's area.

Indeed, subdividing the arc AB (Fig. 21) into an infinite number of in-finitely small parts (not necessarily equal to each other) and joining the divi-sion-points to the center O, we can consider the sector's area OAB as a sum of infinitely many infinitely thin triangles. These triangles all have the same altitude R (radius of the circle) and infinitely small bases, whose sum is the arc $s = \overgroup{\text{AB}}$. The important feature in the introduction of infinitely small bases is the elimination of the curvature which is a phenomenon related essentially to arcs of finite length. An infinitesimal arc has no curvature, so that our triangles can be considered as ordinary triangles to which the formula $\frac{1}{2}bh$ is applicable. Adding their areas, computed with the aid of the formula $\frac{1}{2}bR$ since for them $h = R$, we can pick out the common factor $\frac{1}{2}R$ and add their bases only, so that the sum of their areas (area of the circular sector) is equal to the product $\frac{1}{2}R$ times the sum s of all the bases. Thus, the formula $\frac{1}{2}Rs = \frac{1}{2}wR^2$ is deduced as a corollary of the rule $\frac{1}{2}bh$ for computing triangles areas.

Limit $\lim\limits_{t=0} (\sin t/t)$

The fundamental fact that a circle can be considered as the limiting shape of a regular polygon when the number n of its sides becomes infinite, and its corollaries $\lim\limits_{n=\infty} P_n = 2\pi R$, $\lim\limits_{n=\infty} S_n = \pi R^2$, where P_n and S_n denote the length and the area of a regular polygon with n sides, are equivalent to the following theorem of trigonometry:

THEOREM XXVI. *The limit for $t = 0$ of the ratio $\sin t/t$ of the sine of an angle t to the value t of this angle expressed in radians is equal to 1.*

To justify the equivalence of this theorem to the geometrical formulae $C = 2\pi R$ and $S = \pi R^2$ we have first to deduce the theorem from the expressions for the length and area of a circle and conversely obtain these expressions from the theorem. We begin by the proof of the theorem, giving two versions of this proof. Let us suppose that in Fig. 22 the chord FC represents the side s_n of a regular inscribed polygon with n sides, P_n and S_n denoting its perimeter and area respectively. The central angle $\widehat{FOC}$ subtended by the arc $\widehat{FAC}$ is then the nth part of 2π, that is, $\widehat{FOC} = 2\pi/n$ and $\widehat{AOC} = \pi/n$.

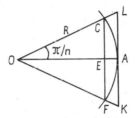

Fig. 16.22

In the right triangle OEC the hypotenuse $OC = R$ is the radius, the two legs being the apothem $a_n = $ OE and half the side $\frac{1}{2}s_n = $ EC of the polygon. By definition of the trigonometric functions sine and cosine of the angle $\widehat{AOC} = \pi/n$, we have $a_n = $ OE $= R \cos(\pi/n)$, $\frac{1}{2}s_n = $ EC $= R \sin(\pi/n)$. Therefore, the perimeter $P_n = n \cdot s_n$ and the area $S_n = P_n \cdot a_n/2$ of the regular polygon with n sides may be expressed in terms of the angle $\widehat{AOC} = \pi/n$ as follows:

$$P_n = n \cdot s_n = 2Rn \cdot \sin(\pi/n) = 2\pi R \cdot [\sin(\pi/n)/(\pi/n)]$$

$$S_n = P_n \cdot a_n/2 = 2\pi R \sin(\pi/n) \cdot R \cos(\pi/n)/(2\pi/n)$$

$$= \pi R^2 [\sin(2\pi/n)/(2\pi/n)],$$

because $2 \sin t \cos t = \sin(2t)$ for any t. Denoting the ratio $\sin x/x$ by the symbol $r(x)$, $r(x) \equiv \sin x/x$ and using the fact that $C = 2\pi R$ and $S = \pi R^2$ we have:

$$P_n = C \cdot r(\pi/n); \quad S_n = S \cdot r(2\pi/n) = \pi R^2 \cdot r(2\pi/n). \tag{19}$$

Letting now n approach infinity, at the limit, for $n = \infty$, we obtain $\lim_{n=\infty} P_n = C$ and $\lim_{n=\infty} S_n = S = \pi R^2$, so that (19) yields $\lim_{n=\infty} r(\pi/n) = 1$, which proves the theorem for the special case, when t approaches zero being of the form $t = \pi/n$, where n tends to infinity. To get rid of this limitation imposed on t we define for each value of the variable t an integer N (depending naturally on t) as follows: N is the largest integer contained in the number π/t, so that $N \leqslant \pi/t$, but N is greater than $\pi/t - 1$. Inverting these inequalities $\pi/t < N + 1$ and $\pi/t \geqslant N$, we obtain

$$\pi/(N + 1) < t \leqslant \pi/N. \tag{20}$$

We observe further that N increases without limit when t tends to zero, so that $\lim N = \infty$. Therefore, passing to the limit for $t = 0$, we can identify this operation with the passage to the limit for $N = \infty$.

We now consider the ratio $r(t) = \sin t/t$, when t approaches zero in any way, without being necessarily of the form $t = \pi/n$. We have to prove that $r(t)$ approaches one when $t \to 0$ and we will deduce it from the limit $\lim_{n=\infty} r(\pi/n)$ $= 1$ the validity of which was just proved. Since the function sine is an increasing function of its argument, when the argument is an acute angle, and because we discuss the behavior of $r(t)$ and $r(\pi/n)$ for small values of $t \to 0$ and for very large values of $N \to \infty$, we have the following inequalities

$$\sin [\pi/(N + 1)] < \sin t \leqslant \sin (\pi/N).$$

Combining them with the inequalities (20), we obtain

$$\sin [\pi/(N + 1)]/(\pi/N) < r(t) = \sin t/t < \sin (\pi/N)/[\pi/(N + 1)].$$

But the lefthand member can be written as $(1 + 1/N)^{-1} \cdot r(\pi/(N + 1))$. Indeed

$$(1 + 1/N)^{-1} \cdot r [\pi/(N + 1)] = N \cdot \sin [\pi/(N + 1)]/ \{(N + 1) \cdot [\pi/(N + 1)]\}$$
$$= \sin [\pi/(N + 1)]/(\pi/N),$$

while the righthand member is equal to $(1 + 1/N) \cdot r(\pi/N)$:

$$\sin (\pi/N)/[\pi/(N + 1)] = [\sin (\pi/N)/(\pi/N)] \cdot (N + 1)/N = (1 + 1/N) \cdot r(\pi/N).$$

Therefore, the ratio $r(t)$ verifies for all values of t the inequalities

$$(1 + 1/N)^{-1} \cdot r [\pi/(N + 1)] < r(t) < (1 + 1/N) \cdot r (\pi/N) \tag{21}$$

and the passage to the limit for $t \to 0$, $N \to \infty$ yields the result $\lim_{t=0} r(t) = 1$, thus providing the theorem, because both the right and lefthand members in (21) have one as their common limit for $N \to \infty$.

Now, inversely, the knowledge of the fact that the limit of the ratio $\sin t/t$ for $t = 0$ is one, entails $\lim\limits_{n=\infty} r\,(\pi/n) = 1$, so that applying Theorem XXVI and passing to the limit for $n = \infty$ in (19), we obtain the formulas $C = 2\pi R$ and $S = \lim\limits_{n=\infty} S_n = \pi R^2$ for the length and area of a circle of radius R.

We add another proof of Theorem XXVI based on the formula $\frac{1}{2}wR^2$ for the area of a circular sector whose central angle is equal to w. Let us denote this time the angle $\overset{\frown}{AOC}$ in Fig. 22 by x, so that the angle $\overset{\frown}{FOC}$ is equal to $2x$. Computing the area of the circular sector OFAC, and supposing that we have to deal with a unit-circle ($R = 1$), we obtain $\frac{1}{2}wR^2 = \frac{1}{2} \cdot 2x \cdot 1^2 = x$. On the other hand, this area OFAC $= x$ is greater than that of the triangle OFC, but less than the area of the triangle OKL:

$$\text{area OFC} < \text{area OFAC} = x < \text{area OKL}.$$

It is easy to compute the two areas OFC and OKL. Since $OE = \cos x$, $EC = \frac{1}{2}FC = \sin x$, $OA = 1$ and $AL = \frac{1}{2}KL = \tan x$, we have the expressions

$$\text{area OFC} = \frac{1}{2}OE \cdot FC = \cos x \sin x\,;$$

$$\text{area OKL} = \frac{1}{2}OA \cdot KL = 1 \cdot AL = \tan x = \sin x/\cos x.$$

Therefore, replacing in our inequalities the areas OFC and OKL by their values, we have

$$\sin x \cdot \cos x < x < \sin x/\cos x.$$

The first inequality $\sin x \cdot \cos x < x$ can easily be reinforced to $\sin x < x$. It holds indeed for any angle and remains therefore true, if we replace in it the angle x by the halfangle $x/2$, which gives $\sin(\frac{1}{2}x) \cdot \cos(\frac{1}{2}x) < x/2$.

Multiplying on both sides by 2 and recalling that the product $2\sin(\frac{1}{2}x) \times \cos(\frac{1}{2}x)$ is equal to $\sin x$, we obtain $\sin x < x$. The second inequality can be written as $\sin x > x \cdot \cos x$ and therefore we finally have

$$x \cos x < \sin x < x.$$

Dividing by x, we prove that the ratio $\sin x/x$ is comprized between $\cos x$ and one:

$$\cos x < \sin x/x < 1.$$

This result deduced for any acute positive angle x holds also for negative acute angles x because all three terms of these inequalities are even functions of x, so that their values do not depend on the sign of x. Passing to the limit for $x = 0$, we achieve the proof of the theorem because $\lim\limits_{x=0} \cos x = 1$.

As a numerical illustration of the important limit $\lim\limits_{x=0} (\sin x/x) = 1$ we reproduce here excerpts from the tables of $\sin x$ to nine decimal places:

Argument x in radians	Values of $\sin x$
0.0100	0.009 999 833
0.0050	0.004 999 979
0.0025	0.002 499 997
0.0020	0.001 999 999
0.0015	0.001 499 999
0.0014	0.001 400 000

Thus, for $x = 0.0014$ radians, that is, $x = 4$ minutes and 49 seconds of arc, the difference between $\sin x$ and x is already so small that it can affect only the tenth decimal after the dot. This is why the values of $\sin x$ and x given in the tables with nine decimal places begin to differ only when x reaches 0.0015 radians.

Returning to the evaluation of the circle's area, we will give here two more deductions of the expression πR^2 for this area, deductions based on the expression $C = 2\pi R$ for the length C of the circumference. Both of them reflect the basic idea of modern mathematics which can be formulated as follows: To evaluate a finite quantity consider it as a sum of infinitely many infinitely small components.

In practice the quantity to be evaluated is decomposed into a sum of n parts and the limit of this sum as n approaches infinity, each part shrinking to zero, is computed.

Drawing n equidistant radii, as in Fig. 21, but for the whole circle, we subdivide the circle's area into n isosceles triangles with curvilinear bases and central angle equal to $2\pi/n$. When n becomes infinite, we can neglect the curvature of the infinitesimal arc which forms the triangle's base and, thus, we can consider each infinitely small triangular part as an ordinary triangle with two finite sides (radii) and a vanishing base. Because of the vanishing of the base the altitude of this triangle is equal to the radius R and therefore its area is equal to the product $\frac{1}{2}R \cdot b$, where the symbol b denotes the length of the infinitely small base.

Adding the areas of all these component parts, we pick out the common factor $\frac{1}{2}R$ and, thus, have to add between the parentheses only the bases b. But, the sum of all the bases is the length $C = 2\pi R$ of the circumference and the circle's area is therefore equal to the product $\frac{1}{2}R \cdot C = \frac{1}{2}R \cdot 2\pi R = \pi R^2$.

We can also decompose a circle's area into a sum of ringshaped, concentric bands (Fig. 23) by dividing the radius $OA = R$ into n equal parts of length R/n, and drawing through the division-points the $n - 1$ concentric circles with radii $r_1, r_2, r_3, \ldots, r_m, \ldots, r_{n-1}$, where $r_m = mR/n$ for $m = 1, 2, 3, \ldots,$ $n - 1$, the radius of the given circle R being also r_n.

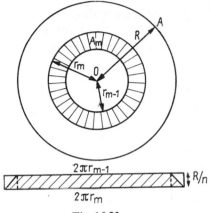

Fig. 16.23

Denoting the mth ring's area included between the circles of radii r_{m-1} and r_m by A_m, we can represent the circle's area S as the sum of all A_m:

$$S = A_1 + A_2 + A_3 + \cdots + A_m + \cdots + A_{n-1} + A_n = \sum_1^n A_m.$$

The direct evaluation of component parts A_m here is impossible because they are bounded by curves (circles). Therefore, we must find the lower and upper bounds for each A_m which will allow us to estimate the lower and the upper bounds for the circle's area S. Increasing then n without limits, we can find the exact expression for S, if the limits of the lower and upper bounds will be found to be equal.

The distance between two concentric circles with radii $r_{m-1} = (m - 1) R/n$ and $r_m = mR/n$, which enclose the area A_m, is equal to R/n. Therefore, the area A_m is included between two lengths $2\pi r_{m-1}$ and $2\pi r_m$, these boundaries being at a distance of R/n from each other. Comparing the area A_m with the area of a rectangle bounded by two equal segments of length $2\pi r_{m-1}$ at a distance R/n from each other, we conclude that A_m is greater than the rectangle's area $2\pi r_{m-1} \cdot (R/n)$ because r_m is greater then r_{m-1}. On the other hand, comparing A_m with the area of a rectangle with a base $2\pi r_m$ and altitude R/n, we conclude that A_m is less that the rectangle's area $2\pi r_m \cdot (R/n)$.

Thus, the lower and upper bounds for A_m are respectively $2\pi r_{m-1} \cdot (R/n)$ and $2\pi r_m \cdot (R/n)$. Computing them, we find $2\pi (m-1) (R/n)^2$ and $2\pi m (R/n)^2$, so that

$$2\pi (m-1) (R/n)^2 < A_m < 2\pi m (R/n)^2. \tag{22}$$

This inequality holds for all component parts A_m, $m = 1, 2, 3, \ldots, n$ of the circle's area S. Adding all these inequalities for $A_1, A_2, \ldots, A_n$ and replacing the constant and common factor $2\pi (R/n)^2$ by $K = 2\pi (R/n)^2$, we obtain finally the following lower and supper bounds for S:

$$K[1 + 2 + 3 + \cdots + (n-1)] < S$$

$$= \sum_1^n A_m < K[1 + 2 + 3 + \cdots + (n-1) + n].$$

The sum of the first k integers was computed in Chapter 2, where the formula $1 + 2 + 3 + \cdots + k = \tfrac{1}{2}k (k+1)$ was deduced. Applying this formula, we have $\tfrac{1}{2} (n-1) n$ and $\tfrac{1}{2} n (n+1)$ as the values of the parentheses in the left- and righthand members respectively. Thus, the lower bound for S is equal to $K \cdot \tfrac{1}{2} (n-1) n = 2\pi R^2 \cdot \tfrac{1}{2} (n-1) n/n^2 = (1 - 1/n) \cdot \pi R^2$, while the upper bound is equal to $K \cdot \tfrac{1}{2} n (n+1) = (1 + 1/n) \cdot \pi R^2$. We have therefore proved the following double inequality for S:

$$\pi R^2 (1 - 1/n) < S < \pi R^2 (1 + 1/n).$$

Subtracting from each member the product πR^2, we transform it into

$$-\pi R^2/n < S - \pi R^2 < \pi R^2/n,$$

where the integer n can be chosen as large as we please because its choice is at our disposal. Increasing this integer n without limit, both the lower and upper bounds for the difference $S - \pi R^2$ tend to zero. At the limit, for $n = \infty$, both these bounds vanish and the equality of S and πR^2 is proved.

Areas of Similar Figures

At the end of this chapter we discuss and prove an almost trivial but very important theorem concerning the areas of similar figures:

THEOREM XXVII. *If the linear dimensions of two similar figures are in a ratio equal to k, the ratio of their areas is equal to k^2.*

Two similar figures bounded by segments of straight lines can be decomposed into similar triangles by drawing their diagonals. On the other hand, any figure bounded by arcs of curves can be considered as a limiting shape of inscribed polygons, that is, of figures bounded by segments of straight lines, when all the sides of the inscribed polygon tend to zero, their number increasing without limit. Therefore, it is sufficient to prove Theorem XXVII for two similar triangles, its extension to two similar polygons and further to any two similar figures being immediate.

Suppose that the two given triangles with sides a, b, c and a', b', c' are similar, the ratio of two corresponding sides being equal to k: $a' = ka$, $b' = kb$, $c' = kc$. Applying the formula $A = [s(s - a)(s - b)(s - c)]^{1/2}$, which expresses the triangle's area A in terms of its three sides a, b, c and half the perimeter $s = \frac{1}{2}(a + b + c)$, to the triangle with sides a', b', c', we observe that half the perimeter of this triangle s' is equal to ks: $s' = \frac{1}{2}(a' + b' + c') = \frac{1}{2}(ka + kb + kc) = k \cdot \frac{1}{2}(a + b + c) = ks$. Therefore, computing the area A' of this triangle, we find

$$A' = [s'(s' - a')(s' - b')(s' - c')]^{1/2}$$

$$= [ks(ks - ka)(ks - kb)(ks - kc)]^{1/2}$$

$$= [k^4 s(s - a)(s - b)(s - c)]^{1/2} = k^2 A,$$

which proves the theorem, because it shows that $A'/A = k^2$.

The Inverse-Square Laws in Physics

A simple and interesting example of application of Theorem XXVII is the physical law which states that the intensity of light emitted by a source of constant brightness decreases with increasing distance as the reciprocal of the square of the distance from the source. In other words, the intensity of light is inversely proportional to the square of distance.

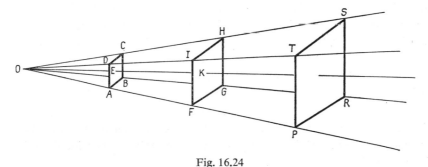

Fig. 16.24

To illustrate this law we consider a very small square ABCD (Fig. 24) at a unit distance from the source of light at O, so that OE = 1, E being the center of symmetry of the square. Denoting the area ABCD by s and the amount of energy emitted per unit of time by the source of light and contained in the interior of the pyramid OPRST by Q, we can characterize the intensity of illumination of the square's area by the quotient Q/s.

The section of the pyramid by a plane parallel to that ABCD and at a distance d = OK from O is a square FGHI similar to ABCD and whose linear dimensions are d times larger than those of ABCD:

$$GH/AB = GK/AE = OK/OE = d/1 = d$$

since the triangles GHK and AEB, OGK and OAE are similar.

Therefore, the area S of the square FGHI is d^2 times greater than the area s of the square ABCD: $S = sd^2$.

If we remove the square ABCD, the amount of light falling in a unit of time on the surface of the square FGHI is the same as on the square ABCD because the rays of light are straight lines. Therefore the same amount Q of light is now spread over d^2 times as large an area as before. Computing the intensity of illumination of FGHI, we obtain $Q/S = Q/sd^2 = (Q/s)/d^2$, which is the mathematical formulation of the physical law cited above.

Electricity and gravitation obey the same inverse-square laws as light, and for the same reason. We see, therefore, that Theorem XXVII explains why the physical phenomena are governed by the inverse-square laws: these laws are a natural corollary of the dispersion of a constant amount of energy emitted per unit of time in the three dimensional space.

If, in the future, physics will be concerned with the propagation of energy emitted by a constant point-source located in a four dimensional space, the intensity of energy falling on a volume in a three-dimensional space will necessarily be considered as inversely proportional to the *cube* of the distance from the source because—as we will see later—the volumes of two similar figures are in a ratio equal to k^3, if k denotes the ratio of their corresponding segments. Thus, we see that the physical inverse-square laws stem from our fundamental assumption that the space in which the physical phenomena take place is three-dimensional. There is no contradiction between the inverse-cube laws of four-dimensional physics and the inverse-square laws of our three-dimensional theories, because, the three-dimensional space being a section of the four-dimensional space, an inverse-cube law of the last space reduces to an inverse-square law in the three-dimensional section of the four-dimensional space.

CHAPTER 17

Some Facts About Non-Euclidean Geometry

Saccheri's Quadrilateral and the Sum of Angles of a Triangle in Riemannian and Hyperbolic Geometries

As was previously stated without proof, in Euclidean geometry the sum of the angles of a triangle is the same for all triangles: namely, equal to two right angles. This is true for Euclidean geometry only; in non-Euclidean geometry the sum of the angles depends on the size of the triangle, so that size and shape are related. In hyperbolic (Lobachevsky's) geometry the sum of the angles of a triangle is less than two right angles and it decreases when the size of the triangle increases. In elliptic (Riemannian) geometry the sum of the angles of a triangle is greater than two right angles and it increases when the size of the triangle increases.

To prove these facts, we will deduce a relation between the area and the sum of the angles of a triangle which holds in non-Euclidean geometry, but is lacking in the particular case of Euclidean geometry.

We begin with another proof of Theorem II, Chapter 14, which states that the sum of the angles of an Euclidean triangle is equal to two right angles. This proof is important because most of it holds in both non-Euclidean geometries, the fifth postulate being used only at the very end of the proof. Since the proof is related to a special figure, we first study this configuration called Saccheri's quadrilateral or *birectangle*.

A birectangle is an isosceles quadrilateral with two right angles at its base so that the equal sides are perpendicular to the base. Nothing is said in this definition about the fourth side and two other angles—called *summit*-angles—so that birectangles exist in non-Euclidean geometry also. They were introduced in 1733 by Girolamo Saccheri with the explicit purpose of studying geometries in which the fifth postulate of Euclid does not hold.

In Euclidean geometry a birectangle becomes a rectangle, since in this geometry the two summit-angles are right also; but rectangles do not exist in non-Euclidean geometries and—as we will see—the sum of four angles of a birectangle exceeds four right angles in Riemannian, while it is less than four right angles in Lobachevsky's geometry.

Given a birectangle ABFD (Fig. 1) with the base DF, right angles ADF = BFD = 90° and two equal sides AD = BF, all that can be stated about its summit-angles DAB and FBA, without using the fifth postulate or a substitute to it, is their equality: DAB = FBA. To prove this, draw the perpendicular OL to the base through its midpoint O, forming two quadrilaterals ADOK and BFOK, where K denotes the point of intersection of lines AB and OL. We shall find that K is the midpoint of AB and that OK is perpendicular to AB, so that the line OL is an axis of symmetry for the birectangle ADFB.

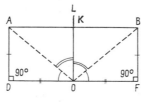

Fig. 17.1

To prove the equality of summit-angles DAB and FBA, draw AO and BO and construct two equal (Theorem V, Chapter 14) triangles ADO and BOF. Therefore, AO = BO and DOA = FOB. Subtracting equal angles DOA and FOB from right angles DOK and FOK respectively, we obtain $\overset{\frown}{AOK} = \overset{\frown}{BOK}$ so that the triangles AOK and BOK are equal (Theorem V, Chapter 14 again). Therefore, we conclude that AK = KB, $\overset{\frown}{OAK} = \overset{\frown}{OBK}$ and $\overset{\frown}{AKO} = \overset{\frown}{BKO}$. Thus, K is the midpoint of AB and OL is perpendicular to AB: $\overset{\frown}{AKO} = \overset{\frown}{BKO} = 90°$ since $\overset{\frown}{AKO} + \overset{\frown}{BKO} = 2 \cdot \overset{\frown}{AKO} = 180°$. Moreover, the angles DAO and FBO are equal and, adding to them the equal angles OAK and OBK respectively, we prove the equality of summit-angles: $\overset{\frown}{DAB} = \overset{\frown}{FBA}$. The value of these two equal angles depends on the type of geometry and they are right angles in Euclidean geometry only.

The sum of the angles of a triangle can be expressed in terms of the value of the summit-angle of a birectangle related to this triangle. To prove this, we draw through the midpoints M and N of sides AC and BC of a given triangle ABC the straight line PMNQ (Fig. 2), and drop on it perpendiculars AD, BF, and CE from the three vertices of our triangle, thus forming four triangles ADM, CEM, BFN, and CEN. By rotating the triangle CEM through 180° about the midpoint M of AC, we make C coincide with A and the line ME

with the line MD. The point E must coincide with the point D since otherwise there would be two different perpendiculars dropped from the point A
on the line MP. Therefore, the triangles CEM and ADM are equal: DM
= ME and $\overset{\frown}{MCE}$ = $\overset{\frown}{DAM}$. The same reasoning proves the equality of triangles CEN and BNF, so that EN = NF and $\overset{\frown}{NCE}$ = $\overset{\frown}{NBF}$. Moreover,

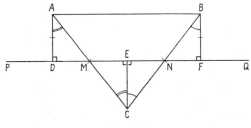

Fig. 17.2

AD = CE as well as CE = BF and, therefore, AD = BF which proves that
the quadrilateral ADFB is a birectangle with the base DF and right angles
ADF and BFD. Since $\overset{\frown}{ACB}$ = $\overset{\frown}{ACE}$ + $\overset{\frown}{BCE}$ = $\overset{\frown}{DAC}$+$\overset{\frown}{FBC}$, the sum of the
angles of our triangle ABC is expressed as follows:

$$s = \hat{A} + \hat{B} + \hat{C} = \overset{\frown}{BAC} + \overset{\frown}{ABC} + \overset{\frown}{DAC} + \overset{\frown}{FBC}$$

$$= (\overset{\frown}{BAC} + \overset{\frown}{CAD}) + (\overset{\frown}{ABC} + \overset{\frown}{CBF}) = \overset{\frown}{BAD} + \overset{\frown}{ABF} = 2 \cdot \overset{\frown}{BAD}$$

Thus, the evaluation of the sum of angles of a triangle is reduced to that
of the summit-angle of a birectangle. The relation $s = 2 \cdot \overset{\frown}{BAD}$ proves that
the sum s exceeds 180° if the summit-angle $\overset{\frown}{BAD}$ is an obtuse angle, while s
is less than 180° if $\overset{\frown}{BAD}$ is an acute angle.

We shall prove that Lobachevsky's postulate of two parallels through a
given point to a given line—one to the left and the other to the right—leads
to an acute angle BAD, while in Riemannian geometry, where there are no
parallel lines at all, the angle BAD is obtuse.

Inverting this proposition, we can also say that a birectangle has two
equal obtuse angles if there is a triangle, the sum of whose angles s is greater
tha 180°: $\overset{\frown}{BAD} = s/2 > 90°$. Or, as we shall show, the sum of the angles of
a triangle cannot exceed 180° if straight lines are infinite in length. This
proves that the straight lines of elliptic geometry are necessarily of finite
length, although they are unbounded, and thus can be produced (extended)

continuously in a straight line without any limitation (Third Axiom of Euclid). Therefore, a straight line of elliptic geometry returns into itself and must be a closed line of finite length.

To establish this characteristic feature of the elliptic plane it is sufficient to prove with Legendre the following theorem:

If straight lines are infinite in extent, the sum of angles of a triangle cannot exceed 180°.

The sixteenth proposition of Euclid states (see Chapter 14) that the exterior angle of a triangle is greater than either of the interior and opposite angles. This theorem is independent from the fifth postulate, since its proof is based on the infinitude of straight lines. Consider now the sum of any two angles of a triangle. Replacing in this sum one of two angles by the exterior angle adjacent to the other angle, we increase this sum and obtain 180° because the exterior angle is greater than the interior. Therefore, the sum of any *two* angles in a triangle must be less than 180°, if the infinitude of straight lines is assumed. To prove our theorem we use the indirect method and suppose that the sum of angles of a triangle ABC (Fig. 3) is greater than 180°,

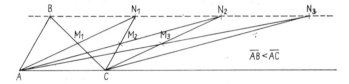

$$\overline{AB} < \overline{AC}$$

Fig. 17.3

namely equal to $180° + h$, where h is positive. Applying to $\triangle ABC$ the same construction as the one used by Euclid in the proof of his proposition number 16, we join the midpoint M_1 of the side BC to the vertex A and mark a point N_1 on the straight line AM_1 such that $M_1N_1 = AM_1$. The two triangles ABM_1 and M_1N_1C are equal (Theorem V, Chapter 14), so that $\overset{\frown}{M_1N_1C} = \overset{\frown}{M_1AB}$; therefore the sum of the angles of triangle AN_1C is the same as that of triangle ABC and thus is equal to $180° + h$. Moreover, since the two parts into which the line AN_1 divides the angle BAC are in general unequal, one of them is less than or at most equal to $\frac{1}{2} \cdot \overset{\frown}{BAC}$. These two parts $\overset{\frown}{BAN_1}$ and $\overset{\frown}{N_1AC}$ are angles of the new triangle AN_1C since $\overset{\frown}{BAN_1} = \overset{\frown}{AN_1C}$. Therefore, the construction just applied to the triangle ABC with AB < AC gives another triangle with the same sum of angles and with an angle $\overset{\frown}{CAN_1}$ which is less or at most equal to $\frac{1}{2} \cdot \overset{\frown}{BAC}$: $\overset{\frown}{CAN_1} \leqslant \frac{1}{2} \cdot \overset{\frown}{BAC}$.

Applying this construction to the triangle CAN_1 and subdividing the angle at the vertex A, we deduce a third triangle N_1AN_2 with the same sum of angles (equal to $180° + h$), and with an angle $\stackrel{\frown}{N_1AN_2}$ at the vertex A which is less or at most equal to $\frac{1}{2} \cdot \stackrel{\frown}{CAN_1} = \frac{1}{4} \cdot \stackrel{\frown}{BAC} : \stackrel{\frown}{N_1AN_2} \leqslant \frac{1}{4} \cdot \stackrel{\frown}{BAC}$.

Because a straight line has by assumption an infinite length, nothing can prevent us from repeating the same construction as many times as we want: we can construct an infinite sequence of points $N_1, N_2, N_3, ..., N_k, ...$ and triangles $CAN_1, N_1AN_2, N_2AN_3, ..., N_kAN_{k+1}, ...$ having, all of them, the same sum of angles as the triangle ABC, namely $180° + h$ by hypothesis. Their angles at the common vertex A decrease when k increases: $\stackrel{\frown}{CAN_1}$ $\leqslant \frac{1}{2} \cdot \stackrel{\frown}{BAC}, \stackrel{\frown}{N_1AN_2} \leqslant \stackrel{\frown}{BAC}/2^2, \stackrel{\frown}{N_2AN_3} \leqslant \stackrel{\frown}{BAC}/2^3$ and in general $\stackrel{\frown}{N_{k-1}AN_k}$ $\leqslant \stackrel{\frown}{BAC}/2^k$.

However small the positive angle h may be in the expression $180° + h$ of the sum of the angle of ABC, a finite integer n can be found such that the product nh exceeds the angle BAC. This integer n may be a very large number, but it is finite and therefore a sufficiently large exponent m can be found such that 2^m is greater than $n : n < 2^m$. We have then $2^m h > nh > \stackrel{\frown}{BAC}$, so that $\stackrel{\frown}{BAC}/2^m < h$.

Consider now the triangle N_mAN_{m+1} of our chain of triangles $N_{k-1}AN_k$. It is obtained for $k = m + 1$ and therefore its angle N_mAN_{m+1} is less than $h/2$:

$$\stackrel{\frown}{N_mAN_{m+1}} \leqslant \stackrel{\frown}{BAC}/2^{m+1} = 1/2 \cdot (\stackrel{\frown}{BAC}/2^m) < h/2.$$

On the other hand, we assumed that the sum of angles of this triangle is equal to $180° + h : \stackrel{\frown}{N_mAN_{m+1}} + \stackrel{\frown}{AN_mN_{m+1}} + \stackrel{\frown}{AN_{m+1}N_m} = 180° + h$, so that the sum of two angles at the vertices N_m and N_{m+1} can be evaluated as follows:

$$\hat{N}_m + \hat{N}_{m+1} = 180° + h - \stackrel{\frown}{N_mAN_{m+1}}.$$

Replacing the term $\stackrel{\frown}{N_mAN_{m+1}}$ by a larger number $\frac{1}{2}h$, we decrease the righthand member and therefore the sum $\hat{N}_m + \hat{N}_{m+1}$ is greater than $180° + h/2$

$$\hat{N}_m + \hat{N}_{m+1} > 180° + h - \frac{1}{2}h = 180° + \frac{1}{2}h$$

which contradicts the fact that the sum of two angles of a triangle cannot exceed 180°. Thus, the initial assumption of the existence of a triangle with a sum of angles greater than 180° is fallacious in a geometry in which straight lines are of infinite length. This proves that the straight lines of elliptic geometry are closed lines of finite length. Being closed, they are boundless and therefore the third axiom of Euclid holds, notwithstanding the fact that they are finite in extent.

One must distinguish between the concepts of boundlessness and infinitude. This important logical refinement was emphasized for the first time in the history of science by Riemann in 1854. In his inaugural dissertation Riemann says: "The boundlessness of space presents a greater empirical certainty than any external experience. But its infinite extent does not follow from this."

In elliptic geometry no two straight lines can be parallel and the Fifth Postulate is replaced by the following

POSTULATE: *Two straight lines always intersect each other.*

We shall now deduce from this postulate the finite length and closure of straight lines. Drawing through two points A and B chosen arbitrarily on a given straight line MN the perpendiculars to this straight line (Fig. 4) and applying the postulate, we form an isosceles triangle ABC since the two perpendiculars intersect in their common point C. The triangle ABC has two equal angles: $\widehat{ABC} = \widehat{BAC} = 90°$; therefore it is isosceles: $AC = BC = \pi R/2$, where $\pi R/2$ denotes the common length of its two equal sides AC and BC.

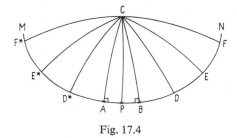

Fig. 17.4

We saw indeed (Chapter 14) that the sixth proposition of Euclid's First Book, namely, "If in a triangle two angles are equal, the opposite sides are equal", is independent from the validity of the Fifth Postulate and therefore holds in non-Euclidean geometry too.

We now prove that the point C defined above is equidistant from all the points of the straight line AB with respect to which it is defined. First of all we construct other intervals equal to the interval AB; for instance BD, DE, EF, etc., such that their extremities A, B, D, E, ... etc., form a sequence of equidistant points on the line AB. Joining them to the point C, we consider the triangles BDC, DEC, EFC, ... etc. It is easy to prove that all of these triangles are equal to the fundamental triangle ABC. Consider the triangle BDC which is a right triangle, the side BC being perpendicular to BD: therefore, $\widehat{CBD} = \widehat{CAB}$, BC = AC and BD = AB, which proves that the triangles ABC and BCD are equal. We deduce from this fact that $\widehat{BDC}$ = ABC = 90° and DC = BC = $\pi R/2$, so that CD, being perpendicular to AF, represents the distance of the point C from the line AB. Since this distance CD is equal to $\pi R/2$ it is proved that C is at the same distance from the point D as from the points A and B.

The same reasoning applies to all the other triangles, proceeding in the order ABC → BDC → DEC → EFC → ⋯ etc., as well as to the left of the point A, to the triangles ACD*, D*CE*, E*CF*, ... etc., such that again AD* = D*E* = E*F* = ⋯ = AB. Thus, the point C is equidistant from all our points A, B, D, D*, E, E*, F, F*, ... etc., extremities of adjacent and equal intervals into which our straight line AB is subdivided.

Any point P on the line AB, if it does not coincide with one of the extremities of these intervals, is interior to an interval, say to the interval AB. We distinguish now between two cases; (a) AP is commensurable with AB and (b) there is no common measure for AP and AB. In the first case AP/AB = m/n and, dividing AP into m equal parts, we construct a third interval AQ = AP/m = AB/n which is the common measure of AP and AB, being contained an integral number of times in AP (m times) and in AB (n times). Joining the point Q to C, we must have QC = BC because the interval AB is a multiple of the interval AQ and we have already proved that the extremities of multiples of a given interval are equidistant from C. But, if QC = BC = $\pi R/2$, then PC = QC = $\pi R/2$ also, since the interval AP is also a multiple of the interval AQ. Therefore, the fact that PC = AC is proved for all points P such that the segment AP is commensurable with AB.

If a point M, interior to AB, is such that AM is incommensurable with AB, an infinite sequence of points $P_1, P_2, P_3, ..., P_n, ...$ can be found such that (1) $\lim_{n=\infty} P_n = M$ and (2) each segment AP_n is commensurable with AB and, therefore, $CP_n = AC = \pi R/2$ for all values of the subscript n running through all the integers. Passing to the limit for $n = \infty$ in $CP_n = \pi R/2$, we find $\lim_{n=\infty} CP_m = CM = \pi R/2$ which completes the proof of the important fact that the point C is equidistant from all points of the line AB.

Thus, to each straight line of the elliptic plane corresponds a point which is equidistant from all the points on that line. It is called *pole* of this line. It is important to observe that the distance $\pi R/2$ from a pole to the corresponding line is the same for all straight lines since the two configurations formed by two distinct straight lines with their poles coincide, if one of two straight lines becomes congruent with the other. Therefore, the constant $\pi R/2$ plays a fundamental role in elliptic geometry and it characterizes an *absolute length* attached to an elliptic plane as its inseparable feature.

Moreover, reflecting Fig. 4 in the straight line AB as in a mirror, we find another pole C* which is symmetrical to C with respect to the line AB. In other words, the two perpendiculars AC and BC, when extended downwards, also intersect in a second pole C* through which pass all the perpendiculars to AB issued from C. Thus, the two poles C and C* define an infinite number of straight lines passing through them instead of one and they constitute an exception to the rule: "two points define one and only one straight line".

Thus, in the elliptic plane two given points define one and only one straight line, except the case when these points are two poles of the same straight line, and this kind of elliptic geometry is well illustrated in spherical geometry, where great circles play the role of straight lines.

But, there is an elliptic geometry of a second kind where there are no exceptions and where any two given points always define a unique straight line. This kind of elliptic geometry is obtained by postulating that the points C and C* coincide, so that each straight line has only one pole. A consistent elliptic geometry is built on this foundation: in it any two lines intersect in only one point and any two points define only one straight line.

Therefore, there are two distinct elliptic planes with two different elliptic geometries. One, which is often called elliptic plane of the spherical type, is a two-sided surface as is the ordinary Euclidean plane, or the spherical surface with its exterior and interior faces. The other, called the single elliptic plane, has only one side since it is possible to pass from one of its faces into the other without piercing the plane. In other words, if one decides to paint the elliptic plane of the second kind by continuously extending the area already painted, only one color is sufficient to paint this plane on both sides because they communicate with each other. To the contrary, the elliptic plane of the first kind will be painted in this way in two different colors, one for its upper face and the other for its lower face because there is no communication between these two faces.

Let us first continue our discussion for elliptic geometry of the spherical type. If C and C* are two poles of the straight line AB, then the lines AC and BC intersect for the second time at C*, so that these two straight lines and, in general, any two lines form a configuration ACBC*A unknown in Euclidean geometry and called a *lune*. A lune is a figure having two equal rectilinear sides and two equal angles; such a figure encloses an area. The common length of both sides is fixed and the same for all lunes, namely $2\pi R/2 = \pi R$, while the angle of a lune $\overset{\frown}{ACB} = \overset{\frown}{AC^*B}$ can vary from zero to 2π. The sides CAC^* and CBC^* have a common perpendicular AB which is an axis of symmetry for the lune.

Consider now the extensions of the sides of a lune (Fig. 5) through the poles C and C^* of the common perpendicular AB and measure off on these extensions from the poles C and C^* the distances $CD = C^*D^* = \pi R/2$ on the extended side CAC^* and the equal distances $CE = C^*E^* = \pi R/2$ on the extended side CBC^*. The points D, D^*, E, E^* are on the line AB since this line is the locus of points at the distance $\pi R/2$ from the points C and C^*. Moreover, the points D and D^* coincide since AB is an axis of symmetry and the same is true for the points E and E^*.

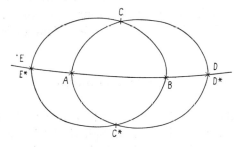

Fig. 17.5

Thus any two straight lines intersect in two points which are the poles of their common perpendicular. Moreover, in an elliptic plane of the spherical type, the total length of a straight line is equal to $4AC = 2\pi R$, and *it is the same for all straight lines,* which are all closed lines.

In the elliptic plane of the second kind the straight lines are also closed. Their finite length is $2AC = \pi R$ because the points C and C^* coincide, a straight line having only one pole in this geometry.

We study now Saccheri's quadrilateral $ABCD$ and prove that its summit angles $BCD = ADC$ are obtuse. Draw the common perpendicular ML to the base AB and the summit CD, M and L being midpoints of AB and CD respectively. The lines AB and CD intersect at the pole N of ML, so that BN is less than $\pi R/2 = MN$. Therefore, a point P on the line AB such that $BP = \pi R/2$ lies behind N with respect to B. This point P is the pole of the straight line BC, so that drawing the line CP, we have $BCP = 90°$ (Fig. 6). The line CN being interior to the triangle BCP, we conclude that the angle

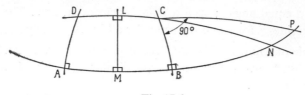

Fig. 17.6

BCN is less than $\overset{\frown}{BCP}$ = 90°, that is, $\overset{\frown}{BCN}$ is an acute angle and thus its supplement, the angle BCD, is an obtuse angle.

We saw that the sum s of the three angles of a triangle is always equal to the double of the summit angle of the corresponding Saccheri's quadrilateral: $s = 2 \cdot \overset{\frown}{BCD}$, so that in elliptic geometry (of both kinds) this sum is greater than 180°. Since the diagonal of a quadrilateral divides it into two triangles whose angles, if added, give the sum of four angles of the quadrilateral, this sum for any quadrilateral is greater than four right angles.

Spherical Excess and Area of a Triangle

The excess of the sum of angles over two right angles is called *excess of the triangle*. In the particular case of spherical triangles, whose sides are arcs of great circles, this excess is called *spherical excess*. This difference $s - 180°$ is a very important quantity since—as we will prove—it is proportional to the area of the triangle.

The fact that the total length of straight lines is finite proves that the distance of two points in an elliptic plane cannot exceed a finite maximum. This maximum distance is πR. Any two points indeed can be joined by a straight line they define and this line is unique, except the case of two points which are poles of a line. The exceptional case corresponds to the maximum value πR of the distance. This case put aside, the unique straight line defined by two given points is a closed line of total extent $2\pi R$. Therefore, the maximum distance is indeed πR.

Thus, an elliptic plane is finite and its total area is finite also. It is divided by a straight line into two equal parts which are symmetric with respect to the straight line. The two poles of the line which are separated by the maximum distance lie symmetrically and are opposite to each other. Elliptic geometry of the first kind is well represented by spherical geometry with the unique difference that the sphere's surface is immersed in the three-dimensional space and therefore appears to us as a curved surface, while the elliptic plane of the spherical type is to be considered as an entity complete in itself and which is not related at all to a higher space. Therefore, the elliptic plane is flat and has no curvature.

On the surface of a sphere the great circles play the role of straight lines of an elliptic plane and in studying the rectilinear triangles in an elliptic plane we can substitute to them the spherical triangles whose sides are arcs of great circles drawn on the sphere's surface. The fundamental configuration we defined and called *lune* appears now as a spherical biangle formed by two half-meridians of the sphere. Let us denote the total area of an elliptic plane by T. For a sphere of radius R this total area is, as we will prove later, expressed by the formula $T = 4\pi R^2$. The total area of an elliptic plane is that of a lune of maximum angle, that is, the lune of angle 2π. In general, the area of a lune is proportional to its angle. Denoting the area by A and the angle of a lune by t, we have $A = kt$. To compute the constant coefficient of proportionality k we observe that $A = T$, when $t = 2\pi$ since then the lune fills out the whole elliptic plane. Therefore, the unknown k verifies the equation $T = 2\pi k$ and solving it, we find $k = T/2\pi$. In the particular case of a spherical lune $T = 4\pi R^2$, so that for a sphere $k = 2R^2$.

Thus the area A of a lune of angle t is equal to $Tt/2\pi$ and, on the sphere, $A = 2tR^2$. The formula $A = T \cdot t/2\pi$ solves the question of finding the area of a triangle whose excess is known. It was stated without proof that this area is proportional to the excess. Now we give the proof and compute also the value of the coefficient of proportionality.

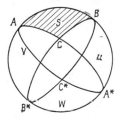

Fig. 17.7

This proof holds for the general elliptic plane of the first kind and is illustrated (Fig. 7) on the example of a sphere of radius R. Three straight lines AB, BC, CA which form a triangle ABC divide the plane (the surface of the sphere) into eight triangles which form four pairs of equal triangles, equal because symmetrical and diametrically opposite point by point. Denoting the points opposite to the vertices A, B, C by A*, B*, C* respectively, we have indeed $\varDelta ABC = \varDelta A^*B^*C^*$, $\varDelta BCA^* = \varDelta B^*C^*A$, $\varDelta C^*A^*B = \varDelta CAB^*$ and $\varDelta A^*B^*C = \varDelta ABC^*$. On the other hand, denoting the excess and the area of the triangle ABC by E and S respectively, so that the sum of angles $A + B + C = 180° + E$, we observe that any two adjacent triangles form a lune. Thus, we have $\varDelta ABC + \varDelta BCA^* =$ lune ABA*CA, as well as $\varDelta ABC + \varDelta CAB^* =$ lune BCB*AB and $\varDelta A^*B^*C^* + \varDelta A^*B^*C =$ lune CA*C*B*C.

The areas of three lunes thus introduced are: area ABA*CA $= T \cdot \hat{A}/2\pi$; area BCB*AB $= T \cdot \hat{B}/2\pi$; area CA*C*B*C $= T \cdot \hat{C}/2\pi$ and the relations between the triangles and the lunes entail the same relations between their areas. Denoting the area of triangles BCA*, CAB* and A*B*C by u, v, w: area BCA* $= u$; area CAB* $= v$; area A*B*C $= w$, we write the relations between areas as follows:

$$S + u = T \cdot \hat{A}/2\pi; \quad S + v = T \cdot \hat{B}/2\pi; \quad S + w = T \cdot \hat{C}/2\pi.$$

Adding them and observing that the sum of three angles A, B, C is equal to two right angles plus the excess E, that is $A + B + C = 180° + E$, we have:

$$3S + u + v + w = T(\hat{A} + \hat{B} + \hat{C})/2\pi = T(180° + E)/2\pi$$

$$= T(\pi + E)/2\pi.$$

Moreover, four distinct triangles ABC, BCA*, CAB* and A*B*C form together half the total elliptic plane (half the sphere's surface), so that the sum of their areas is equal to $T/2$:

$$S + u + v + w = T/2.$$

Using this second relation, we obtain

$$3S + u + v + w = 2S + (S + u + v + w) = 2S + T/2$$

$$= T(\pi + E)/2\pi = T/2 + TE/2\pi$$

that is $2S = TE/2\pi$ and therefore the area S of our triangle ABC is expressed in terms of the excess E of this triangle and of the total area T of the plane:

$$S = (T/4\pi) \cdot E. \tag{1}$$

We restate that this area S is proportional to the excess E of the triangle, the value of the coefficient of proportionality being equal to $T/4\pi$.

In the particular case of a sphere of radius R the total area T is equal to $4\pi R^2$, so that the area of a spherical triangle ABC is equal to the product ER^2, where E is its spherical excess: $E = \hat{A} + \hat{B} + \hat{C} - \pi$.

Let us emphasize two corollaries of this fundamental result. First it can be said that the sum of angles of a triangle in elliptic geometry depends on its size and increases when the size increases. For an equilateral triangle, whose angles are equal, the common value of its angles is determined if its area is given. We have, indeed, for an equilateral triangle $E = 3A - \pi$, so that $E = 4\pi S/T$ becomes in this particular case $3A = \pi(1 + 4S/T)$ which gives the angle A: $A = \pi(1 + 4S/T)/3$. This result proves that there are no similar figures in elliptic geometry: increasing the area of equilateral triangle, we increase also its angles and, therefore, the shape and the size of configuration are not independent contrary to what we know for Euclidean geometry.

The same relation (1), which we transcribe as follows

$$\hat{A} + \hat{B} + \hat{C} = \pi + 4\pi S/T,$$

proves that the sum of angles of a triangle tends to two right angles, when the area S of this triangle approaches zero, that is, when the triangle vanishes. Therefore, an infinitesimal triangle in the elliptic plane is Euclidean in that sense that the sum of its angles is equal to 180°. In other words *in an elliptic plane the infinitely small figures obey Euclidean geometry* which therefore appears as the geometry of infinitely small. We can speak about infinitely small figures in an elliptic plane because there is an absolute constant R (radius of the sphere, in the particular case of spherical geometry) with respect to which an infinitely small length can be considered. In Euclidean geometry the size of a length is relative to the particular length chosen as unit of length and, because this choice is absolutely free and arbitrary, one *cannot* speak about infinitely small or infinitely large figures in an Euclidean plane: the existence of similar figures in it precludes in fact any size differentiation in absolute sense, that is, eliminates the concept of size itself.

The second corollary has important philosophical implications. The universe is so enormously large in comparison to the Earth and even to the Solar System or to our galaxy, the Milky Way, that the region of universe accessible to our direct measurements can be considered as an infinitely small part of the universe. Therefore, *a priori* it is impossible to find out what is the kind of geometry characterizing the physical space around us: our experience which seems to ascribe to the space around us Euclidean structure corresponds to the infinitesimal size of the region which directly affects us and therefore, even if the universe is non-Euclidean, our experience will ascribe to our part of space the structure of Euclidean space. Modern physics indeed is inclined to accept the finiteness of the universe which can correspond only to a non-Euclidean space and, more precisely, to a non-Euclidean geometry of elliptic type. We will see indeed that non-Euclidean geometry of hyperbolic type, that is Lobachevsky's geometry, does not lead to a finite plane: the hyperbolic plane, and with it the hyperbolic space are of infinite extent as are Euclidean plane and space.

THEOREM XXVIII: *Two triangles are equal, if their corresponding angles are equal.*

We know that this theorem does not hold in Euclidean geometry and the reason of it is the existence of similar triangles. We want now to prove this fact. To do it, a lemma is needed which replaces the 16th proposition (Book I) of Euclid by the corresponding lemma of elliptic geometry:

LEMMA. "The exterior angle of a triangle is greater, equal or less than an interior non-adjacent angle, if the median through the midpoint of the side included between the vertices of exterior and interior angles is respectively less, equal or greater than a quarter of the total length of straight line, that is, than $\pi R/2$".

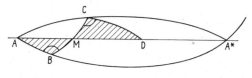

Fig. 17.8 a

If the median AM (Fig. 8a) is shorter than $\pi R/2$, then the proof of the inequality $\overset{\frown}{ABC} < \overset{\frown}{BCA}$* (where AA* = πR so that the sides AB, AC of the triangle ABC and the median AM are concurrent at the point A*) is exactly the same as that of Euclid's proposition 16 (see Chapter 14) since the point D obtained by doubling the median, AD = $2 \cdot$ AM $< \pi R$, is located *above* the straight line ABA*.

Suppose now that the median AM exceeds $\pi R/2$. Then (Fig. 8b) AD $> \pi R$, so that the point D is *below* the line ABA*. Joining this point to the vertex C,

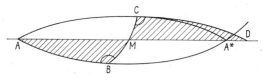

Fig. 17.8 b

we form a triangle MCD which is again equal to the triangle ABM because the equal angles $\widehat{AMB} = \widehat{CMD}$ are included between two pairs and equal sides, AM = MD and BM = MC. Therefore, $\widehat{ABC} = \widehat{BCD}$, but this time the angle BCD is greater than the exterior angle BCA* since the point D is farther from A than the point A*. Thus, if AM > $\pi R/2$ then the interior angle ABC is greater than the exterior angle BCA*.

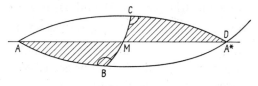

Fig. 17.8c

Finally, if the median AM = $\pi R/2$ then the points A* and D coincide (Fig. 8c) and the exterior angle is equal to the interior: $\widehat{ABC} = \widehat{BCA}*$. This last case will be used in the proof of Theorem XXVIII in the form of the converse proposition, namely: *if an exterior angle BCA* is equal to an interior angle ABC, then the median AM is equal to $\pi R/2$.* This converse proposition can be deduced from our lemma. Suppose that $\widehat{BCA}* = \widehat{ABC}$, while AM $\gtrless$ $\pi R/2$. Since AM $\gtrless$ $\pi R/2$ we must have, applying the lemma, $\widehat{BCA}*$ $\gtrless$ $\widehat{ABC}$, which contradicts the hypothesis $\widehat{BCA}* = \widehat{ABC}$. Therefore, AM is necessarily equal to $\pi R/2$, if it is known that $\widehat{BCA}* = \widehat{ABC}$.

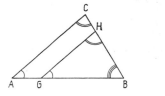

Fig. 17.9a

We pass now to the proof of Theorem XXVIII. By hypothesis the triangles ABC and DEF are equiangular: $\widehat{ABC} = \widehat{DEF}$, $\widehat{BCA} = \widehat{EFD}$, $\widehat{CAB} = \widehat{FDE}$ (Fig. 9a). Should AB be equal to DE, our triangles would coincide as two triangles having equal sides included between equal angles. Let us suppose that AB and DE are unequal and DE < AB (choice of notation). We do not know anything about the sides BC and EF and will therefore consider three possible cases BC > EF, BC = EF and BC < EF. As we will see, all these three cases are incompatible with the equality of angles and this constitutes the proof of Theorem XXVIII.

Suppose first (Fig. 9a) that not only AB > DE, but also BC > EF. Cut off on AB a segment BG equal to DE and also cut off on BC a segment BH equal to EF. Joining G and H, we obtain a triangle GBH whose two sides and the included angle are equal to the corresponding sides and angle of the triangle DEF, so that the triangles BGH and DEF are equal. Therefore $\widehat{EDF} = \widehat{BGH} = \widehat{BAC}$ since $\widehat{EDF} = \widehat{BAC}$, as well as $\widehat{EFD} = \widehat{BHG} = \widehat{BCA}$ since $\widehat{EFD} = \widehat{BCA}$. The sum of four angles of the quadrilateral AGHC is then equal to four right angles, and this is impossible. We have seen indeed that the sum of angles of a triangle exceeds two right angles. Dividing a quadrilateral into two triangles (by drawing one of its diagonals), we find that the sum of its angles must exceed four right angles because it is equal to the sum of angles of two triangles. Thus, we come to the conclusion that the inequality BC > EF leads to a contradiction and therefore is impossible.

The case BC = EF is also impossible because it contradicts the assumption AB > DE: if BC = EF then the triangles are equal and AB must be equal to DE.

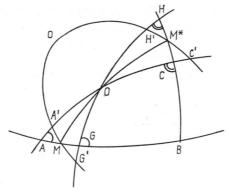

Fig. 17.9 b

We discuss finally the case BC < EF. In this case (Fig. 9b) the lines AC and GH intersect in a point O, the segments BG and BH being defined by BG = ED and BH = EF, so that the triangle BGH is equal to the triangle EDF. Consider now the triangles OAG and OCH. According to our assumption they have exterior angles equal to interior angles: BGO = BAO and BCO = BHO. Applying our lemma, we join the point O to the midpoints M

of AG and M* of CH and state that the medians OM and OM* are equal to
$\pi R/2$, so that the point O is a pole of the straight line MO'M* perpendicular
to OM and to OM*. This straight line intersects OC and OH in C' and H'
and the two right triangles CC'M* and HH'M* are equal, having equal angles
at M* as well as at C and H, and equal sides CM* = HM*. Therefore,
C'M* = H'M* which entails the equality of angles COM* and HOM*,
so that OM* appears as bisector of the angle COH. The same reasoning
applied to the point M proves that the line OM also bisects the angle AOG.
We thus reach the conclusion that the three points M, O, M* are collinear
and therefore the segment MM* is equal to πR: MOM* = πR.

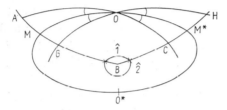

Fig. 17.9c

Since MM* is a straight line we can consider two triangles BMM* having
the points B, M, M* as vertices. There are two such triangles because the line
defined by the points M, O, M* is a closed line (Fig. 9c) and therefore there
are two equal segments MOM* and MO*M* on the closed line MOM*O*M.
The first triangle MBM$_1^*$ has the segment MOM* as its third side opposite
to the angle $\hat{1}$. The second triangle MBM$_2^*$ includes the angle 2 to which is
opposite the side MO*M*. These two triangles are equal since they have
three pairs of equal sides: BM = MB, BM* = MB* and MOM* = MO*M*
= πR. Therefore, angles 1 and 2 are equal. But together they form four right
angles around the point B and therefore their common value is two right
angles. This result proves that the segments AMGB and HM*CB form one
and the same straight line which means that there is no triangle ABC, the
three points A, B, C being collinear.

Thus we see that the assumption AB > DE leads to a contradiction if
BC $\geqslant$ EF; the assumptions AB > DE and BC < EF are impossible because
in this case three points A, B, C are collinear and therefore there is no triangle
ABC at all. We conclude that in two triangles ABC and DEF with equal
angles the side AB cannot be greater than the corresponding side DE of the
second triangle. But it cannot be smaller either because if DE > AB, the

reasoning which was applied to the triangle ABC with AB > DE can now be applied to the triangle DEF. Therefore, it is proved that the equality of angles is incompatible with the inequality of the sides AB and DE and, if the two triangles are equiangular, they must have AB = DE and are therefore equal triangles, having equal sides included between two equal angles.

Equality of Triangles in Hyperbolic Geometry

We saw above that in the elliptic plane the summit-angle of a birectangle is obtuse; the sum of angles of a triangle exceeds two right angles; the area of a triangle is proportional to its excess E, that is, to the difference $E = S - \pi$ between the sum s of its angles and two right angles; and finally we established the truth of Theorem XXVIII and proved that there is only one triangle with three given angles since any other triangle with same angles is congruent to it.

We have now to study how the same questions are solved for hyperbolic geometry in which the Fifth Postulate of Euclid is replaced by the following

LOBACHEVSKY'S POSTULATE: *Through a given point non-incident with a given line more than one line can be drawn not intersecting the given line.*

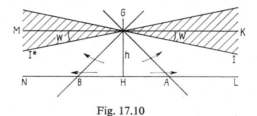

Fig. 17.10

The Euclidean parallel MGK through G to the straight line NHL (Fig. 10) cannot intersect NHL since, by symmetry with respect to the perpendicular HG to NL, it would then intersect it in two symmetrical points to the left and to the right of H. Therefore, in the hyperbolic plane the line MK does not meet NL. But there must be at least one more line through G which does not intersect NL and by symmetry we conclude that there are at least two such lines which are symmetrical with respect to GH. To find them we rotate the ray GA intersecting HL in A counterclockwise, so that the point A moves on the line HL to the right until A disappears at infinity to the right. Denoting the ultimate position of the secant GA when the intersection point A disappears at infinity by GI, we state that the angle $w = \overset{\frown}{KGI}$ cannot vanish since would it be zero, the Fifth Postulate of Euclid in its Playfair's form would follow.

By the reason of symmetry the ultimate position GI* of the secant GB, when its intersection point B moving to the left disappears at infinity, is symmetrical to GI; that is, $\overset{\frown}{MGI^*} = \overset{\frown}{KGI}$. The two straight lines GI and GI* are such that rotating GI* counterclockwise and GI clockwise through an angle as small as we want we obtain straight lines intersecting NL, while any straight line through the point G lying between GI and GK or between GI* and GM does not meet NL. We see thus that, if more than one line can be drawn through G not intersecting the line NL, then there is an infinite number of such lines and they all belong to the shaded angle (Fig. 10) formed by two lines GI and GI*. These important lines are called two parallels to NL through the point G: the line GI is the parallel to the right, or *right parallel*, and GI* is the parallel to the left, or *left parallel*. The lines lying between two parallels and within the angle to which belongs the perpendicular HG, intersect, all of them, the line NL. The lines lying in the shaded region which do not meet NL, even at infinity, are called *ultraparallels*.

The value of the acute angle of parallelism $w = \overset{\frown}{KGI}$ depends on the length GH of the perpendicular dropped from the point G on the line NL, the sense of its variation being opposite to that of the length $h = $ GH: the angle of parallelism decreases when the length $h = $ GH increases and at the limit for $h = \infty$ the angle becomes zero; when h decreases, the angle w increases and becomes equal to a right angle when h vanishes.

The straight line NL and a parallel to it through G have in common their point at infinity, the ultimate position of the intersection point of NL and of the secant which becomes parallel at the limit.

Therefore, in hyperbolic geometry a straight line has two distinct points at infinity, one to the right and the other to the left. These points must be different, otherwise the two parallels, to the right and to the left, through the point G would coincide as having two common points: point G and the unique point of the line NL at infinity — which is impossible.

We saw that the line joining the midpoints of the base and of the summit (side opposite to the base) of a birectangle is perpendicular to both, this result being independent from the postulate of parallels and therefore true in non-Euclidean geometries as well as in Euclidean. Thus, the summit-line considered as a line through the midpoint of the summit lies to the right above the right parallel and to the left above the left parallel. In other words, the summit line is ultraparallel to the base line, and as such does not meet it.

Preparing the study of equality of two triangles, which have equal angles, we begin with the proof that in the hyperbolic plane the equal summit-angles of a birectangle are acute angles. This proof uses some auxiliary facts which are also interesting in themselves since they characterize specific properties and configurations of the hyperbolic geometry. We formulate them as five lemmas I–V.

LEMMA I. "Two infinite triangles ABZ and CDZ* are equal, if they have their finite sides equal, AB = CD, and if their angles ABZ and CDZ* are equal."

A triangle is called infinite if one of its vertices is at infinity, so that two sides are parallel. Thus, in $\triangle$ABZ (Fig. 11) AZ is parallel to BZ. Given two triangles ABZ and CDZ* satisfying the conditions imposed in Lemma I, two cases are possible: the second angles BAZ and DCZ* may be equal or unequal.

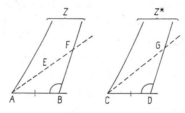

Fig. 17.11

If $\widehat{BAZ} = \widehat{DCZ^*}$ the triangles are congruent and therefore equal. We shall see that the assumption $\widehat{BAZ} \neq \widehat{DCZ^*}$ leads to a contradiction. In this assumption it is sufficient to consider the case $\widehat{BAZ} > \widehat{DCZ^*}$ only, because the same proof holds in the case $\widehat{BAZ} < \widehat{DCZ^*}$, interchanging the roles of the triangles in the proof. Let us assume, therefore, that $\widehat{BAZ} > \widehat{DCZ^*}$.

This assumption allows us to draw through the vertex A and inside the triangle ABZ a line AE making with AB an angle BAE equal to $\widehat{DCZ^*}$: $\widehat{BAE} = \widehat{DCZ^*}$. This line must intersect BZ because it lies below the parallel AZ and can be obtained by rotating this parallel clockwise about A. Let F denote the intersection point of AE and BZ, thus defining a finite segment BF on the line BZ. Plotting on DZ* the segment DG = BF and joining G to C, we obtain two equal triangles (Theorem V, Chapter 14) ABF and CDG, so that the angle BAE, which by construction is equal to the angle DCZ*, is at the same time equal to the smaller angle DCG. This contradiction deduced from the assumption $\widehat{BAZ} > \widehat{DCZ^*}$ proves that $\widehat{BAZ}$ cannot exceed $\widehat{DCZ^*}$. The same contradiction is obtained if we assume that $\widehat{DCZ^*} > \widehat{BAZ}$, and thus Lemma I is proved.

LEMMA II. "The exterior angle GAZ at a vertex A of an infinite triangle ABZ is greater than the interior angle ABZ at the other vertex B: $\widehat{ABZ} < 180° - \widehat{BAZ}$."

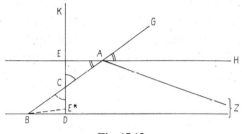

Fig. 17.12

Draw a perpendicular (Fig. 12) DK to BZ through the midpoints C of AB. A perpendicular drawn through A to DK intersects this line at E. The straight line EAH is ultraparallel to BZ since both lines are perpendicular to DK. Therefore, the ray AH, as an ultraparallel, lies above the right parallel AZ to BZ and thus the angle GAH, as a part of the exterior angle GAZ, is less than $\widehat{GAZ}$: $\widehat{GAH} < \widehat{GAZ}$.

To compare the triangles BCD and ACE with right angles at D and at E we rotate the second triangle about its vertex C through 180°. After this rotation CA coincides with CB and the ray CEK coincides with the ray CD since $\widehat{ACE} = \widehat{BCD}$ as vertical angles. We do not know if the segments CE and CD are equal, but we can prove that they must be equal. Suppose, to the contrary, that after the rotation the points E and D do not coincide, the point E occupying the position E* on the line CD. In such a case we would have two different perpendiculars BD and BE* dropped from the point B on the line DCK which is impossible. Therefore, the points E* and D must coincide and CE = CD, the triangles BCD and ACE being congruent: $\triangle BCD = \triangle ACE$. This result entails $\widehat{CAE} = \widehat{CBD}$. But, $\widehat{CAE} = \widehat{GAH} < \widehat{GAZ}$ and thus $\widehat{CBD} = \widehat{ABZ} < \widehat{GAZ}$, which completes the proof of Lemma II.

A line and two parallels (right parallel and left parallel) through a point to this line form a triangle with *two* vertices at infinity. The angle of parallelism is always an acute angle. Therefore, the sum of angles of a triangle with two vertices at infinity is less than two right angles. We know indeed that the angle formed by two parallels at their common point at infinity vanishes. Were it different from zero, it could be decreased further by rotating the parallel which would contradict the definition of a parallel as the ultimate position of a secant.

Now Lemma II expresses the analogous property of a triangle with *one* vertex at infinity: the sum of angles of the triangle ABZ is equal to $\widehat{\text{BAZ}}$ + $\widehat{\text{ABZ}}$ = $\widehat{\text{BAZ}}$ + $\widehat{\text{GAH}}$ < 180°. Therefore, it is less than two right angles, as is the case for triangles with two vertices at infinity. There is in the hyperbolic geometry a third kind of infinite triangle, namely, a triangle with three vertices at infinity. In such a triangle each side is right parallel to one of two other sides and left parallel to the other. All three angles of such an infinite triangle vanish, their sum being zero.

The definition of a line parallel to a given line through a given point does not imply that a parallel to the line L through the point P remains parellel to the same line L, when considered as a line through any other of its points. Therefore, we have to prove that the fact of parallelism does not depend on the particular point P for which it is stated. In other words, we have to prove that a right (left) parallel to L through P is also right (left) parallel to L through any other point Q chosen arbitrarily on it.

LEMMA III. If AB is a parallel to CD through one of its points P, it is also a parallel to CD in the same sense through each of its points.

The point P divides the line AB into two rays (half-lines) and we must distinguish between two cases: the point Q other than P is any point of AB on that side of P which extends in the direction of parallelism; or Q is on the other side of P, opposite to the direction of parallelism.

Let AB be right parallel to CD and choose a point Q on the right of P (Fig. 13). Draw the perpendiculars PR, QS through P, Q to CD. We have to prove that any line through Q and within the angle SQB necessarily intersects SD. Let QX be such a line and E any point on it between AB and CD.

The proof that QX intersects CD is based on the Axiom of Pasch, which asserts that a straight line penetrating inside a triangle through a point of a side leaves it through a point of another side or through the opposite vertex. Join P and E and also draw the line RQ. The line PE intersects CD in a point F since this line is within the angle RPB and PB is parallel to CD. The line QS is also cut by PE because the points P and E are separated by the line QS. Since PE penetrates inside the triangle QRS through its side QS it must intersect one of two sides of this triangle (Pasch's Axiom). It cannot intersect the side RS because RS belongs to the line CD which is cut by PE in F outside of the segment RS. Therefore, the line PE intersects the side QR. Let us denote the intersection point of PE and QR, the existence of which was just proved, by G. The straight line QX intersects the side GF of the triangle RGF in the point E. Applying again Pasch's Axiom to the triangle RGF and the line QX, we come to the conclusion that QX does intersect CD and thus the line AB is right parallel to the line CD through the point Q.

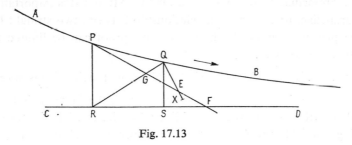

Fig. 17.13

We consider now the second case, the point Q on AB being to the left of the point P (Fig. 14). Let QX be any line through Q within the angle SQB and E any point on this line above the point Q. Joining E to P, we obtain a straight line through P within the angle RPB and therefore EP, produced through P, intersects CD in a point F. The points P and E being separated by the line SQ, the lines EP and SQ intersect in a point G between E and P.

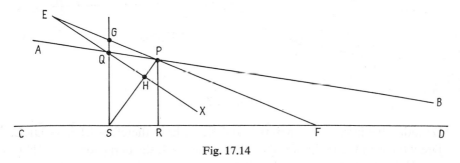

Fig. 17.14

Joining S and P, we consider the triangle GSP. The line EX penetrates inside this triangle through the point Q on the side SG. Therefore, EX must intersect one of two other sides of the triangle GSP. It cannot intersect GP because

17 Kogbetliantz

GP belongs to the line EF which is already intersected by EX in E. Thus, EX must intersect SP. Let us denote the intersection point by H. Now the line EX cuts the side of the triangle SPF in H and therefore it must intersect PF or SF. It cannot intersect the line PF for a second time and therefore EX intersects CD between the points S and F which completes the proof of Lemma III.

This lemma states that a straight line parallel to another line in one of its points is parallel in the same sense and to the same line in all its points. But it does not prove that the relationship of parallelism is reversible and thus mutual. In other words, from the fact that AB is parallel to CD does not follow immediately that CD is parallel to AB and this important property of parallelism to be a mutual relationship between two straight lines is yet to be proved. Lemma III shows that this proof can be limited to a single point chosen on CD.

LEMMA IV. If a line AB is parallel to CD, then the line CD is parallel to AB.

Given two lines AB and CD, suppose that the first AB is known to be parallel to the right to the second line CD (Fig. 15). Draw a transversal HJ cutting both AB and CD in E and F respectively, choose any point G interior to the segment EF and, rotating the line HJ about G, bring it in a new position PQ such that the line PQ makes equal angles with AB and CD.

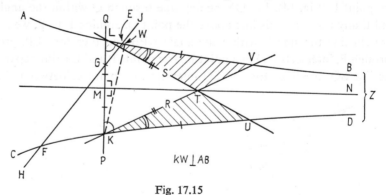

Fig. 17.15

Denoting the intersection points L and K, we have therefore $\overset{\frown}{BLK} = \overset{\frown}{DKL}$. Draw through the midpoint M of the segment KL the perpendicular MN to KL. This line MN, produced in both directions as far as we want, cannot intersect AB since by symmetry it would then also intersect CD at the same point at which it meets AB, so that AB would interesect CD and could not be parallel to it.

For the same reason MN does not meet CD and thus remains, for all its infinite length, between AB and CD separating these two lines from one another.

To prove the lemma we have to show that any straight line through K and lying within the angle LKD intersects AB. Given such a line KR, we draw through the point L a line LS symmetrical to KR with respect to MN, so that $\widehat{RKL} = \widehat{SLK}$. This line LS intersects CD in U because AB is parallel to CD by hypothesis. Therefore, it also intersects MN which separates the point L from the line CD.

Let T denote the intersection point of LS and MN. Joining T to K, we compare the right triangles MTK and MTL. They are equal (Theorem V, Chapter 14). Therefore, $\widehat{TKL} = \widehat{TLK} = \widehat{SLK} = \widehat{RKL}$, so that the line KT coincides with the line KR. Plotting on the line LB a segment LV equal to KU, we define a triangle LTV. We will prove now that the side TV of this triangle is a continuation of the line KT that is, the point V is on the line KR. Comparing the triangles KTU and LTV, we find indeed that they are equal because KU = LV by construction, KT = LT as hypotenuses of two equal right triangles KMT and LMT, and finally the included angles TKD and TLB are equal also:

$$\widehat{TKD} = \widehat{LKD} - \widehat{LKT} = \widehat{KLB} - \widehat{KLT} = \widehat{TLB}.$$

The equality $\varDelta KTU = \varDelta LTV$ entails $\widehat{KTU} = \widehat{LTV}$ so that indeed, the points Q, T, U being collinear, those K, T, V are also collinear and the segments KT and TV form one and the same straight line. Thus, the line KR intersects AB in V and the Lemma IV is proved: any straight line through K and within the angle WKD (KW is perpendicular to AB) intersects the line AB, while CD does not. Therefore, by definition of parallelism, the line CD through the point K is parallel to the right to AB and, therefore (Lemma III), the line CD is the right parallel to AB in general.

To clarify completely the concept of parallelism in hyperbolic geometry, it remains to prove:

LEMMA V. Two lines parallel in the same sense to a third line are parallel to each other in that sense.

Two lines parallel in the same direction to a third line may form two different configurations. (Fig. 16a and 16b) and the two cases are considered separately. Suppose first that the third line L_3 lies between the lines L_1 and L_2 which are parallel to it (Fig. 16a).

Using the indirect method, we suppose to the contrary that the lines L_1 and L_2 are not parallel to the right, although each of them separately is parallel to the right to the line L_3. On the other hand, L_1 and L_2 cannot intersect: they are separated by the line L_3 so that, if they intersect each other, one of them must also cut the line L_3 which would contradict the assumption of its parallelism to L_3. Thus, if the lines L_1 and L_2 are not parallel, they are necessarily ultraparallel to each other.

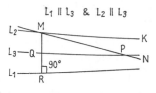

Fig. 17.16a

Therefore, it is possible to draw through any point M on L_2 (Fig. 16a) a parallel MN to L_1 within the angle RMK, where RM is perpendicular to L_1. This parallel to L_1 must intersect L_3 because L_2 is parallel to L_3. Denoting the intersection point of MN and L_3 by P, we obtain two parallels through P in the same direction to the line L_1 which is impossible: there can be one and only one parallel to a given line in a given direction. Therefore, our initial assumption that the lines L_1 and L_2, both parallel in the same direction to L_3, are not parallel to each other is fallacious and Lemma V is proved in this case.

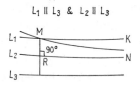

Fig. 17.16b

Consider now L_2 between L_1 and L_3 (Fig. 16b). Assuming again that L_1 and L_2 are parallel to L_3, but L_1 is not parallel to L_2, we state that L_1 and L_2 cannot intersect, otherwise there would be two different parallels in the same direction to L_3 through the intersection point of L_1 and L_2. Therefore, if L_1 and L_2 are not parallel, they are ultraparallel and a line MN parallel to L_2 can be drawn through a point M on L_1 within the angle RMK. Consider now the three lines MN, L_2 and L_3. The lines MN and L_3 are parallel in the same direction to the line L_2 which lies between them. Applying the first case of our Lemma V to the configuration formed by MN which is parallel to L_2, L_2 and L_3 also parallel to L_2, we come to the conclusion that MN and L_3 must be parallel to each other. But this conclusion is impossible because then there would be two different parallels in the same direction to the line L_3 through the point M on L_1. Thus, the second case of Lemma V is proved.

We consider now a birectangle ABCD with the base CD and the summit AB (Fig. 17). We know that the two angles at the summit ABC and BAD are equal. To prove that they are acute angles it is sufficient to show that their sum is less than two right angles. Drawing through the points B and A the parallels BZ and AZ to the base CDZ, we construct two infinite triangles BCZ and ADZ with equal sides BC = AD and equal angles BCD = ADZ $= \pi/2$. Using Lemma I, we state that they are equal and thus $\overparen{CBZ} = \overparen{DAZ}$.

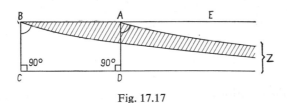

Fig. 17.17

On the other hand, Lemma V proves that the lines BZ and AZ are parallel to each other. The triangle ABZ is also an infinite triangle. Applying to this infinite triangle Lemma II, we conclude that the exterior angle EAZ is greater than the interior angle EBZ: $\overparen{EAZ} > \overparen{EBZ}$. Adding on both sides of this inequality the equal angles DAZ and CBZ, we obtain $\overparen{EBC} < \overparen{EAD}$ since $\overparen{EAD} = \overparen{EAZ} + \overparen{DAZ} > \overparen{EBZ} + \overparen{CBZ} = \overparen{EBC}$.

But $\overparen{EAD} = 180° - \overparen{BAD}$, so that the inequality $\overparen{EBC} < \overparen{EAD}$ becomes $\overparen{EBC} < 180° - \overparen{BAD}$ and therefore the sum of two summit angles of a birectangle $\overparen{EBC} + \overparen{BAD}$ is shown to be less than two right angles: $\overparen{EBC} + \overparen{BAD} < 180°$.

This result has far-reaching consequences. We saw that the sum of angles of a triangle is equal to the sum of two summit angles of a birectangle. Therefore, in hyperbolic geometry the sum of angles of a triangle is less than two right angles. The sum of angles of a quadrilateral is equal to the sum of six angles of two triangles into which the quadrilateral is subdivided by its own diagonal. Therefore, the sum of four angles of any quadrilateral is less than four right angles. We can now prove that Theorem XXVIII also holds in hyperbolic geometry.

THEOREM XXVIII*: *Two triangles are equal if their corresponding angles are equal.*

Given two triangles ABC and DEF (Fig. 18) with equal angles: ABC = DEF, BCA = EFD and CAB = FDE. If any two corresponding sides are equal, then the triangles are equal as having equal sides included between equal angles. Let us suppose the contrary, assuming that no two corresponding sides are equal. We will deduce from this assumption a contradiction and thus prove Theorem XXVIII* by the indirect method.

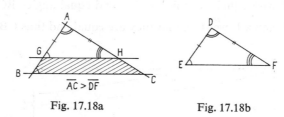

Fig. 17.18a   Fig. 17.18b

We choose the notations so that the two unequal corresponding sides AB and DE verify the inequality DE < AB. Comparing the corresponding sides AC and DF, we distinguish between two possible cases: (a) AC > DF and (b) AC < DF. Since DE < AB we can find on AB such a point G between A and B that AG = DE. It is now easy to deduce a contradiction from our assumptions.

If AC > DF we can plot AH = DF on the side AC and joining G to H build a triangle AGH. This triangle is equal to $\triangle$DEF, having equal angles included between sides. Therefore, we obtain $\overset{\frown}{AGH} = \overset{\frown}{DEF}$ and $\overset{\frown}{AHG} = \overset{\frown}{DFE}$. But by hypothesis $\overset{\frown}{DEF} = \overset{\frown}{ABC}$ and $\overset{\frown}{DFE} = \overset{\frown}{ACB}$, so that the sum of four angles of the quadrilateral BGHC can be shown to be equal to four right angles:

$$\hat{B} + \overset{\frown}{BGH} + \hat{C} + \overset{\frown}{CHG} = \overset{\frown}{DEF} + \overset{\frown}{BGH} + \overset{\frown}{EFD} + \overset{\frown}{CHG}$$

$$= (\overset{\frown}{AGH} + \overset{\frown}{BGH}) + (\overset{\frown}{AHG} + \overset{\frown}{CHG})$$

$$= 180° + 180° = 360°,$$

which is impossible. We saw indeed that since the summit angles of a bireectangle are acute angles, the sum of the angles of a triangle is less than two right angles and, therefore, the sum of the angles of a quadrilateral must be less than four right angles. The contradiction thus obtained proves that the side DF cannot be less than AC which eliminates the case (a).

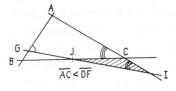

Fig. 17.18c

Suppose now that DF exceeds AC. Plotting the length DF on the line AC we obtain (Fig. 18c) a point I such that C is between I and A and AI = DF. Joining G to I we have again ΔAGI = ΔDEF, so that $\overset{\frown}{AIG}$ = $\overset{\frown}{DFE}$ = $\overset{\frown}{ACB}$. Thus, for the triangle CIJ (the vertex J of which is the intersection point of the line GI with BC), our assumption that DF > AC entails the equality of the interior angle CIJ to the exterior angle ACJ and this is impossible: Legendre's Theorem proved in this chapter states that, if straight lines are infinite in extent, the sum of angles of a triangle cannot exceed 180°, and indeed in the hyperbolic geometry with its infinite straight lines the sum of angles of a triangle is definitely *less* than two right angles. But, if $\overset{\frown}{CIJ}$ = $\overset{\frown}{ACJ}$ then the sum of only two angles of the triangle CIJ will be equal to 180° since $\overset{\frown}{CIJ}$ + ICJ = ACJ + ICJ = 180°. Therefore, the case (b) is also impossible and the assumption, that no corresponding sides are equal although the triangles have equal angles, leads to contradictions.

We add that in the second contradiction the existence of the triangle CIJ can be proved with the aid of Pasch's Axiom. The line GI joining I to G passes through the point G and does not coincide with the line AB. Therefore, it penetrates into the interior of the triangle ABC. Applying Pasch's Axiom we conclude that the line GI must intersect one of the segments AC and BC or leave the interior of the triangle ABC through the vertex C. It cannot pass through the point C nor intersect AC between A and C because in such a case it would have a second point in common with the line AI and therefore coincide with AI, which is precluded because the point G does not belong to AI. Therefore, the line GI intersects BC in a point between B and C and it was this intersection point which we denoted by J.

With the proof that Theorem XXVIII* holds in hyperbolic geometry just achieved, we come to the conclusion that the existence of similar triangles is the characteristic feature of Euclidean geometry. Theorem XXVIII* precludes their existence in both non-Euclidean geometries, so that in them the shape of a triangle determines its size.

No systematic development of hyperbolic geometry can be given here. All we can do is to mention a few more facts omitting their proofs. We want to describe now some fundamental constructions which can be performed with the aid of a compass and a ruler and which are characteristic of hyperbolic geometry. The constructions which are the same in both hyperbolic and Euclidean geometries need not to be described since they can be found in any textbook on Euclidean geometry.

To construct a parallel, right or left, to a given line AB through a given point C non-incident with AB (Fig. 19) draw through C the perpendicular CD to AB and also the perpendicular CE to CD, so that CE and AB are two ultraparallels having as their common perpendicular the line CD. There cannot be more than one common perpendicular to two ultraparallel lines otherwise the two ultraparallels and two common perpendiculars would form a quadrilateral with a sum of angles equal to four right angles which is impossible. The ultraparallels diverge on each side of their common perpendicular which is the shortest distance between the two ultraparallels.

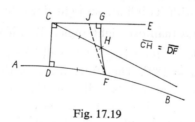

Fig. 17.19

Choosing any point F on the line AB and to the right of D, we drop from F the perpendicular FG on the line CE forming thus a quadrilateral CDFG with three right angles at the vertices D, C, G and with an acute angle DFG. In such a quadrilateral each of two sides of the acute angle is greater than the opposite side: DF > CG and GF > CD. The fact that the angle DFG is less than the right angle CGF precludes the equality CG = DF since were CG = DF then CDFG as a birectangle should have two equal summit angles $\overset{\frown}{DFG} = \overset{\frown}{CGF}$, while $\overset{\frown}{DFG} < \overset{\frown}{CGF}$. The assumption that CG exceeds DF would entail a contradiction also: in the triangle FGJ, where CJ = DF, the interior angle JGF (right angle) would exceed the exterior angle FJC (equal to the angle DFJ which is a part of the acute angle DFG).

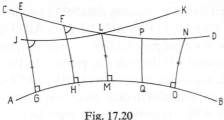

Fig. 17.20

Therefore, a circle of radius DF described from the center C will intersect the line GF at a point H. The straight line CH is the right parallel to AB.

As a second construction let us consider how to draw the common perpendicular to two given ultraparallel lines AB and CD (Fig. 20). Choosing any two points E and F on CD, draw the perpendiculars EG and FH to AB through these two points E and F. If, by chance, EG = FH then the quadrilateral EGHF is a birectangle with the base GH and the summit EF. Joining the midpoints of its base and of its summit we obtain the common perpendicular.

But in general EG and FH are not equal. To fix our ideas we denote by FH the shorter perpendicular, so that EG > FH. Plotting on GE the segment GJ = HF, we draw through the point J a straight line JK such that the angle it makes with GJ is equal to the angle the line CD forms at F with the line HF: $\widehat{\text{GJK}} = \widehat{\text{HFD}}$. The line JK intersects CD at L and we drop from L a perpendicular LM on AB.

We consider now the point N on CD and the point O on AB defining them by the conditions FN = EL and HO = GM, and compare the two quadrilaterals HFNO and GJLM. With the aid of equal triangles we prove that these two quadrilaterals are equal, so that NO = LM and moreover $\widehat{\text{MON}}$ = $\widehat{\text{GML}}$ = 90°. Therefore, the configuration MLNO is a birectangle and the line PQ joining the midpoints of the base MO and of the summit LN is the common perpendicular to two ultraparallels AB, CD.

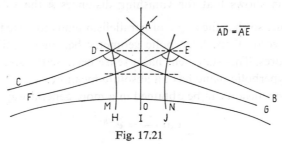

$\overline{AD} = \overline{AE}$

Fig. 17.21

Finally, we describe how a common parallel to two intersecting lines AB, AC can be drawn. Choosing D on AC and E on AB (Fig. 21) at equal distances from A, draw the right parallel DG through the point D to the line AB and also the left parallel EF through the point E to the line AC. Through the points D and E draw also the bisectors DH and EJ of the angles CDG and BEF. They are ultraparallel to each other and their common perpendicular MN is the line which is parallel to the right to AB and parallel to the left to AC.

This last construction also solves the question of how to construct the distance for which a given acute angle is the angle of parallelism. Consider in Fig. 21 the bisector AI of the angle BAC. It is perpendicular to the line MN and intersects it at the point O. The line MN is the right parallel to AB and the left parallel to AC. Therefore, the distance AO just constructed is that distance for which the given angle IAB is the angle of parallelism. Thus, given an acute angle, it is sufficient to reflect it in one of its sides and then construct the common parallel (which is perpendicular to the side which played the role of the mirror) to find the distance corresponding to this angle of parallelism.

The first construction solves the inverse problem, namely: given a distance, find by construction the corresponding angle of parallelism. Together, these constructions show clearly that in hyperbolic geometry distances and angles are related: to each angle corresponds a distance and inversely. This allows the choice of a distance as an *absolute unit of length*, for instance the distance which corresponds to an angle of parallelism equal to 45°.

Exploring the hyperbolic geometry Lobachevsky discovered in 1825 that the functional relationship between the angle of parallelism w at a point G and the distance GH of this point from the straight line NL (Fig. 10) is expressed by the formula

$$\tan \frac{w}{2} = e^{-h}$$

where $h =$ GH is the length of the segment GH.

This relation shows that for vanishing distances h the value of $\tan \frac{w}{2}$ approaches one, so that the angle of parallelism tends to a right angle when GH tends to zero. Thus, hyperbolic geometry becomes Euclidean for infinitesimal figures. This statement has a sense because the size of geometric figures in a hyperbolic plane has an absolute meaning.

The same conclusion can be obtained in a more general way. The relation

$$\tan \frac{w}{2} = e^{-h}$$

is only a particular case of the general relation

$$\tan\frac{w}{2} = e^{-h/c}, \tag{2}$$

where c is a constant length characterizing a particular hyperbolic plane in the same way in which the sphere's radius R specifices a particular elliptic plane. If now the constant c becomes infinite the configurations of finite size (h finite) obey the Euclidean geometry since for them $\tan\frac{w}{2} = 1$ and thus $w = 90°$.

This limiting case is analogous to $R = \infty$ in the elliptic geometry and thus Euclidean geometry is an intermediary case between the elliptic and hyperbolic geometries obtained at the limit, when their characteristic constants (R and c) become infinite.

Areas in Hyperbolic Geometry

The measurement of areas in Euclidean geometry with the aid of a unit-area (unit-square with a side equal to the unit of length) is based on the existence of similar figures. A square with a side equal to n units is similar to the unit-area and therefore it contains n^2 such unit-squares. Any rectangle can be subdivided into equal squares, if its sides are commensurable. One could also use as unit-area regular triangles or regular hexagons because they share with the squares the property of filling completely, if juxtaposed, a part of the Euclidean plane without leaving gaps between them.

No analogy to this situation can be found in a hyperbolic plane. There are of course squares, that is, quadrilaterals having four equal sides and four equal acute angles, but their shapes being determined by the size, a square of side $2a$ does not contain exactly four squares of side a and its area is not equal to four times the area of a square of side a. There are also quadrilaterals with equal opposite sides (which are ultraparallel) and equal angles, but they cannot be subdivided into squares, although these quadrilaterals generalize Euclidean rectangles.

The only way of comparing and measuring areas in a hyperbolic plane is to use congruent triangles, and congruent figures in general. Thus, two areas which can be subdivided into congruent parts are equal even when, the arrangement of parts being different, they have different shape, and thus are not congruent as entities. Since any polygonal area can be partioned into triangles the comparison of triangular areas becomes the foundation of measurement of hyperbolic areas.

Two triangles can have equal areas without being congruent and then the sums of their angles are equal, although their shapes are different and therefore their angles are unequal too. Inversely, if two triangles of different shape have equal sums of angles, their areas are equal. These two converse propositions will be now proved.

Instead of the sum $s = \hat{A} + \hat{B} + \hat{C}$ of angles of a triangle we will consider the difference $d^* = \pi - s = \pi - (\hat{A} + \hat{B} + \hat{C})$ and call it the *defect* of this triangle. The concept of defect in the hyperbolic geometry is analogous to the concept of spherical excess in the elliptic geometry. We will see that the area of a triangle is proportional to its defect and, namely, is equal to the product $c^2 [\pi - (\hat{A} + \hat{B} + \hat{C})]$, where the coefficient of proportionality c^2 is the square of the characteristic constant c of the particular hyperbolic plane to which the triangle belongs.

The expression of the area $c^2 d^*$ is analogous to that $R^2 E$ of the elliptic geometry, where $E = \hat{A} + \hat{B} + \hat{C} - \pi$ is the spherical excess of the triangle. Its proof is based on the following two theorems:

THEOREM XXIX: *Two triangles having equal areas have also equal defects.*

THEOREM XXX: *Two triangles having equal defects have also equal areas.*

Let us call two figures having equal areas equivalent. By definition, two triangles are equivalent if they can be partitioned by straight lines into congruent parts. Drawing supplementary lines, if necessary, we subdivide congruent polygonal parts into congruent triangles, so that two equivalent triangles can always be considered as partitioned into congruent triangles.

Fig. 17.22

We first consider a special kind of partition into triangles, namely the so-called partition into *subtriangles*. This kind of partition is obtained when only *transversals* are used for dividing a given triangle into smaller triangles. A *transversal* of a triangle is the line joining one of its vertices to a point of the side opposite to this vertex. Thus (Fig. 22), a triangle ABC is partitioned by the transversal CD into two subtriangles ACD and BCD.

It is not difficult to prove that *in a partition into subtriangles the defects are added.* Thus, the sum of the defects $\pi - s_1$ and $\pi - s_2$ of ADC and BDC (Fig. 22) is equal to the defect $\pi - s$ of the triangle ABC, if $s_1 = \hat{A} + \widehat{ADC} + \widehat{ACD}$, $s_2 = \widehat{BDC} + \hat{B} + \widehat{BCD}$ and $s = \hat{A} + \hat{B} + \hat{C}$ denote the angle-sums of these triangles:

$$(\pi - s_1) + (\pi - s_2) = \pi - \hat{A} - \hat{B} - (\widehat{ACD} + \widehat{BCD})$$

$$+ \pi - (\widehat{ADC} + \widehat{BDC}) = \pi - (\hat{A} + \hat{B} + \hat{C}),$$

since $\widehat{ACD} + \widehat{BCD} = \hat{C}$ and $\widehat{ADC} + \widehat{BDC} = \pi$.

Now, two congruent triangles have equal areas, equal angles and equal defects. Therefore, if two equivalent triangles are partitioned into subtriangles, their defects are equal because the component defects of subtriangles are the same for both equivalent triangles. This is not yet the proof of Theorem XXIX, since the partition into subtriangles is a particular case. In general, in a partition into triangles the component triangles are not subtriangles because not all the lines establishing the partition are transversals.

The general case is reduced to the particular case of subtriangles because any partition which is not a partition by transversals can be made such by the addition of supplementary lines: it is sufficient to draw transversals from a vertex of the large triangle through each vertex of small triangles in the interior of the large triangle to transform them into subtriangles. Quadrilaterals thus created in certain cases are subdivided into subtriangles by the addition of their diagonals. Thus, Theorem XXIX is proved.

Theorem XXX will be proved in two steps: first we consider a particular case when two triangles having equal defects are supposed, also, to have a side of one equal to a side of the other; then we will reduce the general case to this particular case.

We suppose that two triangles with equal defects ABC and A*B*C* have equal sides AB and A*B*: AB = A*B*. Drawing the lines PQ and P*Q* through the midpoints D, E and D*, E* of the sides BC, AC and B*C*, A*C* of these triangles (Fig. 23), we drop the perpendiculars BF, CG, AH to PQ, and the perpendiculars B*F*, C*G*, A*H* to P*Q*, forming two birectangles BFHA and B*F*H*A*. As we know, the sum of the angles of a triangle is equal to double the summit-angle of the corresponding birectangle. Since the defects of the triangles ABC and A*B*C* are equal, the two birectangles have equal summit-angles. Moreover, their summits are equal also: AB = A*B*. We do not know whether BF and B*F* are equal, but the following reasoning proves that they are. Suppose the contrary, BF $\neq$ B*F*. Then superposing the summits we would have a quadrilateral FF*HH* with four right angles which is impossible. Thus, two birectangles with equal summit angles and equal summits are congruent and therefore they have equal areas.

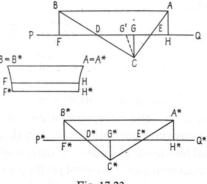

Fig. 17.23

On the other hand, the area of the triangle ABC is equal to the area of the birectangle ABFH: the triangles AEH and CEG are congruent, as well as the triangles BDF and CDG. It is sufficient to prove the congruence of the first pair. Rotating AEH about the vertex E through 180°, we make the point A coincide with the point C, since E is the midpoint of the segment AC. The line EQ after the rotation takes the direction of the line EP. Were the point H non-congruent with G, occupying after the rotation a position G' different from G, we would have two perpendiculars CG and CG' dropped from the point C on the line DE which is impossible. Therefore, the segment EH must be equal to EG and the triangles are congruent. Thus, the area of the birectangle is equal to that of the triangle. The same conclusion is true for the birectangle associated with the triangle A*B*C*. Since the equality of birectangles entails the equivalence of our two triangles, Theorem XXX is proved under the assumption AB = A*B*.

We consider now the general case and assume that no side of A*B*C* is equal to a side of ABC. To fix our ideas we choose the notations so that the segment A*C* is greater than AC, A*C* > AC. To prove the theorem we will construct a third triangle with the same defect as ABC and having one of its sides equal to the side AB of the first triangle and the other equal to the side A*C* of the second triangle. Every one of our two given triangles will be equivalent to this third triangle and therefore they will be equivalent to each other.

Draw the birectangle ABFH associated with the triangle ABC (Fig. 24) and choose to the left of the point E a point I such that AI = $\frac{1}{2} \cdot$ A*C* > $\frac{1}{2} \cdot$ AC = AE. Producing AI, draw AJ = A*C* and join J to B. A third triangle ABJ is thus formed with the base AB and the opposite vertex J. To study it we drop the perpendicular JK to the base FH of the birectangle, forming a right triangle IJK. It is equal to the right triangle AHI since IJ = AI and $\widehat{\text{AIH}}$ = $\widehat{\text{KIJ}}$, the proof being exactly the same as for the triangles AEH and CEG in Fig. 23. Therefore, the perpendicular JK is equal to AH and also to BF since AH = BF. Having established that JK = BF we now compare the triangles JKL and BFL, the letter L denoting the intersection point of BJ and FH. Rotating BFL through 180° about the vertex L, we bring the point F on the line LK. It must coincide with the point K, otherwise (Fig. 24) in any position F_1 to the left of K or F_2 to the right of K it would generate a birectangle F_1B_1JK or KJB_2F_2 (B_1F_1 = BF = JK) with unequal summit-angles which is impossible. In F_1B_1JK we would have an obtuse summit-angle at B_1 and in KJB_2F_2 an obtuse summit-angle at J while the other summit-angle is acute. Therefore, the point F coincides after the rotation with the point K and the triangles BFL and JKL are congruent.

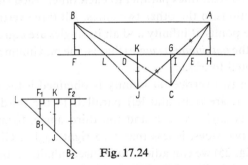

Fig. 17.24

We conclude that the sum of angles of the triangle ABJ is the same as that of the triangle ABC because both are equal to the sum of two summit-angles of the birectangle ABFH. Thus, the defects of these two triangles are equal. But, by hypothesis, the triangles A*B*C* and ABC have the same defect. Therefore, our three triangles ABC, A*B*C* and ABJ have equal defects. Since ABC and ABJ have also equal sides AB = AB, they are equivalent. But the triangles A*B*C* and ABJ have also equal sides A*C* = AJ and therefore they are equivalent too. Finally, the triangles ABC and A*B*C* are equivalent since each of them is equivalent to the same third triangle ABJ. Thus, Theorem XXX is proved.

This discussion justifies the conclusion that area and defect of a triangle must be proportional since two triangles have equal areas if and only if their defects are equal. Moreover, in partitions areas and defects are added. We omit the proof of the fact that the coefficient of proportionality is equal to the square c^2 of the characteristic constant.

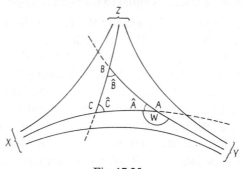

Fig. 17.25

There is a maximum triangle in the hyperbolic geometry. This triangle is formed by three straight lines parallel to each other, each side being parallel in opposite directions to the other two sides. All three vertices of the maximum triangle are points at infinity and all its angles are equal to zero. Therefore, the area of the *maximum triangle* (that is, the maximum area of a triangle in general), is equal to $c^2\pi$.

A triangle with two vertices at infinity is obtained if the two sides, intersecting each other, are right and left parallels to the third side. In such a triangle two of its angles vanish and the third angle, formed at the intersection point of two sides, is less than two right angles. Given an ordinary triangle ABC (Fig. 25) we can adjoin to it three infinite triangles XAY, YBZ and ZCX, the straight lines XY, YZ, ZX being parallel to two sides of the triangle ABC. For instance, XY is parallel to the left to AC, and to the right to BA. Denoting the angles of the triangle ABC by $\hat{A}$, $\hat{B}$, $\hat{C}$, we see that the angle at the vertex A of the triangle XAY is equal to $\pi - \hat{A}$. Likewise, $\pi - \hat{B}$ and $\pi - \hat{C}$ are angles of YBZ and ZCX. Together the four triangles ABC, XAY, YBZ, ZCX form the maximum triangle XYZ and therefore we have area ABC $+ c^2\hat{A} + c^2\hat{B} + c^2\hat{C} =$ area XYZ $= c^2\pi$ which gives again: area ABC $= c^2 (\pi - \hat{A} - \hat{B} - \hat{C})$.

This reasoning proves that the formula for the area of a finite triangle can be obtained easily if it is known that the area of a triangle of the type XAY is expressed by the product $c^2 (\pi - w)$, where w is the angle at the vertex A.

Gauss has deduced the formula $c^2(\pi - w)$ for the area of an infinite triangle with a unique non-vanishing angle w, from the assumption that the area of the maximum triangle is finite. Denoting this maximum area by M, consider with Gauss a triangle formed by two parallels to XY through the point A. Its area is a function of the angle w of two parallels to XY which can be denoted by $f(\pi - w)$. Our problem is to find the function $f(x)$. All what we know about $f(x)$ at this moment is the fact that it vanishes, if $w = \pi$, because $w = \pi$ means that the angle of parallelism is a right angle and therefore the point A is on the line XY, so that there is no triangle and no area: $f(0) = 0$. We know also that for the maximum triangle w vanishes and the area is equal to M, so that $f(\pi) = M$.

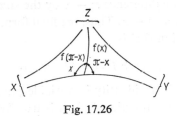

Fig. 17.26

Consider now a partition of the maximum triangle into two subtriangles (Fig. 26) by a parallel to two sides through a point on the third side. This parallel forms the angles x and $\pi - x$ with the side XY, so that the areas of subtriangles are equal to $f(\pi - x)$ and $f(x)$, while their sum is the area M of the maximum triangle:

$$f(\pi - x) + f(x) = M.$$

Take now an interior point P and draw through it three straight lines PX, PY and PZ each parallel to two sides of the maximum triangle (Fig. 27).

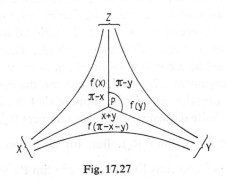

Fig. 17.27

18 Kogbetliantz

Denoting the angles of three infinite triangles XPY, YPZ, ZPX by $\pi - x$, $\pi - y$ and $x + y$ respectively, we find another relation:

$$f(x) + f(y) + f(\pi - x - y) = M,$$

the sum of areas of three triangles being equal to the area M of the maximum triangle.

The first relation $f(\pi - x) + f(x) = M$ gives $M - f(x) = f(\pi - x)$ and thus the second relation can be transformed into

$$f(y) + f(\pi - x - y) = f(\pi - x).$$

Substituting z for the argument $\pi - x - y$ of the function $f(\pi - x - y)$ we must also replace the difference $\pi - x$ by the sum $y + z$ because $z = \pi - x - y$ entails $\pi - x = y + z$. Thus, the final form of the relation verified by our unknown function $f(x)$ is

$$f(y) + f(z) = f(y + z).$$

This relation, which is an identity in variable parameters y and z, is an equation for the unknown function $f(x)$. It is true for all values of y and z. To solve it, that is, to find the structure of the function $f(x)$, we take first $y = z$ which gives $f(z) + f(z) = 2f(z) = f(2z)$. Likewise, for $y = 2z$ the same relation gives $f(2z) + f(z) = 3f(z) = f(3z)$. This suggests that, in general, we will have $nf(z) = f(nz)$ for any positive integer n. Our conjecture is easy to justify by mathematical induction: if $f(nz) = nf(z)$, then for $y = nz$ we obtain $f(nz) + f(z) = (n + 1)f(z) = f[(n + 1)z]$ and, therefore, $f(nz) = nf(z)$, for all integral and positive values of n.

Substituting in this result $z = 1$, we obtain $f(n) = nf(1)$. The value $f(1)$ is a constant and this constant can be denoted by c^2 since it is positive. Thus, we have $f(n) = nc^2$, where n is a positive integer. Replacing z in the formula $f(nz) = nf(z)$ by a rational number m/n, we further conclude that $nf(m/n) = f(m)$, so that $nf(m/n) = mc^2$; that is, $f(m/n) = (m/n)c^2$ which extends the validity of the expression $f(n) = nc^2$ to rational arguments. Here we observe than an area is a continuous magnitude. Therefore, the measure $f(x)$ of an area must be a continuous function. If the value of this function for an irrational argument z is asked, we can use the continuity of $f(z)$ and find the values in question as a limit: suppose that the irrational number z is the limit of an infinite sequence of rational numbers R_k so that $z = \lim_{k = \infty} R_k$, then we also have $f(z) = \lim_{k = \infty} f(R_k)$. But, for all rational arguments R_k we have $f(R_k) = R_k \cdot c^2$ and thus $\lim_{k = \infty} f(R_k) = c^2 \cdot \lim_{k = \infty} R_k = zc^2$.

Thus, for any positive argument z the function $f(z)$ is simply proportional to it, that is, $f(z) = c^2z$. In particular for $f(\pi - w)$ we find the value $c^2(\pi - w)$ and this is the value of the area of an infinite triangle with two vertices at infinity and the angle w at its third vertex. We saw that the formula for the area of a finite triangle follows from this result immediately. This formula, area ABC $= c^2 (\pi - \hat{A} - \hat{B} - \hat{C})$, again indicates that the sum of angles of an infinitesimal triangle tends to 180° when the triangle vanishes: to a vanishing area corresponds a vanishing defect, so that the sum $\hat{A} + \hat{B} + \hat{C}$ becomes equal to 180°. In other words, if the characteristic constant c of a hyperbolic plane becomes infinite, the hyperbolic plane is transformed into an Euclidean plane because the triangles of finite area then have 180° as the sum of their angles: $\pi - \hat{A} - \hat{B} - \hat{C} = $ area ABC$/c^2$ gives at the limit, for $c = \infty$, $\hat{A} + \hat{B} + \hat{C} = 180°$.

CHAPTER 18

Principle of Parity
Trigonometric and Hyperbolic Functions

Applications

In the theory of complex numbers we saw the importance of the principle of separation of real and imaginary. It can easily be extended to functions $f(z)$ of a complex variable $z = x + iy$ whose values are in general complex expressions of the type $u + iv$ where u and v are real functions of two real variables x and y. Thus, for instance, if $f(z) = e^z$, then

$$e^z = e^{x+iy} = e^x e^{iy} = e^x (\cos y + i \sin y) = e^x \cos y + i e^x \sin y = u + iv,$$

so that for this function we have $u = e^x \cos y$ and $v = e^x \sin y$.

But there is another way to approach a systematic study of trigonometric functions based on their property of being even or odd functions of the variable. A function $f(x)$ is by definition *even* if $f(-x)$ is equal to $f(x)$, so that the function does not change if the sign of its argument changes: $f(x) = f(-x)$. If a function $f(x)$ changes its sign when the argument x is replaced by $-x$, then it is called an *odd* function, so that for an odd function we must have $f(-x) = -f(x)$.

These definitions show clearly that, in general, a function is neither even nor odd. Take for instance e^x. The relation between e^{-x} and e^x is neither $f(-x) = f(x)$ nor $f(-x) = -f(x)$, but $f(-x) = 1/f(x)$ since $e^{-x} = 1/e^x$. Nevertheless any function $F(x)$ can be represented as a *sum* of its even and odd parts:

$$F(x) = \tfrac{1}{2} [F(-x) + F(x)] + \tfrac{1}{2} [F(x) - F(-x)] = F_e(x) + F_o(x),$$

where the symbols F_e and F_o denote the even and odd part respectively:

$$F_e(x) = \tfrac{1}{2} [F(x) + F(-x)], \quad F_o(x) = \tfrac{1}{2} [F(x) - F(-x)].$$

Translated into geometric language, these statements become as follows: The graph of an even function $y = F(x)$ is a curve symmetrical with respect to the OY-axis, while the equation $y = G(x)$, where $G(x)$ is an odd function, defines a curve symmetrical with respect to the origin since both x and y change their sign simultaneously. A curve in general does not possess a symmetry with respect to OY-axis neither with respect to the origin, but it can be considered as being obtained by the addition of two curves, one symmetrical with respect to OY and the other symmetrical with respect to the origin.

This decomposition of a curve into two component curves symmetrical with respect to the origin and to the OY-axis is *unique*. To prove this let us consider an identity

$$F_e(x) + F_o(x) \equiv G_e(x) + G_o(x) \tag{*}$$

both members of which are sums of an even and of an odd term. We formulate now the *Principle of Parity*, which states that an equation of the type (*) is equivalent to two equations obtained by equating the even terms of two members as well as their odd terms separately, so that $F_e(x) = G_e(x)$ and $F_o(x) = G_o(x)$.

Changing the sign of x we transform the identity (*) into another identity, namely

$$F_e(x) - F_o(x) \equiv G_e(x) - G_o(x).$$

Adding and subtracting these identities, we prove the principle of parity.

Euler's formula

$$e^{ix} = \cos x + i \sin x$$

together with its corollaries

$$\cos x = \tfrac{1}{2}(e^{ix} + e^{-ix}); \quad i \sin x = \tfrac{1}{2}(e^{ix} - e^{-ix})$$

can now be considered as a definition of the fundamental trigonometric functions $\cos x$ and $\sin x$. From this point of view $\cos x$ and $i \sin x$ are even and odd parts of the function e^{ix}. Many important formulas related to them are simply corollaries of this definition. So (6) p. 207, Chapter 6, simply expresses the fact that by definition $\cos x$ is even, while $\sin x$ is odd. Observing that $e^{i\pi} = -1$, we deduce from the identity $e^{i(\pi+x)} = e^{i\pi}e^{ix} = -e^{ix}$ the relation

$$\cos(180° + x) + i \sin(180° + x) = -\cos x - i \sin x.$$

Applying to this relation the principle of parity, we obtain immediately the formulas

$$\cos(180° + x) = -\cos x, \quad \sin(180° + x) = -\sin x,$$

since $\cos(180° + x) = \cos(-180° + x) = \cos(180° - x)$ is even, while $\sin(180° + x) = \sin(-180° + x) = -\sin(180° - x)$ is odd. The addition formulas are also easy to prove with the aid of the principle of parity as follows:

$$\cos(A + B) + i\sin(A + B) = e^{i(A+B)} = e^{iA}e^{iB}$$

$$= (\cos A + i\sin A)(\cos B + i\sin B).$$

Performing the multiplication, we obtain

$$\cos(A + B) + i\sin(A + B)$$

$$= \cos A \cos B - \sin A \sin B + i(\sin A \cos B + \cos A \sin B).$$

Suppose now that A and B change their signs simultaneously, so that $A + B$ also changes its sign. Applying the principle of parity and observing that the first two terms of the righthand member are even, while the coefficient of i is odd, we conclude that

$$\cos(A + B) = \cos A \cos B - \sin A \sin B;$$

$$\sin(A + B) = \sin A \cos B + \cos A \sin B. \tag{1}$$

Thus, the principle of parity replaces the separation of real and imaginary and, together with Euler's formula, gives the properties of trigonometric functions. In this chapter we complete the study of these functions and discuss the so-called inverse trigonometric functions. Moreover, the same principle of parity applied to the function e^x gives an easy approach to the theory of hyperbolic functions and at the end of this chapter we apply this principle to our study of hyperbolic functions.

Graph of the Function Sin x

The functions $\sin x$ and $\cos x$ are periodic, the period being equal to $360° = 2\pi$: $\sin(360° + x) = \sin x$ as well as $\cos(360° + x) = \cos x$. Their periodicity can be easily established using the addition formulas:

$$\sin(360° + x) = \sin 360° \cos x + \cos 360° \sin x = \sin x$$

$$\cos(360° + x) = \cos 360° \cos x - \sin 360° \sin x = \cos x$$

since $\sin 360° = 0$ and $\cos 360° = 1$. Therefore it is sufficient to study the curve $y = \sin x$ in an interval of length $2\pi = 360°$ and then reproduce its arc in this interval by periodicity. If the interval from $x = -180°$ up to $x = 180°$ is chosen as the fundamental interval, then knowing the graph in the right half-interval $0° \leqslant x \leqslant 180°$, we will know the graph of $y = \sin x$ in the left half-interval $-180° \leqslant x \leqslant 0°$ since the function $\sin x$ being odd, the curve $y = \sin x$ is symmetrical with respect to the origin.

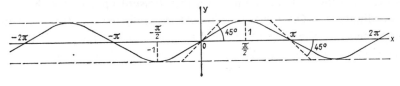

Fig. 18.1 a

Now we know that $\sin x$ increases from zero to one when the argument x increases from zero to $\pi/2 = 90°$, the value one being the maximum of $\sin x$. When x continues to increase from $90°$ to $180°$ the function $\sin x$ decreases from one back to zero, so that its graph (see Fig. 1a) in the interval from zero to $180°$ may be described as a half-wave above OX-axis. This half-wave is completed by another half-wave in the interval from $-180°$ to zero, symmetrical to the first with respect to the origin. The graph is called a *sinusoid* and it extends from minus infinity to plus infinity in identical waves each of which occupies an interval of length $2\pi = 360°$.

We saw (Chapter 9, p. 419) that the ratio $\sin x/x$ approaches one as x tends to zero, $\lim\limits_{x=0} \sin x/x = 1$, so that the curve $y = \sin x$ at the origin cannot be distinguished from the straight line $y = x$. We can state that the tangent to the sinusoid at the point $x = 0$, as well as at all points $x = 2\pi k = 360° k$,

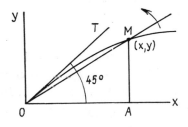

Fig. 18.1 b

where k is an integer, makes an angle of $45°$ with the OX-axis. A tangent line indeed is defined as the ultimate position of a secant when its two intersection points coincide at the limit. Therefore, a tangent OT to the sinusoide at the origin (Fig. 1b) is the limit of the secant OM whose second intersection point M approaches the origin, the first intersection point (at the origin) being fixed. The slope of this secant is equal to the ratio $AM/OA = y/x$, where x and y are coordinates of the point M on the sinusoide. But $AM = y = \sin x$ since the sinusoid is the graph of the function $y = \sin x$. Therefore, the slope of the variable secant OM takes the form $\mathrm{Sin}\, x/x$.

Now, when the variable point M on the sinusoid approaches the origin, its coordinate $x = OA$ tends to zero. At the limit for $x = 0$ the secant is transformed into the tangent OT and the slope of this tangent is the limit of the slope of the secant, that is, one since $\lim\limits_{x=0} \sin x/x = 1$.

Addition Formulas

The expressions of $\sin (A \pm B)$, $\cos (A \pm B)$ in terms of sines and cosines of A and B were obtained in Chapter 11 with the aid of rotation factors, that is, using *complex* numbers. Therefore, they can be considered as translations into trigonometric language of the simplest properties of *rotations*. On the other hand, it is possible to show that the same formulas (1) are also trigonometric forms of very simple geometrical facts concerning triangular *areas*.

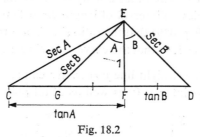

Fig. 18.2

Thus, we also have a proof of addition formulas which deals with *real* numbers only. To begin with $\sin (A \pm B)$, let us consider a triangle CDE whose altitude EF is equal to one (Fig. 2): $EF = 1$. Joining E to a point G between C and F such that $GF = FD$ and denoting the angles $\widehat{CEF}$ and $\widehat{DEF}$ by A and B respectively, so that $\widehat{CEF} = A$ and $\widehat{DEF} = \widehat{GEF} = B$, we have by definition:

$$\tan A = CF, \quad \tan B = FD = GF, \quad CE = \sec A, \quad DE = \sec B,$$

where the trigonometric function sec A (read: *secant* A) is by definition the reciprocal of cos A: $\sec A = 1/\cos A$. Another trigonometric function very often used is *cosecant* A which by definition is the reciprocal of sin A: cosec A = 1/sin A. To complete the study of trigonometric functions we add the definition of the sixth function which is the reciprocal of tan A. It is called *cotangent* A and denoted by cotan A = 1/tan A = cos A/sin A.

The triangular areas in Fig. 2 are related to each other:

$$\triangle CDE = \triangle CFE + \triangle FDE, \quad \triangle CGE = \triangle CFE - \triangle GFE.$$

To evaluate the areas $\triangle CDE$ and $\triangle CGE$, we observe that the angles included between the sides CE = Sec A, DE = Sec B on the one hand, and CE = Sec A, GE = Sec B on the other hand, are equal to A + B and A − B respectively.

Now the area of a triangle, equal to half the product base times altitude, can be expressed also as half the product of two sides times the sine of the included angle. We deduced this expression in Chapter 15 by observing that an altitude is always equal to a side times the sine of the angle included between this side and the base.

Applying this expression of the area to our triangles CDE and CGE and doubling their areas, we obtain $2\triangle CDE = CE \cdot ED \cdot Sin \overset{\frown}{CED}$, $2\triangle CGE = CE \cdot EG \cdot Sin \overset{\frown}{CEG}$, that is:

$$2\triangle CDE = sec\ A\ sec\ B\ sin\ (A + B);$$

$$2\triangle CGE = sec\ A\ sec\ B\ sin\ (A - B).$$

The remaining triangles CFE, FDE and GFE are right triangles, so that their doubled areas are equal to the products of their legs. The common leg EF being equal to one, the areas of these three triangles are numerically equal to $\frac{1}{2}$ tan A and $\frac{1}{2}$ tan B:

$$2\triangle CFE = tan\ A; \quad 2\triangle FDE = 2\triangle GFE = tan\ B.$$

Substituting into the geometric relations between these areas (their expressions in terms of trigonometric functions), we obtain easily

$$sin\ (A + B)\ sec\ A\ sec\ B = tan\ A + tan\ B$$

$$sin\ (A - B)\ sec\ A\ sec\ B = tan\ A - tan\ B.$$

Multiplying these relations by cos A cos B transforms them into the addition formulas (1), since sec A · cos A = 1 and tan A · sec A = sin A. Thus, the addition formulas in trigonometry and the relations between the triangular areas of the Fig. 2 in geometry express one and the same mathematical fact formulated in two different ways.

To deduce the addition formulas for $\cos (A + B)$ with the aid of the same Fig. 2 replace in it the angle B by $90° - B$, so that B will denote the angle $\overset{\frown}{CDE}$ instead of denoting the angle $\overset{\frown}{FED}$ as before. Observing that $\sin [A + (90° - B)] = \sin [90° + (A - B)] = \cos (A - B)$ as well as $\sin (90° - B) = \cos B$, $\cos (90° - B) = \sin B$, $\sec (90° - B) = \operatorname{cosec} B$ and $\tan (90° - B) = \operatorname{cotan} B$, we obtain the desired result from the same geometric relations between the areas which gave us the addition formulas for $\sin (A \pm B)$.

Sum-Formulas for Sine and Cosine

It is easy to verify for numerical values of A and B that the sum of two sines, $\sin A + \sin B$, is not equal to the sine of the sum of two angles $A + B$: $\sin A + \sin B \neq \sin (A + B)$ and the same holds for cosine: $\cos A + \cos B \neq \cos (A + B)$. For the sums of two sines or of two cosines we now deduce the following representations as products of trigonometric functions:

$$\sin A + \sin B = 2 \sin (\tfrac{1}{2}A + \tfrac{1}{2}B) \cos (\tfrac{1}{2}A - \tfrac{1}{2}B) \tag{2}$$

$$\cos A + \cos B = 2 \cos (\tfrac{1}{2}A + \tfrac{1}{2}B) \cos (\tfrac{1}{2}A - \tfrac{1}{2}B).$$

The differences of sines and of cosines have also a similar form:

$$\sin A - \sin B = 2 \cos (\tfrac{1}{2}A + \tfrac{1}{2}B) \sin (\tfrac{1}{2}A - \tfrac{1}{2}B) \tag{3}$$

$$\cos A - \cos B = 2 \sin (\tfrac{1}{2}A + \tfrac{1}{2}B) \sin (\tfrac{1}{2}B - \tfrac{1}{2}A).$$

The sum and the difference of a sine and a cosine can be reduced to these formulas by replacing $\sin A$ by $\cos (90° - A)$ or $\cos A$ by $\sin (90° - A)$, and then denoting $90° - A$ by C.

To prove the conversion formulas (2), (3) we observe that the angles A and B can be represented as follows

$$A = (\tfrac{1}{2}A + \tfrac{1}{2}B) + (\tfrac{1}{2}A - \tfrac{1}{2}B), \quad B = (\tfrac{1}{2}A + \tfrac{1}{2}B) - (\tfrac{1}{2}A - \tfrac{1}{2}B).$$

Therefore, considering the trigonometric functions of A and of B as sines or cosines of the sum and of the difference of two angles $\tfrac{1}{2}A + \tfrac{1}{2}B$ and $\tfrac{1}{2}A - \tfrac{1}{2}B$ and applying to them the addition formulas, we obtain the conversion formulas (2), (3). It is important to observe that in the expression of the difference $\cos A - \cos B$ of two cosines as a double product of two sines, the argument of the second sine is not $\tfrac{1}{2}A - \tfrac{1}{2}B$, but $\tfrac{1}{2}B - \tfrac{1}{2}A$. This is related to the fact that the function cosine is a *decreasing* function of its argument, so that if—in particular—the angles A and B are two acute positive angles such that A is greater than B, then the difference cos A − cos B is a negative number and, therefore, the product of two sines is also negative. Or, the first factor sin $(\frac{1}{2}A + \frac{1}{2}B)$ is positive, so that the second factor must be negative; and it is, since $\frac{1}{2}B - \frac{1}{2}A$ is a negative acute angle, A being greater than B.

EXAMPLES. (1) In Chapter 11 we have examples of applications of the addition formulas for sine and cosine. Here we apply the addition formula for the function tangent to the following example: Find tan (A + B) and tan (A − B), if tan A = $(n - 1)^{-1}$, tan B = $(n + 1)^{-1}$, n being any number except ± 1.

Forming the sum and the difference of two tangents, we have

$$\tan A + \tan B = (n + 1)/(n^2 - 1) + (n - 1)/(n^2 - 1)$$

$$= (n + 1 + n - 1)/(n^2 - 1) = 2n/(n^2 - 1);$$

$$\tan A - \tan B = (n + 1)/(n^2 - 1) - (n - 1)/(n^2 - 1) = 2/(n^2 - 1).$$

The product $\tan A. \tan B$ is equal to $1/(n^2 - 1)$, so that the addition formulas (Chapter 11) give

$$\tan (A + B) = (\tan A + \tan B)/(1 - \tan A \tan B)$$

$$= [2n/(n^2 - 1)]/[1 - 1/(n^2 - 1)] = 2n/(n^2 - 2)$$

$$\tan (A - B) = (\tan A - \tan B)/(1 + \tan A \tan B)$$

$$= [2/(n^2 - 1)]/[1 + 1/(n^2 - 1)] = 2/n^2.$$

If, in particular, $n = 2^{1/2}$ so that tan A = $(2^{1/2} - 1)^{-1} = 2^{1/2} + 1$ and tan B = $2^{1/2} - 1$, then tan (A + B) = ∞ and tan (A − B) = 1. Thus, A + B = 90° and A − B = 45° which gives A = 67° 30′ and B = 22° 30′. We find out that tan 67° 30′ = $\sqrt{2} + 1$ and tan 22° 30′ = $\sqrt{2} - 1$. We. note that the tangents of multiples of 7° 30′ are expressed with the aid of two irrational numbers $\sqrt{3} = 1.73205\cdots$ and $\sqrt{2} = 1.41421\cdots$ only: tan 7°.5 = $(3^{1/2} - 2^{1/2})(2^{1/2} - 1)$, tan 15° = $2 - 3^{1/2}$, tan 37°.5 = $(3^{1/2} - 2^{1/2})(2^{1/2} + 1)$, tan 52°.5 = $(3^{1/2} + 2^{1/2})(2^{1/2} - 1)$, tan 75° = $2 + 3^{1/2}$ and tan 82°.5 = $(3^{1/2} + 2^{1/2})(2^{1/2} + 1)$.

(2) Simplify the sums cos (60° + x) + sin (30° + x), sin (45° + x) + cos (45° + x). Replacing cos (60° + x) and sin (45° + x) by sin (30° − x)

and $\cos (45° - x)$ respectively [see formulae (9), Chapter 6], we use the conversion formulas:

$$\cos (60° + x) + \sin (30° + x) = \sin (30° - x) + \sin (30° + x)$$
$$= 2 \sin 30° \cos x = \cos x;$$

$$\sin (45° + x) + \cos (45° + x) = \cos (45° - x) + \cos (45° + x)$$
$$= 2 \cos 45° \cos x = 2^{1/2} \cos x.$$

(3) Express the products $\sin (A + B) \sin (A - B)$ and $\cos (A + B) \cos (A - B)$ in terms of sine and cosine of A and B. Reading the conversion formulas from the right to the left, we conclude that

$$2 \sin (A + B) \sin (A - B) = -\cos 2A + \cos 2B$$
$$= 1 - \cos 2A - (1 - \cos 2B)$$
$$= 2 (\sin^2 A - \sin^2 B),$$

since $1 - \cos x = 2 \sin^2 (x/2)$, as well as

$$2 \cos (A + B) \cos (A - B) = \cos 2A + \cos 2B$$
$$= 1 + \cos 2A - (1 - \cos 2B)$$
$$= 2 (\cos^2 A - \sin^2 B).$$

Thus, dividing both sides by 2:

$$\sin (A + B) \sin (A - B) = \sin^2 A - \sin^2 B;$$
$$\cos (A + B) \cos (A - B) = \cos^2 A - \sin^2 B.$$

(4) In a triangle the sum of three angles $A + B + C$ is equal to 180°. The trigonometric functions of three angles of a triangle are therefore related to each other by many special formulas which hold only for the three angles A, B, C of a triangle; that is, only in the case when $A + B + C = 180°$. Such are the relations:

$$\left.\begin{array}{c} \tan A + \tan B + \tan C = \tan A \tan B \tan C \\ \cot \tfrac{1}{2}A + \cot \tfrac{1}{2}B + \cot \tfrac{1}{2}C = \cot \tfrac{1}{2}A \cot \tfrac{1}{2}B \cot \tfrac{1}{2}C \\ \sin A + \sin B + \sin C = 4 \cos \tfrac{1}{2}A \cos \tfrac{1}{2}B \cos \tfrac{1}{2}C \\ \cos A + \cos B + \cos C = 1 - 4 \sin \tfrac{1}{2}A \sin \tfrac{1}{2}B \sin \tfrac{1}{2}C. \end{array}\right\} \quad (4)$$

These relations can be proved with the aid of addition formulas and their corollaries, the conversion formulas, using the relation $A + B + C = 180°$ as well as its equivalent $\frac{1}{2}A + \frac{1}{2}B + \frac{1}{2}C = 90°$. Their proofs are left to the reader as an exercise.

Fundamental Formulas

The six trigonometric functions form three groups of two functions whose squares are related:

$$\sin^2 A + \cos^2 A = 1; \quad 1 + \tan^2 A = \sec^2 A; \quad 1 + \cotan^2 A = \cosec^2 A.$$

The first relation was deduced from the definition of sine and cosine [see formula (11), Chapter 6]. Dividing it by $\cos^2 A$ and $\sin^2 A$, we obtain the second and the third relation respectively since

$$\sin A/\cos A = \tan A, \quad 1/\cos A = \sec A,$$

$$\cos A/\sin A = \cotan A, \quad 1/\sin A = \cosec A.$$

It is easy to remember these three fundamental formulas by applying the Pythagorean Theorem to three similar right triangles with an acute angle A at its base (Fig. 3).

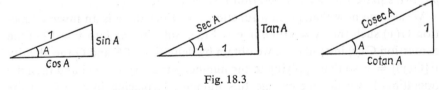

Fig. 18.3

All three of them have one side equal to one. In the first it is the hypotenuse and the corresponding formula states that the sum of squares of sine and cosine of the same angle is one. In the second triangle the side of length one is adjacent to the angle A, so that the opposite side is equal to tan A. This triangle is similar to the first and it is obtained by increasing the sides of the first in the ratio $1/\cos A$ which explains the measure $1/\cos A = \sec A$ of its hypotenuse. This triangle yields the relation $1 + \tan^2 A = \sec^2 A$. Finally the relation $1 + \cotan^2 A = \cosec^2 A$ corresponds to the third triangle the hypotenuse of which is equal to $1/\sin A = \cosec A$, the side one being this time opposite to the angle A.

Inverse Trigonometric Functions

Any function $F(x)$ can be considered as a symbol of an operation applied to the number x. The result of this operation is another number y equal by definition to $F(x)$: $y = F(x)$. The numerical value $\frac{1}{2}$ of the sine of $30° = \pi/6$, for instance, is from this point of view a transform of the number $\pi/6$. The operation by which such a transformation of $\pi/6$ into $\frac{1}{2}$ is carried out is denoted by the symbol sin: $\sin(\pi/6) = \frac{1}{2}$.

Given an operation transforming x into y if there is another operation such that when applied to y, it yields back the original number x, cancelling thus the effect of the first operation, then this second operation is called the *inverse* of the first. Thus, for instance, if $y = x^{1/2}$ is the first, *direct* operation, then $x = y^2$ is the corresponding *inverse* operation. Extraction of square root and squaring are two mutually inverse operations: $(N^{1/2})^2 = N$ as well as $(N^2)^{1/2} = N$. If two mutually inverse operations are applied successively, there is no effect at all. This rule holds under certain limitations which in general are included in the definition of the inverse operation. For instance, there are two square roots, positive and negative, so that $(N^2)^{1/2}$ is equal to $\pm N$ and, beginning with N, we could also have $(N^2)^{1/2} = -N$ instead of N. To justify in this case the statement that two mutually inverse operation sapplied successively have no effect we must choose the extraction of *positive* square root as an operation inverse to squaring.

We assume now that, given a function $y = F(x)$, there is an inverse function $G(y)$ such that $x = G(y)$, if $y = F(x)$. Substituting into $y = F(x)$ the expression $G(y)$ instead of x, we obtain by definition of F and G the identity $F[G(y)] = y$, so that applying to the number y the operation G and then the operation F we do not change this number. Replacing in $x = G(y)$ the argument y by $F(x)$, we obtain also $x = G[F(x)]$, so that the order in which two mutually inverse operations are applied does not matter. In general the functions F and G inverse to each other are different, but if $F(x) = 1/x$, then also $G(y) = 1/y = F(y)$.

Applying this general reasoning to the function sine, we are lead to the conclusion that given the function $y = \sin x$ there must be another function inverse to the sine and such that it expresses the angle x in terms of the value y of its sine, retransforming back the number y into x. This function is called the *arcsine* and it is denoted by the symbol *arcsin* so that $x = \arcsin y$, if $y = \sin x$. The origin of its name is the fact that this function represents the angle x whose sine has the value y. Or, in a circle a central angle and the corresponding arc have the same measure, so that substituting the word *arc* for the word *angle* we can say that the function arcsin y is the *arc* whose *sine* equals y.

Thus, arcsin $\frac{1}{2}$ denotes an angle whose sine has the value $\frac{1}{2}$. We note that there are an infinite number of angles whose sines have the same value $\frac{1}{2}$: such are the angles 30°, 150°, 390°, 510° and in general $30° \pm 360° k$; and also $150° \pm 360° k$, where k is any positive or negative integer. In other words, the equation $\sin x = \frac{1}{2}$ has an infinite number of solutions. Therefore, the expression arcsin $\frac{1}{2}$ has an infinite number of different numerical values. In general, the function arcsin t, whose argument t is a real number between -1 and $+1$ (because it represents the value of a sine), has an infinite number of possible values, is a *multivalued* and, more precisely, an *infinitely multivalued* function of the variable t.

There is always one of these values which lies between $-90° = -\pi/2$ and $90° = \pi/2$ since for a given t satisfying the condition $-1 \leqslant t \leqslant 1$ there is always an acute angle (positive, if $t > 0$, and negative, if $t < 0$) such that its sine is equal to t. This special value of the multivalued function arcsin t is called *principal value* and denoted by Arcsin t. Thus, for $t = \frac{1}{2}$ we find immediately that Arcsin $\frac{1}{2} = 30° = \pi/6$. All the other values of arcsin $\frac{1}{2}$ are related to its principal value by the following two formulas:

$$\text{arcsin } \tfrac{1}{2} = \text{Arcsin } \tfrac{1}{2} + 2k\pi \quad \text{or} \quad \text{arcsin } \tfrac{1}{2} = (2k + 1)\pi - \text{Arcsin } \tfrac{1}{2}$$

and, in general, for any t we have two sets of values for arcsin t:

$$\text{arcsin } t = \text{Arcsin } t + 2k\pi \quad \text{or} \quad \text{arcsin } t = (2k + 1)\pi - \text{Arcsin } t,$$

where the integer k runs through all values from $-\infty$ to $+\infty$.

The principal value Arcsin t of the function arcsin t is a one-valued function of t. It is increasing from $-\pi/2$ to $+\pi/2$ when t increases from -1 to 1, passing through zero for $t = 0$. Figure 4 gives the graph of the function $y = $ Arcsin t.

To each formula expressing a property of the function sine corresponds a formula for the inverse function arcsine. Thus, the relation

$$\text{Arcsin } x + \text{Arcsin } t = \arcsin\left(x\sqrt{1 - t^2} + t\sqrt{1 - x^2}\right) \qquad (5)$$

corresponds to the addition formula for sine that is

$$\sin(u + v) = \sin u \sqrt{1 - \text{Sin}^2 v} + \text{Sin } v \sqrt{1 - \text{Sin}^2 u}.$$

To prove it let $u = $ Arcsin x and $v = $ Arcsin t, so that $x = \sin u$, $t = \sin v$. Since an Arcsin represents always an acute angle, u and v are acute angles and their cosines are positive. Therefore, we have $\cos u = (1 - \sin^2 u)^{1/2}$ and $\cos v = (1 - \sin^2 v)^{1/2}$ which gives

$$\sin(u + v) = x\sqrt{1 - t^2} + t\sqrt{1 - x^2}.$$

Taking the arcsine of both members, we obtain the relation (5) since $\arcsin[\sin(u + v)] = u + v = \text{Arcsin } x + \text{Arcsin } t$. In particular if $t = x$, the relation (5) becomes

$$\arcsin\left(2x\sqrt{1 - x^2}\right) = 2\,\text{Arcsin } x. \tag{6}$$

This property of the function arcsine corresponds to the duplication of the argument in a sine: $\sin(2t) = 2\sin t\cos t$.

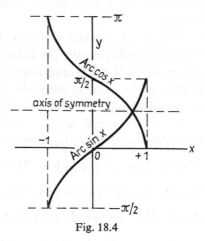

Fig. 18.4

It is important to observe that relations (5) and (6) do not hold in general, if in the right member the function arcsine is replaced by its principal value Arcsine. We illustrate this observation on the example of the particular case (6) of the formula (5), comparing $\text{Arcsin}\left(2x\sqrt{1 - x^2}\right)$ and $2\,\text{Arcsin } x$ for $x = 3^{1/2}/2$: since $\text{Arcsin}\,(3^{1/2}/2) = \pi/3$ and $2(3^{1/2}/2)(1 - \tfrac{3}{4})^{1/2} = 3^{1/2}/2$ we find that for $x = 3^{1/2}/2$ the value of the righthand member $2\,\text{Arcsin}\,(3^{1/2}/2)$ is the double of $\text{Arcsin}\left(2x\sqrt{1 - x^2}\right) = \text{Arcsin}\,(3^{1/2}/2) = \pi/3$.

On the other hand, if the absolute value of the sum $\text{Arcsin } x + \text{Arcsin } t$ does not exceed $\pi/2$ then this sum is equal to the principal value of

$$\arcsin\left(x\sqrt{1 - t^2} + t\sqrt{1 - x^2}\right);$$

that is, to

$$\text{Arcsin}\left(x\sqrt{1 - t^2} + t\sqrt{1 - x^2}\right).$$

We now define the other five inverse trigonometric functions in the exactly similar way, stating that $x = $ arccos t, if $t = \cos x$; $u = $ arctan z, if $z = \tan u$; $y = $ arccotan w, if $w = \cotan y$; $x = $ arcsec y, if $y = \sec x$ and, finally, $z = $ arccosec t, if $t = \cosec z$. They all are infinitely multivalued functions as is the arcsine. Their *principal values* are limited, as for the arcsine, by semicircular arcs as follows: an Arccosine is always a positive angle which does not exceeds 180°; the principal value Arctangent of the function arctangent is always an acute angle whose value lies between $-90°$ and 90°, so that the Arcsine and Arctangent have the same range of variation; the same holds for the Arccotangent and Arccosine whose common range of variation extends from 0° to 180°. Finally, the Arcsecant's range of variation is also the same interval from 0° to 180°, while that of the Arccosecant extends from $-90°$ to 90°.

It is important to mention that the principal values satisfy the following fundamental identities:

$$\text{Arcsin } x + \text{Arccos } x = \pi/2; \tag{7}$$

$$\text{Arctan } x + \text{Arccot } x = \pi/2; \tag{8}$$

$$\text{Arcsec } x + \text{Arccosec } x = \pi/2. \tag{9}$$

To prove the first one we consider Sin (Arcsin $x + $ Arccos x). Denoting Arcsin x and Arccos x by u and v respectively, we have Sin $u = x$, Cos $v = x$. Moreover

$$\cos u = (1 - \sin^2 u)^{1/2} = (1 - x^2)^{1/2}, \quad \sin v = (1 - \cos^2 v)^{1/2} = (1 - x^2)^{1/2},$$

where both square roots are positive since $\cos u$ is the cosine of an acute angle, while $\sin v$ is the sine of a positive angle not exceeding 180°. Therefore, applying the addition theorem, we conclude that

$$\sin (\text{Arcsin } x + \text{Arccos } x) = \sin (u + v) = \sin u \cos v + \cos u \sin v$$

$$= x^2 + (1 - x^2) = 1.$$

The sum Arcsin $x + $ Arccos x is an angle whose value lies between $-90°$ and $90° + 180° = +270°$ and the sine of this angle is equal to one. There is only one angle satisfying these two conditions and this angle is equal to $90° = \pi/2$. Thus, the formula (7) is proved. The limitations $-90° \leqslant $ Arcsin x + Arccos $x \leqslant 270°$ are justified observing that an Arcsine always lies between $-90°$ and $+90°$, while an Arccosine lies between 0° and 180°.

The function Arccos x, equal to the difference $\pi/2 - $ Arcsin x, is a *decreasing* function of the argument x because Arcsin x is an *increasing* function.

19 Kogbetliantz

It decreases from $180° = \pi$ to zero when x increases from minus to plus one (Fig. 4). The addition theorem for cosine takes for the inverse function arccosine the following form

$$\text{Arccos } x + \text{Arccos } y = \arccos [xy - (1 - x^2)^{1/2}(1 - y^2)^{1/2}]. \quad (10)$$

Denoting Arccos x and Arccos y by u and v, we have indeed $\cos u = x$, $\cos v = y$, as well as $\sin u = (1 - x^2)^{1/2}$, $\sin v = (1 - M y^2)^{1/2}$ since u and v are positive and less than $180°$, so that their sines are positive also. Now

$$\cos (u + v) = \cos u \cos v - \sin u \sin v = xy - (1 - x^2)^{1/2}(1 - y^2)^{1/2}$$

which justifies (10). In particular, if $x = y$, this identity becomes

$$2 \text{ Arccos } x = \arccos (2x^2 - 1). \quad (11)$$

In general, the relations (10), (11) do not hold, if the arccosine in the right-hand member is replaced by its principal value. But, if the sum in the left-hand member, Arccos x + Arccos y, is less than $180°$, then the symbol arccosine means the principal value Arccosine of this function, so that if Arccos x + Arccos $y < 180°$, then Arccos x + Arccos $y = $ Arccos $[xy - (1 - x^2)^{1/2} (1 - y^2)^{1/2}]$ and in particular 2 Arccos $x = $ Arccos $(2x^2 - 1)$, if $x < 1$ is positive.

The function Arctan x varies between $-90° = -\pi/2$ and $90° = \pi/2$ when its argument x increases from minus to plus infinity (see Fig. 5).

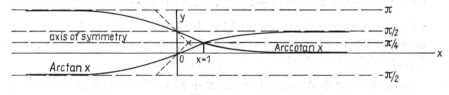

Fig. 18.5

The addition theorem for the tangent gives the corresponding property of the function arctangent:

$$\text{Arctan } x + \text{Arctan } y = \arctan \left(\frac{x + y}{1 - xy}\right), \quad (12)$$

where again the righthand member becomes Arctangent instead of arctangent, if the absolute value of the lefthand member does not exceed $\pi/2$. While the Arctangent is an *increasing* function, the Arccotangent *decreases* when its argument x increases: Arccotan $(-\infty) = \pi$ and it decreases to Arccotan 0

$= \pi/2$ when x increases from minus infinity to zero. For x positive and increasing from zero to plus infinity the Arccotan x continues to decrease from $\pi/2$ to zero and Arccotan $(+\infty) = 0$, as it is seen in the graph (Fig. 5).

Adding the ordinates of two curves in Fig. 4 and Fig. 5, we obtain for each value of x the same constant sum $\pi/2$. This facts correspond to the relations Arcsin x + Arccos $x = \pi/2$ and Arctan x + Arccotan $x = \pi/2$, the first of which was proved above. We now prove the second, deducing it from the addition theorem for the tangent. Let us denote Arctan x and Arccotan x by u and v respectively, so that $\tan u = x$ and $\cot u = x$. Applying the addition theorem to the tangent of the sum $u + v$, we obtain

$$\tan (u + v) = (\tan u + \tan v)/(1 - \tan u \tan v)$$

$$= (x + 1/x)/(1 - x/x) = \infty,$$

because $\tan u = x$ and $\cot u = x$; that is, $\tan v = 1/x$. Since $\tan (u + v) = \infty$, the sum $u + v$ is equal to $\pi/2 + k\pi$, where k is an integer, positive, negative or zero. An Arctangent is always less than $\pi/2$ in absolute value as is $u =$ Arctan x: $-\pi/2 < u < \pi/2$. On the other hand, $v =$ Arccotan x lies between zero and π. Therefore, the sum $u + v = (k + \frac{1}{2})\pi$ lies between $-\pi/2$ and $3\pi/2$ and, thus, the number $k + \frac{1}{2}$ must be greater than $-\frac{1}{2}$ and less than $\frac{3}{2}$, that is, $-1 < k < 1$. Therefore, the integer k necessarily vanishes and the sum $u + v$ is exactly equal to $\pi/2$. This proves the formula (8).

Finally, to prove the third relation Arcsec x + Arccosec $x = \pi/2$ we consider $\cos (u + v)$, where $u =$ Arcsec x, $v =$ Arccosec x, so that $x = \sec u$ and $x = \csc v$. In other words, $\cos u = (\sec u)^{-1} = x^{-1}$ and $\sin v = (\csc v)^{-1} = x^{-1}$. Since an Arcsecant is always an angle in the first or the second quadrant so that $0 < u =$ Arcsec $x < 180°$, we have $\sin u = +(1 - \cos^2 u)^{1/2} = (1 - x^{-2})^{1/2}$. On the other hand, an Arccosecant does not exceed $90°$ in absolute value and therefore $\cos v$ is also positive and $\cos v = (1 - \sin^2 v)^{1/2} = (1 - x^{-2})^{1/2} = \sin u$. Since $\cos u = \sin v$ and also $\sin u = \cos v$ we conclude that

$$\cos (u + v) = \cos u \cos v - \sin u \sin v = \sin v \cos v - \cos v \sin v = 0.$$

Now the sum $u + v$ must be equal to $\pi/2 + k\pi$ since $\cos (u + v) = 0$, but the value of this sum lies between $-\pi/2$ and $3\pi/2$, so that, again, the integer k must vanish and $u + v =$ Arcsec x + Arccosec $x = \pi/2$ proving the formula (9).

These three fundamental relations (7), (8), (9) allow the use of Arcsine, Arctangent and Arcsecant functions instead of Arccosine, Arccotangent and Arccosecant.

If x is positive, Arctan x and Arccotan x are also positive and lie between zero and $\pi/2$. Moreover, Arctan x and Arccotan x are two complementary angles, because their sum is equal to $\pi/2$. If we denote the value of the Arccotan x by u, then cotan $u = x$, so that tan $u = 1/x$ and thus $u = $ Arccotan x is also equal to Arctan $(1/x)$. Therefore, the relation (8) gives for a *positive* argument x

$$\text{Arctan } x + \text{Arctan } (1/x) = \pi/2 \qquad (x \geqslant 0).$$

Changing the sign of x, we change the sign of the lefthand member since both Arctan x and Arccotan x are odd functions. Thus, for *negative* x, $\pi/2$ must be replaced by $-\pi/2$. In the same way, if x is *positive*, then $u = $ Arcos x gives first $x = \cos u$, u being an angle in the first quadrant, so that $0 < u < \pi/2$, and then $\sin u = (1 - \cos^2 u)^{1/2} = (1 - x^2)^{1/2}$. Therefore, $u = $ Arccos x $= $ Arcsin $[(1 - x^2)^{1/2}]$ and thus

$$\text{Arcsin } x + \text{Arcsin } [(1 - x^2)^{1/2}] = \pi/2 \qquad (1 \geqslant x \geqslant 0)$$

while for *negative* x, $-1 \leqslant x < 0$, Arcsin x must be replaced by its absolute value. Finally, if x is a *positive* number greater than one, we will prove that

$$\text{Arcsec } x + \text{Arcsec } [x/(x^2 - 1)^{1/2}] = \pi/2 \qquad (1 \leqslant x).$$

Let Arccosec $x = u$, so that $x = $ cosec u and $\sin u = 1/x$. Since u belongs to the first quadrant, $\cos u$ is positive and equal to $(1 - \sin^2 u)^{1/2} = (1 - x^{-2})^{1/2}$; that is sec $u = 1/\cos u = 1/(1 - x^{-2})^{1/2} = x/(x^2 - 1)^{1/2}$. Thus $u = $ Arccosec $x = $ Arcsec $[x/(x^2 - 1)^{1/2}]$, if $x \geqslant 1$.

Now we obtain our formula from the relation Arcsec $x + $ Arccosec x $= \pi/2$ replacing in it Arccosec x by the equivalent expression Arcsec $[x/(x^2 - 1)^{1/2}]$. If x is negative, $x \leqslant -1$, Arcsec x must be replaced by $-$Arcsec x.

EXAMPLES. We illustrate the general properties of inverse trigonometric functions by the following numerical examples:

(1) Above (page 324, Ch. 7) we computed $\sin 18° = (5^{1/2} - 1)/4$, $\sin 54°$ $= (5^{1/2} + 1)/4$ and $\sin 72° = (10 + 2 \cdot 5^{1/2})^{1/2}/4$. Therefore, we find that Arcsin $[(5^{1/2} - 1)/4] = \pi/10$, Arcsin $[(5^{1/2} + 1)/4] = 3\pi/10$ and Arcsin $[(10 + 2 \cdot 5^{1/2})^{1/2}/4] = 4\pi/10$. Letting $x = (5^{1/2} - 1)/4$, $y = (5^{1/2} + 1)/4$, $z = (10 + 2 \cdot 5^{1/2})^{1/2}/4$ it is seen that

$$\text{Arcsin } x + \text{Arcsin } y = \text{Arcsin } z.$$

Applying now (5), we deduce that z must be equal to $x(1 - y^2)^{1/2} + y(1 - x^2)^{1/2}$. To verify that it is so we compute the square of the last expression and multiply it by 16:

$$16 [x (1 - y^2)^{1/2} + y (1 - x^2)^{1/2}]^2$$

$$= 16 (x^2 + y^2) - 32x^2y^2 + 32xy (1 - x^2)^{1/2}(1 - y^2)^{1/2}$$

$$= (5^{1/2} - 1)^2 + (5^{1/2} + 1)^2 - 2 (5^{1/2} - 1)^2(5^{1/2} + 1)^2/16$$

$$+ 2 (5^{1/2} - 1) (5^{1/2} + 1) (10 + 2 \cdot 5^{1/2})^{1/2}(10 - 2 \cdot 5^{1/2})^{1/2}/16$$

$$= 12 - 2 (5 - 1)^2/16 + 2 (5 - 1) (100 - 20)^{1/2}/16$$

$$= 12 - 2 + 80^{1/2}/2 = 10 + 2 \cdot 5^{1/2} = 16z^2.$$

(2) We computed also in this chapter $\tan (3\pi/8) = 2^{1/2} + 1$ and $\tan (\pi/8) = 2^{1/2} - 1$, so that Arctan $(2^{1/2} + 1) = 3\pi/8$ and Arctan $(2^{1/2} - 1) = \pi/8$. Since Arctan $1 = \pi/4$, we have the numerical equality

$$\text{Arctan } (2^{1/2} - 1) + \text{Arctan } 1 = \text{Arctan } (2^{1/2} + 1).$$

The relation (12) applied to the case $x = 2^{1/2} - 1$, $y = 1$ shows that $z = 2^{1/2} + 1$ must be equal to $(x + y)/(1 - xy)$ and we will check it computing the numerical value of this expression:

$$(2^{1/2} - 1 + 1)/[1 - (2^{1/2} - 1)] = 2^{1/2}/(2 - 2^{1/2}) = 1/(2^{1/2} - 1)$$

$$= 2^{1/2} + 1 = z.$$

On the other hand applying (12) to the case when $x = 2^{1/2} + 1$, $y = 1$ we have no right to expect that Arctan x + Arctan y = Arctan $[(x + y)/(1 - xy)]$ since in that case $(x + y)/(1 - xy) = (2^{1/2} + 2)/(1 - 2^{1/2} - 1) = -(2^{1/2} + 1)$ and therefore Arctan $[(x + y)/(1 - xy)] = $ Arctan $[-(2^{1/2} + 1)] = -3\pi/8$, while Arctan x + Arctan $y = 3\pi/8 + \pi/4 = 5\pi/8$. Here we have an example of (12) where

$$\text{Arctan } x + \text{Arctan } y = \text{arctan } [(x + y)/(1 - xy)]$$

since Arctan $(2^{1/2} + 1)$ + Arctan $1 = \pi$ + Arctan $[-(2^{1/2} + 1)]$, that is

$$\text{Arctan } x + \text{Arctan } y = \pi + \text{Arctan } [(x + y)/(1 - xy)].$$

The right-hand member is one of the values $k\pi$ + Arctan t of the multi-valued function arctan t, namely that for which $k = 1$. It is worthwhile to tabulate the ranges of variation for the principal values of various inverse trigonometric functions together with the ranges of variation of the argument x within which the values of these functions remain real:

	Range of variation	
Function $y = f(x)$	of x	of y
Arcsin x	$-1 \leqslant x \leqslant 1$	
Arctan x	$-\infty \leqslant x \leqslant +\infty$	$-\pi/2 \leqslant y \leqslant \pi/2$
Arccosec x	$1 \leqslant \lvert x \rvert < \infty$	
Arccos x	$-1 \leqslant x \leqslant 1$	
Arccotan x	$-\infty \leqslant x \leqslant +\infty$	$0 \leqslant y \leqslant \pi$
Arcsec x	$1 \leqslant \lvert x \rvert < \infty$	

Inverse Trigonometric Functions as Logarithms

We saw in Chapter 11 that the natural logarithm $y = \log x$ is also an infinitely multivalued function

$$y = \log x = \text{Log } x + 2k\pi i,$$

where Log x denotes the *principal value* of the natural logarithm that is the value which vanishes for $x = 1$; Log $1 = 0$. Thus, inverse trigonometric functions share with natural logarithms the property of infinite multivaluedness.

The natural logarithm is also an inverse function, namely a function inverse to the exponential function e^x. On the other hand, the trigonometric functions are combinations of exponential functions e^{ix} and e^{-ix} since

$$\sin x = (e^{ix} - e^{-ix})/2i, \quad \cos x = (e^{ix} + e^{-ix})/2$$

and therefore the four other trigonometric functions can be expressed also in terms of e^{ix} and e^{-ix}. Thus, the inverse trigonometric functions are functions inverse to combinations of exponential functions e^{ix} and e^{-ix}.

This fact strongly suggests that there must be some relation between inverse trigonometric functions and natural logarithms. This relation will correspond to the direct relation between e^{ix} and $\sin x$, $\cos x$ which we studied under the name of Euler's Formula. Therefore Euler's Formula

$$e^{ix} = \cos x + i \sin x, \tag{13}$$

when properly transformed will give us the relations between the inverse trigonometric functions and the natural logarithms.

First of all we take the logarithms of both members of (13). Dividing them by i we transform Euler's Formula into an equivalent formula which relates the variable x to the rotation factor through x, that is, to $\cos x + i \sin x$:

$$(\log e^{ix})/i = x = [\log (\cos x + i \sin x)]/i = 2k\pi + \text{Log } [(\cos x + i \sin x)]/i.$$

To determine the value of the integer k it is sufficient to substitute zero for x. This gives the numerical equality

$$2k\pi + (\text{Log } 1)/i = 0$$

But $\text{Log } 1 = 0$ and therefore $k = 0$. The final result is as follows:

$$x = i^{-1} \text{Log } (\cos x + i \sin x). \tag{14}$$

Suppose now that $-1 \leqslant t \leqslant 1$ and $x = \text{Arcsin } t$, so that $\sin x = t$ and $\cos x = (1 - t^2)^{1/2}$, the square root being positive because x (as an Arcsine) represents an acute angle and therefore $\cos x$ is positive. Replacing in (14) x, $\sin x$ and $\cos x$ by their values, we obtain

$$\text{Arcsin } t = i^{-1} \text{Log } \left(\sqrt{1 - t^2} + it\right) \qquad (|t| \leqslant 1). \tag{15}$$

Taking now $-1 \leqslant t \leqslant 1$ but $x = \text{Arccos } t$, so that $0 \leqslant x \leqslant \pi$, $\cos x = t$ and $\sin x = (1 - t^2)^{1/2}$, we deduce from (14) the corresponding expression of the function Arccos x as a logarithm:

$$\text{Arccos } t = i^{-1} \text{Log } \left(t + i\sqrt{1 - t^2}\right) \qquad (|t| \leqslant 1). \tag{16}$$

We can now prove relation (7), simply adding (15) and (16), member by member:

$$\text{Arcsin } t + \text{Arccos } t = i^{-1} \text{Log } \left[\left(\sqrt{1 - t^2} + it\right)\left(t + i\sqrt{1 - t^2}\right)\right]$$

$$= i^{-1} \text{Log } [t (1 - t^2)^{1/2} + it^2 + i(1 - t^2) - t(1 - t^2)^{1/2}]$$

$$= i^{-1} \text{Log } i.$$

But the formula (14) gives for $x = \pi/2$

$$\pi/2 = i^{-1} \text{Log } (\cos 90° + i \sin 90°) = i^{-1} \text{Log } i,$$

so that, finally, $\text{Arcsin } t + \text{Arccos } t = \pi/2$.

Suppose now t positive and consider $x = \text{Arctan } t$, so that $0 < x < \pi/2$. We have $\tan x = t > 0$, $\sec x = (1 + \tan^2 x)^{1/2} = (1 + t^2)^{1/2}$, $\cos x = (1 + t^2)^{-1/2}$ and $\sin x = \tan x \cdot \cos x = t(1 + t^2)^{-1/2}$. Substituting these values of x, $\cos x$ and $\sin x$ into relation (14), we find

$$\text{Arctan } t = i^{-1} \text{Log } [(1 + it)/(1 + t^2)^{1/2}].$$

Replacing $1 + t^2$ by $(1 + it)(1 - it)$, we transform $(1 + it)/(1 + t^2)^{1/2}$ into $[(1 + it)/(1 - it)]^{1/2}$ and therefore

$$\text{Arctan } t = (2i)^{-1} \text{Log } [(1 + it)/(1 - it)]. \tag{17}$$

It is now easy to justify relation (17), which is proved only for t positive, also for *negative* t. If t is negative, we apply (14) to Arctan $(-t)$:

$$\text{Arctan}\,(-t) = -\text{Arctan}\,t = (2i)^{-1}\,\text{Log}\,[(1-it)/(1+it)] \qquad (t < 0)$$

Multiplying both members by -1, we obtain

$$\text{Arctan}\,t = -(2i)^{-1}\,\text{Log}\,[(1-it)/(1+it)] = (2i)^{-1}\,\text{Log}\,[(1+it)/(1-it)]$$

and this result justifies (17) for $t < 0$.

To find the expression of Arccot t we use the relation (8)

$$\text{Arccot}\,t + \text{Arctan}\,t = \pi/2 = i^{-1}\,\text{Log}\,i = (2i)^{-1}\,\text{Log}\,(-1).$$

Solving it for Arccot t, we obtain:

$$\text{Arccot}\,t = (2i)^{-1}\,\text{Log}\,[(t+i)/(t-i)]. \tag{18}$$

We have indeed

$$\text{Arccot}\,t = \pi/2 - \text{Arctan}\,t = (2i)^{-1}\{\text{Log}\,(-1) - \text{Log}\,[(1+it)/1 - it]\}$$

$$= (2i)^{-1}\,\text{Log}\,[(it-1)/(it+1)] = (2i)^{-1}\,\text{Log}\,[(t+i)/(t-i)].$$

Now, if the absolute value of t exceeds 1, $|t| \geqslant 1$, and $x = \text{Arcsec}\,t$, then $\sec x = t$ and therefore $\cos x = 1/\sec x = t^{-1}$. Applying to $x = \text{Arccos}(t^{-1})$ the expression (16), we obtain

$$\text{Arcsec}\,t = \text{Arccos}\,(t^{-1}) = i^{-1}\,\text{Log}\,[t^{-1} + i\,(1-t^{-2})^{1/2}],$$

so that

$$\text{Arcsec}\,t = i^{-1}\,\text{Log}\,\{[1 + i\,(t^2-1)^{1/2}]/t\}. \tag{19}$$

Finally, the similar relation Arccosec $t = \text{Arcsin}\,(1/t)$ gives, replacing Arcsin $(1/t)$ by natural logarithm,

$$\text{Arccosec}\,t = i^{-1}\,\text{Log}\,\{[(t^2-1)^{1/2} + i]/t\}. \tag{20}$$

Hyperbolic Functions

The trigonometric functions were studied up to now as functions of a *real* argument x. Let us now ask what are their values for a complex argument $z = x + iy$? Before studying this general question we discuss its particular case and the values of trigonometric functions for purely imaginary values iy of the argument. Substituting in Euler's Formula $e^{ix} = \cos x + i \sin x$ a pure imaginary iy for x, we obtain

$$e^{i^2y} = e^{-y} = \cos(iy) + i\sin(iy),$$

where $\cos(iy)$ and $i\sin(iy)$ are even and odd parts of the function e^{-y}.

Changing the sign of y we have therefore another relation

$$e^y = \cos(iy) - i\sin(iy).$$

Adding and subtracting these two relations member by member, we obtain

$$\cos(iy) = \tfrac{1}{2}(e^y + e^{-y}); \quad -i\sin(iy) = \tfrac{1}{2}(e^y - e^{-y}).$$

This result shows that the values of $\cos(iy)$ and $-i\sin(iy)$ are real numbers. The functions $\tfrac{1}{2}(e^y + e^{-y})$ and $\tfrac{1}{2}(e^y - e^{-y})$, have special names and they are called the *hyperbolic cosine* and the *hyperbolic sine*, respectively. The usual notation is Sh for hyperbolic sine and Ch for hyperbolic cosine, so that, by definition, the two functions Sh y and Ch y thus introduced are:

$$\text{Sh } y = \tfrac{1}{2}(e^y - e^{-y}), \quad \text{Ch } y = \tfrac{1}{2}(e^y + e^{-y}). \tag{21}$$

Thus, $\sin(iy) = i \text{ Sh } y$ and $\cos(iy) = \text{Ch } y$. Recalling the representation of e^y by infinite series, namely

$$e^y = 1 + y/1! + y^2/2! + y^3/3! + y^4/4 + \cdots + y^n/n! + \cdots$$

as well as

$$e^{-y} = 1 - y/1! + y^2/2! - y^3/3! + y^4/4! - \cdots + (-1)^n y^n/n! + \cdots,$$

the corresponding expansions of Sh y and Ch y are:

$$\text{Sh } y = \sum_0^\infty y^{2n+1}/(2n+1)! = y + y^3/3! + y^5/5! + y^7/7! + \cdots \tag{22}$$

$$\text{Ch } y = \sum_0^\infty y^{2n}/(2n)! = 1 + y^2/2! + y^4/4! + y^6/6 + \cdots \tag{23}$$

Comparing these series with the expansions (38), Chapter 9 p. 421, of trigonometric sine and cosine, we have again

$$\text{Sin}(iy) = i \text{ Sh } y, \quad \text{Sh}(ix) = i\sin x, \quad \cos(iy) = \text{Ch } y, \quad \text{Ch}(ix) = \cos x. \tag{24}$$

Therefore, hyperbolic and trigonometric sines of a purely imaginary argument have also purely imaginary values, while cosines $\cos(iy)$ and $\text{Ch}(ix)$ are real. Moreover, the trigonometric cosine of a purely imaginary argument is greater than one, as the series (23) shows, except for $y = 0$ since $\text{Ch } 0 = 1$.

Hyperbolic cosines of a purely imaginary argument have real values between minus and plus one since they are equal to trigonometric cosines of a real argument.

The definitions of the four other hyperbolic functions are similar to those of the corresponding trigonometric functions:

$$\text{Th } z = \text{Sh } z/\text{Ch } z, \quad \text{Cth } z = (\text{Th } z)^{-1} = \text{Ch } z/\text{Sh } z, \quad \text{Sech } z = (\text{Ch } z)^{-1},$$

$$\text{Csch } z = (\text{Sh } z)^{-1},$$

where Th, Cth, Sech and Csch mean hyperbolic tangent, cotangent, secant and cosecant respectively. For purely imaginary argument they are reduced to trigonometric functions:

$$\text{Th}\,(iy) = i \tan y, \quad \text{Cth}\,(iy) = -i \cot y, \quad \text{Sech}\,(iy) = \text{Sec } y,$$

$$\text{Csch}\,(iy) = -i \csc y.$$

Therefore, the periodicity of trigonometric functions entails the corresponding property of hyperbolic functions: they are also periodic with a period equal to $2\pi i$ for hyperbolic sine, cosine, secant and cosecant, while the period of hyperbolic tangent and cotangent is πi. We have, for instance,

$$\text{Th}\,(iy + \pi i) = \text{Th}\,[i\,(y + \pi)] = i \tan\,(y + \pi) = i \tan y = \text{Th}\,(iy).$$

Since their periods πi and $2\pi i$ are purely imaginary, the hyperbolic functions of a *real* variable are not periodic and their graphs (Fig. 6) reveal this circumstance clearly:

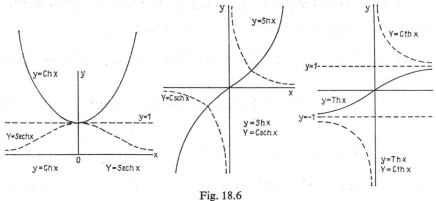

Fig. 18.6

The behavior of hyperbolic functions of a *real* variable can be described as follows: Sh x and Th x increase when the argument x increases, but their reciprocals Csch x and Cth x are decreasing functions of x, with a discontinuity (infinite jump from minus to plus infinity) at the origin; Ch x and its reciprocal Sech x have at the origin a minimum and a maximum respectively: Ch $0 =$ Sech $0 = 1$. Their ranges of variation when x increases from minus to plus infinity are as follows ($\nearrow$ = increases, $\searrow$ = decreases):

Function	$-\infty \nearrow x \nearrow 0 \nearrow x \nearrow +\infty$
Sh x	$-\infty \nearrow y \nearrow 0 \nearrow y \nearrow +\infty$
Ch x	$+\infty \searrow y \searrow 1 \nearrow y \nearrow +\infty$
Th x	$-1 \nearrow y \nearrow 0 \nearrow y \nearrow 1$
Cth x	$-1 \searrow y \searrow \pm\infty, \pm\infty \searrow y \searrow 1$
Sech x	$0 \nearrow y \nearrow 1 \searrow y \searrow 0$
Csch x	$0 \searrow y \searrow \pm\infty, \pm\infty \searrow y \searrow 0$

The definitions of hyperbolic functions are extended to complex values of their argument. Thus, if $z = x + iy$ denotes a complex variable, we define Ch z and Sh z as even and odd parts of the function e^z, so that $e^z =$ Ch z + Sh z and

$$\text{Sh } z = \tfrac{1}{2}(e^z - e^{-z}), \quad \text{Ch } z = \tfrac{1}{2}(e^z + e^{-z}) \tag{25}$$

Squaring these functions and subtracting Sh$^2 z$ from Ch$^2 z$, we obtain one:

$$\text{Ch}^2 z - \text{Sh}^2 z = (\text{Ch } z + \text{Sh } z)(\text{Ch } z - \text{Sh } z) = e^z \cdot e^{-z} = e^{z-z} = e^0 = 1.$$

Dividing both members of this fundamental relation by Sh$^2 z$ on one hand, and by Ch$^2 z$ on the other, we have two more relations between the squares of hyperbolic functions, namely

$$\text{Ch}^2 z - \text{Sh}^2 z = 1; \quad \text{Cth}^2 z - 1 = \text{Csch}^2 z; \quad 1 - \text{Th}^2 z = \text{Sech}^2 z \tag{26}$$

Gudermanian

Let us consider the particular case when the argument of the hyperbolic functions is a real variable x. Interpreting the three relations (26) as expressions of the Pythagorean Theorem, we obtain three similar triangles (Fig. 7)

Fig. 18.7.

The acute positive angle $\theta = \overset{\frown}{ABC}$ is called *Gudermanian*. It is a function of the real variable x with the aid of which a complete correlation can be established between the values of hyperbolic and trigonometric functions. Applying the definitions of trigonometric functions of this acute angle θ, we deduce immediately the following six correlation formulas:

$$\text{Sh } x = \tan \theta \qquad \text{Ch } x = \sec \theta \qquad \text{Th } x = \sin \theta$$
$$\text{Sech } x = \cos \theta \quad \text{Csch } x = \cotan \theta \quad \text{Cth } x = \csc \theta. \tag{27}$$

These formulas, established by Guderman, helped very much in the tabulation of hyperbolic functions; once the Gudermanian θ was tabulated as a function of x, the tables of hyperbolic functions were obtained simply by a rearrangement of trigonometric tables.

The tabulation of θ can be deduced from that of the inverse function x considered as a function of θ. It is easy to tabulate x because the expression of x in terms of θ is very simple:

$$x = \text{Log } [\tan (\pi/4 + \theta/2)] \qquad (0 \leqslant \theta \leqslant \pi/2). \tag{28}$$

Inverse Hyperbolic Functions

To prove (28) we need the inverse hyperbolic functions, more precisely we need their expressions as natural logarithms. As for the trigonometric functions, the inverse hyperbolic functions are denoted by a prefix which in this case is not the word *arc*, but an abbreviation *arg* of the word *argument*. Thus, if the value of Sh u is denoted by v, $v = $ Sh u, then the symbol u means the argument of a hyperbolic sine whose value is equal to v. This long sentence defines u as an inverse function and it is condensed in the notation Argsh v (read: argument of hyperbolic sine of value v). Therefore, $u = $ Argsh v is equivalent to $v = $ Sh u. Likewise, if $v = $ Th u then $u = $ Argth v, if $w = $ Ch u then $u = $ Argch w and so on.

It is sufficient to deduce the logarithmic expressions for three functions Argsh v, Argch v and Argth v because the three others are related to them by simple formulas which follow. If $u = $ Argcth v, then $v = $ Cth u so that, by the definition of Cth u, we have also $v^{-1} = 1/\text{Cth } u = $ Th u and therefore the same u which denotes Argcth v is also equal to Argth (v^{-1}): Argcth v $= $ Argth $(1/v)$. Since Sech v and Csch v, as Cth v, are reciprocals of Ch v and Sh v respectively, the same reasoning proves that Argsech $v = $ Argch$(1/v)$

and Argcsch v = Argsh $(1/v)$:

$$\text{Argcth } t = \text{Argth } (1/t); \quad \text{Argsech } t = \text{Argch } (1/t);$$

$$\text{Argcsch } t = \text{Argsh } (1/t). \tag{29}$$

We begin with Argch $v = u$, where both u and v are *real* variables. The function Ch u being even (that is, Ch $(-u)$ = Ch u), the real inverse function Argch v is necessarily double–valued and its two values corresponding to the same argument v are equal in absolute value and opposite in sign, one being positive and the other negative. We now study the *positive* inverse function u = Argch $v > 0$.

Since $u > 0$ the function Sh u is positive and therefore, using (26), we have Sh $u = (\text{Ch}^2 u - 1)^{1/2}$. The fundamental relation e^u = Ch u + Sh u now becomes e^u = Ch $u + (\text{Ch}^2 u - 1)^{1/2}$. Taking the logarithms, we write it

$$u = \text{Log } [\text{Ch } u + (\text{Ch}^2 u - 1)^{1/2}],$$

which for v = Ch u, u = Argch $v \gtrless 0$ gives the expression of the inverse hyperbolic function Argch v in the form of a natural logarithm

$$\text{Argch } v = \pm \text{Log } [v + (v^2 - 1)^{1/2}] \quad (v \geqslant 1), \tag{30}$$

the double sign corresponding to two possible values of Argch v.

On the other hand, the hyperbolic cosine is always positive and therefore Ch $u = (1 + \text{Sh}^2 u)^{1/2}$, so that $e^u = (1 + \text{Sh}^2 u)^{1/2}$ + Sh u, that is,

$$u = \text{Log } [(1 + \text{Sh}^2 u)^{1/2} + \text{Sh } u],$$

which for Sh $u = v$, u = Argsh v gives

$$\text{Argsh } v = \text{Log } [(1 + v^2)^{1/2} + v]. \tag{31}$$

Finally, transforming $e^{2u} = (\text{Ch } u + \text{Sh } u)^2$, we can write

$$e^{2u} = \text{Ch}^2 u \cdot (1 + \text{Th } u)^2 = (1 + \text{Th } u)^2/\text{Sech}^2 u = (1 + \text{Th} u)^2/(1 - \text{Th}^2 u)$$

since $\text{Ch}^2 u = \text{Sech}^{-2} u = (1 - \text{Th}^2 u)^{-1}$. The factor $1 + \text{Th } u$ appears in both numerator and denominator of the righthand member. Reducing this member to its lowest terms, we obtain

$$e^{2u} = (1 + \text{Th } u)/(1 - \text{Th } u),$$

that is, passing to logarithms,

$$u = \tfrac{1}{2} \text{Log } [(1 + \text{Th } u)/(1 - \text{Th } u)].$$

This result is equivalent to

$$\text{Argth } v = \tfrac{1}{2} \text{Log} \left[(1 + v)/(1 - v) \right] \tag{32}$$

because if $v = \text{Th } u$, then $u = \text{Argth } v$.

With the aid of the relations (29) the formulas (30), (31), (32) yield the corresponding expressions of the other three inverse hyperbolic functions in terms of natural logarithms:

$$\text{Argcth } v = \tfrac{1}{2} \text{Log} \left[(v + 1)/(v - 1) \right]; \quad \text{Argsech } v = \text{Log} \left[v^{-1} + (v^{-2} - 1)^{1/2} \right];$$

$$\text{Argcsch } v = \text{Log} \left[(v^{-2} + 1)^{1/2} + v^{-1} \right].$$

Reverting to the Gudermanian θ, we invert now the formulas $\tan \theta = \text{Sh } x$ and $\sin \theta = \text{Th } x$ and obtain, using (31) and (32):

$$x = \text{Argsh} (\tan \theta) = \text{Log} (\sec \theta + \tan \theta);$$

$$x = \text{Argth} (\sin \theta) = \tfrac{1}{2} \text{Log} \left[(1 + \sin \theta)/(1 - \sin \theta) \right].$$

Both expressions of x give (28) because, dividing $\sec \theta + \tan \theta$ by $(\sec^2 \theta - \text{Tan}^2 \theta)^{1/2} = 1$, we have

$$\sec \theta + \tan \theta = (\sec \theta + \tan \theta)/(\sec^2 \theta - \tan^2 \theta)^{1/2}$$

$$= [\cos \theta (\sec \theta + \tan \theta)]^{1/2}/[\cos \theta (\sec \theta - \tan \theta)^{1/2}]$$

$$= (1 + \sin \theta)^{1/2}/(1 - \sin \theta)^{1/2}$$

$$= [1 - \cos (\pi/2 + \theta)]^{1/2}/[1 + \cos (\pi/2 + \theta)]^{1/2}$$

since $\sin \theta = \cos (\pi/2 + \theta)$. Now $1 - \cos t = 2 \cdot \sin^2 (t/2)$ and $1 + \cos t = 2 \cdot \cos^2 (t/2)$, so that

$$\sec \theta + \tan \theta = [2 \sin^2 (\pi/4 + \theta/2)^{1/2}/[2 \cos^2 (\pi/4 + \theta/2)^{1/2}$$

$$= \tan (\pi/4 + \theta/2)$$

which proves the formula (28). This formula, if inverted, gives also

$$\theta = 2 \cdot \text{Arctan} (e^x) - \pi/2$$

so that a direct tabulation of the Gudermanian θ is also possible.

Addition Formulas

Functions of a sum $A + B$ of two complex arguments A and B can be expressed in terms of functions of A and B only, if they possess the so-called addition theorem. This is the case with hyperbolic functions, as with trigonometric, and the addition theorem for hyperbolic sine and cosine is stated as follows

$$\text{Sh} (X + Y) = \text{Sh } X \cdot \text{Ch } Y + \text{Ch } X \cdot \text{Sh } Y$$

$$\text{Ch} (X + Y) = \text{Ch } X \cdot \text{Ch } Y + \text{Sh } X \cdot \text{Sh } Y \tag{33}$$

These formulas are easy to deduce with the aid of the principle of parity from the identity $e^{x+y} = e^x \cdot e^y$. Recalling that $e^t = \text{Ch } t + \text{Sh } t$, we write this identity as $\text{Ch}(x + y) + \text{Sh}(x + y) = (\text{Ch } x + \text{Sh } x)(\text{Ch } y + \text{Sh } y)$, that is, performing the multiplication

$$\text{Ch}(x + y) + \text{Sh}(x + y) = \text{Ch } x \cdot \text{Ch } y + \text{Sh } x \cdot \text{Sh } y + \text{Sh } x \cdot \text{Ch } y$$
$$+ \text{Ch } x \cdot \text{Sh } y.$$

Changing the signs of both x and y, we change the sign of their sum $x + y$, so that we can apply the principle of parity. Thus, the even and odd parts $\text{Ch}(x + y)$ and $\text{Sh}(x + y)$ of the left-hand member are equal respectively to the even and odd parts $\text{Ch } x \cdot \text{Ch } y + \text{Sh } x \cdot \text{Sh } y$ and $\text{Ch } x \cdot \text{Sh } y + \text{Sh } x \cdot \text{Ch } y$ of the right-hand member and this establishes the addition formulas (33). In them X and Y denote any two complex numbers. Applying (33) to the particular case in which $X = x$ is real while $Y = iy$ is purely imaginary, so that their sum $X + Y = z = x + iy$ being complex, we obtain the complex values of hyperbolic sine and cosine of *complex* argument $x + iy$:

$$\text{Sh}(x + iy) = \text{Sh } x \cos y + i \,\text{Ch } x \sin y$$

$$\text{Ch}(x + iy) = \text{Ch } x \cos y + i \,\text{Sh } x \sin y, \tag{34}$$

where we have replaced $\text{Sh}(iy)$ and $\text{Ch}(iy)$ by $i \sin y$ and $\cos y$ respectively.

On the other hand, the trigonometric sine and cosine of a complex argument are also complex numbers and their components can be computed using the formulas (24). We have indeed $\text{Sh}(iz) = i \sin z$ as well as $\text{Ch}(iz) = \cos z$ for any complex $z = x + iy$, since $e^{iz} = \text{Ch}(iz) + \text{Sh}(iz) = \cos z + i \sin z$. Applying the principle of parity to the identity

$$\text{Ch}(iz) + \text{Sh}(iz) \equiv \cos z + i \sin z,$$

we find that $\text{Ch}(iz) \equiv \cos z$ (even parts) and $\text{Sh}(iz) \equiv i \sin z$ (odd parts).

Therefore, $\sin (x + iy) = -i \, \text{Sh} \, (ix - y)$ and $\cos (x + iy) = \text{Ch} \, (ix - y)$. With the aid of (34) applied to $\text{Sh} \, (ix - y)$ and $\text{Ch} \, (ix - y)$, we obtain:

$$\sin (x + iy) = \sin x \cdot \text{Ch} \, y + i \cos x \cdot \text{Sh} \, y$$
$$\cos (x + iy) = \cos x \cdot \text{Ch} \, y - i \sin x \cdot \text{Sh} \, y. \tag{35}$$

These formulas prove that the trigonometric addition formulae for sine and cosine of a sum hold for complex argument $x + iy$ too because $\sin (iy) = i \, \text{Sh} \, y$ and $\cos (iy) = \text{Ch} \, y$.

The result (35) shows clearly that trigonometric and hyperbolic sine, as well as cosine, of a real variable, form one and the same function of a complex variable. We see indeed that $\text{Sin} \, (x + iy)$ becomes the trigonometric $\text{Sin} \, x$, if $y = 0$, while for $x = 0$ it is equal to $i \, \text{Sh} \, y$. This unification of two different functions of a *real* variable into a unique function of a *complex* variable is a characteristic feature of the use of complex numbers.

What happens now to the fundamental relation $\sin^2 x + \cos^2 x = 1$, when the real variable x becomes complex? Since the values of a sine and cosine of complex variable are also complex numbers their squares are complex numbers too, but the sum of these squares $\sin^2 (x + iy) + \cos^2 (x + iy)$ remains equal to one, so that $\sin^2 z + \cos^2 z = 1$ for any complex argument z. This is easy to prove, using the formulas (35):

$$\sin^2 (x + iy) + \cos^2 (x + iy) = \sin^2 x \cdot \text{Ch}^2 y - \cos^2 x \cdot \text{Sh}^2 y$$

$$+ \cos^2 x \cdot \text{Ch}^2 y - \sin^2 x \cdot \text{Sh}^2 y = (\sin^2 x + \cos^2 x) \, \text{Ch}^2 y$$

$$- (\cos^2 x + \sin^2 x) \, \text{Sh}^2 y = (\sin^2 x + \cos^2 x)(\text{Ch}^2 y - \text{Sh}^2 y) = 1$$

since $\sin^2 x + \cos^2 x = 1$, $\text{Ch}^2 y - \text{Sh}^2 y = 1$.

More interesting is the value of the sum of squares of *absolute* values:

$$|\sin (x + iy)|^2 + |\cos (x + iy)|^2$$

$$= \sin^2 x \cdot \text{Ch}^2 y + \cos^2 x \cdot \text{Sh}^2 y + \cos^2 x \cdot \text{Ch}^2 y + \sin^2 x \cdot \text{Sh}^2 y$$

$$= \text{Ch}^2 y + \text{Sh}^2 y = \text{Ch}^2 y - \text{Sh}^2 y + 2 \, \text{Sh}^2 y = 1 + 2 \, \text{Sh}^2 y \geqslant 1.$$

Thus, in general, $|\sin z|^2 + |\cos z|^2 > 1$, except when z is real.

Dividing member by member the formulas (33), we have the addition theorem for the hyperbolic tangent and cotangent

$$\text{Th} \, (X + Y) = (\text{Th} \, X + \text{Th} \, Y)/(1 + \text{Th} \, X \cdot \text{Th} \, Y)$$
$$\text{Cth} \, (X + Y) = (\text{Cth} \, X \cdot \text{Cth} \, Y + 1)/(\text{Cth} \, X + \text{Cth} \, Y). \tag{36}$$

The addition theorems give for $X = Y$ formulas for the duplication of the argument.

$$\text{Sh } 2X = 2\text{Sh } X \cdot \text{Ch } X, \quad \text{Ch } 2X = \text{Ch}^2 X + \text{Sh}^2 X,$$

$$\text{Th } 2X = 2\text{ Th } X/(1 + \text{Th}^2 X) = 2(\text{Cth } X + \text{Th } X)^{-1}.$$

Combining $\text{Ch } 2X = \text{Ch}^2 X + \text{Sh}^2 X$ with $\text{Ch}^2 X - \text{Sh}^2 X = 1$, we deduce

$$\text{Ch } 2X + 1 = 2\text{ Ch}^2 X, \quad \text{Ch } 2X - 1 = 2\text{ Sh}^2 X$$

which gives, dividing member by member:

$$\text{Th}^2 X = (\text{Ch } 2X - 1)/(\text{Ch } 2X + 1).$$

Solving this relation with respect to $\text{Ch } 2X$, we transform it into

$$\text{Ch } 2X = (1 + \text{Th}^2 X)/(1 - \text{Th}^2 X).$$

Expanding the righthand member with the aid of the geometric progression

$$1/(1 - \text{Th}^2 X) = 1 + \text{Th}^2 X + \text{Th}^4 X + \text{Th}^6 X$$
$$+ \text{Th}^8 X + \cdots + \text{Th}^{2n} X + \cdots$$

and dividing by two, we obtain an infinite series which converges for all real values of the variable X to the sum $\frac{1}{2}\text{ Ch } 2X$:

$$\frac{1}{2} + \sum_{n=1}^{\infty} \text{Th}^{2n} X = \frac{1}{2} + \text{Th}^2 X + \text{Th}^4 X + \cdots + \text{Th}^{2n} X + \cdots = \frac{1}{2}\text{ Ch } 2X.$$

Substituting for X a purely imaginary argument ix, where x is a real number, we find the corresponding trigonometric expression

$$\frac{1}{2} + \sum_{n=1}^{\infty} (-1)^n \tan^{2n} x = \frac{1}{2} - \tan^2 x + \tan^4 x - \cdots + (-1)^n \tan^{2n} x + \cdots$$
$$= \frac{1}{2}\cos 2x$$

which converges only if $\tan x$ remains less than one in absolute value; that is, only when $-\pi/4 < x < \pi/4$.

De Moivre's Theorem

The identity $e^{nz} \equiv (e^z)^n$ leads to the analogue of De Moivre's Theorem for hyperbolic functions.

$$(\text{Ch } z + \text{Sh } z)^n = \text{Ch } (nz) + \text{Sh } (nz). \tag{37}$$

20 Kogbetliantz

Expanding the nth power of the sum $\mathrm{Ch}\, z + \mathrm{Sh}\, z$ with the aid of the binomial theorem and applying the principle of parity, we deduce the following expressions of hyperbolic sine and cosine of a multiple of z in terms of powers of hyperbolic sine and cosine of z:

$$\mathrm{Ch}\, nz = \sum_{0}^{n/2} \binom{n}{2m} \mathrm{Ch}^{n-2m} z \cdot \mathrm{Sh}^{2m} z$$

$$\mathrm{Sh}\, nz = \sum_{0}^{(n-1)/2} \binom{n}{2m+1} \mathrm{Ch}^{n-2m-1} z \cdot \mathrm{Sh}^{2m+1} z.$$

Thus, for instance, the cases $n = 3$, $n = 4$ give

$$\mathrm{Ch}\,(3z) = \mathrm{Ch}^3 z + 3\,\mathrm{Ch}\, z \cdot \mathrm{Sh}^2 z = 4\,\mathrm{Ch}^3 z - 3\,\mathrm{Ch}\, z$$

$$\mathrm{Sh}\,(3z) = 3\,\mathrm{Ch}^2 z \cdot \mathrm{Sh}\, z + \mathrm{Sh}^3 z = 4\,\mathrm{Sh}^3 z + 3\,\mathrm{Sh}\, z$$

$$\mathrm{Ch}\,(4z) = \mathrm{Ch}^4 z + 6\,\mathrm{Ch}^2 z \cdot \mathrm{Sh}^2 z + \mathrm{Sh}^4 z = 8\,\mathrm{Ch}^4 z - 8\,\mathrm{Ch}^2 z + 1$$

$$\mathrm{Sh}\,(4z) = 4\,\mathrm{Ch}^3 z \cdot \mathrm{Sh}\, z + 4\,\mathrm{Ch}\, z \cdot \mathrm{Sh}^3 z = 4\,\mathrm{Ch}\, z\,(\mathrm{Sh}\, z + 2\,\mathrm{Sh}^3 z).$$

In general, all formulas and properties of hyperbolic functions are parallel to those of trigonometric functions. They can be deduced from the trigonometric formulas by substituting for the real argument of trigonometric functions a purely imaginary number and applying the appropriate relations.

Solution of Algebraic Equations by the Method of Auxiliary Angle

The computation of expressions involving a square root can be performed with the aid of trigonometric functions of an auxiliary angle definition of which is chosen precisely in such a way that the square-root involved is expressed as a trigonometric function of this auxiliary angle.

Let us study as an example of the method of auxiliary angle the numerical computation of the roots of a quadratic equation. In the case when these roots are real, we take the quadratic equation in the standard form

$$x^2 + px + q = 0, \quad (p^2 > 4q) \tag{38}$$

where by hypothesis the condition of real roots is fulfilled: $p^2 > 4q$.

Beginning with the case of a positive constant term, $q > 0$, we have to simplify the square root $(p^2 - 4q)^{1/2}$. Picking out under the square root the square of p^2 (first term) and extracting the square root of it, we have

$$(p^2 - 4q)^{1/2} = [p^2(1 - 4q/p^2)]^{1/2} = |p| [1 - (2q^{1/2}/|p|)^2]^{1/2}$$

Now the difference $1 - t^2$, where t^2 is less than one, can be written as a perfect square if $t^2 = \text{Sin}^2 2A$, the auxiliary angle A being defined by the equality $t = \text{Sin } 2A$, since for such a choice of A we obtain $1 - t^2 = \text{Cos}^2 2A$. Therefore, instead of computing the numerical value of the difference $1 - (2q^{1/2}/|p|)^2$ and then extracting the square root of this value, we can introduce an auxiliary angle A (A < 45°), defining it by $\text{Sin } 2A = 2q^{1/2}/|p|$. Then $[1 - (2q^{1/2}/|p|)^2]^{1/2} = \text{Cos } 2A$, so that

$$(p^2 - 4q)^{1/2} = |p| \cdot \text{Cos } 2A. \qquad (p \gtrless 0)$$

This result, when used in the formula expressing the two roots of (38), gives:

$$x_1, x_2 = \tfrac{1}{2}(-p \pm p \cdot \text{Cos } 2A) = -\tfrac{1}{2}p(1 \pm \text{Cos } 2A)$$

But, $1 - \text{Cos } 2A = 2 \text{Sin}^2 A$ and $1 + \text{Cos } 2A = 2 \text{Cos}^2 A$, so that finally the two real roots of the equation (38) are expressed in terms of trigonometric functions of the auxiliary angle:

$$x_1 = -p \, \text{Sin}^2 A; \qquad x_2 = -p \, \text{Cos}^2 A$$
$$(\text{Sin } 2A = 2q^{1/2}/|p|).$$

It is easy to check the fundamental relations $x_1 + x_2 = -p$ and $x_1 x_2 = q$ which must be verified by the two roots:

$$x_1 + x_2 = -p(\text{Sin}^2 A + \text{Cos}^2 A) = -p;$$
$$x_1 x_2 = p^2 \cdot \text{Sin}^2 A \cdot \text{Cos}^2 A = (p^2 \cdot \text{Sin}^2 2A)/4 = q$$

since by definition $\text{Sin}^2 2A = 4q/p^2$.

We pass now to the case of a negative constant term, $q < 0$, when the difference $p^2 - 4q$ is in fact a sum of two positive terms, that is, $p^2 + 4|q|$.

In this case we have under the square root a sum of the type $1 + t^2$:

$$(p^2 - 4q)^{1/2} = |p| \cdot [1 + (2|q|^{1/2}/|p|)^2]^{1/2}.$$

To compute the square root $(1 + t^2)^{1/2}$ replace t^2 by $\text{Tan}^2 2A$, since then $(1 + \text{Tan}^2 2A)^{1/2} = \text{Sec } 2A = 1/\text{Cos } 2A$. Therefore, this time we define the auxiliary angle by a tangent, choosing such an angle A < 45° that

$$\text{Tan } 2A = 2|q|^{1/2}/|p|. \qquad (39)$$

Since with such a choice of A the value of the square root $(p^2 - 4q)^{1/2}$ is equal to $|p|$ Sec 2A $= |p|/$Cos 2A, the roots of (38) are now represented by

$$x_1, x_2 = \tfrac{1}{2}(-p \pm p/\text{Cos } 2A) = -\tfrac{1}{2}p \text{ (Cos } 2A \mp 1)/\text{Cos } 2A$$
$$= \pm\tfrac{1}{2}p \text{ (1} \mp \text{Cos } 2A)/\text{Cos } 2A$$

The final expressions are:

$$x_1 = \tfrac{1}{2}p \text{ (1} - \text{Cos } 2A)/\text{Cos } 2A = p \cdot \text{Sin}^2 A \cdot \text{Sec } 2A$$

$$x_2 = -\tfrac{1}{2}p \text{ (1} + \text{Cos } 2A)/\text{Cos } 2A = -p \cdot \text{Cos}^2 A \cdot \text{Sec } 2A,$$

where the auxiliary angle A is to be computed with the aid of (39).

The check is easy:

$$x_1 + x_2 = -p \text{ Sec } 2A(-\text{Sin}^2 A + \text{Cos}^2 A) = -p \cdot \text{Sec } 2A \cdot \text{Cos } 2A = -p$$

$$x_1 x_2 = -p^2 \text{ Sec}^2 2A \cdot \text{Sin}^2 A \text{ Cos}^2 A = -p^2 \text{ Sin}^2 2A \cdot \text{Sec}^2 2A/4 = q$$

since $\text{Tan}^2 2A = 4|q|/p^2$ by definition and $-|q| = q$, if q is negative.

EXAMPLE 1. In general, the auxiliary angle is computed with the aid of logarithms, but in our example we will consider very simple equations so that the logarithms are not needed. It is easy to see by inspection that the equation

$$x^2 - 4x + 3 = 0$$

has the two roots $x_1 = 1$ and $x_2 = 3$. Since the constant term $q = 3$ is positive we introduce the auxiliary angle with the aid of the definition Sin 2A $= 2q^{1/2}/|p|$ which for our equation gives Sin 2A $= 2\sqrt{3}/4 = \sqrt{3}/2$, so that 2A $= 60°$ and A $= 30°$. Thus, Sin A $= \tfrac{1}{2}$ and Cos A $= \sqrt{3}/2$ which yields

$$x_1 = -p \text{ Sin}^2 A = 4(\tfrac{1}{2})^2 = 1 \quad \text{and} \quad x_2 = -p \text{ Cos}^2 A = 4(3^{1/2}/2)^2 = 3.$$

EXAMPLE 2. In the equation

$$x^2 - 2x - 3 = 0$$

the constant term $q = -3$ is negative and therefore we define A with the aid of (39): Tan 2A $= 2 \cdot \sqrt{3}/2 = \sqrt{3}$. Thus, 2A $= 60°$, A $= 30°$, Sin^2 A $= (\tfrac{1}{2})^2 = \tfrac{1}{4}$ and Cos^2 A $= (3^{1/2}/2)^2 = \tfrac{3}{4}$. We obtain

$$x_1 = p \cdot \text{Sin}^2 A \cdot \text{Sec } 2A = -2 \cdot (\tfrac{1}{4}) \cdot 2 = -1;$$
$$x_2 = -p \text{ Cos}^2 A \cdot \text{Sec } 2A = 1(3/4) \cdot 2 = 3,$$

since Sec 2A $=$ Sec 60° $= 1/$Cos 60° $= 1/(\tfrac{1}{2}) = 2$.

We add that instead of the trigonometric sine and tangent, hyperbolic functions Th 2A and Sh 2A (defined by the same formulas: Th 2A $= 2q^{1/2}/|p|$, if $q > 0$; and Sh 2A $= 2|q|^{1/2}/|p|$, if $q < 0$) could be used. The new auxiliary argument 2A, naturally, is different from the angle 2A which is the argument of trigonometric functions.

Case $q > 0$. If $2q^{1/2}/|p| =$ Th 2A, then $(p^2 - 4q)^{1/2} = |p|(1 - \text{Th}^2 2A)^{1/2}$ $= |p|$ Sech 2A, so that the roots are expressed as follows: $\frac{1}{2}(-p \pm |p| \cdot \text{Sech} 2A)$ $= -\frac{1}{2}p$ Sech 2A (Ch 2A $\pm$ 1), that is,

$$x_1 = -p \, \text{Sh}^2 A \cdot \text{Sech} \, 2A, \quad x_2 = -p \, \text{Ch}^2 A \cdot \text{Sech} \, 2A.$$

Case $q < 0$. If $2|q|^{1/2}/|p| =$ Sh 2A, then $(p^2 - 4q)^{1/2} = (p^2 + 4|q|)^{1/2}$ $= |p| \cdot$ Ch 2A, so that the roots become: $\frac{1}{2}(-p \pm |p| \, \text{Ch} \, 2A) = \pm p$ $\cdot \frac{1}{2}(\text{Ch} \, 2A \mp 1)$; that is,

$$x_1 = p \cdot \text{Sh}^2 A, \quad x_2 = -p \cdot \text{Ch}^2 A.$$

In these formulas the root of smaller absolute value is denoted by x_1, so that $|x_1| < |x_2|$. The auxiliary angle A, indeed, is less than 45° and positive, when the trigonometric functions are used, so that Sin A < Cos A; in the case when the hyperbolic functions are applied, $\text{Sh}^2 A < \text{Ch}^2 A$, since $\text{Sh}^2 A = \text{Ch}^2 A - 1$.

A quadratic equation (38) with real coefficients has conjugate complex roots $x_1 = a + ib$ and $x_2 = a - ib$, when its discriminant $p^2 - 4q$ is negative. This can happen only if the constant term q is positive: the inequality $p^2 - 4q < 0$ gives $4q > p^2$ so that q is positive. Using the polar form for the complex numbers $a \pm ib$ and denoting $(a^2 + b^2)^{1/2}$ by r, we have $x_1 = r \cdot e^{it}$ and $x_2 = r \cdot e^{-it}$, where r and t are to be found.

Now $x_1 + x_2 = -p$ and $x_1 x_2 = q$ become $r(e^{it} + e^{-it}) = -p$ and $r^2 = q$, so that $r = \sqrt{q}$ and $2q^{1/2} \text{Cos} \, t = -p$. Therefore, to find the conjugate complex roots of (38) we first determine the auxiliary angle $t < \pi$ by $\text{Cos} \, t = -p/2q^{1/2}$ and then compute the numerical value of Sin t, the two roots being given by $x_1 = q^{1/2}(\text{Cos} \, t + i \cdot \text{Sin} \, t)$ and $x_2 = q^{1/2}(\text{Cos} \, t - i \cdot \text{Sin} \, t)$.

Trigonometric Solution
of Cubic Equation with Three Real Roots

As it was proved in Chapter 8, a cubic equation with real coefficients

$$x^3 + px + q = 0 \tag{40}$$

can have two complex conjugate and a real root or three real roots. Its three roots are real, if the expression $q^2/4 + p^3/27$ has a negative value.

In what follows we suppose that this condition of real roots

$$(q/2)^2 + (p/3)^3 < 0 \tag{41}$$

is fulfilled. Since its first term $(q/2)^2$ is positive, it implies that the coefficient p must be negative: $p < 0$. Moreover, this coefficient must be sufficiently large in absolute value to insure the inequality (41); that is, we must have the inequality $q^2/4 < |p|^3/27$ which can be written also as

$$\tfrac{1}{2}|q| < (|p|/3)^{3/2}. \tag{42}$$

The three real roots of (40) are expressed (see Chapter 8, p. 348) as sums of complex conjugate numbers:

$$x_1 = R^{-1}u + Rv; \quad x_2 = u + v; \quad x_3 = Ru + R^{-1}v, \tag{43}$$

where R denotes the complex radical $R = \sqrt[3]{1} = (e^{2\pi i})^{1/3} = e^{2\pi i/3}$, so that R^{-1} is the conjugate radical equal to $\sqrt[3]{1} = e^{-2\pi i/3}$, while u and v denote conjugate complex cubic roots, namely

$$u = [-q/2 + (q^2/4 + p^3/27)^{1/2}]^{1/3};$$

$$v = [-q/2 - (q^2/4 + p^3/27)^{1/2}]^{1/3}. \tag{44}$$

This case of three real roots was called by the early algebraists the *irreducible* case since they did not know how to extract cube roots of complex numbers. We do know how to find them, but nevertheless the numerical computations are not easy to perform. The method of auxiliary angle simplifies them enormously since the use of trigonometric functions not only eliminates the extraction of square root $(q^2/4 + p^2/27)^{1/2}$ but also transforms the complicated complex expressions of real quantities into a real form.

The application of this method to the cubic equation (40) is based on the formula (31) p. 234 Chapter 6, namely

$$\text{Cos } 3t = 4 \text{ Cos}^3 t - 3 \text{ Cos } t \tag{45}$$

We again consider separately the two cases $q > 0$ and $q < 0$.

Case $q > 0$. To solve equation (40) let us use the substitution $x = k \text{ Cos } t$, where the unknown t replaces x while k is a constant, the choice of which is at our disposal and will be fixed later.

Multiplying equation (40) by $4k^{-3}$, we rewrite it as follows

$$4(x/k)^3 + 4pk^{-2}(x/k) + 4qk^{-3} = 0,$$

so that the substitution $x = k \cdot \text{Cos } t$ transforms it into

$$4 \cos^3 t + 4pk^{-2} \cos t + 4qk^{-3} = 0. \tag{46}$$

Comparing this equation with the identity (45), we come to the conclusion that the equation (46) will be easy to solve, if the coefficient $4pk^{-2}$ of the term with Cos t could be replaced by -3. Here we remember that the choice of the constant k is free and therefore we can choose it in such a way that indeed $4pk^{-2} = -3$. Thus, we define k^2 by the condition $k^2 = -4p/3$ $= 4|p|/3$, where the coefficient p is, as we know, necessarily negative.

For k itself we have two possible values, namely $\pm 2 \, (|p|/3)^{1/2}$. If q is positive, we choose the negative value of the square root and define k by

$$k = -2 \, (|p|/3)^{1/2}. \qquad (q > 0)$$

Using this value of k in the constant term $4q \cdot k^{-3}$ of (46), we give to this constant term the form $-\frac{1}{2}q \, (|p|/3)^{-3/2}$ and therefore our final equation for the unknown t is

$$\text{Cos } 3t = \tfrac{1}{2}q \, (|p|/3)^{-3/2}. \tag{47}$$

The lefthand member is Cos $3t$ since $4 \text{ Cos}^3 t + 4pk^{-2} \text{ Cos } t = 4 \text{ Cos}^3 t$ $- 3 \text{ Cos } t = \text{Cos } 3t$ as result of our choice of k. The righthand member is positive and less than one as it can be seen from (42), so that the auxiliary angle t defined by equation (47) is real, one of its principal values being the positive and acute angle t_0, $0 < 3t_0 < 90°$. This principal value (which is less than 30°) can easily be found with the aid of logarithms of trigonometric functions.

The general solution of the equation (47) is $3t = 3t_0 + 2m\pi$, where m is an arbitrary integer, $m \gtreqless 0$. Therefore,

$$t = t_0 + 2m\pi/3.$$

Having found the auxiliary angle t, we can express the three roots x_1, x_2, x_3 of the cubic equation (40) in terms of t, using the substitution's formula $x = k \cdot \text{Cos } t$. Thus,

$$x = -2 \, (|p|/3)^{1/2} \cdot \text{Cos } (t_0 + 2m\pi/3).$$

Since Cos t is a periodic function with 2π as its period, only three different values for Cos $(t_0 + 2m\pi/3)$ can be obtained for any choice of the arbitrary integer m. They correspond to three roots of (40). Thus, giving to m the values $-1, 0, 1$, we obtain the three roots of (40):

$$x_1 = -2 \, (|p|/3)^{1/2} \cdot \text{Cos } (t_0 - 2\pi/3); \quad x_2 = -2 \, (|p|/3)^{1/2} \, \text{Cos } t_0;$$
$$x_3 = -2 \, (|p|/3)^{1/2} \cdot \text{Cos } (t_0 + 2\pi/3). \tag{48}$$

Case $q < 0$. If q is negative, the same substitution is used, the only difference with the case $q > 0$ being in the choice of the sign in the expression for the constant $k = \pm 2\,(|p|/3)^{1/2}$: the positive value of the square root must be chosen, if q is negative, so that now

$$k = 2\,(|p|/3)^{1/2} \qquad\qquad (q < 0).$$

Using this value of k in the equation (46), we obtain for the lefthand member $\mathrm{Cos}\, 3t$ the value $-4q \cdot k^{-3} = -\tfrac{1}{2}q\,(|p|/3)^{-3/2} = \tfrac{1}{2}|q|\,(|p|/3)^{-3/2}$, that is,

$$\mathrm{Cos}\, 3t_0 = \tfrac{1}{2}\,|q|(|p|/3)^{-3/2} \qquad\qquad (49)$$

This time the three roots of (40) are given by the expression

$$x_n = 2\,(|p|/3)^{1/2} \cdot \mathrm{Cos}\,(t_0 + 2n\pi/3) \qquad (n = -1, 0, 1)$$

Denoting the sign of the constant term q by the symbol *sign* (q), we can summarize the discussion of both cases $q \gtrless 0$ as follows. The three real roots of the cubic equation (40) are expressed in terms of the auxiliary angle t_0 defined by the equation (49). They are given by

$$x_n = -2\,(|p|/3)^{1/2} \cdot \mathrm{Cos}\,(t_0 + 2n\pi/3)\,sign\,(q). \qquad (n = -1, 0, 1) \quad (50)$$

Cubic Equation with Complex Roots

When the quantity $q^2/4 + p^3/27$ is positive the equation $x^3 + px + q = 0$ has only one real root, two other being complex and conjugate. Their computation with the aid of Tartaglia's formulas given in Chapter 9 is not difficult because in this case no complex expressions are involved in general expressions of three roots except the radicals $R = e^{2\pi i/3}$ and $R^{-1} = e^{-2\pi i/3}$. Nevertheless, these computations can be enormously simplified by the method of auxiliary argument, not angle but argument because in this case the *hyperbolic* functions are used. The simplification in question is based on the analogue of De Moivre's theorem for the hyperbolic functions which states that $\mathrm{Ch}\, t \pm \mathrm{Sh}\, t = \sqrt[n]{\mathrm{Ch}\,(nt) \pm \mathrm{Sh}\,(nt)}$, and more exactly on its particular case when $n = 3$:

$$\sqrt[3]{\mathrm{Ch}\,(3t) \pm \mathrm{Sh}\,(3t)} = \mathrm{Ch}\, t \pm \mathrm{Sh}\, t.$$

Moreover, we recall the formula

$$4\,\mathrm{Sh}^3\, t + 3\,\mathrm{Sh}\, t = \mathrm{Sh}\,(3t)$$

which is needed when the equation $x^3 + px + q = 0$ is transformed with the aid of the substitution $x = k \cdot \mathrm{Sh}\, t$. Multiplying the cubic equation by $4k^{-3}$ and replacing x/k by $\mathrm{Sh}\, t$, we obtain

$$4\,\mathrm{Sh}^3\, t + 3\,\mathrm{Sh}\, t = -4q \cdot k^{-3},$$

if k verifies the condition $4p \cdot k^{-2} = 3$, that is, $k = \pm 2\,(p/3)^{1/2}$.

The condition imposed on k implies that the coefficient p is positive: $p = 3k^2/4 > 0$. Therefore, the case of a negative p, which is characterized by the double inequality

$$-3 \cdot (|q|/2)^{2/3} < p < 0, \tag{51}$$

will be considered separately.

Choosing for k the definition $k = 2\,(p/3)^{1/2}$, we obtain for the righthand member $-4q \cdot k^{-3}$ the real value $-\tfrac{1}{2}q\,(p/3)^{-3/2}$, so that the unknown t verifies the equation

$$\mathrm{Sh}\, 3t = -\tfrac{1}{2}q \cdot (3/p)^{3/2}. \tag{$p > 0$}$$

The solution $t = t_0$ of this equation is easily obtained with the aid of the table of logarithms for the hyperbolic sine and its sign is opposite to that of the constant term q since the hyperbolic sine is an odd function and has the same sign as its argument.

Having computed t_0, we can replace $-q/2$ in Tartaglia's formulas (44) by $(p/3)^{3/2} \cdot \mathrm{Sh}\, 3t_0$, so that the square root $(q^2/4 + p^3/27)^{1/2}$ takes the value $(p/3)^{3/2} \cdot \mathrm{Ch}\, 3t_0$ and the two cube roots u and v of formulas (44) become:

$$u = [(p/3)^{3/2}\,(\mathrm{Sh}\, 3t_0 + \mathrm{Ch}\, 3t_0)]^{1/3} = (p/3)^{1/2}\,(\mathrm{Ch}\, t_0 + \mathrm{Sh}\, t_0)$$

$$v = [-(p/3)^{3/2}\,(-\mathrm{Sh}\, 3t_0 + \mathrm{Ch}\, 3t_0)]^{1/3} = (p/3)^{1/2}\,(-\mathrm{Ch}\, t_0 + \mathrm{Sh}\, t_0).$$

Using now the expressions (43) of three roots x_1, x_2, x_3 and observing that $R^{-1} + R = -1$, while $R^{-1} - R = -i\sqrt{3}$, we finally obtain

$$x_1 = -(p/3)^{1/2}\,(\mathrm{Sh}\, t_0 + i\sqrt{3}\,\mathrm{Ch}\, t_0); \quad x_2 = 2\,(p/3)^{1/2}\,\mathrm{Sh}\, t_0;$$

$$x_3 = -(p/3)^{1/2}\,(\mathrm{Sh}\, t_0 - i\sqrt{3}\,\mathrm{Ch}\, t_0),$$

these expressions solving the question in the case of a positive p.

We emphasize that the original substitution $x = k\,\mathrm{Sh}\, t = 2\,(p/3)^{1/2}\cdot\mathrm{Sh}\, t$ gives only the *real* root x_2, the other two roots being obtained from the general formulas (43).

Case $-3(|q|/2)^{2/3} < p < 0$. Here we use again the symbol *sign* (q) which by definition is equal to plus one, if q is positive, and to minus one if q is negative. An auxiliary argument t_0 is defined by the equation

$$\text{Ch } 3t_0 = \tfrac{1}{2}q \cdot (|p|/3)^{-3/2} \cdot sign\,(q),$$

so that $q/2$ is to be replaced by $sign\,(q) \cdot (|p|/3)^{3/2} \cdot \text{Ch } 3t_0$.

With this value for $q/2$ we deduce that the square root $(q^2/4 + p^3/27)^{1/2}$ s equal to $(|p|/3)^{3/2} \cdot \text{Sh } 3t_0$ which entails for u and v the following transformation:

$$
\begin{aligned}
u &= \{-sign\,(q) \cdot (|p|/3)^{3/2}\,[\text{Ch } 3t_0 - sign\,(q) \cdot \text{Sh } 3t_0]\}^{1/3} \\
&= -sign\,(q)\,(|p|/3)^{1/2}\,[\text{Ch } t_0 - sign\,(q) \cdot \text{Sh } t_0] \\
v &= \{-sign\,(q) \cdot (|p|/3)^{3/2}\,[\text{Ch } 3t_0 + sign\,(q) \cdot \text{Sh } 3t_0]\}^{1/3} \\
&= -sign\,(q)\,(|p|/\,3)^{1/2}\,[\text{Ch } t_0 + sign\,(q) \cdot \text{Sh } t_0].
\end{aligned}
$$

Using the values of u and v in terms of t_0 in the expressions (43) of roots x_1, x_2, x_3 and replacing $[sign\,(q)]^2$ by 1, we find finally

$$x_1 = (|p|/3)^{1/2}\,[sign\,(q)\,\text{Ch } t_0 - i\,\sqrt{3}\,\text{Sh } t_0];$$

$$x_2 = -2 \cdot sign\,(q) \cdot (|p|/3)^{1/2}\,\text{Ch } t_0;$$

$$x_3 = (|p|/3)^{1/2}\,[sign\,(q) \cdot \text{Ch } t_0 + i\,\sqrt{3}\,\text{Sh } t_0].$$

Therefore, in all three cases (a) $p < -3\,(|q|/2)^{2/3}$ (that is, three real roots), (b) $p > 0$ and (c) $-3\,(|q|/2)^{2/3} < p < 0$ the computation of roots of the cubic equation $x^3 + px + q = 0$ with the aid of trigonometric or hyperbolic functions reduces to the solution of a very simple equation which is

(a) $\text{Cos } 3t_0 = \tfrac{1}{2}\,|q|\,(|p|/3)^{-3/2}$ $[p < -3\,(|q|/2)^{2/3}]$

(b) $\text{Sh } 3t_0 = -\tfrac{1}{2}\,q \cdot (p/3)^{-3/2}$ $(p > 0)$

(c) $\text{Ch } 3t_0 = \tfrac{1}{2}\,|q|\,(|p|/3)^{-3/2}$ $[0 > p > -3\,(|q|/2)^{2/3}]$

Examples. To form a cubic equation with given three real roots x_1, x_2, x_3 it is sufficient to multiply out the three linear factors $x - x_1$, $x - x_2$, $x - x_3$ which vanish for $x = x_1$, $x = x_2$ and $x = x_3$ respectively, and equate their product to zero. Suppose, for instance, that we want to form a cubic equation having as its three real roots the numbers 1, 2 and -3. We chose these three numbers so that their sum $1 + 2 - 3$ is zero, in order to obtain a cubic equation without the term involving x^2. Indeed, the product $(x - 1)\,(x - 2)\,(x + 3)$ multiplied out yields the cubic equation

$$x^3 - 7x + 6 = 0.$$

The condition (41) is verified since $(q/2)^2 + (p/3)^3 = -100/27 < 0$.

We are in the case (a) and thus the auxiliary angle t_0 is defined by Cos $3t_0$ = $\frac{1}{2}q\,(|p|/3)^{-3/2} = 3\,(7/3)^{-3/2} = 3^{5/2} \cdot 7^{-3/2}$. The common logarithm of Cos $3t_0$ is therefore equal to $\frac{1}{2}(5\log 3 - 3\log 7) = \bar{1}.92515$ and $3t_0$ = $32° 40' 52.5''$. Dividing the angle $3t_0$ by 3, we find $t_0 = 10° 53' 37.5''$.

The three roots are given by the formulas (48) which in our case yield the following numerical values

$$x_1 = -2(7/3)^{1/2}\,\text{Cos}\,(-109° 6' 22.5'') = 2(7/3)^{1/2}\sin 19° 6' 22.5''$$

$$x_2 = -2(7/3)^{1/2}\,\text{Cos}\,10° 53' 37.5''$$

$$x_3 = -2(7/3)^{1/2}\,\text{Cos}\,(130° 53' 37.5'') = 2(7/3)^{1/2}\,\text{Sin}\,40° 53' 37.5''$$

Computing the logarithms of x_1, $|x_2|$, x_3, we find first the log $2(7/3)^{1/2}$ which is equal to $\log 2 + \frac{1}{2}(\log 7 - \log 3) = 0.48502$ and then the logarithms of trigonometric functions, namely log Sin $19° 6' 22.5'' = \bar{1}.514975$, log Cos $10° 53' 37.5'' = \bar{1}.99210$ and log Sin $40° 53' 37.5'' = \bar{1}.816014$. Adding to them the logarithm of $2(7/3)^{1/2}$, that is 0.48502, we obtain:

$$\log x_1 = \bar{1}.514975 + 0.48502 = \bar{1}.999995; \quad \log|x_2| = 0.47712;$$

$\log x_3 = \bar{1}.816014 + 0.48502 = 0.301034$. These results give $x_1 = 1$, $x_2 = -3$, $x_3 = 2$ because, rounding off the sixth decimal in the logarithms of x_1 and x_3, we obtain the exact tabular values of $\log 1 = 0$ and $\log 2$ = 0.30103.

Our next example is the equation $x^3 - 11x + 20 = 0$. Here the absolute value 11 of the coefficient $p = -11$ is less than $3(q/2)^{2/3} = 3\sqrt[3]{100} = 13.9\ldots$, so that this example belongs to the case (c). Therefore, the auxiliary argument t_0 is defined by Ch $3t_0 = 10 \cdot (3/11)^{2/3}$ and log Ch $3t_0 = 0.15360$.

With the aid of tables of logarithms for the hyperbolic functions we find that $3t_0 = 0.89139$ and thus $t_0 = 0.29713$. The expressions of roots are: $x_1 = 11^{1/2}\,\text{Ch}\,t_0/3^{1/2} - i \cdot 11^{1/2}\,\text{Sh}\,t_0$; $x_2 = -2\,(11/3)^{1/2}\,\text{Ch}\,t_0$; $x_3 = 11^{1/2}$ $\cdot\,\text{Ch}\,t_0/3^{1/2} + i \cdot 11^{1/2}\,\text{Sh}\,t_0$. Computing the logarithms of hyperbolic cosine and sine of $t_0 = 0.29713$, we find log Ch $t_0 = 0.01890$ and log Sh t_0 = $\bar{1}.47927$. With the aid of these logarithms, it is found that the real parts of x_1 and x_3 are equal to 2; $x_2 = -4$; and log $(11^{1/2}\,\text{Sh}\,t_0) = \bar{1}.99997$ instead of zero (the difference being caused by the inaccuracy of tables of logarithms). Thus, $x_1 = 2 - i$, $x_2 = -4$ and $x_3 = 2 + i$.

The root $x_2 = -4$ is evaluated exactly as it can be shown by direct substitution: $(-4)^3 - 11(-4) + 20 = 0$. If we eliminate this root, dividing the lefthand member $x^3 - 11x + 20$ of our equation by $x - (-4) = x + 4$, the two other roots will be found by solving the equation $x^2 - 4x + 5 = 0$, where $x^2 - 4x + 5$ is the quotient of the division of $x^3 - 11x + 20$ by $x + 4$. Thus, the two other roots are $x_1 = 2 - i$ and $x_3 = 2 + i$. We see, therefore, that the exact value of $11^{1/2} \operatorname{Sh} t_0$ is one, so that indeed $\log(11^{1/2} \operatorname{Sh} t_0) = 0$.

Finally we consider the case (b) to which belongs the cubic equation $x^3 + x - 10 = 0$. Since $p = 1 > 0$ we begin by computing t_0, root of the equation $\operatorname{Sh} 3t_0 = -\frac{1}{2}q(p/3)^{-3/2} = 5 \cdot (1/3)^{-3/2} = 15\sqrt{3}$. The value of $\log \operatorname{Sh} 3t_0$ is 1.41465, so $3t_0 = 3.950875$ and $t_0 = 1.316958$. The expressions of the roots are

$$x_1 = -(\operatorname{Sh} t_0/3^{1/2} + i \cdot \operatorname{Ch} t_0); \quad x_2 = 2 \operatorname{Sh} t_0/3^{1/2};$$

$$x_3 = -(\operatorname{Sh} t_0/3^{1/2} - i \cdot \operatorname{Ch} t_0).$$

The values of hyperbolic sine and cosine of t_0 (namely, $\operatorname{Sh} t_0 = 1.7320...$ $= 3^{1/2}$ and $\operatorname{Ch} t_0 = 2.0000$) give

$$x_1 = -(1 + 2i); \quad x_2 = 2; \quad x_3 = -(1 - 2i)$$

and the direct substitution proves that the solution is correct.

Solution of Trigonometric Equations

Another important application of the method of the auxiliary angle is the following solution of trigonometric equation of the type

$$a \cdot \operatorname{Cos} x + b \cdot \operatorname{Sin} x = c, \tag{52}$$

where a, b, c are three given and known numbers, the unknown in this equation being the argument x of sine and cosine.

To solve this equation we introduce an auxiliary angle A such that the coefficients a and b are proportional to Cos A and Sin A respectively. Denoting the unknown coefficient of proportionality by k

$$a = k \cdot \operatorname{Cos} A, \qquad b = k \cdot \operatorname{Sin} A,$$

and dividing equation (52) by k, we transform it into

$$(a/k) \operatorname{Cos} x + (b/k) \operatorname{Sin} x = \operatorname{Cos} A \cdot \operatorname{Cos} x + \operatorname{Sin} A \cdot \operatorname{Sin} x = c/k.$$

To find k it is sufficient to square and then add the expressions of a and b:

$$a^2 + b^2 = k^2 \operatorname{Cos}^2 A + k^2 \operatorname{Sin}^2 A = k^2 (\operatorname{Cos}^2 A + \operatorname{Sin}^2 A) = k^2.$$

Therefore, $k = (a^2 + b^2)^{1/2}$ while, on the other hand, the lefthand member Cos A Cos x + Sin A. Sin x is equal to Cos $(x - A)$. Thus, equation (52) is now written as follows:

$$\text{Cos } (x - A) = c/(a^2 + b^2)^{1/2}$$

and its solution can be expressed in terms of the auxiliary angle A by

$$x = A \pm \text{Arccos } (c/(a^2 + b^2)^{1/2}] + 2n\pi,$$

where n is an arbitrary integer.

The auxiliary angle A is easy to find: its tangent is known

$$\tan A = b/a \tag{53}$$

and the signs of Sin A and Cos A are those of b and a, the coefficient of proportionality k being positive by definition. This is important since the equation (53) gives for A an expression

$$A = \text{Arctan } (b/a) + m\pi,$$

where the integer m can be even or odd and the choice of parity for m depends on the sign of Cos A: if Cos A is positive (positive a), then the integer m is even; if Cos A is negative, then m is odd.

It is important to observe that the argument of the Arccosine in the expression of x, namely the fraction $c/(a^2 + b^2)^{1/2}$, cannot exceed one in absolute value unless the value of the Arccosine, and with it the value of the unknown x, become complex numbers. Therefore, we must emphasize that the solution x of the equation (52) is real only when the condition

$$|c| < (a^2 + b^2)^{1/2} \tag{54}$$

is fulfilled. Its necessity is easily deduced from the fact that the value $c/(a^2 + b^2)^{1/2}$ of the cosine Cos $(x - A)$ must be less than or at most equal to one in absolute value, if the argument $x - A$ of this cosine is to be real.

EXAMPLE. Given 3 Cos x + 5 Sin x = 4, find x. First of all, we check the condition for a real solution for x. Here, $c = 4 < (3^2 + 5^2)^{1/2} = (a^2 + b^2)^{1/2}$ and this condition is verified. To find A we form Tan A = $b/a = \frac{5}{3}$ = 1.66666··· which gives two values for A: A_1 = 59°02′11″ and $A_2 = A_1$ + 180°. Both a and b being positive, Cos A and Sin A are positive and therefore the angle A belongs to the first quadrant and A = A_1; the second value A_2 being in the third quadrant, it must be rejected.

The ratio $c/(a^2 + b^2)^{1/2}$ is equal to $4/34^{1/2} = 0.68599\cdots$ and thus the Arccosine of it is equal to 46°41′11″. The final result is x = 59°02′11″ ± 46°41′11″ + $2n\pi$, that is, x = 105°43′22″ or x = 12°21′00″.

An equation of this type $a \cos x + b \sin x = c$ can be solved with the aid of a quadratic equation into which it is transformed, if $\sin x = z$ is considered as an auxiliary unknown, but this indirect method has the following defect. Reducing the trigonometric equation to a quadratic equation, we must replace $\cos x$ by $\pm (1 - \sin^2 x)^{1/2} = \pm(1 - z^2)^{1/2}$: $\pm a (1 - z^2)^{1/2} = c - bz$ and then square both members to get rid of the radical $(1 - z^2)^{1/2}$. Thus,

$$(a^2 + b^2)z^2 - 2bcz + (c^2 - a^2) = 0$$

is the equivalent quadratic equation. Solving it for $z = \sin x$, we obtain two different numerical values for $\sin x$ and therefore *four* different angles because to each numerical value v of $\sin x$ there correspond two different angles: Arcsin v and $180° -$ Arcsin v. Two of them are solutions of the original trigonometric equation, but two others are extraneous solutions of the quadratic equation which do not satisfy the trigonometric equation. Thus, if the reduction to a quadratic equation is used, a subsequent study of four solutions obtained is necessary to isolate and reject the extraneous solutions.

For instance, the equation just solved by the method of auxiliary angle can also be written $3 \cos x = 4 - 5 \sin x$. Squared, it becomes $9 - 9 \sin^2 x = 16 - 40 \sin x + 25 \sin^2 x$ that is $34z^2 - 40z + 7 = 0$. It yields for $\sin x = z$ two values: $\sin x = 0.96259$ and $\sin x = 0.21389$. To the first of them correspond two angles $x_1 = 74°16'38''$, $x_2 = 180° - x_1$. Likewise, to the second correspond two other angles $x_3 = 12°21'$, $x_4 = 180° - x_3$. Comparing them with the solution obtained by the method of auxiliary angle, we see that x_1 and x_4 are extraneous solutions which do not satisfy the given equation $3 \cos x + 5 \sin x = 4$ because they are solutions of the equation $-3 \cos x + 5 \sin x = 4$. This last equation was introduced by the operation of squaring since the expression $9 - 9 \sin^2 x$ is the square not only of $3 \cos x$ but also of $-3 \cos x$.

The analogous hyperbolic equation $a \operatorname{Ch} t + b \operatorname{Sh} t = c$ can also be solved with the aid of a quadratic equation taking as an auxiliary unknown $z = \operatorname{Sh} t$, or by applying the method of an auxiliary argument A such that the lefthand member of the equation becomes $\operatorname{Ch}(t + A)$ or $\operatorname{Sh}(t + A)$; but the best way consists in replacing the hyperbolic functions by exponentials. Thus, we obtain instead of $a \operatorname{Ch} t + b \operatorname{Sh} t = c$

$$(a + b) e^{2t} - 2c \cdot e^t + (a - b) = 0.$$

Using the auxiliary unknown $u = e^t$ and solving the quadratic equation

$$(a + b) u^2 - 2c \cdot u + (a - b) = 0,$$

we find the value of $e^t = u$:

$$e^t = [c \pm (b^2 + c^2 - a^2)^{1/2}]/(a + b). \tag{55}$$

This expression shows that there is a condition of real solution imposed on the data a, b, c: the quantity under the square root, $b^2 + c^2 - a^2$, must be positive or at least zero, otherwise e^t has a complex value and its argument t cannot be real. Looking for real solutions, we suppose that this condition

$$a^2 \leqslant b^2 + c^2 \tag{56}$$

is satisfied. Moreover, an exponential e^t cannot have negative values if its exponent is a real number. Therefore, the positiveness of the righthand member in (55) is another condition of real solution and the necessary condition (56) is not sufficient. We do not study the second condition of real solution because in each particular case the sign of the righthand member in (55) is obtained by computing its value. We observe only that in general there are two solutions t_1 and t_2 given by

$$t_1 = \mathrm{Log} \{[c + (b^2 + c^2 - a^2)^{1/2}]/(a + b)\};$$
$$t_2 = \mathrm{Log} \{[c - (b^2 + c^2 - a^2)^{1/2}]/(a + b)\} \tag{57}$$

They are real, if both expressions under the logarithm symbol are positive, or there can be one real and one complex, or finally two complex solutions. There is one solution only, if the coefficients a, b, c satisfy the relation $a^2 = b^2 + c^2$, namely $t = \mathrm{Log} [c/(a + b)]$.

EXAMPLES. The equation $5 \mathrm{Ch}\, t - 4 \mathrm{Sh}\, t = 3$ has only one solution $t = \mathrm{Log}\, 3$ because $a^2 = 5^2 = 4^2 + 3^2 = b^2 + c^2$. This solution is easy to check by direct substitution: $5 \mathrm{Ch}\, t = 5 (e^{\mathrm{Log}\, 3} + e^{-\mathrm{Log}\, 3})/2 = 5 (3 + \frac{1}{3})/2$ $= \frac{25}{3}$; $4 \mathrm{Sh}\, t = 2 (e^{\mathrm{Log}\, 3} - e^{-\mathrm{Log}\, 3}) = 2 (3 - \frac{1}{3}) = \frac{16}{3}$, so that indeed $5 \mathrm{Ch}\, t - 4 \mathrm{Sh}\, t = \frac{25}{3} - \frac{16}{3} = \frac{9}{3} = 3$.

In our second example $24 \mathrm{Ch}\, t - 20 \mathrm{Sh}\, t = 15$, where $a = 24 < (20^2 + 15^2)^{1/2} = (b^2 + c^2)^{1/2}$, we have two real solutions:

$$t_1 = \mathrm{Log} [(15 + 7)/4] = \mathrm{Log}\, 5.5 \qquad t_2 = \mathrm{Log} [(15 - 7)/4] = \mathrm{Log}\, 2.$$

Checking them we have indeed

$$24 \mathrm{Ch} t_1 - 20 \mathrm{Sh}\, t_1 = 12 (5.5 + \tfrac{2}{11}) - 10 (5.5 - \tfrac{2}{11})$$
$$= 11 + \tfrac{44}{11} = 15$$
$$24 \mathrm{Ch}\, t_2 - 20 \mathrm{Sh}\, t_2 = 12 (2 + \tfrac{1}{2}) - 10 (2 - \tfrac{1}{2}) = 4 + \tfrac{22}{2}$$
$$= 4 + 11 = 15.$$

Finally, changing the sign of c, we have the equation $24 \operatorname{Ch} t - 20 \operatorname{Sh} t + 15 = 0$ which verifies the condition (56), but nevertheless has only complex roots, namely $t_1 = \operatorname{Log}(-2)$ and $t_2 = \operatorname{Log}(-\frac{11}{2})$.

Solution of Triangles

The six elements of a triangle, three sides a, b, c and three respectively opposite angles A, B, C, are not independent. Not only do the angles satisfy the condition $A + B + C = 180°$ and the sides satisfy the inequalities $a < b + c, b < c + a, c < a + b$ (which entail also $a > |b - c|, b > |c - a|, c > |a - b|$), but also there are relations between the angles and sides the effect of which is to limit the number of independent elements to three.

The three independent elements necessarily include at least one side because there are similar triangles having equal angles but different size. It is sufficient to know the three sides a, b, c, for instance, to deduce from them the values A, B, C of the angles. Or, if two angles A and B and the included side c are given, the three other elements C, a and b can be computed. Finally, one angle and two sides also determine a triangle, but in this case we must distinguish between two variants: if the known angle is included between two given sides, the triangle is perfectly determined and unique; if the given angle is opposite to one of two known sides there may be two different triangles with the same three elements, or one triangle or none. Therefore, we must distinguish in all four cases: always denoting a side and the opposite angle by same letter (capital letter for the angle and small for the side), the three elements considered as given and known in the four cases (I) to (IV) are:

(I) a, b, c; (II) A, B, c; (III) A, b, c (included angle); (IV) A, a, b (opposite angle).

The *solution of a triangle* in each of these four cases consists in the computation of three unknown elements with the aid of formulas expressing these unknown elements in terms of the given three elements. The expressions used in the computation are deduced from general relations between the six elements of a triangle studied and proved in Chapter 15. One of them is the so-called

Sine Law

$$a/\sin A = b/\sin B = c/\sin C = 2R \qquad (58)$$

which expresses the proportionality of sides a, b, c to sines of their opposite angles, the coefficient of proportionality being equal to the diameter $2R$ of the circumscribed circle.

The proof of this sine law given in Chapter 15 was based on the equality o two angles inscribed in a circle and subtended by two equal arcs or by the same arc. This proof was limited to the case of an acute-angles triangle and now we complete it by considering the case of a triangle with an *obtuse* angle, $\overset{\frown}{ACB} > 90°$ (Fig. 8).

In this case the opposite side $AB = c$ does not play the same role as the two other sides opposite acute angles $\overset{\frown}{CAB}$ and $\overset{\frown}{CBA}$. Therefore, drawing the diameter BB*, we must consider the right triangle ABB*. In this triangle the side $AB = c$ is opposite to the angle $\overset{\frown}{AB^*B}$ subtended by the arc $\overset{\smile}{ACB} = \overset{\smile}{AC}$ $+ \overset{\smile}{CB}$, so that the angle $\overset{\frown}{AB^*B}$ is equal to the sum $A + B$ of two angles $\overset{\frown}{CAB} = A$ and $\overset{\frown}{CBA} = B$ subtended by the arcs $\overset{\smile}{AC}$ and $\overset{\smile}{CB}$ respectively.

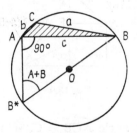

Fig. 18.8

Since the hypotenuse of the triangle ABB* is equal to $2R$ (R being the radius of the circumscribed circle), we obtain for side c opposite the obtuse angle C the following relation: $\mathrm{Sin}\,(A + B) = c/2R$. But the sum of angles $A + B + C$ is equal to 180°, so that $A + B = 180° - C$. Thus, $\mathrm{Sin}\,(A + B) = \mathrm{Sin}(180° - C) = \mathrm{Sin}\,C$ and, therefore, $c/2R = \mathrm{Sin}\,C$; that is, $c/\mathrm{Sin}\,C = 2R$ and this completes the proof of the sine law in the case of an obtuse angle.

Tangent Law

With the aid of the sine law it is easy to evaluate the ratio $(a - b)/(a + b)$ in terms of opposite angles A and B. This transformation of the sine law is known under the name of the tangent law since the ratio of the difference and sum of two sides $(a - b)/(a + b)$ is expressed as a ratio of two tangents, namely, $(a - b)/(a + b) = \text{Tan} [\frac{1}{2} (A - B)]/\text{Tan} [\frac{1}{2} (A + B)].$ (59)

The sine law gives $a = 2R \cdot \text{Sin A}$ and $b = 2R \cdot \text{Sin B}$, so that $a - b = 2R (\text{Sin A} - \text{Sin B})$ and $a + b = 2R (\text{Sin A} + \text{Sin B})$. Therefore, $(a - b)/(a + b) = (\text{Sin A} - \text{Sin B})/(\text{Sin A} + \text{Sin B})$ and to achieve the deduction of the tangent law (59) we recall the formulas (2) and (3) of this chapter

$$\text{Sin A} + \text{Sin B} = 2 \text{Sin} [\frac{1}{2} (A + B)] \cdot \text{Cos} [\frac{1}{2} (A - B)]$$
$$\text{Sin A} - \text{Sin B} = 2 \text{Cos} [\frac{1}{2} (A + B)] \cdot \text{Sin} [\frac{1}{2} (A - B)].$$

Dividing these relations member by member, we prove the tangent law. The tangent law can also be deduced from the definitions of sine and cosine with the aid of the following geometrical configuration (Fig. 9):

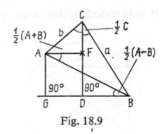

Fig. 18.9

Draw CD bisecting the angle $\widehat{ACB} = C$, so that $\widehat{ACD} = \widehat{DCB} = \frac{1}{2}C$, and drop the perpendiculars AF and BD on the bisector CD. In the triangle AFC thus formed, the angle at A is equal to $\frac{1}{2} (A + B)$. We have indeed

$$\widehat{CAF} = 90° - \frac{1}{2}C = 90° - \frac{1}{2} (180° - A - B) = \frac{1}{2} (A + B).$$

Therefore, the angle $\widehat{FAB}$ adjacent to $\widehat{CAF}$ is equal to $A - \frac{1}{2} (A + B) = \frac{1}{2} (A - B)$ and, since the line BDG is parallel to AF, the alternate interior angle $\widehat{ABG}$ is also equal to $\frac{1}{2} (A - B)$: $\widehat{ABG} = \frac{1}{2} (A - B)$. The point G is defined as the intersection point of BD and of the perpendicular AG dropped from the vertex A on the line BD, so that the triangle ABG is rightangled at G, $\widehat{AGB} = 90°$.

On the other hand, in the right triangle BCD, the angle at the vertex B is equal to $\frac{1}{2}(A + B)$: $\widehat{DBC} = \widehat{ABG} + \widehat{ABC} = \frac{1}{2}(A - B) + B = \frac{1}{2}(A + B)$. The two right triangles BCD and ACF yield the following expressions of their sides AF, FC, BD, DC:

$$AF = b \cdot \mathrm{Cos}\left[\tfrac{1}{2}(A + B)\right]; \quad FC = b \cdot \mathrm{Sin}\left[\tfrac{1}{2}(A + B)\right];$$
$$BD = a \cdot \mathrm{Cos}\left[\tfrac{1}{2}(A + B)\right]; \quad CD = a \cdot \mathrm{Sin}\left[\tfrac{1}{2}(A + B)\right].$$

Considering now the ratio AG/BG of two legs in the right triangle ABG, we note that it is equal to the tangent of the angle $\widehat{ABG} = \frac{1}{2}(A - B)$:

$$\tan\left[\tfrac{1}{2}(A - B)\right] = AG/BG = (CD - FC)/(AF + BD)$$
$$= \frac{a \cdot \mathrm{Sin}\left[\tfrac{1}{2}(A + B)\right] - b \cdot \mathrm{Sin}\left[\tfrac{1}{2}(A + B)\right]}{b \cdot \mathrm{Cos}\left[\tfrac{1}{2}(A + B)\right] + a \cdot \mathrm{Cos}\left[\tfrac{1}{2}(A + B)\right]}$$

so that, finally
$$= (a - b)\,\mathrm{Sin}\left[\tfrac{1}{2}(A + B)\right]/(a + b)\,\mathrm{Cos}\left[\tfrac{1}{2}(A + B)\right],$$

$$\mathrm{Tan}\left[\tfrac{1}{2}(A - B)\right] = \{(a - b)/(a + b)\} \cdot \mathrm{Tan}\left[\tfrac{1}{2}(A + B)\right]$$

which yields the proof of the tangent law (59).

In Chapter 15 we deduced from the cosine law the following formulas

$$\mathrm{Tan}\,(\tfrac{1}{2}A) = \left[(s - b)(s - c)/s(s - a)\right]^{1/2};$$
$$\mathrm{Tan}\,(\tfrac{1}{2}B) = \left[(s - c)(s - a)/s(s - b)\right]^{1/2};$$
$$\mathrm{Tan}\,(\tfrac{1}{2}C) = \left[(s - a)(s - b)/s(s - c)\right]^{1/2}, \tag{60}$$

where $s = (a + b + c)/2$. We now study the first case in the solution of triangles.

FIRST CASE: Given three sides a, b, c. Find the three angles A, B, C.

The solution is contained in the formulas (60) which can be rewritten in the form

$$\mathrm{Tan}\,(\tfrac{1}{2}A) = r/(s - a); \quad \mathrm{Tan}\,(\tfrac{1}{2}B) = r/(s - b); \quad \mathrm{Tan}\,(\tfrac{1}{2}C) = r/(s - c),$$

where $r = \left[(s - a)(s - b)(s - c)/s\right]^{1/2}$ is the radius of the inscribed circle. The numerical computation of the half-angles proceeds as follows. Forming s, $s-a$, $s-b$, $s-c$, their logarithms are written down and $\log r = \frac{1}{2}\left[\log(s-a) + \log(s-b) + \log(s-c) - \log s\right]$ is computed. This gives now the three logarithms

$$\log \mathrm{Tan}\,(\tfrac{1}{2}A) = \log r - \log(s - a); \quad \log \mathrm{Tan}\,(\tfrac{1}{2}B) = \log r - \log(s - b);$$
$$\log \mathrm{Tan}\,(\tfrac{1}{2}C) = \log r - \log(s - c).$$

The half-angles $\frac{1}{2}$A, $\frac{1}{2}$B, $\frac{1}{2}$C are then computed, using the table of logarithms of tangents, and as a check the sum $\frac{1}{2}$ (A + B + C) is compared to 90°.

EXAMPLE: Given $a = 11$, $b = 25$ and $c = 30$. Therefore, $a + b + c = 2s$ = 66 and $s = 33$, $s - a = 22$, $s - b = 8$, $s - c = 3$. Their logarithms are: $\log s = 1.51851$; $\log (s - a) = 1.34242$; $\log (s - b) = 0.90309$; $\log (s - c)$ = 0.47712. Computing $\log r = 0.60206$, we find log Tan $(\frac{1}{2}$A$) = \bar{1}.25964$; log Tan $(\frac{1}{2}$B$) = \bar{1}.69897$ and log Tan $(\frac{1}{2}$C$) = 0.12494$. These logarithms give $\frac{1}{2}$A $= 10° 18' 17.5''$; $\frac{1}{2}$B $= 26° 33' 54.5''$; $\frac{1}{2}$C $= 53° 07' 48.5''$, so that $\frac{1}{2}$ (A + B + C) exceeds 90° only by half a second of arc. This difference is small for the five-place table of logarithms we used: in general, with this table the seconds are only approximately correct.

SECOND CASE: *Given two angles* A, B *and a side c. Find* C *and a, b.*

What side is given has no importance because when two angles are given the third is known also: C $= 180° - $ A $- $ B. To find the sides a and b use the sine law: $a/\text{Sin A} = c/\text{Sin C}$ yields $a = c \cdot \text{Sin A}/\text{Sin C}$ and likewise $b = c \cdot \text{Sin B}/\text{Sin C}$. To check the computations the tangent law can be applied.

EXAMPLE: We take the same triangle we studied in the first example and suppose that A $= 20° 36' 35''$, B $= 53° 07' 49''$ and $c = 30$ are known. The third angle C is found to be equal to $106° 15' 36''$, so that the logarithm of the ratio $c/\text{Sin C}$ is equal to $\log 30 - \log \text{Sin} (90° + 16° 15' 36'') = 1.47712$ $- \bar{1}.98227 = 1.49485$. Adding to it $\log \text{Sin A} = \bar{1}.54654$ and $\log \text{Sin B}$ $= \bar{1}.90309$, we obtain the logarithms of a and b: $\log a = 1.04139$; $\log b$ $= 1.39794$, so that $a = 11$, $b = 25$. The check proceeds as follows: $a + b$ = 36, $b - a = 14$, $\frac{1}{2}$ (A + B) $= 36° 52' 12''$ and $\frac{1}{2}$ (B $-$ A) $= 16° 15' 37''$. Therefore, on one hand $\log [(b - a)/(b + a)] = \log (\frac{14}{36}) = \log (\frac{7}{18}) = \log 7$ $- \log 18 = \bar{1}.58983$, while on the other hand, $\log [\text{Tan} \frac{1}{2} (B - A)/\text{Tan} \frac{1}{2} (B + A)]$ $= \log \text{Tan} 16° 15' 37'' - \log \text{Tan} 36° 52' 12'' = \bar{1}.46489 - \bar{1}.87506$ which is exactly equal to $\bar{1}.58983$. Thus, the check shows that our computation is right.

THIRD CASE. *Given two sides b, c and included angle* A. *Find two other angles* B *and* C *and the third side a.* The sum B + C of two unknown angles is known since B + C $= 180° - $ A. To find B and C it will be sufficient to know their difference or half of it, $\frac{1}{2}$ (C $-$ B).

Therefore, the tangent law must be applied. Taking it in the form

$$\text{Tan} [\tfrac{1}{2} (C - B)] = [(c - b)/(c - b)] \cdot \text{Tan} [\tfrac{1}{2} (C + B)],$$

we can compute log Tan $[\frac{1}{2}$ (C $-$ B)$]$ and hence obtain the value of $\frac{1}{2}$ (C $-$ B). Combining it with the known value of $\frac{1}{2}$ (C + B), we deduce the value of the angles B and C, so that all three angles are known. The third side is obtained with the aid of the sine law.

EXAMPLE: If $c = 30$, $b = 25$ then $c - b = 5$ and $c + b = 55$, so that $(c - b)/(c + b) = \frac{1}{11}$ and $\log (\frac{1}{11}) = \bar{2}.95861$. Since $\frac{1}{2} (C + B) = 90° - \frac{1}{2}A = 90° - 10°18'17.5'' = 79°41'42.5''$, $\log \mathrm{Tan} [\frac{1}{2} (C + B)] = 0.74036$ and thus $\log \mathrm{Tan} [\frac{1}{2} (C - B)] = \bar{1}.69897$ which gives $\frac{1}{2} (C - B) = 26°33'54.5''$. Adding to and subtracting from it $\frac{1}{2} (C + B) = 79°41'42.5''$, we have $C = 106°15'37''$ and $B = 53°07'48''$. To find a we use the relation $a = c \cdot \mathrm{Sin}\, A/\mathrm{Sin}\, C$ which yields $\log a = \log 30 + \bar{1}.54654 - \bar{1}.98227 = 1.04139 = \log 11$, so that $a = 11$.

FOURTH CASE: We pass now to the fourth case which is not as simple as the first three cases. It needs a discussion because when two sides a, b and an angle opposite to one of them, for instance angle A, are given the existence of solutions and their number depend on the numerical values of the data. We must distinguish between two variants: angle A is acute or A > 90°. We consider first the case of an acute angle A.

(I)   A < 90°.

Let us begin with the geometric construction of the triangle for which the lengths a and b of two sides and the value of acute angle A are given (Fig. 10).

The known angle A is included between the unknown side c and the one of two given sides b. Choosing c as the base, we draw a line AG, which makes with the base AD an angle equal to the given angle A, and measure on it the length AC = b.

Since the angle at the vertex C included between the sides b and a, is unknown, the direction of the side a cannot be chosen. But, because the distance BC of the vertex B from the vertex C is equal to a known length a, BC = a, this third vertex B of our triangle lies on a circle with the center C and the radius a. At the same time this unknown vertex B must lie on the straight line AD taken as base of our triangle.

Therefore, the point B can be plotted as the intersection point of the line AD and the circle of radius a drawn around the center C.

There is a triangle ABC, if this intersection is possible. But if the length $b \cdot \mathrm{Sin}\, A$ of the perpendicular CE dropped from the point C on the line AD exceeds the given length a, then the circle of radius a with the center at C is above the line and does not meet it at all. Therefore, in the case when the three data a, b, A verify the inequality $a < b \, \mathrm{Sin}\, A$ (see Fig. 10a) there is no

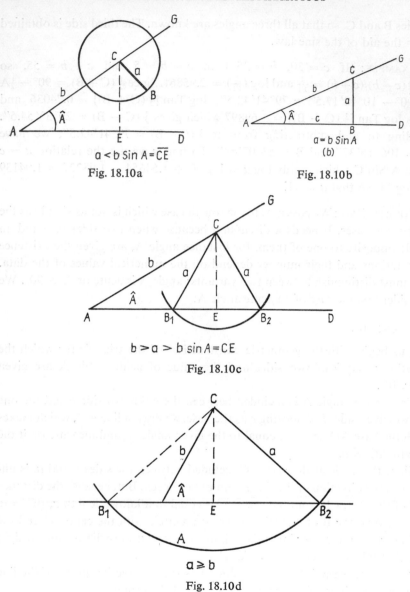

$a < b \sin A = \overline{CE}$

Fig. 18.10a

$a = b \sin A$

(b)

Fig. 18.10b

$b > a > b \sin A = CE$

Fig. 18.10c

$a \geqslant b$

Fig. 18.10d

solution of our problem: a triangle with sides a, b and angle A opposite to a and verifying the condition $a < b \sin A$ is impossible.

If $a = b \cdot \sin A$, then there is a solution (Fig. 10b) and this unique solution is a right triangle $\widehat{ABC}$ with B $= 90°$.

We now consider the case when $a > b \cdot \text{Sin A}$ and distinguish in this case two possibilities: $a < b$ and $a \geqslant b$. If a is greater than $b \cdot \text{Sin A}$ and less than b, $b \text{ Sin A} < a < b$, then the circle about C with the radius a intersects the base line AD in *two* points B_1 and B_2 to the right of the point A (Fig. 10c). Therefore, in the case $b > a > b \cdot \text{Sin A}$ two different triangles can be constructed having both the same elements a, b, A, but different sides $c_1 = AB_1$, $c_2 = AB_2$ as well as different angles opposite to the side b: an obtuse angle $\overset{\frown}{AB_1C}$ at B_1 and an acute angle $\overset{\frown}{AB_2C}$ at B_2. In the first triangle AB_1C the side $c_1 = AB_1$ is less than $AC = b$ since AC as opposite to the obtuse angle $\overset{\frown}{AB_1C}$ is the largest side of this triangle.

Finally, if a is equal to or greater than b (Fig. 10d), then there is only one solution AB_2C, the point B_1 being to the left of A when $a > b$, or coinciding with A when $a = b$. When the point B_1 is to the left of A the resulting triangle B_1AC cannot be considered as a solution of our problem because its angle at the vertex A is not equal to the given acute angle A: $\overset{\frown}{B_1AC}$ $= 180° - A$.

After this geometrical study of the fourth case in which two sides a, b and an acute angle A *opposite* to one of them are given, it becomes clear that before proceeding to solve the triangle a criterion must be applied which allows one to distinguish between the existence and the lack of solutions in general. This criterion is the value obtained for the sine of the unknown angle B with the aid of the sine law. We have indeed

$$\text{Sin B} = b \cdot \text{Sin A}/a,$$

where the righthand member consists of known quantities.

If a is less than $b \cdot \text{Sin A}$ (which corresponds to the lack of solution, the data a, b, A being such that no triangle can be constructed with them), then the value of the righthand member $b \cdot \text{Sin A}/a$ is greater than one. But the value of a sine cannot exceed one and therefore, in the case $a < b \text{ Sin A}$, there is no real angle B satisfying the condition $\text{Sin B} = b \cdot \text{Sin A}$. If logarithms are used, log Sin B must be negative or, at most, zero. But, if $a < b \text{ Sin A}$, then computing $\log \text{Sin B} = \log (b \text{ Sin A}) - \log a$ we find for it a positive number which proves that B as a *real* angle does not exist.

Therefore, the criterion is found and it must be applied before proceeding to solve the triangle. If one finds that the formula $\text{Sin B} = b \text{ Sin A}/a$ yields a real value for the angle B because $a \geqslant b \text{ Sin A}$, then to distinguish between one and two solutions it is sufficient to compare b to a: if $a \geqslant b$ (which entails *a fortiori* the existence of solution), then there is one solution only;

if $a < b$ but $a > b$ Sin A, then there are two triangles with the sides a, b and the *acute* angle A.

(II) A $\geqslant 90°$.

We study now the variety of case IV, in which the angle A is a right or an obtuse angle. In this variety there cannot be two solutions as one can see in Fig. 11. If $a \leqslant b$, then no triangle can be constructed with two sides a, b and A $\geqslant 90°$. If $a > b$, then only the triangle ACB_2 represents the solution for

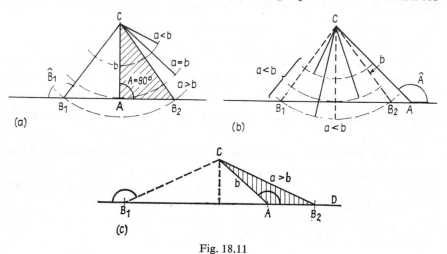

Fig. 18.11

the obtuse angle A, while for right angle A both triangles ACB_1 and ACB_2 are good but they are identical and represent one and the same solution.

Summing up this long discussion, we state that:

(1) for $a > b$ there is one solution only, the angle A being acute, right or obtuse, so that its value does not matter, if $a > b$;

(2) for $a = b$ there is no solution, if A is an obtuse or right angle, but if A is an acute angle, then there is one solution;

(3) for $a < b$ there is no solution, if A is an obtuse or right angle, but if A is an acute angle, then there are three possibilities:

no solution if $a < b \cdot$ Sin A, one solution if $a = b \cdot$ Sin A, two solutions if $a > b \cdot$ Sin A.

When the existence of a solution is assured, first the value of the angle B must be found with the aid of the relation Sin B $= b \cdot$ Sin A$/a$. In general, two supplementary angles B_2 and $B_1 = 180° - B_2$ are found. In our notation B_1 denotes an obtuse angle and B_2 the supplementary acute angle.

After finding B, determine C from the relation $A + B + C = 180°$ and then evaluate the side c with the aid of the sine law: $c = a \cdot \text{Sin } C/\text{Sin } A$. If only one solution is possible, one value is found for C and c, but if both B_1 and B_2 correspond to a solution, then the relation $A + B + C = 180°$ yields two corresponding values of the third angle C: $C_1 = 180° - A - B_1$ and $C_2 = 180° - A - B_2$, whose sum must be equal to the difference $180° - 2A$. When two solutions are to be found, these two values C_1 and C_2 entail two different values for the third side c: $c_1 = a \cdot \text{Sin } C_1/\text{Sin } A$ and $c_2 = a \cdot \text{Sin } C_2/\text{Sin } A$. Thus, the six elements of two triangles are: first solution—a, b, c_1, A, B_1, C_1; second solution—a, b, c_2, A, B_2, C_2.

EXAMPLES. Given $A = 30°$, $a = 8$, $b = 18$. Forming the product $b \cdot \text{Sin } A = 18 \cdot \text{Sin } 30° = 18 \cdot \frac{1}{2} = 9$, we compare $a = 8$ to $b \cdot \text{Sin } A = 9$ and find out that $a < b \cdot \text{Sin } A$. Thus, no solution exists and no triangle can be constructed with these elements. If we try to compute a real angle B with the aid of $\text{Sin } B = b \text{ Sin } A/a = \frac{9}{8}$, we obtain for Sin B an impossible value $\frac{9}{8}$: the solution of the equation $\text{Sin } B = \frac{9}{8}$ can be shown to be the complex number $B = (2m + \frac{1}{2})\pi \pm i \cdot \text{Log } [(9 + 17^{1/2})/8]$.

If $A = 30°$, $a = 8$ and $b = 14$, then $b \cdot \text{Sin } A = 14 \cdot \frac{1}{2} = 7 < 8 = a$ and therefore two triangles can be constructed with sides 8 and 14 and an angle $A = 30°$ opposite the side $a = 8$. This time $\text{Sin } B = b \cdot \text{Sin } A/a = \frac{7}{8}$ and its logarithm is negative: $\log \text{Sin } B = \log 7 - \log 8 = \overline{1}.94201$, so that $B_2 = 61°02'43''$, $B_1 = 118°57'17''$. Continuing the first solution, we find that $C_2 = 180° - A - B_2 = 88°57'17''$ which gives for the logarithm of the third side $c_2 = a \cdot \text{Sin } C_2/\text{Sin } A = 16 \text{ Sin } 88°57'17''$ the value $\log c_2 = 1.20412 + \overline{1}.99993 = 1.20405$, so that $c_2 = 15.9974\cdots$ On the other hand, if $B = B_1 = 118°57'17''$, then $C_1 = 31°02'43''$ and $\log c_1 = \log 16 + \log \text{Sin } 31°02'43'' = 1.20412 + \overline{1}.71241 = 0.91653$, so that in the second triangle the third side is equal to $c_1 = 8.2514\cdots$.

To check the two solutions we can apply the formula $\text{Tan } (\frac{1}{2}A) = [(s - b) \times (s - c)/s (s - a)]^{1/2}$ for the tangent of the half angle $\frac{1}{2}A = 15°$. For the first triangle $2s = 8 + 14 + 15.9974 = 37.9974$, so that $s = 18.9987$, $s - a = 10.9987$, $s - b = 4.9987$ and $s - c = 3.0013$. Computing the logarithms of these four numbers, we obtain $\log \text{Tan } (\frac{1}{2}A) = \frac{1}{2}(0.69885 + 0.47731 - 1.27872 - 1.04134 = \overline{1}.42805$ which is exactly equal to the tabular value of the logarithm of tangent of $15°$. Therefore, the value of c_2 is correct.

As third example we choose an obtuse angle $A = 118°57'17''$, $a = 14$ and $b = 8$, so that the condition of the existence of a solution, $a > b$, is fulfilled.

Computing $\log \operatorname{Sin} B = \log (b \cdot \operatorname{Sin} A/a) = \log (\frac{4}{7}) + \log \operatorname{Sin} 118°57'17''$ $= -0.30103$, we find the value of the $\log \frac{1}{2} = -0.30103$, so that $\operatorname{Sin} B = \frac{1}{2}$ and $B = 30°$. The third angle $C = 180° - A - B = 31°02'43''$ and this yields $c = b \operatorname{Sin} C/\operatorname{Sin} B = 8 \operatorname{Sin} 31°02'43''/\frac{1}{2}$. We obtain $\log c = 0.91653$ and thus $c = 8.2514\cdots$.

Having now studied the four classical cases, we add that sometimes the three given elements of a triangle include the radius r of the inscribed circle or the radius R of the circumscribed circle. Thus, for instance, it may happen that three sides of a triangle are to be found, knowing its angles and the radius r of the inscribed circle. Such a problem is easy to solve with the aid of the sine law, if it is known that the common value of ratios $a/\operatorname{Sin} A$ $= b/\operatorname{Sin} B = c/\operatorname{Sin} C = 2R$ is equal also to $\frac{1}{2}r/(\operatorname{Sin} \frac{1}{2}A \cdot \operatorname{Sin} \frac{1}{2}B \cdot \operatorname{Sin} \frac{1}{2}C)$.

To prove this important fact we write the side a as the sum of two differences $s - b$ and $s - c$ and then apply the relations $s - b = r \cdot \operatorname{Cotan} \frac{1}{2}B$ and $s - c = r \cdot \operatorname{Cotan} \frac{1}{2}C$:

$$a = 2s - b - c = (s - b) + (s - c) = r (\operatorname{Cotan} \frac{1}{2}B + \operatorname{Cotan} \frac{1}{2}C)$$

$$= r (\operatorname{Sin} \tfrac{1}{2}C \cdot \operatorname{Cos} \tfrac{1}{2}B + \operatorname{Sin} \tfrac{1}{2}B \cdot \operatorname{Cos} \tfrac{1}{2}C)/(\operatorname{Sin} \tfrac{1}{2}B \cdot \operatorname{Sin} \tfrac{1}{2}C)$$

$$= r \cdot \operatorname{Sin} (\tfrac{1}{2}B + \tfrac{1}{2}C) \operatorname{Sin} \tfrac{1}{2}A/(\operatorname{Sin} \tfrac{1}{2}A \cdot \operatorname{Sin} \tfrac{1}{2}B \cdot \operatorname{Sin} \tfrac{1}{2}C)$$

But $2 \operatorname{Sin} \frac{1}{2}A \cdot \operatorname{Sin} (\frac{1}{2}B + \frac{1}{2}C) = \operatorname{Cos} (\frac{1}{2}B + \frac{1}{2}C - \frac{1}{2}A) - \operatorname{Cos} (\frac{1}{2}A + \frac{1}{2}B + \frac{1}{2}C)$, where the second term vanishes since $\frac{1}{2} (A + B + C) = 90°$. On the other hand, $\frac{1}{2} (B + C) - \frac{1}{2}A = \frac{1}{2} (A + B + C) - A = 90° - A$, so that the first term $\operatorname{Cos} (\frac{1}{2}B + \frac{1}{2}C - \frac{1}{2}A)$ is equal to $\operatorname{Cos} (90° - A) = \operatorname{Sin} A$. The final result is as follows

$$a = r \cdot \operatorname{Sin} A/(2 \cdot \operatorname{Sin} \tfrac{1}{2}A \cdot \operatorname{Sin} \tfrac{1}{2}B \cdot \operatorname{Sin} \tfrac{1}{2}C)$$

which proves that the sine law can also written as

$$a/\operatorname{Sin} A = b/\operatorname{Sin} B = c/\operatorname{Sin} C = 2R = r/(2 \cdot \operatorname{Sin} \tfrac{1}{2}A \cdot \operatorname{Sin} \tfrac{1}{2}B \cdot \operatorname{Sin} \tfrac{1}{2}C). \quad (61)$$

Incidentally we obtain for the ratio r/R of the radii of inscribed and circumscribed circles an expression in terms of sines of half-angles:

$$r/R = 4 \cdot \operatorname{Sin} \tfrac{1}{2}A \cdot \operatorname{Sin} \tfrac{1}{2}B \cdot \operatorname{Sin} \tfrac{1}{2}C. \quad (62)$$

Returning to the problem: find the three sides of a triangle, knowing its angles and the radius r of the inscribed circle, we see that it is solved with the aid of the expressions (61) of sides in terms of radius r and trigonometric functions of angles.

The solution of triangles just discussed is a particular case of a more general theory of solution of spherical triangles which will be studied in Chapter 22.

CHAPTER 19

Solid Geometry.
Point, Straight Line and Plane in Space.
Restricted Duality in Solid Geometry

The three-dimensional Euclidean space to which the configurations considered in solid geometry belong is perfectly homogeneous: the neighborhood of any of its points is identical to that of any other point. A space S_3 of three dimensions can be considered as imbedded in a higher four-dimensional space S_4 exactly as a two dimensional surface is imbedded in our Euclidean three-dimensional space. Therefore, we can imagine spaces S_3 having such an intrinsic structure that when considered from outside, in an S_4, they appear curved, as for instance a sphere is a curved surface in our space.

Spaces having different amounts of bending at their differents points are said to have a variable curvature which means that their inner, intrinsic structure at two different points is not the same, the variable curvature depending on the point where it is considered. Such spaces of variable curvature are not homogeneous: the neighborhoods of two different points cannot coincide because their structure is not the same. Thus the space S_3 of solid geometry, being perfectly homogeneous, cannot have a variable curvature.

These considerations suggest the question as to whether the Euclidean space of solid geometry has a constant curvature or no curvature at all, being perfectly flat in all directions. Even if it it were curved the fact that its curvature is constant would ensure its perfect homogeneity: consider as an example the surface of a sphere which is perfectly homogeneous precisely because its curvature is constant and, thus, the same at each point.

To answer this question let us first analyze the perfect flatness of the Euclidean plane. We know that a straight line belongs entirely to a plane if two of its points are in this plane and this is so precisely because a plane is a perfectly flat surface. There is only one perfectly flat surface, the plane, and for no other surface it can be said that any straight line through any two points of this surface lies entirely on it.

Therefore, to discuss whether the Euclidean three-dimensional space possesses a constant curvature or is a perfectly flat space, we must consider how a plane is located in it. This brings us to the axioms of solid geometry which define the properties of Euclidean space.

Taking the point as the fundamental and simple element, we define a plane with the aid of the first axiom, namely:

Through three noncollinear points one and only one plane can be drawn.

If the three given points lie on a straight line instead of defining three different straight lines, there are an infinite number of planes through these three *collinear* points, namely all the planes which pass through the straight line incident with three given points. Eliminating this exceptional case, the axiom states that three non-collinear points define a unique plane.

The meaning of the first axiom also includes the assumption that a finite part of a plane containing the three points which define this plane can be extended in all directions as far as we want. Thus, the whole infinite plane belongs entirely to the three-dimensional space, if three of its points are incident with this space. Since an Euclidean plane is a perfectly flat surface devoid of any curvature, it can be imbedded wholly, in its entirety, only into a perfectly flat space. Thus, the Euclidean space has no curvature at all and is perfectly flat as straight lines and planes are.

In three-dimensional space plane and point are dual transforms of each other. Therefore, the dual form of the first axiom states that:

Three non-collinear planes have in common one and only one point.

Two planes intersect along a straight line and a third plane, if it does not pass through this straight line, has in common with the line only one point, namely the intersection point of the three planes. In the exceptional case when the third plane contains the intersection line of the first two planes, it is said to be collinear with them and in this case the three planes have in common all the points of their common intersection line. Disregarding this exceptional case, let us analyze more closely how two planes define their common straight line. If they meet at a finite distance from the observer, they intersect along a straight line which is *defined* by these two planes. But what can be said about two planes which do not meet in the finite part of the space? Two such planes which have no common points at a finite distance from the observer are said to be *parallel* to each other. To prove the existence of parallel planes we define the concept of *perpendicular* planes. Consider two planes P and Q intersecting along the line *ll* (Fig. 1). They form four so-called *dihedral* angles bounded by two half-planes and forming two pairs of vertical and equal dihedral angles: $\hat{1} = \hat{2}$ and $\hat{3} = \hat{4}$, which in general are not equal: $\hat{2} \neq \hat{3}$. But, if two intersecting planes form four equal dihedral angles, they are said to be perpendicular, and the equal dihedral angles are called *right dihedral* angles.

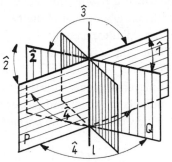

Fig. 19.1

We consider now two planes P and Q perpendicular to a third plane T (Fig. 2) and such that the intersection lines of P and Q with T are parallel: $ll \parallel mm$. The configuration thus formed is symmetrical with respect to the plane T, so that the two planes P, Q perpendicular to T cannot intersect at a finite distance from the plane T. Indeed, if they do intersect on one side of the plane T, then by symmetry they must intersect also on the other side of

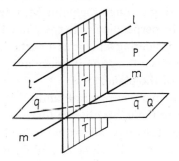

Fig. 19.2.

T. Since P and Q have no common points in the plane T itself, their two intersection lines will be distinct and three points can be chosen, two on one line and the third one on the other line, such that they are non-collinear and nevertheless two distinct planes P and Q pass through them. Thus, the assumption that P and Q meet at a finite distance contradicts the first axiom, and the existence of parallel planes is established. The fact that parallel planes do not meet in the finite region of space does not predetermine their behavior at infinity.

Consider now two parallel lines lying in two parallel planes. They define a third plane which can be called a *transversal* plane. The intersection of two parallel planes by a third transversal plane along two parallel lines defines a point common to these three planes, namely the point at infinity where the two parallel lines meet. Thus, three planes define a point even when two of them are parallel.

Suppose again that a transversal plane T cutting two given parallel planes P and Q (Fig. 3) is perpendicular to them and passes therefore through their common normal MN. The new concept of the *normal* of a plane is defined as

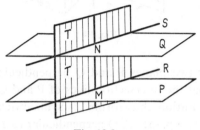

Fig. 19.3

follows: a straight line MN which is perpendicular to *all* straight lines lying in the plane P and passing through the point M, where the line MN pierces the plane P, is said to be perpendicular to the plane P and is called a *normal* of the plane P. Thus, considering a plane as a part of space, we ascribe to it a *new* property: a plane has a direction in space and this direction is characterized by the normal of the plane.

Returning to our two parallel planes P and Q (Fig. 3) with a transversal plane T perpendicular to them, we observe that these planes meet at the infinity at a point common to two parallel straight line MR and NS along which the plane T intersects the parallel planes P and Q. Rotating now this transversal plane T about the normal MN, we find out that two parallel planes meet at infinity *in every direction*, so that their straight lines at infinity *coincide*. Therefore, it can be said that two planes always have a straight line in common, the line defined by two planes being the line at infinity, if they are parallel. If three given planes are parallel to each other their lines at infinity coincide: three parallel planes belong to the exceptional configuration of three *collinear* planes, they do not define a point and have in common all the points of their common straight line at infinity.

Any straight line *q* lying in a plane Q which is parallel to a given plane P (Fig. 2) cannot meet the plane P at a finite distance. Nevertheless, the point at infinity of this line belongs to the line at infinity of the plane Q and therefore lies also on the line at infinity of the plane P because P and Q are parallel. Therefore, the straight line we are considering meets the plane P to which it is parallel at infinity. Thus, a plane and a line always define a point. The point is in the finite region of space, if they intersect, and it is at infinity, if line and plane are parallel.

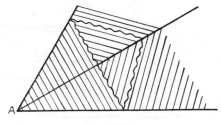

Fig. 19.4

Two planes always define a straight line. Therefore, three noncollinear planes define three straight lines and these three lines are concurrent lines because they pass necessarily through the point defined by the three planes and which is their common point. When this point A is at a finite distance the configuration formed by three planes, three straight lines and the point A is called a *trihedral angle* (= "angle with three faces", Fig. 4), the point A being *vertex* of the trihedral angle.

But it can happen that the point common to three lines and three planes is at infinity, as for instance in the case when two of three planes are parallel to each other. There is another case, when the point defined by three planes is at infinity although no two planes are parallel. The situation arises if three intersection-lines of three planes are parallel to each other (Fig. 5).

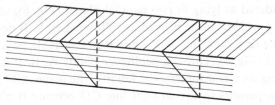

Fig. 19.5

Three parallel lines indeed pass all three through their common point at infinity because they are parallel and at the same time they define three different planes since each pair of parallel lines defines a plane. These three planes are distinct, if the three parallel lines are not *coplanar*, that is, if they do not belong to one and the same plane. And all three planes pass through the point at infinity which is common to their intersection lines. The configuration just described is the ultimate shape of a trihedral angle when its vertex is rejected to infinity, its three edges (straight lines) becoming parallel at the limit. It is called an infinite triangular *prism*.

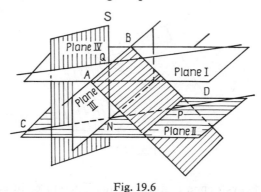

Fig. 19.6

We emphasize that among the three elements—point, straight line and plane—point and plane can be considered as fundamental elements, but not the line: a straight line is defined by two points or by two planes incident with it, but no point and no plane correspond to two straight lines taken arbitrarily in a three-dimensional space. Such two lines in general do not meet and have no common elements, if we discard a special case of two intersecting or parallel lines. Two intersecting lines (parallel, if their intersection point is at infinity) do define a plane to which they belong so that they in fact are two lines considered in a two-dimensional space. But, in general, two straight lines belonging to a three-dimensional space are not parallel and do not intersect. Such two lines are said to be *skew*. Now any two skew lines can be considered as lying in two parallel planes (Fig. 6), the existence and uniqueness of which can be proved as follows. Let A, B denote two points chosen on the first skew line AB, while P is a variable point on the second skew line CD (Fig. 6). Three noncollinear points A, B, P define a plane. If now P moving on CD disappears at infinity, the plane ABP in its final position becomes parallel to the straight line CD because it meets this line at infinity. Thus, there is a plane through AB which is parallel to CD and therefore, there is also another plane through CD and parallel to AB. Let us call the plane through AB "plane I" and that through CD "plane II", so that plane I‖CD and plane II‖AB. It remains to prove that these two planes are parallel. They have two distinct points at infinity in common, namely the points at infinity on CD and on AB. These two points define a straight line at infinity which lies in both planes I and II. Therefore, the planes I and II are parallel as having the same line at infinity.

Consider now a plane III through the line AB and perpendicular to the plane I and also a fourth plane IV through the line CD and perpendicular to the plane II. The plane III intersects the line CD at a point denoted on Fig. 6 by N and the plane IV is pierced by the line AB at the point Q. The points N and Q define the straight line NQS which is perpendicular to both planes I and II. The concept of a straight line perpendicular to a plane implies that this line is perpendicular to every line drawn in the plane through its foot and the definition of a normal can be rephrased as follows: a line perpendicular to all straight lines drawn in the plane through its foot and thus perpendicular to this plane is called a normal.

We set out now to prove that a line PQS meeting a plane π at Q and perpendicular to *two* straight lines lying in the plane π and passing through Q is perpendicular to *every* straight line through Q and incident with the plane, and therefore this line PS is perpendicular to the plane π.

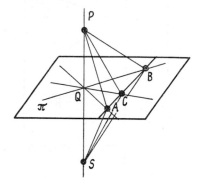

Fig. 19.7

Suppose that PQ ⊥ QA and PQ ⊥ QB (Fig. 7), where the symbol ⊥ means perpendicularity, and draw in the plane π through the point Q any straight line QR intersecting AB in C. Let S denote a point on the line PQ symmetrical to P with respect to the point Q so that PQ = SQ. Joining A, B, C to P and to S, we consider three pairs of symmetrical triangles PQA and

SQA, PQB and SQB, PQC and SQC. The right triangles PQA and SQA have equal legs: PQ = SQ and QA = QA. Therefore, they are equal and AP = AS. Applying the same reasoning to two other right triangles PQB and SQB, we conclude that BP = BS. Consider now the triangles ABP and ABS. They are also equal as having three sides of the one equal to three sides of the other. Therefore, $\widehat{PAB} = \widehat{SAB}$ as opposite equal sides, and this is sufficient to conclude that the two triangles ASC and APC are equal since they have equal angles $\widehat{PAB} = \widehat{SAB}$ included between equal sides AP = AS and AC = AC. Finally, their sides opposite to equal angles are equal: PC = SC, and this proves that the triangles PQC and SQC are equal because their sides one by one are equal: PC = SC, QC = QC, PQ = SQ.

Having proved that triangles PQC and SQC are equal, we conclude that their angles at the point Q are equal: $\widehat{PQC} = \widehat{SQC}$. But, on the other hand, the sum of these two angles is equal to 180° and therefore both are *right* angles: $\widehat{PQC} = 90°$. Thus, the following lemma is proved:

LEMMA I: A line, perpendicular to two lines in the plane which pass through the point P common to this line and to the plane, is perpendicular to every line in the plane which passes through the point P.

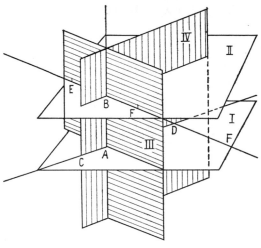

Fig. 19.8

Returning back to our two skew lines lying in two parallel planes I, II and considering two other planes III and IV, both perpendicular to the two parallel planes (Fig. 8), we draw a straight line AB along which two perpendicular planes intersect each other. This line AB is perpendicular to each of the two parallel planes. Consider for instance the upper plane II. At point B there can be only one normal to this plane II and any plane through point B and perpendicular to plane II must pass through it. Therefore, the normal to plane II at the point B belongs to both planes III and IV because they are perpendicular to plane II by construction. Thus, the intersection line AB of these planes III and IV is the common normal of two parallel planes I and II. As such it is perpendicular to both skew lines CAD and EBF and this common perpendicular of two given straight skew lines is unique by construction. Thus: *two skew lines imbedded in a three-dimensional space define together a third line, namely, their common perpendicular.*

But this definition is possible only with the aid of planes which play here the role of fundamental elements since two skew lines do not define a plane or a point, while points define line and plane as well as planes define line and point.

Thus, the configurations of solid geometry can be build with points taken as fundamental element or with planes, but *not with lines.* The dualism in three-dimensional space is based on the interchangeability of points and planes as it is expressed already in the dual form of the first axiom of solid geometry:

Three noncollinear points define one and only one plane and three noncollinear planes define one and only one point.

The fact that the concept of straight line is implicitly involved in the word "noncollinear" does not matter because a line is defined by two points or two planes and thus the notion of noncollinearity of three points (or planes) can be brought in as follows: three points (or three planes) are said to be collinear, when the three straight lines *they define* coincide.

A straight line is self-dual in three-dimensional space: a line defined by two points A, B is transformed by duality into the line of intersection of two planes *a, b* which are dual images of points A, B. Thus lines of a configuration remain lines when this configuration is transformed by duality.

In solid geometry two skew straight lines form a configuration unknown in the plane geometry. Therefore, the addition of a new dimension to the plane brings with it new possibilities in combinations of simple elements. Two planes cannot be skew in the three-dimensional geometry, but in general they are skew, that is, do not meet at all, neither in the finite region nor at infinity, if they are imbedded in a five-dimensional space S_5. If considered in a four-dimensional space S_4, two planes cannot be skew and they intersect necessarily (parallelism being considered as a particular case of intersection, when the intersection takes place at infinity), but they intersect in one point only except the special case when they belong to the same three-dimensional region S_3 of the four-dimensional space S_4.

We propose now to explore systematically all possible relative locations of simple elements such as point, straight line, plane, three-dimensional space S_3, etc., depending on the dimensions' number of the *imbedding* space. These simple elements will be denoted by a generic symbol s_m, where m characterizes their dimensions' number. So for instance a point is s_0 since it is dimensionless object, while straight line must be denoted by s_1 being one-dimensional. A plane is two-dimensional and it is denoted by s_2. Our three-dimensional space, if imbedded in a higher space, becomes one of simple elements of this higher space and as such must be denoted by s_3. The n-dimensional space S_n in which the relative location of two simple elements is studied *(imbedding space)* will always be denoted by *capital* letter S with a subscript n which again denotes its dimensionality.

In general, there can be only three different relative locations of two simple elements: incidence, intersection (parallelism included as a special case), and avoidance (skewness). If s_m is entirely inside some s_n (which presupposes that m is less or at most equal to n) we say that s_m and s_n are incident with each other.

EXAMPLE: A plane located in our space S_3 is incident with it.

If s_m and s_n have some of their elements in common, but not all for either of them, they are said to intersect each other. Finally, if s_m and s_n have no elements in common, they avoid each other, so that avoidance is negation of both incidence and intersection. The intersections can be classified accordingly to the dimensionality of the set of common elements. So, for instance, two lines can intersect in one point only so that their intersection may be called intersection of order zero. But the intersection of two planes in our three-dimensional space along a line is an intersection of order one, since a straight line has one dimension.

We consider first two *skew* elements of m and n dimensions, s_m and s_n. They do not meet at all, that is, are non-parallel and non-intersecting. To realize this complete avoidance we must immerse s_m and s_n in a space S_k whose dimensionality k is larger than the sum $m + n$. We know indeed that a plane s_2 ($m = 2$) and a line s_1 ($n = 1$) intersect or are parallel (that is have a common point at infinity) in an S_3 (our space) for which $k = m + n = 2 + 1 = 3$. Thus, two simple elements s_m, s_n can be entirely outside of each other only in a space whose number of dimensions exceeds the sum $m + n$ of their dimensions. If $k \leqslant m + n$, then s_m and s_n necessarily intersect each other, either at a finite distance from the observer or at infinity.

To study the order of the *intersection* it is important to clarify completely our ideas about the space S_k in which this intersection of s_m and s_n is considered. We must assume that k does not exceed the sum $m + n$, but we add that k denotes the *minimum* number of dimensions of S_k, so that s_m and s_n cannot be considered as imbedded in a lower space of less than k dimensions. Let us take as example the case of two planes $m = n = 2$ immersed in an S_5. If they cannot be considered as belonging to some S_4 and are immersed in the S_5, then $k = 5 > 4 = m + n$ and the planes are skew planes, that is, non-parallel and non-intersecting (avoidance). But if $k = 4$, so that, although two planes cannot be considered as located in the same three-dimensional space, they belong to some four-dimensional space, these two planes necessaarily intersect each other in a point, that is in a S_0 because would they intersect along a line, they would define and belong to a three-dimensional space. We emphasize that the order of intersection, namely zero, is equal to $m + n - k = 2 + 2 - 4 = 0$ and this is a general rule:

The order of intersection of s_m and s_n imbedded in an S_k, with $k \leqslant m + n$, but not belonging to the same S_{k-1}, is equal to $m + n - k$.

In the case of incidence we have $k = m > n$, so that the order of intersection $m + n - k$ is equal to n and this means precisely that the space S_n of *smaller* dimensionality n is immersed entirely in that S_m of *greater* dimensionality. The case of avoidance can be interpreted as intersection of *negative* order since $m + n - k$ is negative, if $k > m + n$.

Elements of Four-dimensional Space S_4

We want to consider now relative locations of simple elements such as point (s_0), straight line (s_1), plane (s_2) and three-dimensional space (s_3) in a flat Euclidean four-dimensional space S_4 which will play the role of our universe and will be called so, while any three-dimensional space immersed in it will be called simply "space".

In his book *The Expanding Universe* Eddington says, discussing the role of four-dimensional configurations in the modern picture of our physical enviroment: "However successful the theory of a four-dimensional world may be, it is difficult to ignore a voice inside us which whispers — "At the back of your mind you know that a fourth dimension is all nonsense. I fancy that voice must often have had a busy time in the past history of physics. What nonsense to say that this solid table is a collection of electrons moving with prodigious speed in empty spaces which relatively to electronic dimensions are so wide as the spaces between the planets in the solar system. ... Let us not be beguiled by this voice. It is discredited."

Here we do not have to discuss the objective reality of the four-dimensional world as it is pictured by the modern physical theories because we are not concerned at all with the structure of our physical environment. In pure geometry, spaces of any number of dimensions have equal right to existence and must be studied with the same interest. From this point of view the omission of elements of four-dimensional geometry in the textbooks of modern geometry is an error because the knowledge of four-dimensional configurations is necessary for the study of the modern physics.

It is also useful for the better understanding of the three-dimensional configurations. In particular rotations about a plane and through the four-dimensional space play the same role in simplifying the proofs in solid geometry as the role played by the rotations about a line and through the three-dimensional space in the proofs of theorems in plane geometry.

There are many indirect indications which seem to justify the impression that the evolution of creative mind through the ages (in different species, including mankind as the last phase), proceeded in the direction of increasing the dimensions of space as a *frame of reference* into which the thinking brain *projects* its perceptions. In other words, it seems that mankind is moving towards better understanding and wider use of the fourth dimension and, if this is true, the study of elements in the four-dimensional space is completely justified.

Thus, to begin this study of the four-dimensional universe S_4 let us imagine a space s_3 immersed in the universe S_4 and a point s_0, non-incident with s_3 but belonging to the universe. The relation of avoidance (non-incidence) is possible because $m + n = 3 + 0 < 4 = k$. Joining this point (exterior to s_3) to a point of s_3, we draw a straight line s_1 which cannot belong entirely to s_3: all its points, except one, are exterior to s_3 because if two points of a line were in s_3 the whole line would be imbedded in s_3 and no point on this line could be exterior to s_3. Or, we know that at least one point of the line s_1 is exterior to s_3. Therefore, in a S_4 a straight line s_1 intersects s_3 in one point only which corresponds to the fact that $m + n = 3 + 1 = 4 = k$.

Any space s_3 and any straight line s_1 belonging to the same universe S_4 must have in common a point since the order of their intersection is zero: $m + n - k = 3 + 1 - 4 = 0$. If this single common point is at infinity, the line is *parallel* to the space, otherwise they intersect in the finite region of the universe S_4. A straight line non-incident with and non-parallel to the space s_3 is divided by this space into two *rays* (infinite half-lines) which are separated by the point of intersection of space and line.

The lines intersecting the space s_3 fill out the whole universe S_4. All of them are divided by s_3 into two halves, so that the whole universe is cut by the space s_3 into half-universes separated from one other by this space s_3. This situation is analogous to the division of our space into two half-spaces by a plane imbedded in it: the half-space above a horizontal plane is separated from the half-space below the plane and a continuous path leading from a point taken above the plane to any other point below the plane necessarily pierces the plane at a point. Likewise, let S_4^I and S_4^{II} denote two half-spaces into which our four-dimensional universe is split by the space s_3. If a point A is in S_4^I while another point B belongs to S_4^{II}, so that both points are non-incident with s_3 and are separated from each other by s_3, any continuous path leading from A to B pierces the space s_3 in *one* point only. We see, incidentally, that a three-dimensional space s_3 *has no thickness* in the universe S_4.

Up to now we studied the configuration formed by a space s_3, a straight line s_1 non-incident with s_2 and a point P defined by s_3 and s_1 as their intersection-point. The space s_3 contains infinitely many planes s_2 incident with it. Some of them pass through the point P, others avoid it. We now draw through the point P all the planes s_2^P contained in s_3 and passing through this point. The straight line s_1 pierces every plane s_2^P in just one point P because otherwise the line would belong to s_2^P and therefore to s_3 which is contrary to our assumptions. Any one of these planes s_2^P together with the line s_1 defines a space *distinct* from the space s_3 we are considering. Let us fix our attention on a particular plane s_2^* defining, together with s_1, a particular space s_3^*. In this space s_3^* the line s_1 can form with the plane any angle between zero and right angle. Varying the direction of the plane s_2^* inside s_3, we not only change the corresponding space s_3^*, but also modify the angle formed by s_2^* and s_1 within the space s_3^*. Moving the plane s_2^* within s_3 in such a way that the angle increases, we reach a position of s_2^* for which the angle between s_2^* and s_1 becomes a right angle. Therefore, for any choice of the relative location of s_3 and s_1, there is always a plane s_2^* in s_3 which is perpendicular to s_1.

Now we can prove that if there are *two* planes in s_3 perpendicular to the line s_1, then *all* the planes through the point P and within s_3 will be perpendicular to the straight line s_1. To justify our assertion it is sufficient to point out that any third plane within s_3 and through the point P intersects the first two planes (which are by hypothesis perpendicular to s_1) along two straight lines to which the line s_1 must be perpendicular because they belong to planes perpendicular to s_1. But, by Lemma I, a line perpendicular to two straight lines in a plane is perpendicular *eo ipso* to the whole plane, so that s_1 will be perpendicular to all the planes through P, if it is perpendicular to two planes through P.

Definition: A straight line intersecting a space in a point P is said to be perpendicular to this space, if this line is perpendicular to all the planes contained in this space and passing through the point P.

We emphasize again that a line perpendicular to two planes through P and within s_3 *eo ipso* is perpendicular to the whole space s_3. Such a line is called the *normal* of the space s_3. The existence of a normal related to a space s_3 when this space is imbedded in a higher space S_4 proves that *a flat Euclidean space s_3 possesses in a four-dimensional universe a direction characterized by its normal*. A normal of s_3 by definition is perpendicular to all planes contained in s_3 and which pass through the foot P of the normal. Therefore, the normal is also perpendicular to all straight lines within s_3 which pass through the point P. A line perpendicular to any *three* non-coplanar straight lines through P will be perpendicular to all the lines through P because three lines define two planes to which our line is perpendicular. Thus, a straight line through P and non-incident with s_3 is a normal of the space s_3, at the point P, if it is perpendicular to three non-coplanar straight lines belonging to s_3 and passing through the point P.

Suppose now that we draw through P and within s_3 three planes forming right dihedral angles with each other. Such a configuration is called a *right trihedral* angle. The three edges of a right trihedral angle are represented by three mutually perpendicular straight lines.

This right trihedral angle can be rotated about its vertex P, taking all possible positions in the space s_3 around P, but it will always remain perpendicular to the straight line s_1 which is the normal of s_3 at the point P. Thus, in our four-dimensional universe S_4 the four straight lines, s_1 (the normal at P) and the three edges of the right trihedral angle in s_3 with vertex P, form a group of four mutually perpendicular lines. Any three of them define a space to which they belong, so that four different spaces cut off a part of universe S_4 included inside a so-called *tetraspatial* angle with its four spaces, six planes, four edges and one vertex. In general, the spaces forming the boundary of a tetraspatial angle need not to be perpendicular, but the tetraspatial angle just described is a *right tetraspatial* angle, because its four spaces are perpendicular to each other. Since the direction of a space is characterized by its normal, two spaces with perpendicular normals are said to be perpendicular to each other.

There are *eight* right trihedral angles around a point in a space s_3: a plane subdivides the space into two parts, and therefore three planes—faces of the right trihedral angle—divide the space into $2^3 = 8$ *octants*, each octant being a right trihedral angle. In other words, eight equal cubes can be juxtaposed around a point in a three-dimensional space and they fill out all the space around this point. Likewise, in a four-dimensional world the four perpendicular spaces intersecting at a point P divide the whole universe S_4 into $2^4 = 16$ right tetraspatial angles, having the point P as their common vertex.

We describe now the intersection in S_4 of a space s_3 ($m = 3$) and a plane s_2 ($n = 2$) non-incident with s_3. Their intersection is a straight line because $m + n - k = 3 + 2 - 4 = 1$. If it is at infinity, plane and space are said to be parallel, otherwise they intersect each other and thus have common points in the finite region of the universe. It is important to observe that rotating a space s_3 about one of *its* straight lines, we do not modify neither its direction nor its location in the four-dimensional world S_4, so that its normal remains at rest during the rotation of s_3 *on itself*. Thus, the intersection-line of two non-incident s_2 (plane) and s_3 (space) can be chosen as rotation-axis of s_3 on itself and in such a case the space s_3 is free to rotate about this line in spite of its intersection with a fixed plane along the line.

Finally, two non-incident distinct spaces s_3 and t_3, imbedded in S_4, intersect in a plane P because for $m = n = 3$, $k = 4$ the order of intersection is equal to $3 + 3 - 4 = 2$. If the plane P whose points are common points of two spaces s_3 and t_3 is at infinity in S_4, the spaces are said to be parallel. Eliminating the special case of two parallel spaces, we consider a *fixed* plane P within a *fixed* space s_3 and a *variable* space t_3 intersecting the fixed space s_3 along the fixed plane P.

Let O be a point in the plane P and OM a straight line in s_3 perpendicular to P (Fig. 9). We denote also by OS and OT the normals to two spaces s_3 and t_3 respectively. Two straight lines OM and OS define a plane MOS intersecting the fixed plane P at a *single* point O and this plane, which will be called plane Q, is also a fixed plane because the lines OM and OS are two fixed lines.

The plane Q cannot have more than one point O in common with the plane P: the order of their intersection must be equal indeed to $2 + 2 - 4 = 0$. These two planes are perpendicular to each other since OM and OS are both perpendicular to P, the last one because, as the normal to s_3, it is perpendicular to all planes incident with s_3 and passing through the point O.

The plane Q and the space s_3 intersect along the straight line OM, so that except this line the whole plane Q is outside of the space s_3. Through a point of S_4 there can be in general no more than four mutually perpendicular planes and at the point O three of them, namely the planes AOB, BOM and MOA, belong to s_3. Therefore, the plane Q which is the fourth perpendicular plane at O is the unique plane perpendicular to the plane P and lying outside of s_3.

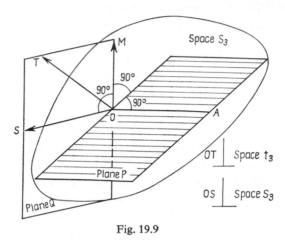

Fig. 19.9

We reach thus the important conclusion that all the straight lines through the point O which do not belong to the space s_3 and only pierce it at O and which are perpendicular to the plane P at this point, lie in and belong to the plane Q. Suppose indeed that a straight line through O and perpendicular to P without belonging to s_3 were non-incident with the plane Q. Such a line would define together with any line through O and in the plane Q a fifth plane perpendicular to four planes AOB, BOM, MOA, MOS and belonging to the four-dimensional space S_4 which is impossible, five dimensions being needed for such a configuration.

Rotation about a Plane in S_4

Now we are prepared to discuss and define the very important concept of rotation around a fixed plane which is a characteristic feature of the four-dimensional universe, distinguishing it from three-dimensional space in which such a rotation is impossible.

We consider the straight line OT defined above and which is perpendicular to the plane P since it is the normal of the space t_3 to which the plane P belongs. This line OT lies in the plane Q because it is perpendicular to the plane P.

When the normal of a space changes its direction, the space moves in the universe S_4. The space t_3 changes its position in S_4 when its normal OT rotates in the plane Q about the point O and during this motion t_3 always passes through the plane P because the normal of t_3 remains in Q and therefore remains perpendicular to the plane P. Thus, in the motion of t_3 around this plane P only the plane P remains fixed and plays the role of a stable *axis-plane* around which the space t_3 moves. Since the normal of t_3 performs a rotation, the motion of t_3 is also a rotation, so that the plane P is the *axis-plane* of this rotation. Since the normal OT and the space t_3 define together a four-dimensional universe S_4 we can consider this rotation around the axis-plane P as a rotation of the universe S_4 on itself and around the plane P. Such a rotation of S_4 generalizes the rotation of a three-dimensional space S_3 on itself around a fixed line as well as the rotation of a plane s_2 on itself around a fixed point. If we compare rotations in spaces of different dimensions, we come to the conclusion that the dimensions' number of a fixed axis around which the rotation is performed, is *two units less* than the dimensionality of the universe in which the rotation is considered: no rotation is possible inside a straight line s_1; in a plane s_2 rotations are performed about points s_0 which are *centers* of rotations; in our three-dimensional space s_3 we have straight lines s_1 as *rotation axes* so that again in a three-dimensional space a one-dimensional element (a straight line) plays the role of rotation axis. Thus, there is nothing surprising in the fact that in a four-dimensional universe rotations are possible which are performed around fixed and immovable planes which for this reason are called *rotation axis-planes*: a two-dimensional element of an S_4 can stand still while the whole universe S_4 rotates on itself about it because $4 - 2 = 2$.

Moreover, we can now understand that during the rotation of the whole universe S_4 about a plane, its three-dimensional element s_3 which intersects the rotation-axis (plane) along a line must seem to a three-dimensional observer, located within s_3 and having neither perceptions nor concept of the existence outside of his world s_3 of an infinitely larger universe S_4, to be in a state of rotation about a *line* because in his world only the intersection-line of this world s_3 and of the fixed plane (rotation-axis-plane in S_4) will stand still.

Returning to the rotation within S_4 of the variable space t_3 around the plane P which is the intersection-plane of this space t_3 with a fixed space s_3, let us study what happens to a three-dimensional configuration located within t_3 and rotating together with t_3 around the plane P. Suppose to fix our ideas that a tetrahedron ABCD (Fig. 10) is at rest within t_3 when the whole space t_3 rotates around the plane P to which belongs the face ABC of our tetrahedron. If in its initial position the variable space t_3 coincides with the space s_3 (the space s_3 remaining at rest within S_4 while t_3 rotates), the tetrahedron ABCD occupies within s_3 a position denoted by ABCH. When the rotation of t_3 begins the tetrahedron simply vanishes for a three-dimensional observer within s_3, only its base ABC remaining for him. It reappears again,

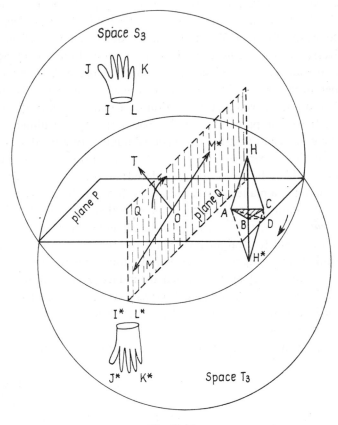

Fig. 19.10

and in the same position ABCH after a complete revolution through 360° of the space t_3 about the rotation axis-plane P. The normal OT of t_3, meanwhile, has also performed a complete revolution within the plane Q and about the point O: at the beginning OT coincided with OM and after a complete revolution OT returns again in s_3 and coincides with OM. But after half a revolution, through 180°, the normal OT coincides with the ray OM*; that is, with the normal to s_3 but pointing in the opposite direction to this normal OM. Therefore, the space t_3 coincides with s_3 also after half a revolution through 180° with the *reversal* of symmetry with respect to plane P within s_3.

This means that after half a revoslution the tetrahedron ABCD is again within the space s_3 but in a new position ABCH* which is symmetrical to ABCH with respect to the fixed plane P. The triangle ABC, the base of the tetrahedron, is located in the fixed plane P and remains therefore at rest when the fourth vertex H and the three edges AH, BH, GH rotate about it. In a more general way, a solid body—for instance, a *right* glove IJKL located in its initial position within s_3—after half a revolution through four-dimensional universe S_4 about the plane P reappears again in S_3, but transformed into the symmetrical *left* glove I*J*K*L* without being subjected to any regrouping of its parts and uniquely by the effect of a simple travel during its motion through the fourt dimension.

This important result proves that the concept of symmetry depends on the dimensionality of space to which it is applied: right and left gloves for us, with our essentially three-dimensional thinking, are two *different* solides. They cannot be brought into coincidence by motion only, though all their constituent parts considered separately are identical: the spatial arrangement of these intrinsically identical and therefore congruent parts is different with respect to our three-dimensional space (that is, for our three-dimensional *mind*), and this explains why for us they are not congruent, more precisely, why they *seem* to be not congruent to three-dimensional thinking and mind.

The same right and left gloves imbedded in a higher four-dimensional space coincide by rotating one of them through 180° around their plane of symmetry. Thus, the reflection in this plane of symmetry P, considered as a mirror, is equivalent to a rotation through 180° about the same plane in a four-dimensional space.

The situation described here is not new to us: in our three-dimensional space we can consider two coplanar and symmetrical plane figures as identical because they coincide if one of them is rotated in space about their *line* of symmetry. At the same time the line of symmetry can be considered as a linear mirror, so that each of two plane symmetrical figures appears to us as a reflection of the other in this linear mirror. Thus, generalizing, we state that a mirror s_{k-2} located in a space s_k and reflecting a geometric configuration C_{k-1} (which has $k-1$ dimensions) onto a symmetrical configuration C_{k-1}^*

can also be considered as fixed base of a rotation around it and this rotation in the space s_k brings C^*_{k-1} into coincidence with C_{k-1} if the rotation angle is 180°. In other words, a symmetry in s_{k-1} becomes an identity in s_k: immersing two symmetrical figures in a higher space with a dimensions' number one unit greater than the number of dimensions of space where these two non-congruent figures are symmetrical, we eliminate completely the apparent difference between the spatial arrangement of identical parts of two symmetrical figures, that is, we eliminate the symmetry.

One is tempted to conclude that there is no symmetry in general, but this conclusion is premature: increasing the number of dimensions of space, we not only transform the apparent symmetry observable in a lower space into an identity, but also create a new kind of symmetry, namely, the symmetry of figures with dimensionality equal to that of the higher space. Thus, although the two three-dimensional left and right gloves become identical in a four-dimensional space, there are in this higher space four-dimensional symmetrical configurations composed of identical parts but non-congruent (reflection in a three-dimensional mirror).

Therefore, if general geometry is defined as a study of spaces of finite dimensionality, the phenomenon of symmetry cannot be eliminated and it will always be present as a characteristic feature of fundamental space with largest dimensions' number. But, if—to the contrary—general geometry is defined as a study of configurations in a space of infinite dimensionality then in such a general geometry no symmetry can exist in itself: it will be a kind of illusion generated by immersing two symmetrical figures in a space of the same dimensions' number as that of figures themselves. This illusion vanishes and the two figures become congruent, when they are imbedded in a higher space which is always there because—as we know well—there is no last integer. The space of infinite dimensionality can have only aleph-null dimensions (denumerable infinity), that is, as many as the number of all integers.

Distances

Having justified the assertion stated without proof at the end of Chapter 13 about the essential identity of two symmetrical figures, we shall discuss now the definitions of distances in a three-dimensional space. We begin this discussion with an analysis of the fundamental fact about distances, namely, the fact that in a flat space a segment of a straight line is the *shortest path* between its two endpoints.

This assertion presupposes a definition of length valid for any path between two given points A and B whatever shape it may possess. Such a definition must be based on the use of rectilinear segments because only the length of a segment of a straight line is measurable directly with the aid of a unit of length. Studying the length of a circle's circumference, we saw that it is defined as a limit of length of an inscribed regular polygon; that is, as a limit of length of an inscribed broken line.

The definition of length of an arc $\overset{\frown}{ABC}$ of any curve (Fig. 11) is also based on the use of circumscribed and inscribed broken lines, all the segments of which are rectilinear. Consider first the chord AB. Choose an interior point C on the arc $\overset{\frown}{AB}$ between A and B and join it to points A and B, forming a triangle ABC.

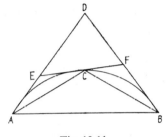

Fig. 19.11

We know that the sum of two sides AC + CB of this triangle is greater than the third side AB: AC + CB > AB. Thus, subdividing the arc $\overset{\frown}{AB}$ into two arcs $\overset{\frown}{AC}$ and $\overset{\frown}{CB}$ and comparing the sum of their chords to the chord AB, we find that the sum of two chords subtending the parts $\overset{\frown}{AC}$, $\overset{\frown}{CB}$ of the arc $\overset{\frown}{AB}$ is greater than the chord AB of the original arc. Now this process can be continued and nothing can stop the subdivisions of each of 2^n arcs obtained in n steps into two parts during the $(n + 1)$-th step, so that 2^{n+1} parts are obtained after $n + 1$ steps. During this process of endless dichotomy the total length L_n of chords of 2^n small arcs into which the arc $\overset{\frown}{AB}$ was divided after the n-th step can only increase since $L_{n+1} > L_n$. If we suppose that the successive subdivisions are carried out in such a way that the length of the largest chord among the chords obtained in the n-th subdivision tends to zero, when n increases without limit, it can be said that the broken line tends to coincide with the curved arc $\overset{\frown}{ACB}$, when the number 2^n of its segments increases indefinitely with $n \to \infty$.

The lengths $L_1, L_2, ..., L_n, L_{n+1}, ...$ of broken lines inscribed i ı the arc $\overset{\frown}{AB}$ by successive subdivisions form an *increasing* sequence which approaches a finite limit because it is bounded from above and is therefore convergent. The fact that it is bounded will be proved in what follows, and anticipating this proof we state that the length of the curved arc can be defined as the limit of the length of the inscribed broken lines L_n for $n \to \infty$:

DEFINITION: length $\overset{\frown}{AB} = \lim\limits_{n = \infty} L_n$

To prove that the sequence L_n is bounded from above we consider broken lines circumscribed to the arc AB. Two tangent lines at the endpoints A and B intersect at D (Fig. 11) and the chord AB is less than the sum AD + BD. The first division of the arc $\overset{\frown}{AB}$ by the point C which yields two chords AC, CB also replaces the first circumscribed broken line ADB by a *shorter* line AECFB where the segment EF is on the tangent line having its contact point at C. The new polygonal line is shorter because its segment EF replaces two segments ED, DF whose sum exceeds EF. Thus, we have here a regular process which can be applied at every new subdivision and this process creates an infinite sequence of polygonal circumscribed lines of *decreasing* length.

On the other hand, a circumscribed polygonal line of a determined subdivision is associated with the corresponding inscribed polygonal line and the length of the inscribed line is always less than the length of the associated circumscribed line. Take, for instance, ACB and AECFB. Since each segment of the inscribed line appears as a third side in a triangle, two other sides of which belong to the corresponding circumscribed line, the proof is achieved. Denoting the decreasing sequence of lengths of circumscribed polygonal broken lines by $M_1, M_2, ..., M_n, ...$, we have the inequalities $M_{n+1} > L_n$ which hold for all values of the integer n. But, M_n is less than M_1, so that all the terms L_n of the increasing sequence L_n are less than a fixed length $M_1 = AD + DB$ which proves that this sequence is bounded from above and thus ensures the existence of the limit $\lim\limits_{n = \infty} L_n$. This limit is also equal to the limit $\lim\limits_{n = \infty} M_n$ of the decreasing sequence M_n bounded from below: $M_n > AB$.

The definition of a curved length $\overset{\frown}{AB}$ yields another proof of the fundamental fact that a segment of straight line is the shortest path between its two end-points A and B. Any other path, if it crosses the segment AB in many points between A and B, can be considered as a sum of arcs of the type $\overset{\frown}{AC}$ (Fig. 12) which does not cross the chord AC. Since each such arc has a length greater than the length of its chord, the total length of a non-rectilinear path is greater than the total length of all chords; that is, of the straight line segment AB: AB < $\overgroup{AB}$.

We know that the distance between a point P and a straight line AB is by definition the minimum distance beween P and an arbitrary point M of AB.

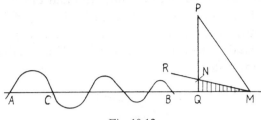

Fig. 19.12

A perpendicular PQ dropped from P on the line AB is a third side of a triangle PQM where M is any point of AB distinct from the foot Q of the perpendicular. To prove that PQ < PM we observe that there can be only three logically possible cases: PQ = PM, PQ > PM and PQ < PM and they are mutually exclusive. Since the angle at Q is a right angle it follows that $\overgroup{PMQ}$ is an acute angle and this is sufficient to disprove the case PQ = PM: were the triangle PQM an isosceles one with equal sides PQ and PM, then we would have $\overgroup{PQM} = \overgroup{PMQ}$ and this is not so. Suppose now that PQ > PM and draw the line MNR which cuts off on PQ a segment PN = PM. Then the triangle PMN is isosceles and the two angles $\overgroup{PNM}$ and $\overgroup{PMN}$ must be equal. But, on the one hand, $\overgroup{PMN}$ as a part of an acute angle is less than 90°, while on the other hand, $\overgroup{PNM}$, as an exterior angle of the shaded triangle MNQ, is greater than the interior non-adjacent angle $\overgroup{PQM}$; that is, greater than 90°. Therefore, the angles $\overgroup{PMN}$ and $\overgroup{PNM}$ cannot be equal and the case PM < PQ is also disproved. Therefore only the third case is valid and the proof that PQ < PM is achieved; a perpendicular dropped on a line from a point non-incident with this line is the shortest path from this point to a point on the line and is, therefore, the measure of the distance from the point to the line.

Having restated the facts related to the definitions of distances in plane geometry, we emphasize that in every case what is called a distance between two geometric objects is always a *minimum* of all possible distances between any two points of these objects. The same observation holds for distances in our space and in higher spaces.

23 Kogbetliantz

Given a plane *p* and a point P non-incident with the plane (Fig. 13), we draw a straight lime PM joining P to any point M in the plane and we drop also a perpendicular PQ to the plane. Two intersecting lines PM, PQ define a plane *q* and in this plane lies the straight line QM. The perpendicular to the plane PQ is also perpendicular to the line MQ and therefore its length is shorter than the length of the segment PM, M being any point of the plane other than Q. Thus, the shortest path from a point P to any point in a plane is the perpendicular dropped from P on the plane. The length of this perpendicular is called the distance from the point to the plane.

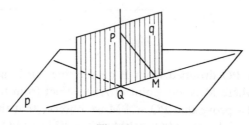

Fig. 19.13

Given two skew straight lines CC and DD (Fig. 14), there is a unique straight line intersecting them and perpendicular to both of them. Its segment AB joining the intersection points is the shortest path between any two points taken on these two skew lines and it is the measure of their distance.

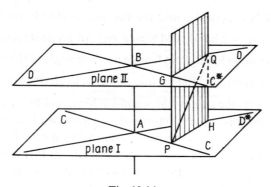

Fig. 19.14

To prove it we draw through CC and DD two planes I and II perpendicular to AB. Therefore, the plane I is parallel to DD and the plane II is parallel to CC. Let AD* in I be parallel to BD, AD* ∥ BD, as well as BC* ∥ CC. Taking on the lines CC and DD the points P and Q distinct from A and B, we draw also through the line PQ a plane III parallel to AB and therefore perpendicular to our two planes I and II. In it, PGQH is a rectangle the sides PG and QH of which are parallel and equal to the segment AB between the two skew lines CC and DD. Naturally, the diagonal PQ is greater than the side PG = AB, so that PQ > AB. Thus, indeed, AB is the minimum distance between any two points taken on CC and DD.

What now about the distances in the four-dimensional space S_4? Without giving all the proofs, we state here some facts about distances in S_4. A point P which does not belong to a three-dimensional space s_3 defines within s_3 a unique point Q such that the straight line PQ which pierces s_3 in the point Q is perpendicular to s_3. This follows from the uniqueness of the perpendicular dropped from P on the space s_3: Q is the foot of the normal of s_3 which passes through P. If M denotes any point in s_3 distinct from Q the distance PM is greater than PQ, so that the length PQ of the perpendicular is again the measure of the distance between a point P and a space s_3. Two parallel spaces s_3 and t_3, $s_3 \parallel t_3$, have common normals and through P non-incident with s_3 and t_3 passes one such common normal which pierces s_3 in a point Q and t_3 in a point T. The distance between these two parallel spaces s_3 and t_3 is therefore equal to PT − PQ = TQ and its measure is the length of the segment TQ on the common normal comprised between the two parallel spaces.

The distances from a point to a line or to a plane are defined in S_4 exactly as in an s_3 because point and line determine a plane, as well as point and plane determine an s_3 to which they both belong.

But the *distance* between a plane P and a straight line L which are skew in S_4 (that is, do not belong to the same three-dimensional space s_3 and therefore do not meet) is again a new concept unknown in s_3. It is defined as the *minimum* of all distances between two variable points A in the plane P and B on the line L. The plane P and the point B on the line L define a space s_3 (B). In this space the segment BA_B, perpendicular to the plane P, is the measure of the distance between the point B and the plane P. Therefore, for any point A in P, BA > BA_B. The line L pierces the threedimensional space s_3(B) in one point only (namely, in B), but the whole straight line BA_B belongs to s_3(B).

Thus, to each point B taken on the line L corresponds in the plane P a point A_B, the foot of the perpendicular BA_B dropped from B on P. When B travels on the line L the point A_B moves in the plane P and the length BA_B varies. At the same time the three-dimensional section s_3(B) of S_4 rotates about the fixed plane P and turns around B as on a pivot changing its direction in S_4. Therefore, the normal to s_3(B) at B turns and the angle ω it makes with the fixed straight line L varies. The acute angle θ between the line L and the variable space $s_3(B)$ which is complementary to ω, $\theta = 90° - \omega$, depends on the position of the point B on L. There is only one position B* of B on L such that θ reaches its maximum and becomes a right angle, while ω vanishes, the normal to $s_3(B)$ coinciding with the line L. The corresponding position s_3^* of the variable space $s_3(B)$ defined by the plane P and the point B*, is perpendicular to the line L and therefore each element (line or plane) within s_3^* is also perpendicular to L. In particular, the segment B*A* which by construction is perpendicular to the plane P, is also perpendicular to the straight line L. This proves the existence and uniqueness of a common perpendicular to a plane and a straight line which are skew in the four-dimensional space S_4.

The relative locations of points on the line L and in the plane P around this unique common perpendicular are symmetrical with respect to B* on L and its counterpart A* (the foot of the common perpendicular) in P. Thus, there are always many equal distances BA for any choice of B on L, except for B*, the distance B*A* on the common perpendicular being unique. The uniqueness characterizes an extremum, that is, a maximum or a minimum. But the maximum of distances BA in case of skew plane P and line L does not exist, the segment BA increasing without limit when B or A recedes to infinity. Therefore, the segment B*A* is the shortest distance between the points of the plane P and the points on the line L. As such it is, by definition, their distance in the four-dimensional universe S_4. As in the case of two straight lines skew in our three-dimensional world, this distance is intercepted by the plane and the line on their common perpendicular which is uniquely determined by plane and line skew in S_4.

Considering now the common perpendicular A*B* to the line L and plane P together with the line L, we state that these two straight lines intersecting at the point B* define a plane Q containing L and AB. The point A* incident with the plane P belongs to the plane Q too, but no other point of Q is a common point of the two planes P and Q since otherwise the plane Q would be contained within the space s* which is impossible because we know that the line L lying entirely within Q peirces s* in the only point B*. Therefore, the planes P and Q intersect in only one point A*.

The plane Q and the space s* intersect each other along the straight line A*B* and have no other points in common because in S_4 the order of intersection $m + n - k$ of plane ($m = 2$) and a space ($n = 3$) is equal to one: $k = 4$ and thus $3 + 2 - 4 = 1$.

Since the line L is perpendicular to the space s*, any plane within s* and passing through the point B*, where L pierces s^*, is perpendicular to the line L. Among these planes all the planes containing the whole line A*B* are perpendicular not only to the line L but also to the plane P, and thus we see that there are an infinite number of common perpendicular planes to line L and plane P, skew in S_4: these common perpendicular planes form a pencil of collinear planes with the common perpendicular line A*B* as the axis of this pencil of planes.

Duality in S_3

We saw already that in a three-dimensional universe s_3 plane and point are dual transforms of each other. We shall study now some examples of transformations by duality in s_3. Let us begin with a segment AB defined by two points A and B and lying on a straight line L through these two points. Two planes a and b which are dual images of A, B intersect along a line L* so that the dual transform of a line is another straight line. But the segment AB whose length is the measure of distance between A and B is transformed into the dihedral angle of two planes a, b with the edge L*, this dihedral angle being the measure of the angular distance between a and b.

The planes a and b form two dihedral angles, one acute and the other obtuse, which are supplementary (their sum is equal to 180°). The straight line L is also divided by two points A, B into two segments because a straight line is a closed line. One of them which is of *finite* length is called segment AB; the other, containing the point at infinity as its interior point, is infinite in length. Thus, two dihedral angles formed by a and b are dual transforms of these two segments.

Next we consider three straight lines λ, μ, ν belonging to a plane p and forming a triangle with vertices A, B, C (Fig. 15): Straight lines, in general, will be denoted by Greek letters followed sometimes by capital letters in parentheses, for instance $\lambda(AC)$, to indicate the points defining the line.

The triangle ABC involves six more elements: three sides (segments) and three angles, so that the configuration we are describing has in all thirteen elements. To build up the dual configuration we take first three planes a, b, c which pass through their common point P, the dual image of the plane p. Thus, a trihedral angle is the dual transform of a triangle in s_3. Three straight lines λ, μ, ν are transformed into three edges λ^*, μ^*, ν^* of the trihedral angle and the sides 1, 2, 3 of the triangle ABC become dihedral angles $\hat{1}$, $\hat{2}$, $\hat{3}$ formed by the planes a, b, c at the edges. Finally, three angles of our triangle are transformed into three plane angles at the point P with sides λ^*, μ^*, ν^*. Thus, in S_3 a plane angle is self-dual, its vertex being transformed into the plane of its dual image and vice-versa.

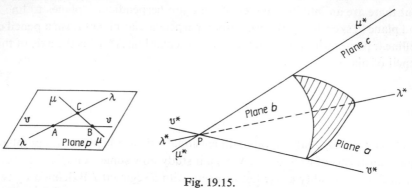

Fig. 19.15.

We pass now to the configuration (Fig. 16) formed by four noncoplanar points A, B, C, D; that is, to the figure called a tetrahedron. A tetrahedron ABCD has four vertices, four faces [planes e(ABC), f(BCD), g(CDA), h(DAB) defined by four sets of three vertices] which are opposite to the respective vertices, six edges [straight lines (AB), (BC), (CD), (DA), (AC),

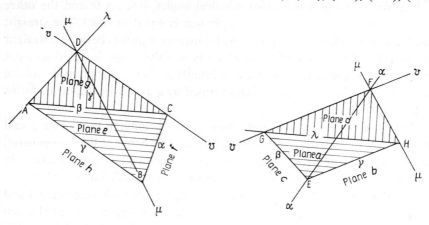

Fig. 19.16

(BD) defined by six pairs of adjacent vertices], and a volume which is the measure of the amount of space interior to the tetrahedron and bounded by the four planes of faces. Moreover, in a tetrahedron we distinguish three different kinds of angles: four trihedral angles at the four vertices, six dihedral interior and six dihedral exterior angles at the six edges, and twelve plane angles (three within each face). To all these elements we must also add six segments, the sides of four triangles ABC, BCD, CDA, DAB as well as the four areas of these triangles.

As we will see, a tetrahedron is self-dual insofar as the global result of its transformation by duality is concerned. But, naturally, separate parts undergo exchanges by duality: four faces (planes) e, f, g, h become vertices, E, F, G, H while vertices A, B, C, D are transformed into faces a, b, c, d; triangles become trihedral angles and vice-versa; edges remain straight lines, but sides of triangles are transformed into dihedral angles and dihedral angles into sides; plane angles remain plane angles. Perhaps the most interesting feature of the dual transformation is the fact that the interior and the exterior of a tetrahedron are exchanged: to the space interior to a tetrahedron corresponds as its dual image the exterior of the transformed tetrahedron.

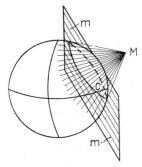

Fig. 19.17

As in plane geometry, the dual transformations in S_3 can be realized in many different ways. Let us describe one of them based on the use of a sphere called the fundamental sphere and which remains invariant, being self-dual. From any exterior point M an infinite number of lines tangent to the fundamental sphere can be drawn (Fig. 17). They form a circular cone tangent to the sphere along a circle C and therefore define a plane m whose intersection with the sphere is the circle C. Thus, by definition, we consider the circle's plane m as the dual image of the exterior point M. Conversely, given a secant plane m which cuts the sphere along a circle C, we associate with m as its dual transform the exterior point M such that a circular cone with the vertex in M is tangent to the sphere along the circle C.

These constructions enable us to find also the dual images of points interior to the fundamental sphere, and of planes non-intersecting it. Given an interior point N, we draw through it three different planes r, s, t. Since these planes are intersecting the sphere we obtain three exterior points R, S, T as the dual images of three planes r, s, t. Now since the interior point N is incident with these planes r, s, t, its dual image, the plane n, is also incident with three points R, S, T and this is sufficient to define and draw this plane n. By the same token, we see that the dual image N of a plane n which does not meet the fundamental sphere can be found by choosing any three points R, S, T incident with the plane n and drawing their dual images, planes r, s, t. The point N is then the intersection point of the three planes r, s, t.

If a plane e intersects the fundamental sphere along a great circle, the cone tangent to the sphere along this great circle is in fact a circular cylinder, that is, its vertex is rejected to infinity. Thus, the dual image of a plane e through the center of the sphere is a point E_∞ at infinity in the direction of the normal to this plane e (Fig. 18).

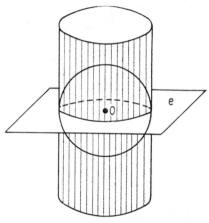

Fig. 19.18

If the interior point is located in the center O of the sphere, then the plane o, its dual transform, is the plane at infinity because to three planes through the center O correspond as their dual images three points at infinity, the plane o defined by these three points at infinity is the plane at infinity of s_3.

To complete the description of tde dual transformation it remains to consider the dual transform of a point on the fundamental sphere as well as the dual image of a plane tangent to the sphere. The contact-point of a tangent plane and this plane itself are dual images of each other, and this can be proved by continuity, approaching an exterior point to the spherical surface: consider a cone with vertex in M and tangent to the sphere along a circle C

(Fig. 17), and suppose that the vertex M tends to a point N on the surface of sphere. The tangent cone opens more and more when M approaches N, the contact circle C shrinks towards the point N and at the limit, when M coincides with N, the circle's plane becomes tangent to the sphere at N. This tangent plane is, at the same time, the limiting shape of the tangent cone which flattens completely out and becomes a plane when its vertex lies on the sphere. Thus, (Fig. 19) a point N of the sphere and a plane *n* tangent to the sphere at this point form a dual pair. Thus, the fudamental sphere—a *locus of points* on it—transforms by duality into itself but is considered now as an *envelope of its tangent planes*.

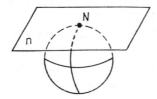

Fig. 19.19

The dual relation between triangle and trihedral angle leads to an easy formulation of many properties of a trihedral angle. Any property of a triangle (which belongs to plane Geometry) transformed by duality becomes a corresponding property of a trihedral angle (which is a proposition of solid Geometry). Thus, the duality establishes a kind of bridge between the results of plane and solid geometry, with the aid of which a theorem of plane geometry, when transformed by duality, yields as its dual companion a theorem of solid geometry.

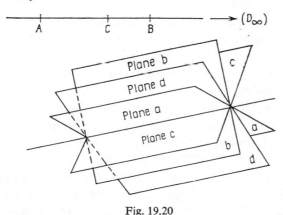

Fig. 19.20

Since a straight line segment AB is the dual companion of a dihedral angle with faces a and b, the point at infinity D_∞ on the line AB and the midpoint C of the segment AB (Fig. 20) are the dual images of two planes which pass through the edge of the dihedral angle and *bisect* this angle. We know that the dual transformation exchanges exterior and interior, so that the midpoint C has as its dual image the exterior bisector-plane c of the dihedral angle, while the interior bisector-plane d corresponds to the point at infinity D on AB.

Therefore, to six bisector-planes of three dihedral angles in a given trihedral angle (Fig. 21) correspond in the dual image of the trihedral angle—that is, in the triangle ABC—the three midpoints E, D, G of its sides CA, BC, AB and three points at infinity of these lines (denoted respectively by the Greek letters α, β, γ). In this correspondence the interior bisector-planes of a trihedral angle are the dual images of points at infinity on the lines AB, BC, CA. A parallel δ to the base γ (we use Greek letters to denote straight lines: δ for DE, ε for DG etc.) through the midpoints E and D of sides AC and BC passes through the point at infinity F_∞ on the line γ, so that the three points E, D, F_∞ are collinear. The dual image of three collinear points are three collinear planes and in this case to the points E and D correspond the *exterior* bisector-planes e and d of dihedral angles formed by the faces a, c and b, c respectively while to the point F_∞ at infinity corresponds the *interior* bisector-plane f of the dihedral angle with faces a and b. These three bisector-planes are therefore collinear and thus we obtain one of the properties of a trihedral angle, namely:

An interior bisector-plane of a trihedral angle passes through the straight line which is the intersection-line of two exterior bisector-planes through two other edges of the trihedral angle.

Moreover, three points at infinity on three lines δ(ED), ε(DG), η(EG), are collinear also, because they belong to the line at infinity of the triangle's plane p. Their dual images are three interior bisector-planes of dihedral angles. Thus these three interior bisector-planes are also collinear: *interior bisector-planes of a trihedral angle pass through a straight line which is called an axis of a trihedral angle.* Therefore the six bisector-planes of a trihedral angle meet by groups of three along four straight lines through the vertex P, one (the axis ω) being interior and the three others exterior to the trihedral angle.

To three medians λ(AD), μ(BE), ν(CG) in the plane p correspond the three intersection-lines (denoted by the same letters) of faces of the trihedral angle with exterior bisector-planes of opposite dihedral angles λ (a, d); μ (b, e) and ν (c, g). Since the medians of a triangle are *concurrent* lines intersecting at the

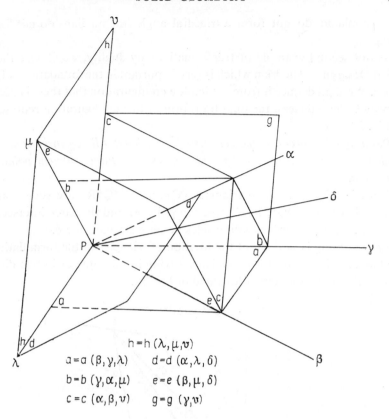

$$h = h\,(\lambda,\mu,\upsilon)$$

$$a = a\,(\beta,\gamma,\lambda) \qquad d = d\,(\alpha,\lambda,\delta)$$

$$b = b\,(\gamma,\alpha,\mu) \qquad e = e\,(\beta,\mu,\delta)$$

$$c = c\,(\alpha,\beta,\upsilon) \qquad g = g\,(\gamma,\upsilon)$$

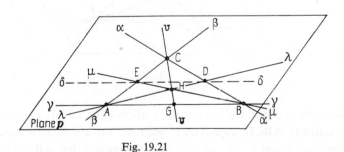

Fig. 19.21

center of gravity H of the triangle, the three intersection-lines of faces *a, b, c* with the exterior bisector-planes *d, e, g* are *coplanar*, that is, they belong to the same plane *h*, dual image of the center of gravity H. They pass through the vertex P of the trihedral angle (the medians belong to the plane *p*), but being coplanar do not form a trihedral angle (the medians do not form a triangle).

As our second example of tranformations by duality, we choose the so-called Desargues' Theorem which is very important in the foundations of geometry. We shall deduce it from so simple a configuration that there is nothing to prove. Nevertheless, the dual transform of this configuration represented in Fig. 23 is the

Desargues' Theorem. If the vertices of two triangles lie on three concurrent straight lines, their corresponding sides intersect in three collinear points and vice versa.

Thus, in Fig. 23 the two triangles PQR and P*Q*R* are such that the straight lines PP*, QQ*, RR* meet at a point M and the three intersection-points F, G, H of corresponding sides lie on a straight line δ.

Since nothing is said about the location of triangles in the formulation of the theorem, it is valid for two triangles lying in the same or in two distinct planes, the first case being illustrated in Fig. 24.

Configuration I

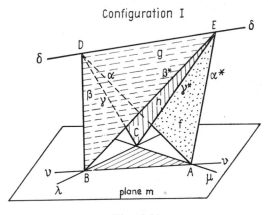

Fig. 19.22

We now describe the first configuration (Fig. 22). It consists of the two tetrahedrons ABCD and ABCE built up on a common base ABC with vertices at D and E. We denote their common edges AB, BC, CA incident with the plane m(ABC) of the base by λ(BC), μ(CA), ν(AB); the six other edges are α(DA), β(DB), γ(DC) for ABCD and α*(EA), β*(EB), γ*(EC) for ABCE. Adding to these nine lines the line δ(DE), we obtain in all ten lines.

The five points A, B, C, D, E define ten planes because the number of various combinations of three items which can be formed within a given set of five items is equal to $C_3^5 = 10$. These planes are the seven face-planes $m(ABC)$, $p(ABD)$, $q(BCD)$, $r(CAD)$, $p^*(ABE)$, $q^*(BCE)$, $r^*(CAE)$ of two tetrahedrons and the three collinear planes through the line δ, namely, the planes $f(ADE)$, $g(BDE)$ and $h(CDE)$. The last three planes f, g, h can also be defined by pairs of lateral edges of two tetrahedrons intersecting at common vertices A, B, C and non-incident with the plane m of the common base ABC. Thus, the plane $f(ADE)$ is also the plane defined by the edges $\alpha(AD)$ and $\alpha^*(AE)$ and we express this by writing $f(ADE) = f(\alpha, \alpha^*)$. Likewise, we have $g(BDE) = g(\beta, \beta^*)$ and $h(CDE) = h(\gamma, \gamma^*)$.

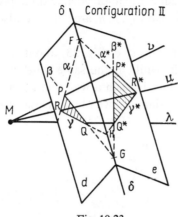

Fig. 19.23

Our first configuration I involves in all five points, ten lines and ten planes. The list of all twenty-five elements together with their dual transforms which form another configuration II (Fig. 23), follows (the elements in the same row are incident):

	Configuration I (Fig. 22)		*Configuration II* (Fig. 23)		
Point	*Lines*	*Planes*	*Plane*	*Line*	*Points*
A	$\mu, \nu, \alpha, \alpha^*$	m, f, p, r, p^*, r^*	a	$\mu, \nu, \alpha, \alpha^*$	M, F, P, R, P*, R*
B	$\nu, \lambda, \beta, \beta^*$	m, g, q, p, q^*, p^*	b	$\nu, \lambda, \beta, \beta^*$	M, G, Q, P, Q*, P*
C	$\lambda, \mu, \gamma, \gamma^*$	m, h, r, q, r^*, q^*	c	$\lambda, \mu, \gamma, \gamma^*$	M, H, R, Q, R*, Q*
D	$\delta, \alpha, \beta, \gamma$	f, g, h, p, q, r	d	$\delta, \alpha, \beta, \gamma$	F, G, H, P, Q, R
E	$\delta, \alpha^*, \beta^*, \gamma^*$	f, g, h, p^*, q^*, r^*	e	$\delta, \alpha^*, \beta^*, \gamma^*$	F, G, H, P*, Q*, R*

Transforming dually the configuration I (Fig. 22), we obtain the dual configuration II (Fig. 23) consisting of a trihedral angle with its vertex at M (dual image of the triangle ABC in the plane m) and three face-planes

$a(\mu, \nu) = a(\text{MPR})$, $b(\nu, \lambda) = b(\text{MQP})$, $c(\lambda, \mu) = c(\text{MRQ})$ cut by two other planes $d(\text{PQR})$ qnd $e(\text{P*Q*R*})$ (dual images of the two points D and E) which pass through the straight line δ. The intersections of the trihedral angle at M and of these two planes d and e define two triangles PQR and P*Q*R* (dual images of two trihedral angles at D and E) which satisfy the hypothesis of the Desargues' Theorem.

Considering now the three pairs of straight lines $\alpha\alpha^*$, $\beta\beta^*$, $\gamma\gamma^*$ first as elements of configuration I and then as elements of configuration II, we observe that in Fig. 22 they define three collinear planes f, g, h incident with the line δ, while in Fig. 23 their dual companions define three points F, G, H, which as the dual images of three planes f, g, h, are collinear also so that Desargues' Theorem follows.

Now rotating the two planes d, e (Fig. 23) about the axis δ and making them coincide at the limit, while at the same time the triangles PQR and P*Q*R* move in their planes in such a way that at the limit their ultimate positions are two different triangles, we obtain Desargues' Theorem for two triangles lying in the same plane (Fig. 24).

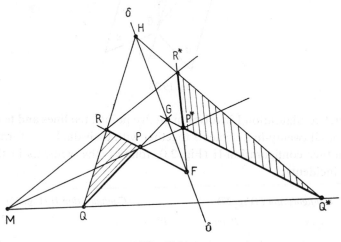

Fig. 19.24

A natural generalization of Desargues' Theorem is the following proposition concerning two tetrahedrons:

If the vertices of two tetrahedrons lie by pairs on four concurrent straight lines, then the four intersection-lines of their corresponding faces are coplanar and vice versa.

The proof of this proposition is based on Desargues' Theorem the use of which yields six coplanar points aligned by triplets on four concurrent straight lines.

As our last example of dual theorems in solid geometry we now study how simple properties of a tetrahedron (which are very easy to justify) become sources of more complicated and difficult to prove theorems which are their dual companions and therefore can be obtained by duality. The results which will be discussed here are only a few of the properties of a tetrahedron, the study of which occupies the next chapter 20.

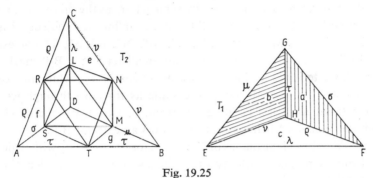

Fig. 19.25

Fig. 25 represents two tetrahedrons T_1 and T_2 which are dual transforms of each other. Their edges are selfdual and for this reason they are denoted by the same Greek letters; the planes are denoted by small letters and their dual images, points, by capital letters, the same letter being used for transformed element. Thus, to small letters in one tetrahedron correspond capital letters in the other, and vice versa.

The relation of incidence is invariant in a transformation by duality. It will be denoted by the symbol $\supset\subset$, for instance in T_1 four faces a, b, c, d are incident with vertices FGH, GHE, HEF and EFG respectively, while the vertices E, F, G, H are incident with faces bcd, cda, dab and abc, and these facts are expressed as follows: FGH $\supset\subset a$, GHE $\supset\subset b$, HEF $\supset\subset c$, EFG $\supset\subset d$, $abc \supset\subset$ H, $bcd \supset\subset$ E, $cda \supset\subset$ Γ and $dab \supset\subset$ G.

The six edges $\lambda, \mu, \nu, \varrho, \sigma, \tau$ of T_1 verify the following relations of incidence:

$$\lambda\mu\nu \supset\subset E, \lambda\varrho\sigma \supset\subset F, \mu\sigma\tau \supset\subset G, \nu\tau\varrho \supset\subset H$$

$$ab \supset\subset \tau, bc \supset\subset \nu, cd \supset\subset \lambda, da \supset\subset \sigma, bd \supset\subset \mu, ac \supset\subset \varrho.$$

Let us now study the intersection-points of twelve bisector-planes of six dihedral angles in T_1 by the method of dual transformation. The dual images of these B-P's (B-P is used as an abbreviation for the term "bisector-plane") are midpoints of sides and points at infinity of edges in T_2 so that propositions related to these midpoints and points at infinity become by duality properties of B-P's for T_1. It is important to recall that the interior of T_1 is dual image of the exterior of T_2, so that to the midpoints of sides in T_2 correspond exterior B-P's in T_1 while its interior B-P's are images of the points at infinity on edges of T_2.

We denote the midpoints of sides by the same capital letters as Greek letters denoting the corresponding edges, so that for instance $L \supset \subset \lambda$. The points at infinity, which are marked by same letters as the midpoints, will be characterized by asterisks, so that the point at infinity on the edge λ is L^*. To twelve points L, M, N, R, S, T, L^*, M^*, N^*, R^*, S^*, T^* correspond twelve B-P's in T_1 denoted by same but small letters; a B-P marked by a letter with asterisk is an interior bisector-plane in T_1, while an exterior B-P is denoted by a small letter (the same as for edge through which it passes) without asterisk. To take an example, two B-P's s and s^* pass through the edge σ, s^* being an interior and s an exterior B-P.

We consider now eight planes in T_2: the plane z^* at infinity with which are incident the six points at infinity on six edges of T_2, so that denoting the plane at infinity by z^*, we have

$$L^*, M^*, N^*, R^*, S^*, T^* \supset \subset z^*;$$

the three planes u, v, w parallel to pairs of opposite edges of T_2 and passing each through four midpoints of four other sides, so that

$$M, N, R, S \supset \subset u \parallel \lambda, \tau; \quad L, N, S, T \supset \subset v \parallel \mu, \varrho;$$

$$L, M, R, T \supset \subset w \parallel \nu, \sigma;$$

and, finally, four planes e^*, f^*, g^*, h^* parallel to faces e, f, g, h and passing each through three midpoints of sides, so that

$$R, S, T \supset \subset e^* \parallel e; \quad M, N, T \supset \subset f^* \parallel f; \quad L, N, R \supset \subset g^* \parallel g;$$

$$L, M, S \supset \subset h^* \parallel h.$$

The first plane z^* contains six points, but each of the seven others just defined also contain six points. Consider, for example, the plane u which by definition is parallel to the two skew straight lines λ and τ. Because of this parallelism the plane u contains the points at infinity L^* and T^* belonging to lines λ and τ to which it is parallel. The same applies to planes v and w:

$$L^*, M, N, R, S, T^* \supset \subset u; \quad L, M^*, N, R^*, S, T \supset \subset v;$$

$$L, M, N^*, R, S^*, T \supset \subset w.$$

Consider again the plane e^* which is parallel to the face e and therefore parallel to the three straight lines λ, μ, ν lying in the plane e. Being parallel to the three edges λ, μ, ν, the plane e^* contains their points at infinity L^*, M^*, N^* and the same reasoning applies to three other planes f^*, g^*, h^*:

$$L^*, M^*, N^*, R, S, T \supset\subset e^*; \quad L^*, M, N, R^*, S^*, T \supset\subset f^*;$$
$$L, M^*, N, R, S^*, T^* \supset\subset g^*; \quad L, M, N^*, R^*, S, T^* \supset\subset h^*.$$

Thus, each one of our eight planes contains a group of six points chosen among twelve, six midpoints of sides plus six points at infinity of edges. The first plane, plane z^*, contains six points at infinity. Each of the three planes u, v, w contains four midpoints and two points at infinity. Each of the four planes e^*, f^*, g^*, h^* contains three points at infinity and three midpoints.

Transforming T_2 by duality into T_1, we obtain eight points which are dual images of our eight planes and through each of these eight points pass six bisector-planes of dihedral angles of the tetrahedron T_1. Through the image Z of the plane z^* pass all six interior B-P's of T_1 because they are dual images of six points at infinity on the edges of T_2 which are incident with z^*. This point Z is also common point of the four axes of trihedral angles of T_1. Since the bisector-plane of a dihedral angle is the locus of points equidistant from both faces of the dihedral angle, the axis of a trihedral angle is the locus of points equidistant from all three faces of the trihedral angle. Thus, *the point Z, intersection-point of all four axes of a tetrahedron, is equidistant from the four faces of tetrahedron and therefore is the center of a sphere interior to the tetrahedron and tangent to its faces.* This sphere is called the *inscribed sphere* and its center Z is one of the remarkable points of a tetrahedron. The point Z is often called the *incenter*.

To four planes e^*, f^*, g^*, h^* correspond, as their dual images, four points E^*, F^*, G^*, H^* exterior to the tetrahedron T_1 because through each of these four points pass three exterior B-P's as well as three interior B-P's of T_1:

$$l^*, m^*, n^*, r, s, t \subset E^*; \quad l^*, m, n, r^*, s^*, t \subset F^*;$$
$$l, m^*, n, r, s^*, t^* \subset G^*; \quad l, m, n^*, r^*, s, t^* \subset H^*.$$

These four points are centers of four escribed spheres, tangent to all faces of the tetrahedron but exterior to it, so that three of four contact-points for each one of the four escribed spheres are exterior to the triangles of T_1. The centers of escribed spheres are sometimes called *excenters*.

Finally, to the three planes u, v, w also correspond three points U, V, W through each of which pass six B-P's of T_1:

$$l^*, m, n, r, s, t^* \subset U; \quad l, m^*, n, r^*, s, t \subset V; \quad l, m, n^*, r, s^*, t \subset W.$$

Thus, the points U, V, W are also equidistant from faces of T_1, so that they may play the role of centers of tangent spheres, if they are not points at infinity. As we shall discuss this question in greater detail in chapter 20, it will be sufficient to mention here only that four different cases are possible and take place for different tetrahedrons, namely: all three points U, V, W are at infinity; two of them are at infinity; one only is at infinity and, finally, no point among U, V, W is at infinity.

The example we studied shows how easily incidence theorems can be proved with the aid of dual transformations of the simplest facts—facts which are almost self-evident as for instance the incidence of points at infinity with the plane at infinity. We terminate this chapter by deducing from the existence of the *centroid* of a tetrahedron and its definition as intersection-point of four medians another property of tetrahedrons with the aid of our method of dual transformation.

Each of the four faces of a tetrahedron possesses three medians of a triangle formed by the three vertices of the tetrahedron lying in this face and the medians are concurrent in the centroid of this triangle. Joining a vertex of the tetrahedron to the centroid of the opposite face, we obtain the median of tetrahedron.

Anticipating the theorem which will be proved in chapter 20, we observe that the four medians of a tetrahedron are concurrent lines: they intersect in the centroid of the tetrahedron, a point lying on each median at one quarter of its length from the face. Now, through the four medians pass the six planes which are called median-planes of a tetrahedron because each of them contains an edge and the midpoint of the opposite edge. A median-plane necessarily passes through the centroid of a tetrahedron because it contains two medians and the centroid is the common point of all four medians. Therefore, the six median-planes of a tetrahedron meet at the centroid.

We want now to formulate the dual transform of this theorem. The dual image of a median-plane is a point, namely, the intersection-point of an edge with the exterior bisector-plane through the opposite edge. To show this we observe that a median-plane in T_2, for instance the plane CDT, is defined as a plane incident with an edge and with the midpoint of the opposite edge. Therefore, its dual image is a point incident with an edge and with the exterior B–P through the opposite edge, that is, the intersection-point of this B-P with the edge. The dual image of the median-plane CDT is the intersection-point of the edge EF in T_1 with the exterior B-P through the opposite edge GH. Thus, the fact that the six median-planes pass through the centroid yields, after the dual transformation, the following statement:

In a tetrahedron the six intersection-points of edges with exterior B-P through the opposite edge belong to the same plane (are coplanar).

This theorem is a generalization for tetrahedrons of the corresponding property of triangles, namely: in a triangle the three intersection-points of sides with the exterior bisectors of opposite angles belong to the same straight line (are collinear).

We pass now to detailed study of the most important three-dimensional configuration, the tetrahedron, by purely geometric considerations and without using the dual transformation.

CHAPTER 20

Tetrahedron

A closed surface such as a sphere divides the tridimensional space into two parts separated by the surface. To clarify the meaning of the term "separation", consider two points A and B such that the point A belongs to the interior of the closed surface, while the point B is exterior to the surface. Any path joining A to B necessarily traverses the closed surface, piercing it at some point; and it is precisely this fact which characterizes the division of the space into two parts separated by a closed surface. The part of space interior to the surface is finite and it is said to be *bounded* by the surface. The exterior part is infinite.

A closed surface may be formed by intersecting planes and in this case its interior is bounded by plane polygonal faces, whose edges belong to inter-section-lines of different planes. These faces, connected at their common edges, form *dihedral* angles. They meet also at common vertices, where their planes form *polyhedral* angles. The closed surface formed by intersecting planes is called a *polyhedron*. A polyhedron consists of vertices, edges and faces as well as of plane, dihedral, and polyhedral angles.

The simplest polyhedron is that one which has the least number of faces being formed by the least number of intersecting planes. Now we know that the configuration formed by three planes does not cut off a finite part of space: three planes form an *infinite* trihedral angle. Therefore, four planes are needed to form the simplest polyhedron and, indeed, cutting a trihedral angle by a fourth plane which does not pass through its vertex, we obtain a polyhedron with four faces, each of which is a triangle. Thus, the simplest polyhedron is a triangular pyramid with four triangular faces, as its name, *Tetrahedron*, indicates (Greek: tetra = four and hedra = base, face). In this chapter we use the symbol "TH" as an abbreviation for the word "tetrahedron".

TH plays in space the same role of fundamental geometric configuration as the triangle does in the plane. Some of a TH's properties are spatial generalizations of corresponding properties of a triangle, but others are new.

A plane quadrilateral can be considered as a degenerated TH which has four coplanar vertices. Therefore, properties of a quadrilateral are limiting cases of a TH's properties when the fourth vertex of a TH is brought down on to the plane of the opposite face.

A TH has four trihedral angles at four vertices, six interior and six exterior dihedral angles at six edges, and twelve plane angles in four triangular faces. Its six edges are coplanar by groups of three and also concurrent at the vertices by groups of three. Two skew (non-coplanar and therefore non-concurrent) edges are called *opposite*. There are three pairs of such opposite edges because four points (vertices) A, B, C, D form three different combinations of two pairs of points: AB and CD, AC and BD, AD and BC (Fig. 1).

Midlines, Medians, Centroid

A triangle possesses four remarkable points: *centroid* (intersection-point of medians), *incenter* (center of inscribed circle), *circumcenter* (center of circumscribed circle) and *orthocenter* (intersection-point of altitudes). It is natural to ask whether an arbitrary TH possesses the same remarkable points? Before answering this question we must define the altitudes, the medians and inscribed and circumscribed spheres of a TH.

A perpendicular dropped from a vertex on the opposite face is called the altitude of a TH. A TH has four altitudes and, as we will prove later, in general these four altitudes do not meet: in general a TH has no orthocenter. But a particular class of TH's does exist such that a TH belonging to this class has an orthocenter, its altitudes being concurrent straight lines. Such a TH is called *orthocentric*. We will study orthocentric TH's later.

A sphere tangent to four faces of a TH and belonging to its interior is called *inscribed* into a TH. A sphere incident with the four vertices of a TH is called *circumscribed* to a TH. These two spheres exist for every TH. Thus, each TH possesses an incenter and an circumcenter. We shall discuss them later and now begin the study of remarkable points of a TH.

Centroid

The midpoints of edges play an important role, as we saw in Chapter 15 where a metric property of a TH was studied by anticipation. The segments joining the midpoints of opposite edges are called *midlines*, and there are three midlines in a TH. Theorem XXII, Chapter 15, states that the sum of squares of six edges of a TH is equal to four times the sum of squares of three midlines.

The definition of medians is more intricate and to generalize correctly the concept of a median of a triangle, we observe that in the case of a TH the part of the boundary opposite to a vertex is an area: namely, the area of the triangular face, and as such it has no midpoint at all. Therefore, the median of a triangle is to be redefined as a segment joining the centroid of a side to the opposite vertex. The centroid of a segment of straight line is, indeed, at the midpoint of this segment. In the case of a TH, the side is replaced by a face and the centroid of the face plays the role of the midpoint. We define therefore the median of a TH as a segment joining a vertex to the centroid of the opposite face.

We complete the definition of medians by introducing the so-called median-planes. Consider a pair of opposite edges, for instance AB and CD (Fig. 1) with midpoints M and N. The edge AB and the midpoint N of the opposite edge CD define a median-plane ABN. Likewise, the edge CD and the mid-point M of the opposite edge AB define another median-plane CDM. The intersections of these planes with the faces of TH define the medians AN, BN, CM, DM of *faces* (triangles) ACD, BCD, ABC, ABD. On the other

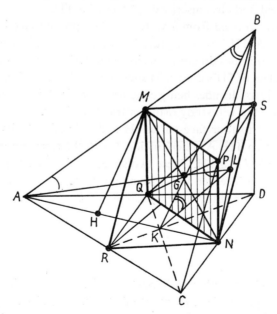

Fig. 20.1

hand, the midline MN belongs to the intersection-line of two median-planes which pass through two opposite edges, AB and CD.

Through each vertex pass three different median-planes. They are collinear and their common intersection-line is the median of the TH through this vertex. Therefore, the four medians of a TH are intersection-lines of four groups of three median-planes each. On the other hand, each median-plane contains two medians of TH. Take, for instance, the median-plane ABN (Fig. 1). It contains the medians AN, BN of two faces ACD and BCD. The centroids of these two faces of TH belong to the medians AN, BN and they are on them at one-third of median from the side CD. Denoting these centroids by K and L, we have

$$NL/BN = NK/AN = KL/AB = \tfrac{1}{3}.$$

Joining A to L and B to K, we obtain the two medians AL, BK of the TH which belong to the median-plane ABN. We conclude that any two medians of TH intersect. We set now to prove the THEOREM: *The four medians of a TH intersect in their common point which lies on each median at one quarter of its length from the face and at three quarters from the vertex of the TH.*

Denoting the intersection-point of medians AL and BK by G, we first observe that the segment KL, dividing the two sides AN, BN of the triangle ABN proportionally, is parallel to the third side AB of this triangle. Therefore, the transversals AL and BK of parallel lines AB and KL form equal angles with two parallels: in two triangles GKL and ABG the angles $\hat{A}$ and $\hat{L}$, as well as $\hat{B}$ and $\hat{K}$ are equal, $\hat{A} = \hat{L}, \hat{B} = \hat{K}$. Thus, these two triangles are similar and we have the proportions

$$GL/AG = GK/BG = KL/AB = \tfrac{1}{3},$$

which proves that the point of intersection of two medians lies on each of these two medians at one quarter of its length from the corresponding face.

On the other hand, any two medians meet. Therefore, the points where three medians intersect the fourth median cannot be different: they coincide at the point, on each median, which is at one quarter of the median's length from the face. The theorem is proved. The point G common to all four medians of a TH is called the *centroid* of the TH. We state also that all six median-planes of a TH pass through the centroid of TH.

Also, the three midlines must pass through the centroid because they are intersection-lines of median-planes; thus the point common to all these planes is necessarily the common point of three midlines. It is not difficult to prove that *the midlines bisect each other at the centroid*. Consider the midpoint H of the segment AK and join it to the midpoint M of the edge AB. The segment HM is parallel to KB and equal to $\frac{1}{2}$KB. Consider now the segment KG in the triangle HMN: the point K is the midpoint of side HN and the straight line KB is parallel to the side HM. Therefore, this line bisects the side MN, and the point G (centroid) is the midpoint of the midline MN.

Thus, the centroid of a TH is the midpoint for all three midlines and it belongs to seven segments: four medians and three midlines. The midlines, grouped by two, are diagonals of three parallelograms the vertices of which are the midpoints of the edges. This brings us to the consideration of three skew quadrilaterals formed by four edges of a TH, when a pair of opposite edges is omitted. Suppose we discard the two opposite edges AC and BD (Fig. 1). The remaining four edges form a skew quadrilateral ABCD whose two diagonals AC and BD are two skew straight lines. The four midpoints M, N, P, Q form a parallelogram because MP and NQ are equal and parallel: each of these two segments is indeed equal and parallel to $\frac{1}{2}$AC. Likewise each of the two segments MQ and NP is equal and parallel to $\frac{1}{2}$BD. The midlines MN and PQ of the TH are diagonals of this parallelogramm MNPQ and they bisect each other. Adding to this picture the two midpoint R and S of edges AC and BD and joining them to the four vertices of the parallelogram MNPQ, we obtain an *octahedron* MNPQRS, inscribed into the TH and whose vertices are midpoints of the edges of the TH.

This octahedron is characterized by many special features: four of its triangular faces belong to the faces of the TH and each of the four other faces is equal and parallel to one of the first four faces. For instance, the face MPS is equal and parallel to the face NQR which is similar to the face ACD of the TH and belongs to this face. The centroid G of the TH is a center of symmetry for the inscribed octahedron, and its three diagonals bisect each other at this point. The TH itself might be very irregular, but the inscribed octahedron is always symmetrical. This fact represents a perfect analogy to the circumstance that the inscribed quadrilateral formed by the midpoints of four sides of an arbitrary plane quadrilateral is always a parallelogram.

The six midpoints of edges of a TH define $C_2^{(6)} = 15$ straight lines. The twelve edges of the inscribed octahedron and three midlines are segments of these 15 straight lines, so that the edges of the octahedron can be defined as segments joining the midpoints of edges of the TH and lying in its faces.

The inscribed octahedron divides the interior of the TH into five regions: four small tetrahedrons lying between the octahedron and the vertices of the TH and the interior of the octahedron. The four small tetrahedrons are equal to each other; they are similar to the large TH from which they are cut off by planes parallel to the faces and passing through the three midpoints of three edges of each of four trihedral angles of the TH. These four planes are called *midplanes* of the TH. The ratio of linear dimensions of a small tetrahedron to those of the large TH is equal to one half. Therefore, the ratio of their volumes is $(\frac{1}{2})^3 = \frac{1}{8}$ and the total volume of four small tetrahedrons is equal to half the volume of the large TH. Thus, the volume of the inscribed octahedron is equal to half the volume of the TH into which it is inscribed. In this too the inscribed octahedron is analogous to the inscribed parallelogram: the area of the parallelogram inscribed into a quadrilateral is equal to half the area of this quadrilateral. It is easy to prove this proposition by using the fact that the vertices of the parallelogram are at the midpoints of sides of the quadrilateral.

Circumcenter

The uniqueness of the sphere circumscribed to a TH can be beduced from the fact that through four given non-coplanar points passes one and only one perfectly determined sphere. We set out to prove this fact. The center of a sphere passing through four given points is equidistant from them. Therefore, we must study the following question: what is the locus of points equidistant from *four* given points? If this locus reduces to a single point the uniqueness of the sphere through four given points will be established. Let us first discuss a simpler problem: find the locus of points equidistant from *two* given points A and B.

In a plane the locus of points equidistant from two given points A, B is the perpendicular MN to the segment AB through its midpoint M. Rotating

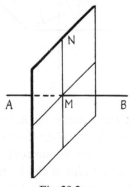

Fig. 20.2

this plane configuration (Fig. 2) around the straight line AB, we obtain a plane perpendicular to the segment AB and passing through its midpoint M. This plane is the locus of points equidistant from two given points A, B because it is described by the perpendicular bisector MN of the segment AB. In other words, the locus of points equidistant from A and B is a *plane* perpendicular to AB and passing through its midpoint. Such a plane is called a *perpendicular bisector plane* of the segment considered.

We take now *three* points A, B, C and ask the same question: find the locus of points equidistant from three vertices of a triangle ABC. In the plane of this triangle there is only one point equidistant from A, B and C: it is the circumcenter of this triangle ABC. But our question concerns the points in space. The locus in question must belong to two planes through the midpoints of AB and AC and which are respectively perpendicular to these two sides of the triangle ABC (Fig. 3). Therefore, it is a straight line: namely, the intersection-line of two perpendicular bisector planes of AB and AC. All the points of this straight line are equidistant from A and B on one hand, and from A and C on the other hand. Therefore, they are also equidistant from B and C which proves that the locus belongs also to a third perpendicular bisector plane: namely, the plane perpendicular to the side BC of the triangle ABC and passing through the midpoint of this side BC.

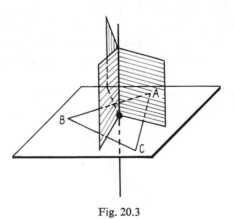

Fig. 20.3

Therefore, we conclude: Three perpendicular bisector planes of three sides of a triangle ABC pass through a straight line which is perpendicular to the plane ABC and passes through the circumcenter of the triangle ABC. Any point of this straight line, as a point of the locus, is equidistant from three given points A, B, C and, as such, can be taken as the center of a sphere through three points A, B, C. We see now that there are an *infinite* number of spheres passing through *three* given points.

Consider now *four* points which are not coplanar and form, therefore, a TH. The locus of points equidistant from all four vertices A, B, C, D of the TH is obtained if we choose among points equidistant from A, B, C those which are also equidistant from C and D. Now the locus of points equidistant from the vertices A, B, C of the face ABC is a straight *line,* while the locus of points equidistant from C and D is the perpendicular bisector *plane* through the midpoint of CD. The points equidistant from four points A, B, C, D are points common to the straight line and to the plane, but there can be one and only one point common to a plane and a line. Thus, there is one and only one point equidistant from four given points and this point is the center of the *unique* sphere circumscribed to a TH the vertices of which are precisely the four given points. It is called the *circumcenter* of a TH.

The circumcenter of a TH is equidistant from three points of each of four triplets of points: (A, B, C); (B, C, D); (C, D, A); (D, A, B). Therefore, it belongs to four straight lines perpendicular to four faces of the TH and passing through the circumcenters of these faces. These four perpendiculars to the faces through their circumcenters are concurrent at the circumcenter of the TH. Moreover, the circumcenter of a TH lies in each of six perpendicular bisector planes of the six edges of the TH because it is equidistant from the two extremities of each edge. We state that the six perpendicular bisector planes of the edges of a TH pass through a common point instead of defining $C_3^{(6)} = 20$ different points. Thus, four straight lines and six planes meet at the circumcenter of a TH, each straight line being an intersection-line for three planes among six, and every plane containing two of four lines. A straight line perpendicular to the plane of the triangle ABC and passing through its circumcenter is called the *axis of the face ABC,* if the triangle ABC belongs to a TH. The perpendicular bisector plane of a segment AB is sometimes called the *mediator of AB.* Using this terminology, we can say that six mediators of edges and four axes of faces of a TH pass through its circumcenter.

A detailed study of the TH is out of the scope of this book. This is why we are obliged to omit the proofs of many properties of the TH formulated and discussed here. This is the case of certain metric relations in a TH discovered by different authors. The first example of such as important metric relation is the expression of the length of radius of the circumscribed sphere in terms of the lengths of six edges. It is well known that a TH is perfectly defined by its six edges, so that the measures of all its elements can be expressed in terms of lengths of its six edges. The expression of R, radius of the circumscribed sphere, was found by Von Staudt. It gives the value of the product 6VR where V is the volume of the TH, in the form of area of a triangle whose sides are equal to products of lengths of opposite edges of the TH. Denoting the opposite edges by same letter, Latin for one and Greek for the opposite edge, for instance a and α, b and β, c and γ, where a, b and c denote three coplanar edges, we consider a triangle with edges αa, βb, γc and form the corresponding expression of the area A for this triangle. It is plain that dimensionwise A is not an area, but a square of an area because the sides of the auxiliary triangle αa, βb, γc are in fact areas. Von Staudt's formula

$$6RV = A \tag{1}$$

gives the length R as a ratio A/6V of square of an area to a volume.

We know how to find the expression A in terms of αa, βb, γc, but what about V? The expression of the volume V in terms of $a, \alpha, b, \beta, c, \gamma$ is difficult to deduce and we shall merely reproduce it here:

$$
\begin{aligned}
144 \cdot V^2 = {}& a^2\alpha^2(b^2 + \beta^2 + c^2 + \gamma^2 - a^2 - \alpha^2) \\
&+ b^2\beta^2(c^2 + \gamma^2 + a^2 + \alpha^2 - b^2 - \beta^2) \\
&+ c^2\gamma^2(a^2 + \alpha^2 + b^2 + \beta^2 - c^2 - \gamma^2) \\
&- a^2b^2c^2 - a^2\beta^2\gamma^2 - b^2\gamma^2\alpha^2 - c^2\alpha^2\beta^2 .
\end{aligned}
$$

This formula implies that the three edges a, b, c are *coplanar* and α, β, γ are concurrent.

Spheres Tangent to Four Faces

To facilitate the study of different cases which are encountered when the number of spheres tangent to all four faces of a TH is discussed, we shall first review the question of circles tangent to three sides of a triangle from a new, purely algebraic point of view; then we shall study the straight lines and planes whose intersections define the centers of spheres tangent to four faces; finally, we shall apply the algebraic method in order to classify the different cases.

A triangle ABC divides the plane into seven regions which are of three different types: interior (denoted in what follows by I), three trunkated angles (denoted by tA, tB, tC) bounded by one side and the extensions of two other sides, and three exterior angles (denoted by eA, eB, eC) bounded by extensions of two sides (Fig. 4).

Denoting the lengths of sides opposite to angles $\hat{A}$, $\hat{B}$, $\hat{C}$ by s_1, s_2, s_3 and the altitudes corresponding to them by h_1, h_2, h_3 respectively, we can express the area A of the triangle ABC as $\frac{1}{2}s_1h_1 = \frac{1}{2}s_2h_2 = \frac{1}{2}s_3h_3 = A$, so that $2A/s_1 = h_1$ and likewise $2A/s_2 = h_2$, $2A/s_3 = h_3$.

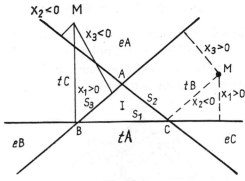

Fig. 20.4

The position of any point M of the plane ABC with respect to the triangle ABC might be characterized by three numbers x_1, x_2, x_3 which represent the distances of this point M to three straight lines BC, CA and AB respectively. Introducing these distances, we must distinguish between two half-planes into which a straight line divides the plane. This can be done by ascribing positive and negative values to the distances x_1, x_2, x_3 and considering such a distance as positive if the point M is on the same side of the straight line as the vertex of the triangle non incident with this line. If, for instance, the point M is on the same side of the line BC as the vertex A, then its distance x_1 to the line BC is a positive number (Fig. 4), but x_2 is negative.

Since the position of a point in a plane is completely characterized by its two coordinates, it is plain that three numbers x_1, x_2, x_3 cannot be independent and must verify a relation. This relation is easily obtained by joining M to the three vertices of triangle ABC and considering the areas of the three triangles ABM, BCM, CAM together with the area ABC. In doing so, we must study three separate cases when M belongs to the interior I of the triangle ABC, either to a region of the type tA, or to that of the type eA.

If M belongs to I, all three distances x_1, x_2, x_3 are positive (Fig. 5) and the areas of triangles BCM, CAM, ABM are equal to $\frac{1}{2}s_1x_1$, $\frac{1}{2}s_2x_2$, $\frac{1}{2}s_3x_3$. On the other hand, adding these three areas, we obtain the area of the triangle

ABC, that is, A. Therefore, the relation verified by three distances is

$$2A = s_1x_1 + s_2x_2 + s_3x_3.$$

Dividing all the terms of this relation by 2A and observing that the quotient $s_1/2A$ is equal to the reciprocal of the altitude h_1, $s_1/2A = h_1^{-1}$, we can also write this relation as follows:

$$x_1/h_1 + x/h_2 + x_3/h_3 = 1.\qquad(3)$$

The relation (3) solves the question of circles tangent to the sides of a triangle. It holds for all positions of the point M in the plane and before we apply it to the study of tangent circles, we must finish the proof of its general validity by considering M in eA and in tB.

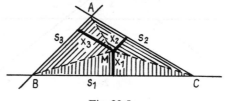

Fig. 20.5

If M belongs to a truncated angle, for instance to tB (Fig. 4), two of three distances remain positive but the third is negative. So, when M is in tB, we have positive x_1 and x_3, but x_2 is negative. At the same time the areas ABM, BCM, CAM change their configurations relative to the area ABC and instead of the relation ABC = ABM + BCM + CAM which characterizes the case when M is inside the triangle ABC, we have the relation

$$\text{ABC} = \text{ABM} + \text{BCM} - \text{ACM}.$$

These four areas are always positive and therefore their expressions in terms of sides and distances are: BCM = $\frac{1}{2}s_1x_1$, ABM = $\frac{1}{2}s_3x_3$, while ACM = $-\frac{1}{2}s_2x_2$ because x_2 is a negative number. Substituting these expressions into the relation between areas, we obtain again our fundamental relation (3).

When M belongs to an exterior angle, for instance to eA, two of three distances are negative and only one remains positive; but the expression of the area ABC in terms of areas ABM, BCM, CAM is again such that the relation (3) is finally obtained. Take, for instance, M in eA (Fig. 4): ABC is now equal to BCM − CAM − ABM = $\frac{1}{2}s_1x_1 - (-\frac{1}{2}s_2x_2) - (-\frac{1}{2}s_3x_3)$ since x_2 and x_3 are negative. Therefore, the relation (3) is justified for *any* position of M in the plane ABC.

If a circle is tangent to three sides of a triangle, three distances of its center to the sides become equal (equal to the radius r of this circle). Since the distances, as represented by numbers x_1, x_2, x_3, are algebraic quantities which may sometimes be negative, whereas the radius r is a positive quantity, we have in general $|x_1| = |x_2| = |x_3| = r$; that is, $r = x$, if x is positive, but $r = -x$, if x is negative.

Consider now the inscribed circle which, by definition, belongs to the region I. For this circle's center (that is, for the *incenter*), we have all three distances positive so that $x_1 = x_2 = x_3 = r$ and the general relation (3) yields the known expression $r(s_1 + s_2 + s_3) = 2A$ which becomes $rs = A$, if the perimeter $s_1 + s_2 + s_3$ is denoted by $2s$. The fact that (3) yields for r a positive value proves the *existence* of the incenter and with it of the inscribed circle.

We study now the question of the existence of escribed circles, placing the point M (center of such a circle) in the region tA. Three distances of the center of an escribed circle, belonging to the truncated angle tA, are characterized by $-x_1 = x_2 = x_3 = r_1$, where r_1 denotes the radius of this escribed circle (x_1 is a negative number, $x_1 < 0$). Substituting r_1 into (3) instead of x_2 and x_3, while x_1 is replaced by $-r_1$, we obtain the following relation: $r_1(-s_1 + s_2 + s_3) = 2A$, where the value of the parentheses $s_2 + s_3 - s_1$ is positive since the sum of any two sides of a triangle is greater than the third side. Therefore, we find for each of three truncated angles tA, tB, tC an escribed circle and their radii are expressed as follows:

$$r_1 = 2A/(-s_1 + s_2 + s_3); \quad r_2 = 2A/(s_1 - s_2 + s_3);$$
$$r_3 = 2A/(s_1 + s_2 - s_3).$$

These expressions are identical with those obtained in Chapter 15, pp. 669, 700.

Consider the exterior angles eA, eB, eC, where, as we know, no circle can be constructed tangent to all three sides of ABC. This fact is evident geometrically, but it is important to correlate it with (3). Suppose that a point belonging to eC, for instance, is equidistant from the sides of ABC. Denoting the absolute value of the distance by R (radius of circle tangent to three sides of ABC), we must have $x_1 = -R$, $x_2 = -R$, $x_3 = R$ because x_1 and x_2 are negative for a point located in eC. We compute R with the aid of (3), substituting there $-R$ for x_1 and x_2, R for x_3. This substitution leads to a *contradiction:* $\quad R(s_3 - s_1 - s_2) = 2A,$

since a positive number 2A cannot be equal to a negative number standing in the lefthand member. The first factor R of this member is positive, while the second factor, namely $s_3 - s_1 - s_2$, is negative because a side of a triangle is always shorter than the sum of two other sides. Thus, our hypothesis (the supposition of the existence in the region eC of a point equidistant from three straight lines AB, BC, CA, which underlies the introduction and the use of the symbol R), is wrong: there cannot be a circle tangent to three sides of ABC with the center belonging to the region eA.

Here we meet again an example of backfiring to which leads the use of algebraical symbolism in the case of a wrong initial assumption: we try to find a numerical value for the radius of a *non-existing* circle, that is, we try to measure a non-existent object, applying algebraical formulas. The answer is obtained, but by its very nature it constitutes a refutation of our wrong assumption: the radius of a circle is essentially a positive quantity and we obtain a negative value for it which is impossible. In other cases, when a negative answer has a meaning, as well as a positive solution, the wrong initial assumption leads to a complex number instead of a real answer, pointing again to our error. It is curious to observe this backfiring of algebraical symbolism in action: very often an inexperienced mind asks algebra to answer meaningless or impossible questions without knowing that he is wrong. The algebraical symbolism reveals itself as much more clever than its user: it backfires, clearly indicating the meaninglessness of the question raised. This ability of mathematical symbolism to correct logical errors in human thinking may seem mysterious, but its explanation is simple: the invention by Vieta of algebraical symbolism has opened the way to the accumulation of results of mathematical work of many generations. The mathematics of today with its symbolisms of different kinds synthesizes the collective experience accumulated by mankind in the domain of thought during many thousands of years. There is nothing surprising in the fact that the collective experience can correct individual errors. We could say, paraphrasing the same explanation, that Vieta's or Newton's thinking is not extinguished, has not lost its vitality. It continues its wonderful work and continues to live and act in the disguised form of mathematical methods and formulas. In other words, what backfires in algebraical symbolic form is the thinking of powerful brains who have created this symbolism, perpetuating thus their knowledge for the benefit of all of us.

To define the center of a sphere tangent to four planes, we first study the locus of points equidistant from two given planes. If they are parallel, this locus is a third plane parallel to two given planes and passing through the midpoint of their common perpendicular. This particular case does not interest us because in a TH no two planes (faces) are parallel. If two given planes form a dihedral angle, the locus of points equidistant from the faces of the dihedral angle is a plane through the edge of the dihedral angle and which bisects this angle. Two planes form two supplementary dihedral angles and their bisector-planes are perpendicular to each other. One of them lies completely outside of the TH, having in common with it only the edge of the TH. It is called an exterior bisector-plane. The other passes through the TH's interior and intersects the opposite edge at a point between two vertices of the TH. It is called an interior bisector-plane. Thus, a TH has twelve bisector-planes of its dihedral angles, six interior and six exterior.

At a vertex of the TH meet six bisector-planes of three dihedral angles formed by three faces of the trihedral angle belonging to this vertex. Three among them are interior bisectors and they pass through a straight line which is called *axis* of the trihedral angle. Two interior bisectors intersect indeed along a straight line and each point on this line is equidistant from three faces of the trihedral angle. Therefore, this line belongs also to the third interior bisector associated with the trihedral angle. Thus, the *locus of points equidistant from three faces of a trihedral angle is a straight line, namely the axis of this trihedral angle.*

Inscribed Sphere

Consider now (Fig. 6) the axis AH of the trihedral angle at the vertex A of the TH ABCD and the interior bisector plane CDK through the edge CD. The point H, where the axis intersects the opposite face BCD, is below the plane CDK while the vertex A is above it. Therefore, AH pierces the plane CDK at a point I. This point I is equidistant from three faces which meet at A and at the same time is it equidistant from two faces ACD and BCD because it belongs to the interior bisector plane through the edge CD.

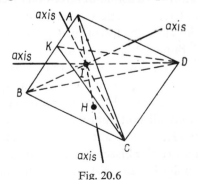

Fig. 20.6

Therefore, the point I is equidistant from all four faces of the TH. It is called the *incenter* and is the center of a sphere tangent to four of the TH and comprised entirely inside the TH. The sphere is called *inscribed* and we see that there is one and only one inscribed sphere.

Since the incenter is equidistant from all four faces, it belongs to all six interior bisector planes as well as to all four axes of trihedral angles of the TH. In other words, the *four axes are concurrent straight lines and their common point is the incenter*. The radius r of the inscribed sphere can be expressed in terms of edges, observing that the volume of the TH can be subdivided into four parts, joining by axes the incenter to four vertices of TH. Four smaller tetrahedrons ABCI, BCDI, CDAI and DABI are thus formed and the volume V of ABCD is the sum of their volumes. Anticipating the study of volumes, we use here the expression of the volume of a tetrahedron, namely the formula $V = Sh/3$, where S and h denote the area of a face and the corresponding altitude of the TH. The four small tetrahedrons have the same altitude r (radius of the inscribed sphere), if the faces of the large TH ABCD are considered as their bases. Denoting the areas of triangles BCD, CDA, DAB, ABC by S_1, S_2, S_3, S_4 respectively, we have

$$3V = rS_1 + rS_2 + rS_3 + rS_4 = r (S_1 + S_2 + S_3 + S_4),$$

so that

$$r = 3V/(S_1 + S_2 + S_3 + S_4).$$

Escribed Spheres

Severing the interior of the TH from each of its four trihedral angles, we consider four truncated trihedral angles. These infinite regions, bounded at the top by a face and laterally by extensions of three other faces, are exterior to the TH. The axis AE of the trihedral angle at A passes through the corresponding truncated part of it (Fig. 7). At the top of such a truncated trihedral angle and at three edges of the TH's face BCD are located three exterior dihedral angles whose bisector-planes (exterior with respect to the TH) intersect the axis AE at their common point E. This point E is indeed equidistant from three planes, faces of the trihedral angle, because it belongs to the axis of this trihedral angle. But it is also equidistant from each one of these planes and from the fourth face BCD of the TH, which is at the top of the truncated angle, because this point belongs to the exterior bisector-plane of the corresponding dihedral angle. Therefore, the point E is equidistant from all four faces of the TH and belongs also to two other exterior bisector-planes. We conclude that three interior and three exterior bisector-planes pass through the point E which is called the *excenter*. Thus, it is the center of a sphere tangent to four faces of the TH and located outside of it, namely in the truncated trihedral angle. At

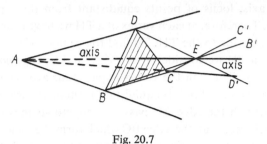

Fig. 20.7

the top of the truncated trihedral angle we have also three exterior *trihedral* angles with vertices at B, C, D. Their axes BE, CE, DE, called *exterior axes*, also pass through the excenter. Thus, *one interior and three exterior axes meet at an excenter*. We resume our discussion as follows:

There are four escribed spheres and four excenters, one in each of four truncated trihedral angles. They are analogous to three escribed circles of a triangle which also belong to truncated angles.

Opposite (with respect to the interior of the TH) to a truncated trihedral angle is situated the exterior trihedral angle formed by the extensions of three faces of the TH in the opposite direction. No sphere located inside an exterior trihedral angle can be tangent to the fourth face of the TH because this fourth plane lies completely outside of the exterior trihedral angle, being separated from it by the TH. Therefore, *there is no sphere tangent to four faces of TH and located in an exterior trihedral angle*.

In all we have considered up to now nine regions of space among fifteen determined by four planes (faces) of a TH: interior, four truncated and four exterior trihedral angles. It is easy to verify that in all there are fifteen regions defined by four planes: at a vertex of the TH pass three planes which divide the space into eight separated regions. The fourth plane subdivides each one of them, except the exterior trihedral angle opposite to this plane, into two. Thus, we obtain in all $7 \cdot 2 + 1 = 15$ regions.

The remaining six regions are related to the six edges: to each *interior* dihedral angle corresponds an equal and opposite exterior dihedral angle which is its "vertical" dihedral angle. This vertical dihedral angle is truncated on both sides of the edge by two other planes (faces) of the TH, so that the region of space thus delimitated has the shape of an irregular roof with its ridge at the edge (Fig. 8).

At each vertex of a TH the three planes which meet at this vertex divide the space into four pairs of equal and vertical trihedral angles. Each pair possesses one axis, locus of points equidistant from three planes incident with the vertex. Therefore, at each vertex of a TH we have four axes: one interior and three exterior to the TH. To find the centers of spheres tangent to all four faces of a TH we consider a vertex, A, and an edge *non incident* with it, BC for instance. Through the vertex A pass four axes which, considered together, form the locus of points equidistant from three faces of the trihedral angle at A. Through the edge BC pass two bisector-planes of exterior and interior dihedral angles at the edge BC which form the locus of points equidistant from the two faces incident with the edge BC, one of which is opposite to A. A point equidistant from all four faces must belong at the same time to one of four axes through A and to one of two bisector-planes through BC. Therefore, the center of a sphere tangent to four faces of the TH must be a point of intersection of one of four axes and of one of two bisector-planes we are considering. The maximum number of points defined by intersections of four lines and two planes being eight, we find there can be no more than eight spheres tangent to four faces of a TH.

We know already than five of them are always there: one inscribed and four escribed spheres. Therefore, in the six twice truncated exterior dihedral

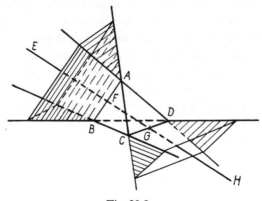

Fig. 20.8

angles we can find at most three tangent spheres. Let us call these regions *roof*. The six roofs can be grouped into three pairs of opposite roofs because there are three pairs of opposite edges. In the Fig. 8 two opposite roofs are drawn, their ridges being opposite edges AB and CD. The interior bisector-planes through AB and CD belong to these two roofs and therefore their intersection line traverses both of them. This straight line EFGH, called an *axis of two opposite roofs*, is locus of points which on one hand are equidistant from faces ACD and BDC, and on the other hand are equidistant from faces ABC and ABD. Consider now the exterior bisector-plane through the edge BC. This plane passes through the opposite roofs we are discussing and it is the locus of points equidistant from the faces ABC and DBC. The center of a sphere tangent to four faces and located in either of two opposite roofs must belong to their axis EH and to the exterior bisector-plane through BC. But a plane and a straight line intersect in a single point and, therefore, there can be only one such point on the axis EH: *there can be only one tangent sphere in two opposite roofs.*

This discussion explains the fact that in six roofs there can be at most three tangent spheres. We will now find out that there are four different cases: no tangent sphere at all in six roofs, the total number of tangent spheres being five; one tangent sphere in six roofs and a total of six; two tangent spheres belonging to different pairs of opposite roofs and a total of seven tangent spheres; and finally one tangent sphere in each of three pairs of opposite roofs and thus in all eight tangent spheres.

To discuss these four cases we use the distances from faces as in the example of circles tangent to sides of a triangle. As for a triangle, we consider a point M anywhere in space and denote by x_1, x_2, x_3 and x_4 its distances from four faces BCD, CDA, DAB and ABC respectively. Thus, the corresponding altitudes h_1, h_2, h_3, h_4 pass through the vertices A, B, C, D, the subscripts 1, 2, 3, 4 indicating the alphabetical order of letters marking the vertices. A distance of the point M from a face is considered positive if M belongs to the same half-space with respect to the face's plane as the vertex opposite to the face; it is negative if the face's plane separates M and the opposite vertex. The faces areas are denoted by S_1, S_2, S_3, S_4, where the subscripts are those of opposite vertices.

The fifteen domains into which the four planes of a TH divide the space belong to four different classes: the interior of the TH, denoted in what follows by I, constitutes a class by itself; the six roofs, denoted by R, also form a class; the four truncated trihedral angles, denoted by TT, belong to a third class; finally, the last class contains the four exterior trihedral angles denoted by ET. These four classes of regions are characterized by the number of negative distances among the four distances x_1, x_2, x_3, x_4.

If the point M belongs to the interior I of the TH, all four numbers x_k are positive. When it traverses a face, the sign of one distance changes and the point penetrates into a region of the class TT. Therefore, if M is in TT, three distances remain positive but the fourth is negative. A roof is adjacent to a truncated trihedral angle, so that when our traveling point M leaves a TT and enters an R, it traverses again one of four planes of the TH. Thus, a point which belongs to a region of class R has two positive and two negative distances. Finally, an exterior trihedral angle ET is surrounded by roofs, so that a point in ET has only one positive distance, three others being negative. No point of space can have four negative distances. The vertices have three vanishing distances each. Points on the edges, other than vertices, have two vanishing distances and those in the faces, other than points of edges, are characterized by one vanishing distance. In what follows we do not consider points belonging to four planes of the TH, but only points interior to one of fifteen regions I, TT, ET, R.

The position of a point in space is completely determined by its three coordinates. On the other hand the four distances just introduced also characterize the position of a point. Therefore, they cannot be independent and must verify a relation. This relation is easy to find when the point M belongs to the interior I of the TH. Joining it to the vertices, we form four tetrahedrons ABCM, BCDM, CDAM and DABM (see Fig. 9) with volumes equal to $x_4 S_4/3$, $x_1 S_1/3$, $x_2 S_2/3$ and $x_3 S_3/3$ respectively. The sum of these volumes is equal to the volume V of the TH ABCD and, therefore, the four distances x_1, x_2, x_3, x_4 verify the relation

$$x_1 S_1 + x_2 S_2 + x_3 S_3 + x_4 S_4 = 3V. \tag{4}$$

This particular case was already deduced and it enabled us to find the expression of the radius of inscribed sphere because, if the point M coincides with the center of the insribed sphere, then $x_1 = x_2 = x_3 = x_4 = r$.

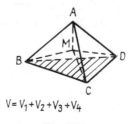

$$V = V_1 + V_2 + V_3 + V_4$$

Fig. 20.9

We have now to justify (4) for all possible positions of the point M in any of fifteen regions I, TT, ET, R. To do this, it is sufficient to consider three cases when the point M is in TT, either in ET or in R. Denoting the volumes of four tetrahedrons BCDM, CDAM, DABM, ABCM by V_1, V_2, V_3, V_4 respectively, we will study the relations between the five volumes V, V_1, V_2, V_3, V_4, where V is the volume of the tetrahedron ABCD.

As Fig. 10 shows, if the point M is in a TT, the volume V is equal to the difference between the sum of three volumes V_k and the fourth volume of the same type. For instance, if M is in the trihedral angle with the vertex A but not in I, then $V + V_1 = V_2 + V_3 + V_4$ and, therefore, $V = V_2 + V_3 + V_4 - V_1$.

Now, for this position of the point M we have a negative distance x_1, so that the expression of the volume $3V_1$ is $|x_1| S_1 = -x_1 S_1$. Using it, we again obtain the relation (4), justifying it for M in any region of the type TT.

If M is in an ET, then (see Fig. 11) on one hand x_2, x_3, x_4 are negative and, on the other hand, $V = V_1 - V_2 - V_3 - V_4$, where $3V_2 = -x_2 S_2$, $3V_3 = -x_3 S_3$, $3V_4 = -x_4 S_4$. We verify easily that (4) holds also in this case.

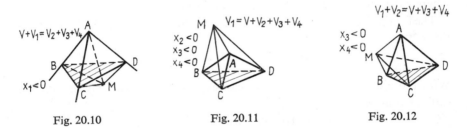

Fig. 20.10   Fig. 20.11   Fig. 20.12

Finally, if M is in an R, then two of its distances are negative and the corresponding volumes are involved with minus signs in the expression of the volume V, so that again the relation (4) holds. For instance, in Fig. 12 we have on one hand $x_3 < 0$, $x_4 < 0$ and, on the other hand, $V = V_1 + V_2 - V_3 - V_4$.

Radii of Four Escribed Spheres

We use the relation (4) in the computation of radii of *escribed* spheres, denoting them by r_1, r_2, r_3, r_4 in such a way that the radius of the sphere tangent externally to the face of area S_k is r_k for $k = 1, 2, 3, 4$. The center of this sphere has three distances positive while the fourth, namely x_k, is negative. The absolute value of these distances being equal to r_k, we have: $x_k = -r_k$, while the other three distances are equal to r_k.

Substituting these values in (4), we obtain for $k = 1, 2, 3, 4$ the four relations:

$$(-S_1 + S_2 + S_3 + S_4) r_1 = (S_1 - S_2 + S_3 + S_4) r_2$$

$$= (S_1 + S_2 - S_3 + S_4) r_3 = (S_1 + S_2 + S_3 - S_4) r_4 = 3V.$$

The reciprocals of radii r_k are therefore equal to:

$$1/r_1 = (-S_1 + S_2 + S_3 + S_4)/3V; \quad 1/r_2 = (S_1 - S_2 + S_3 + S_4)/3V;$$

$$1/r_3 = (S_1 + S_2 - S_3 + S_4)/3V; \quad 1/r_4 = (S_1 + S_2 + S_3 - S_4)/3V.$$

Adding them and recalling that $1/r = (S_1 + S_2 + S_3 + S_4)/3V$, we obtain

$$1/r_1 + 1/r_2 + 1/r_3 + 1/r_4 = 2/r,$$

where r denotes the radius of the *inscribed* sphere.

The four altitudes h_k of a TH are related to the quotients $S_k/3V$ by the relations

$$1/h_k = S_k/3V \quad (k = 1, 2, 3, 4).$$

With the aid of these relations we can express the reciprocals of our five radii as follows:

$$1/r = 1/h_1 + 1/h_2 + 1/h_3 + 1/h_4,$$

$$1/r_1 = -1/h_1 + 1/h_2 + 1/h_3 + 1/h_4; \quad 1/r_2 = 1/h_1 - 1/h_2 + 1/h_3 + 1/h_4$$

$$1/h_3 = 1/h_1 + 1/h_2 - 1/h_3 + 1/h_4; \quad 1/r_4 = 1/h_1 + 1/h_2 + 1/h_3 - 1/h_4.$$

The fact that no tangent sphere can exist in an ET is evident geometrically. It can be proved by applying the relation (4) to the computation of the radius of such a sphere. Take for instance the exterior trihedral angle at the vertex A. Since in it (Fig. 11) the distances x_2, x_3, x_4 are negative, we have $x_2 = x_3 = x_4 = -r$, while $x_1 = r$. The relation (4) becomes $3V = r (S_1 - S_2 - S_3 - S_4)$ which is impossible. Indeed, the sum of the areas of three faces of a TH being always larger than the area of the fourth face, the factor $S_1 - S_2 - S_3 - S_4$ is negative so that the product standing in the righthand member is negative, while the lefthand member is positive.

The inequality $S_1 < S_2 + S_3 + S_4$ expresses a minimum property of plane areas which is true in the most general case when the area's boundary is any closed curve. It can be formulated as follows:

Given a closed plane curve C, the area of any curved surface bounded by the curve C is larger than the plane area interior to the curve C.

This proposition is easy to deduce from the minimum property of segments of straight line, which are shortest paths between their extremities, if

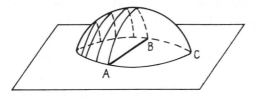

Fig. 20.13

we use the principle of Cavalieri and consider an area (plane or curved) as a sum of its sections. Intersecting the curved surface and the plane area bounded by the same closed curve C by planes perpendicular to the plane of the curve C, we find (Fig. 13) that each section AB of the plane area enclosed by C is a segment of straight line joining two points A and B of the boundary curve, while the corresponding section of the curved surface is a curved path between the same points A and B. Therefore, each section of the curved surface has a greater length than the corresponding section of the plane area. Therefore their sum, the area of the curved surface, is greater than the sum of rectilinear sections, that is the plane area enclosed by C.

We pass now to the study of tangent spheres located in roofs. To fix the ideas we denote the areas of the faces by S_1, S_2, S_3, S_4 in the order of decreasing magnitude, so that $S_1 \geqslant S_2 \geqslant S_3 \geqslant S_4$. The six roofs are characterized by the following six groups of inequalities:

(R1)	$x_1 > 0, x_2 > 0$, but $x_3 < 0, x_4 < 0$
(R1*)	$x_1 < 0, x_2 < 0$, but $x_3 > 0, x_4 > 0$
(R2)	$x_1 > 0, x_3 > 0$, but $x_2 < 0, x_4 < 0$
(R2*)	$x_1 < 0, x_3 < 0$, but $x_2 > 0, x_4 > 0$
(R3)	$x_1 > 0, x_4 > 0$, but $x_2 < 0, x_3 < 0$
(R3*)	$x_1 < 0, x_4 < 0$, but $x_2 > 0, x_3 > 0$,

where the opposite roofs are marked 1) and 1*), 2) and 2*), 3) and 3*).

The conditions of the existence of tangent spheres located in roofs are found with the aid of the relation (4) because the absolute values of distances of the center of such a tangent sphere from the face planes, that is $|x_1|$, $|x_2|$, $|x_3|$, $|x_4|$ are equal to the radius r.

Thus, replacing the distances x_1, x_2, x_3, x_4 by plus or minus r, we obtain for r equations of the general type

$$r\,(\pm S_1 \pm S_2 \pm S_3 \pm S_4) = 3V, \tag{5}$$

where two of double signs $\pm$ are plus signs, while the two other are minus signs. The equation (5) is possible only when the left hand member is positive because 3V is positive. Now, if a sphere with radius r does exist, the value of the radius is also a positive number. Therefore, when the factor in parentheses which multiplies r in the lefthand member is negative or zero, the radius r cannot have a positive and finite value which means that there cannot be a tangent sphere in this case.

Our choice of notation for the areas S_k entails the corollaries $S_1 + S_2 \geqslant S_3 + S_4$ and $S_1 + S_3 \geqslant S_2 + S_4$, where the signs of equality are not precluded. If a sphere with its center in the roof R1 is considered, the distances of the center from faces are $x_1 = r$, $x_2 = r$, $x_3 = -r$ and $x_4 = -r$, so that the equation (5) for the radius of a tangent sphere located in R1 becomes

$$r\,(S_1 + S_2 - S_3 - S_4) = 3V.$$

If the expression $S_1 + S_2 - S_3 - S_4$ vanishes, then r becomes infinite which means that there cannot be a tangent sphere in the roof R1. But, if $S_1 + S_2 > S_3 + S_4$, then r has a finite and positive value and the existence of a tangent sphere in R1 is proved. For the radius of a tangent sphere located in the opposite roof R1* we have $r\,(-S_1 - S_2 + S_3 + S_4) = 3V$ and this equation is certainly impossible because the factor of r is negative or zero. Therefore, there cannot be a tangent sphere in R1*. The same holds for the roof R2* because $-S_1 + S_2 - S_3 + S_4$ is negative or zero.

The combination $S_1 - S_2 - S_3 + S_4$ may be positive, negative or zero. If it vanishes, then we have also $-S_1 + S_2 + S_3 - S_4 = 0$, so that in such a case either one of opposite roofs R3 and R3* is devoid of a tangent sphere. The two expressions $S_1 - S_2 - S_3 + S_4$ and $-S_1 + S_2 + S_3 - S_4$, if they do not vanish, have opposite signs. Therefore, if there is a tangent sphere in one of two opposite roofs R3, R3*, there cannot be such a sphere in the opposite roof.

To study the conditions of one, two, three or none tangent spheres in six roofs let us consider the first relation $S_1 + S_2 \geqslant S_3 + S_4$. Two cases are possible: it is an exact inequality or the sign of equality holds. If it reduces to $S_1 + S_2 = S_3 + S_4$, then the inequality $S_2 \geqslant S_3$ entails also the corollary $S_1 \leqslant S_4$. But the relation $S_1 \geqslant S_4$ precludes the sign $<$ and therefore

$S_1 = S_4$, if $S_1 + S_2 = S_3 + S_4$. This result $S_1 = S_4$, combined with $S_1 \geqslant S_2 \geqslant S_3 \geqslant S_4$, proves that the condition $S_1 + S_2 = S_3 + S_4$ is satisfied only when all four faces of a TH have equal areas, that is if $S_1 = S_2 = S_3 = S_4$. It does not mean that they are congruent triangles: triangles of different shape may have the same area. It can be shown that in such an *equifacial* TH the oppsoite edges are necessarily equal, but in general the adjacent edges are of different length, so that an equifacial TH is not a regular TH (a TH is called *regular*, if all its six edges are equal, the faces being equilateral triangles).

We can state now that *an equifacial TH has no tangent spheres in roofs* because the equations (5) yield for the roofs $r = \infty$, if $S_1 = S_2 = S_3 = S_4$.

We study now the case, when $S_1 + S_2 > S_3 + S_4$. The second relation $S_1 + S_3 \geqslant S_2 + S_4$ may be an exact inequality or an equality. We discuss first the case, when $S_1 + S_3 = S_2 + S_4$. Since $S_1 \geqslant S_2$ we must have $S_3 \leqslant S_4$. But we know that $S_3 \geqslant S_4$, so that S_3 must be equal to S_4: $S_3 = S_4$. Then the relation $S_1 + S_3 = S_2 + S_4$ yields $S_1 = S_2$. Since $S_1 + S_2 > S_3 + S_4$ we conclude that the combination of this inequality with the equality $S_1 + S_3 = S_2 + S_4$ is possible only when $S_1 = S_2 > S_3 = S_4$. In this case only one of six expressions $\pm S_1 \pm S_2 \pm S_3 \pm S_4$ does not vanish and is not negative. It is the expression $S_1 + S_2 - S_3 - S_4$ and there is only one tangent sphere in six roofs, located in R1.

We pass now to the case when both our relations are exact inequalities: $S_1 + S_2 > S_3 + S_4$ and $S_1 + S_3 > S_2 + S_4$. Consider the expression $S_1 - S_2 - S_3 + S_4$. If it vanishes, there are only two tangent spheres in roofs: one in R1 and the other in R2. But if $S_1 + S_4 \gtrless S_2 + S_3$, then there will a third tangent sphere in one of two opposite roofs R3 and R3*. Thus, assuming that the areas of four faces are denoted by S_1, S_2, S_3, S_4 in order of decreasing magnitude, so that $S_1 \geqslant S_2 \geqslant S_3 \geqslant S_4$, we can formulate the conditions as follows:

Number of tangent spheres in roofs   *Condition*

(1)   none $S_1 = S_2 = S_3 = S_4$

(2)   one $S_1 = S_2 > S_3 = S_4$

(3)   two $S_1 - S_2 = S_3 - S_4 > 0$

(4)   three $S_1 - S_2 \neq S_3 - S_4$.

In the case (4) we have indeed $S_1 > S_2$ or $S_3 > S_4$ and both alternatives entail $S_1 + S_2 > S_3 + S_4$ as well as $S_1 + S_3 > S_2 + S_4$.

Orthocentric Tetrahedron (OTH)

The four altitudes of a TH in general do not meet, so that usually there is no orthocenter in a TH. But there are particular TH's such that their altitudes are concurrent in a common point called the *orthocenter* and denoted by ω. Such particular TH's are called *orthocentric*. They are characterized by special properties which we can only describe, omitting their proofs.

An important feature of an OTH (abbreviation for orthocentric TH) consists in the perpendicularity of opposite edges, which form three pairs of perpendicular straight lines. The converse theorem is also very interesting. It states that if *two* pairs of opposite edges of a TH are perpendicular lines, the third pair of opposite edges is also formed by two perpendicular lines and the TH is an OTH.

We know that two skew lines have one and only one common perpendicular. Thus, in a TH there are three straight lines which are common perpendiculars of three pairs of opposite edges. These three straight lines of an OTH pass through the orthocenter ω which therefore appears as a common point of seven straight lines, four altitudes and three common perpendiculars of three pairs of opposite edges.

In an OTH the feet of altitudes are orthocenters of faces, so that the orthocenters of faces appear as orthogonal projections of the orthocenter ω of the OTH on the planes of faces.

Three remarkable points of an OTH, namely centroid, circumcenter and orthocenter, are collinear. Moreover the centroid is midway between the circumcenter and orthocenter, being at the midpoint of the segment defined by the last two points.

We describe now the special metric properties of an OTH which do not hold for a general TH. Let a, b, c denote the lengths of three concurrent edges of an OTH, while the same but Greek letters α, β, γ designate the lengths of their opposite edges. The sums of squares of opposite edges, namely $a^2 + \alpha^2$, $b^2 + \beta^2$, $c^2 + \gamma^2$, are different in general, but for an OTH they are equal:

$$a^2 + \alpha^2 = b^2 + \beta^2 = c^2 + \gamma^2.$$

In any TH the sum of squares $S_1^2 + S_2^2 + S_3^2 + S_4^2$ of four face areas S_1, S_2, S_3, S_4 can be expressed in terms of six edge-lengths and three angles $\widehat{a; \alpha}$, $\widehat{b; \beta}$, $\widehat{c; \gamma}$ formed by pairs of opposite edges as follows:

$$4(S_1^2 + S_2^2 + S_3^2 + S_4^2) = a^2\alpha^2 \operatorname{Sin}^2 \widehat{a; \alpha} + b^2\beta^2 \operatorname{Sin}^2 \widehat{b; \beta} + c^2\gamma^2 \operatorname{Sin}^2 \widehat{c; \gamma}. \quad (6)$$

Now in an OTH the opposite edges are perpendicular, so that the angles $\widehat{a;\alpha}$, $\widehat{b;\beta}$ and $\widehat{c;\gamma}$ are right angles. Therefore, for an OTH the general formula (6) yields

$$S_1^2 + S_2^2 + S_3^2 + S_4^2 = \tfrac{1}{4}(a^2\alpha^2 + b^2\beta^2 + c^2\gamma^2).$$

The six dihedral angles of an OTH are also characterized by two conditions which express the equality of products of cosines of opposite dihedral angles. Denoting the dihedral angle at the edge a by the same letter with a circumflex, $\hat{a}$, and likewise for the five other dihedral angles, we have in an OTH:

$$\text{Cos } \hat{a} \cdot \text{Cos } \hat{\alpha} = \text{Cos } \hat{b} \cdot \text{Cos } \hat{\beta} = \text{Cos } \hat{c} \cdot \text{Cos } \hat{\gamma}.$$

Finally, the five points A, B, C, D (the four vertices of an OTH) and ω (orthocenter) form a so-called *orthocentric* set of five points: any one of these five points is the orthocenter of the tetrahedron formed by the four other points, so that all the five different TH which can be formed with the aid of these five points are orthocentric.

Equifacial Tetrahedron (EFTH)

Equilateral triangles form an important particular group among triangles. They are also equiangular and are called regular triangles because they have equal sides and equal angles. Among TH's those whose four faces are equal regular triangles are called *regular* TH's. A regular TH has equal edges, equal plane angles ($= 60°$), as well as equal dihedral angles and equal trihedral angles.

But a more general class of TH's can be found which generalize equilateral triangles without being regular. To the side length in a triangle corresponds the face area in a TH. Therefore, a TH with four equal face-areas $S_1 = S_2 = S_3 = S_4$ represents a generalization of an equilateral triangle. Such TH's are called *equifacial* (in what follows, EFTH by abbreviation) because the equality of *areas* of faces entails the equality of opposite edges:

$$a = \alpha, \quad b = \beta, \quad c = \gamma,$$

and thus the equality of four faces themselves which therefore are congruent triangles. But the face-triangle of an EFTH is not regular and its three sides a, b, c in general are different from one other. Thus, in the three-dimensional space an EFTH is not an equiangular TH, while in the plane an equilateral triangle is *eo ipso* equiangular.

Nevertheless the four trihedral angles of an EFTH are equal and in this respect it is similar to the equilateral triangle. But the dihedral angles of an EFTH are not equal: though the opposite dihedral angles are equal $\hat{a} = \hat{\alpha}$, $\hat{b} = \hat{\beta}$, $\hat{c} = \hat{\gamma}$, in general $\hat{a}$, $\hat{b}$, $\hat{c}$ are unequal. The three plane angles of a face are also unequal angles and the face of an EFTH is not a regular triangle.

The four altitudes of an EFTH are necessarily equal, but they do not meet: an EFTH, in general, is not orthocentric. The three other remarkable points, centroid, incenter and circumcenter, of an EFTH coincide as they do in a regular triangle. Conversely, if two of these three remarkable points coincide, the TH is equifacial and the third remarkable point coincides with the first two.

In an EFTH the four excenters (centers of escribed spheres) lie on the circumscribed sphere and they are diametrically opposed to the four vertices. The orthocenters of faces are contact-points of escribed spheres and faces, while the other twelve contact-points of escribed spheres with the lateral walls of truncated trihedral angles are on the circumscribed sphere. An EFTH has only five tangent spheres since there are no tangent spheres in roofs. The four escribed spheres are equal and their common radius ϱ is equal to the diameter $2r$ of the inscribed sphere. We deduce from $S_1 = S_2 = S_3 = S_4 = S$: $4S \cdot r = 3 \cdot V$ as well as $(S_1 + S_2 + S_3 - S_4) \cdot \varrho = 3 \cdot V = 2S \cdot \varrho$, so that $\varrho = 2r$. The altitude H of an EFTH is equal to the diameter of escribed sphere because $H \cdot S = 3 \cdot V$ gives $H = 2\varrho = 4r$. The radius R of the circumscribed sphere is given by the relation $8R^2 = a^2 + b^2 + c^2$.

The midlines of an EFTH (lines joining the midpoints of opposite edges) are at the same time common perpendiculars of pairs of opposite and equal edges. They have the remarkable property of being mutually perpendicular and an EFTH is characterized by the same symmetry as the regular triangle: it has three axes of symmetry which are precisely the three midlines. Thus, an EFTH possesses three mutually perpendicular axes of symmetry.

Regular Tetrahedron (RTH)

A TH which is orthocentric and equifacial is necessarily a regular TH (denoted by RTH). A RTH is characterized by equal edges and, conversely, if in a TH all six edges are equal the other elements are equal too and the TH is regular. Now for a TH which is orthocentric and equifacial the two conditions $a^2 + \alpha^2 = b^2 + \beta^2 = c^2 + \gamma^2$ and $a = \alpha$, $b = \beta$, $c = \gamma$ are fulfilled simultaneously, so that $a = \alpha = b = \beta = c = \gamma$ and the TH is regular.

Denoting the length of its edges by a, we have for the area of a face which is regular triangle with side a, $S = a^2 3^{1/2}/4$. On the other hand, the formula (2) gives for an RTH: $V = a^3 2^{1/2}/12$. Therefore, $4r = H = 3V/S = a(2/3)^{1/2}$, as well as $8R^2 = 3a^2$ and $R = \frac{1}{2}a(3/2)^{1/2}$.

Comparing the radii R and r of the circumscribed and inscribed spheres, we find that their ratio R/r is equal to 3 in the case of an RTH. It is interesting to observe that, in general, this ratio R/r exceeds 3, so that its value in an RTH appears as a minimum value attained only for RTH's.

An RTH possesses many other extremum properties, among them the following ones. If the total surface of a TH has a fixed prescribed value K (that is, if the sum of four face areas $S_1 + S_2 + S_3 + S_4$ is equal to K, where K is a known constant), one can ask what is the shape of the TH which possesses *maximum volume for a given total surface* K? The answer is an RTH: an RTH realizes maximum volume included in a given total surface K. Since, for an RTH, $K = 4S = a^2 3^{1/2}$ while $V^2 = a^6/72$, we obtain for the volume of an RTH with total surface K the following expression:

$$216V^2 \sqrt{3} = K^3,$$

so that for all other TH (non regular) we have the inequality

$$216V^2 \sqrt{3} < K^3.$$

If, conversely, we ask what is the shape of the TH which realizes the *least total surface* K *for a prescribed and fixed volume* V, we find the general result

$$K \geqslant \left(216V^2 \sqrt{3}\right)^{1/3},$$

the sign of equality (least total surface) being valid only for an RTH with volume V.

Likewise, given a sphere of fixed radius, an inscribed TH with maximum volume is regular, while among TH's circumscribed to that sphere, the RTH possesses the least volume.

CHAPTER 21

Pythagorean Theorem in Space.
Spherical Trigonometry

The classic Pythagorean theorem in plane geometry is intimately related to the determination of a direction in a plane with the aid of two cosines called *direction cosines*. Let us denote by α and β the two angles a given direction (a given straight line) makes with two axes of coordinates OX and OY

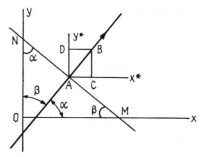

Fig. 21.1

(Fig. 1). Projecting a segment AB lying on this line on parallels AX*, AY* to axes OX, OY through the point A, we obtain $AC = AB \cdot \text{Cos}\,\alpha$ and $AD = CB = AB \cdot \text{Cos}\,\beta$.

Now the Pythagorean theorem applied to the right triangle ABC yields the relation

$$AC^2 + CB^2 = AB^2.$$

Replacing AC and CB by $AB \cdot \text{Cos}\,\alpha$ and $AB \cdot \text{Cos}\,\beta$ respectively and dividing both members by AB^2, we deduce the important relation

$$\text{Cos}^2\alpha + \text{Cos}^2\beta = 1 \tag{1}$$

between the direction cosines $\text{Cos}\,\alpha$ and $\text{Cos}\,\beta$ of any given direction. As a matter of fact we find nothing new, but this form of the Pythagorean theorem is very important in analytic geometry. We add that the direction of a straight line such as, for instance, MAN can also be characterized perfectly well by the direction of its normal AB, that is, by two direction cosines of the normal (we call *normal* any segment perpendicular to the line) $\cos \alpha$ and $\cos \beta$.

The segment MN has two projections on axes, namely OM and ON. If L denotes its length, $L = MN$, then denoting the lengths of the projections parallel to OY and to OX by L_y and L_x respectively, we obtain $L_y = OM = L \cdot \cos \beta$ and $L_x = ON = L \cdot \cos \alpha$. Therefore, expressed in terms of projections' lengths L_x, L_y, the same Pythagorean theorem becomes:

$$L^2 = L_x^2 + L_y^2. \tag{2}$$

We shall see that these relations are particular cases of relations which hold in three-dimensional space for three direction cosines of any direction (straight line) in space. They also hold for squares of plane areas A_x, A_y, A_z lying in three mutually perpendicular planes YOZ, ZOX, XOY and which are projections parallel to axes OX, OY, OZ respectively of any given plane area A. To prove our assertion we need the Pythagorean theorem in space and we set out to deduce it.

The plane Pythagorean theorem deals with the measures of three parts (hypotenuse and two legs) of the boundary of a right triangle. In space, a tetrahedron plays the role of a triangle in a plane. A tetrahedron is called a right tetrahedron, if one of its trihedral angles is a right angle. At the vertex of the right trihedral angle the three faces form three right dihedral angles, so that among the four triangles which form the boundary of a right tetrahedron, three are right triangles while the fourth is not.

Choosing the vertex of a right trihedral angle as the origin O and the three faces concurrent at this vertex as planes of coordinates, we denote the three vertices lying on the axes OX, OY, OZ by A, B, C respectively (Fig. 2). The lengths of edges OA, OB, OC are a, b, c: $a = OA$, $b = OB$, $c = OC$. The triangle ABC opposite to the right trihedral angle is called the *hypotenuse* of the right tetrahedron OABC, its three *legs* being the right triangles OAB, OBC, OCA. Their areas OAB, OBC, OCA can be obtained by projecting the area ABC of the hypotenuse parallel to axes OZ, OX and OY respectively.

We know that the area of the projection of any plane figure on a plane making an angle t with the plane of the original figure equals the area of this figure multiplied by the cosine of the angle t. Therefore, the areas OAB $= S_z$, OBC $= S_x$, OCA $= S_y$ of legs of a right tetrahedron can be deduced

26 Kogbetliantz

from the measure S of the area S = ABC of its hypotenuse, if we know the angles their planes make with the plane of the hypotenuse.

These angles can be characterized as follows. Dropping the perpendicular OPQ from the origin O on the plane ABC, we observe that the direction

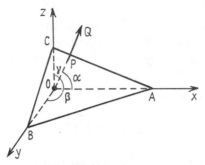

Fig. 21.2

of the plane ABC is perfectly defined by that of its normal OPQ. We denote the angles this normal OPQ makes with the three axes OX, OY, OZ by α, β, γ respectively. Now the angle between two planes is equal to the angle between their normals, so that the plane ABC makes the angles α, β, γ with the three coordinate-planes YOZ, ZOX and XOY respectively. Take, for example, the angle α formed by two lines OPQ and OX. The first is the normal of the face ABC while the other, axis OX, is perpendicular to the plane YOZ. Therefore, the angle α is also angle of two planes ABC and YOZ, so that the triangle BOC is obtained as projection parallel to OX of the triangle ABC. Likewise, projecting the hypotenuse ABC of the right tetrahedron OABC parallel to the axes OY and OZ, triangles COA and AOB are obtained.

Therefore, the measures S_x, S_y, S_z of projections BOC, COA, AOB of the area S = ABC are:

$$BOC = S_x = S \cdot Cos\,\alpha; \quad COA = S_y = S \cdot Cos\,\beta; \quad AOB = S_z = S \cdot Cos\,\gamma,$$

and this fact is analogous to $L_x = L \cdot Cos\,\alpha$, $L_y = L \cdot Cos\,\beta$ of the plane case.

We formulate now the Pythagorean theorem in space:

THEOREM: *The square of the area S of the hypotenuse of a right tetrahedron is equal to the sum of squares of areas S_x, S_y, S_z of its three other faces:*

$$S_x^2 + S_y^2 + S_z^2 = S^2. \tag{3}$$

The proof can be based on the well-known classical formula for the area K of a plane triangle with sides a, b, c (see Chapter 15):

$$4K = [(a + b + c)(-a + b + c)(a - b + c)(a + b - c)]^{1/2}.$$

A simple algebraical transformation of the corresponding expression for $16S^2$ yields the desired result (Fig. 2):

$$16S^2 = (AB + BC + CA)(-AB + BC + CA)(AB - BC + CA) \times$$
$$\times (AB + BC - CA)$$
$$= [(AB + BC)^2 - CA^2] \cdot [AC^2 - (AB - BC)^2]$$
$$= (AB^2 + BC^2 - CA^2 + 2 \cdot AB \cdot BC) \times$$
$$\times (2 \cdot AB \cdot BC + CA^2 - AB^2 - BC^2)$$
$$= 4 \cdot AB^2 \cdot BC^2 - (AB^2 + BC^2 - CA^2)^2.$$

On the other hand, the three right triangles AOB, BOC, COA yield the expressions of squares of their hypotenuses AB, BC, CA, namely:

$$AB^2 = a^2 + b^2; \quad BC^2 = b^2 + c^2; \quad CA^2 = c^2 + a^2,$$

where $a = OA$, $b = OB$ and $c = OC$. Therefore, the expression of $16S^2$ becomes

$$16S^2 = 4(a^2 + b^2)(b^2 + c^2) - (a^2 + 2b^2 + c^2 - a^2 - c^2)^2$$
$$= 4(a^2b^2 + b^4 + a^2c^2 + b^2c^2 - b^4) = 4(a^2b^2 + b^2c^2 + c^2a^2).$$

The areas S_x, S_y, S_z of right triangles are equal to $S_x = \frac{1}{2}bc$, $S_y = \frac{1}{2}ca$, $S_z = \frac{1}{2}ab$ and therefore

$$S^2 = \frac{1}{4}(a^2b^2 + b^2c^2 + c^2a^2) = \frac{1}{4}(4S_z^2 + 4S_x^2 + 4S_y^2) = S_x^2 + S_y^2 + S_z^2.$$

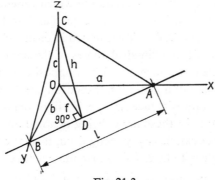

Fig. 21.3

Another, shorter proof is the following: denoting by D the point on the side AB where this side is cut by a plane OCD through the opposite side OC and perpendicular to AB, we have (Fig. 3), joining D to O and C by the altitudes $f = $ OD and $h = $ CD of triangles OAB and OCD:

$$c^2 + f^2 = h^2; \quad a^2 + b^2 = AB^2 = l^2; \quad 2S_x = bc, \quad 2S_y = ac,$$

Thus,
$$2S_z = fl \quad \text{and} \quad 2S = hl.$$

$$4\,(S_x^2 + S_y^2 + S_z^2) = (b^2 + a^2)\,c^2 + f^2 l^2 = l^2(c^2 + f^2) = l^2 h^2 = 4S^2.$$

Substituting in the Pythagorean theorem (3) the expressions $S_x = S \cdot \mathrm{Cos}\,\alpha$, $S_y = S \cdot \mathrm{Cos}\,\beta$, $S_z = S \cdot \mathrm{Cos}\,\gamma$ and dividing by S^2, we obtain another form of the same theorem:

$$\mathrm{Cos}^2\alpha + \mathrm{Cos}^2\beta + \mathrm{Cos}^2\gamma = 1 \qquad (4)$$

which generalizes relation (1) and reduces to it, if the straight line is parallel to the plane XOY. This relation allows us to extend the validity of the relation $S^2 = S_x^2 + S_y^2 + S_z^2$ to any *plane* area S bounded by any closed curve. If the normal to this plane area S makes the angles α, β, γ with the coordinate-axes, then the areas of its projections on the planes YOZ, ZOK and XOY are equal to $S_x = S \cdot \mathrm{Cos}\,\alpha$, $S_y = S \cdot \mathrm{Cos}\,\beta$, $S_z = S \cdot \mathrm{Cos}\,\gamma$ respectively. Thus, with the aid of the relation (4) we find, indeed, that the Pythagorean theorem (3) holds not only for a triangular plane area S for but any area S, provided it is a plane area (see Fig. 4).

In plane geometry the Pythagorean theorem $c^2 = a^2 + b^2$ was extended into the so-called cosine law $c^2 = a^2 + b^2 - 2ab\,\mathrm{Cos}\,C$, considering any triangle instead of a right triangle.

In solid geometry we have also a theorem which generalizes the cosine law of plane geometry and which concerns a general tetrahedron. In this theorem the square of area of a face is expressed in terms of areas of three other faces and of cosines of three dihedral angles of the opposite trihedral angle. Let us denote the area of a face v which is opposite to a vertex V by S_v, so that, if the four vertices of a general tetrahedron are A, B, C, D (see Fig. 5), then the areas of the opposite faces a, b, c, d will be denoted by S_a, S_b, S_c, S_d respectively, the planes of these areas being denoted also by $a, b, c,$ and d.

The dihedral angles can be easily recognized, if we use the following notation. A dihedral angle with faces (planes) a and b will be denoted by the symbol $\widehat{ab}$. Thus, three dihedral angles which belong to the trihedral angle opposite to a face, for instance to the face a, are those in the notation of which the letter denoting this face is lacking: for instance, $\widehat{bc}$, $\widehat{bd}$, $\widehat{cd}$ are opposite to a. Having defined our notations, we now formulate the following generalization of Pythagorean theorem for right tetrahedron:

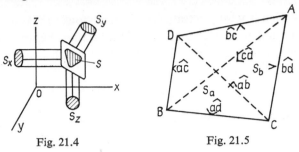

Fig. 21.4 Fig. 21.5

Cosine Law for a Tetrahedron

Given a tetrahedron with face-ares S_a, S_b, S_c, S_d and dihedral angles $\widehat{ab}$, $\widehat{ac}$, $\widehat{ad}$, $\widehat{bc}$, $\widehat{bd}$, $\widehat{cd}$, the square of each face-area can be expressed in terms of other areas and dihedral angles opposite to it as follows:

$$S_a^2 = S_b^2 + S_c^2 + S_d^2 - 2S_bS_c \, \mathrm{Cos}\, \widehat{bc} - 2S_cS_d \, \mathrm{Cos}\, \widehat{cd} - 2S_dS_b \, \mathrm{Cos}\, \widehat{db}, \quad (5)$$

so that there are four relations of this type.

The proof of this theorem which for a right tetrahedron reduces to the Pythagorean theorem (3) may be deduced from the following important linear relations between the four areas S_a, S_b, S_c, S_d:

$$
\left.
\begin{aligned}
S_a &= S_b \, \mathrm{Cos}\, \widehat{ab} + S_c \, \mathrm{Cos}\, \widehat{ac} + S_d \, \mathrm{Cos}\, \widehat{ad} \\
S_b &= S_c \, \mathrm{Cos}\, \widehat{bc} + S_d \, \mathrm{Cos}\, \widehat{bd} + S_a \, \mathrm{Cos}\, \widehat{ba} \\
S_c &= S_d \, \mathrm{Cos}\, \widehat{cd} + S_a \, \mathrm{Cos}\, \widehat{ac} + S_b \, \mathrm{Cos}\, \widehat{bc} \\
S_d &= S_a \, \mathrm{Cos}\, \widehat{ad} + S_b \, \mathrm{Cos}\, \widehat{bd} + S_c \, \mathrm{Cos}\, \widehat{cd}
\end{aligned}
\right\} \quad (6)
$$

They are obtained by projecting three areas onto the plane of the fourth area, the sum of projections being equal to this fourth area. For example, if the areas S_a, S_b, S_c (see Fig. 5) are projected on the plane of the triangle ABC, the area S_d of this triangle is obtained and the last of the four relations (6) expresses this result.

Multiplying them by S_a, S_b, S_c, S_d so that their lefthand members become squared, adding the three obtained relations member by member and subtracting the fourth relation, we prove the cosine law for the tetrahedron. Thus, adding the three squares $S_b^2 + S_c^2 + S_d^2$ and subtracting S_a^2, the relation (5) is found.

Since the cosine law for a tetrahedron is analogous to that for a plane triangle, it is natural to expect that there is a relation between the sines of dihedral angles and face-areas of a tetrahedron which is analogous to the sine law of plane trigonometry.

Sine Law for a Tetrahedron

And indeed such a relation does exist but it is not at all so simple as the sine law of plane trigonometry, and also involves the edges. We formulate this relation without proving it:

$$\frac{S_a S_b \operatorname{Sin} \widehat{ab}}{CD} = \frac{S_a S_c \operatorname{Sin} \widehat{ac}}{BD} = \frac{S_a S_d \operatorname{Sin} \widehat{ad}}{BC} = \frac{S_b S_c \operatorname{Sin} \widehat{bc}}{AD}$$

$$= \frac{S_b S_d \operatorname{Sin} \widehat{bd}}{AC} = \frac{S_c S_d \operatorname{Sin} \widehat{cd}}{AB} = \frac{3}{2} V.$$

Here the sine of a dihedral angle is multiplied by areas of its faces and divided by length of its edge. The common value of these six equal ratios is equal to $3V/2$, where V denotes the volume of the tetrahedron. The proof of this relation is obtained by combining the sine laws of plane and spherical trigonometry applied to four plane triangular faces and to four spherical triangles with vertices of the tetrahedron playing the role of centers of spheres.

An interesting form of the same relation is obtained by multiplying them by pairs related to opposite angles:

$$\frac{\operatorname{Sin} \widehat{ab} \cdot \operatorname{Sin} \widehat{cd}}{AB \cdot CD} = \frac{\operatorname{Sin} \widehat{ac} \cdot \operatorname{Sin} \widehat{bd}}{AC \cdot BD} = \frac{\operatorname{Sin} \widehat{ad} \cdot \operatorname{Sin} \widehat{bc}}{AD \cdot BC} \tag{7}$$

The common value of these three equal ratios is equal to $9 \cdot V^2$ divided by $4 \cdot S_a \cdot S_b \cdot S_c \cdot S_d$. For an equifacial tetrahedron whose opposite edges and opposite dihedral angles are equal, the relation (7) takes a very simple form

$$\frac{\operatorname{Sin} \widehat{ab}}{AB} = \frac{\operatorname{Sin} \widehat{bc}}{BC} = \frac{\operatorname{Sin} \widehat{ca}}{CA} = \frac{3V}{2S^2} \qquad (S_a = S_b = S_c = S_d = S)$$

Volumes

We begin the study of volumes by the simplest case of a right parallelepiped whose six faces are rectangles, so that all its eight trihedral angles are right trihedral angles, the opposite faces being parallel and equal rectangles. We denote its three edges concurrent at a vertex by a, b and c, where a is the length, b the breadth and c the height of parallelepiped.

The base area is equal to the product ab and any horizontal section of the parallelepiped's volume is equal to the base and has the same area ab. Applying the principle of Cavalieri which states that a volume is the sum of areas of all its sections parallel to a given plane, we come to the conclusion that the volume we are studying is sum of equal areas each of which is ab, so that the measure of this volume is obtained by multiplying ab by the "number" of horizontal sections contained in the volume.

Through each point of the edge c of parallelepiped passes a horizontal plane and therefore there are as many horizontal sections of area ab as many points in the segment of length c, that is a continuum of sections. But the continuum of points in the segment c is expressed in the measure of its length and therefore the product $(ab)c = abc$ is the measure of the volume of our right parallelepiped of dimensions a, b and c.

The same measure of this volume is obtained by the passage to the limit, this passage being necessary in the general case of incommensurable segments a, b, c. Suppose all three of them are commensurable and therefore have a common measure λ, so that three integers m, n, p may be found such that $a = m \cdot \lambda$, $b = n \cdot \lambda$, $c = p \cdot \lambda$. In this case the use of absolute infinity in the form of the passage to the limit is not necessary and the same result $V = abc$ is obtained by subdividing the volume V of the right parallelepiped into mnp small cubes by planes parallel to faces, the distance between two parallel planes being equal to λ. Choosing this length λ as our unit of length and defining the unit of volume as the volume of a cube whose edges are units of length, we obtain the measure of volume of our right parallelepiped simply by counting the number of unit-cubes it contains. This number is mnp because the dimensions of the parallelepiped a, b, c expressed in terms of the unit of length λ, being equal to m, n, p respectively, there are mn unit-squares at the base and p unit-cubes above each square. On the other hand, $a = m$, $b = n$ and $c = p$ with our choice of unit of length and therefore $V = mnp = abc$ which proves our assertion.

Let us now study the general case of *incommensurable* edges a, b, c. This case necessitates a passage to the limit which means that without the concept

of absolute infinity embodied in this operation, no justification for the rule
V = abc can be found and no measure of volumes can be performed, this
rule V = abc being the foundation for the measurement of volumes.

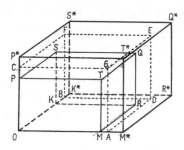

Fig. 21.6

Given a unit of length, we try to measure three segments a, b, c with the
aid of the N-th part of this unit; that is, with the aid of the segment of length
1/N. Naturally we cannot find an integer N such that the segment of length
1/N is contained an integral number of times in each of the three segments
a, b, c because by hypothesis they are incommensurable. Nevertheless the
axiom of Archimedes says that for any fixed N, however large we choose it,
any given length is comprised between two successive multiples of 1/N.
Thus, three pairs of successive integers $(m, m + 1)$; $(n, n + 1)$; $(p, p + 1)$ can
be found such that (Fig. 6)

$$m/N < a < (m + 1)/N; \quad n/N < b < (n + 1)/N;$$

$$p/N < c < (p + 1)/N. \tag{8}$$

This means the vertices A, B, C of the right paralellepiped OABCDEFG
fall between the points M and M*, K and K*, P and P* respectively: m/N
$= OM < a = OA < OM* = (m + 1)/N;$ $n/N = OK < b = OB < OK*$
$= (n + 1)/N;$ $p/N = OP < c = OC < OP* = (p + 1)/N.$

The four points O, M, K, P define a right parallelepiped OMKPQRST
whose edges are commensurable with the unit of length: $OM = m/N$, OK
$= n/N$, OP $= p/N$. Therefore, the measure of its volume V_i is equal to the
product $(m/N) (n/N) (p/N)$: $V_i = mnp/N^3$. Since this parallelepiped is comprised entirely within our incommensurable parallelepiped we have for the
volume V of the last parallelopiped the inequality $V > V_i$.

On the other hand, the four points O, M*, K*, P* define another right
parallelepiped with commensurable edges, too: $OM* = (m + 1)/N$, OK*
$= (n + 1)/N$ and $OP* = (p + 1)/N$ which contains our incommensurable

parallelepiped in its interior. Therefore, the volume V is less than the volume V_e of the parallelepiped OM*K*P*Q*R*S*T*: $V < V_e$. Now the measure of V_e is equal to the product $(m+1)(n+1)(p+1)/N^3$, so that finally the volume V we are studying satisfies the double inequality $V_i < V < V_e$; that is,

$$mnp/N^3 < V < (m+1)(n+1)(p+1)/N^3. \tag{9}$$

Our purpose consists in proving that $V = abc$. Therefore, we study now the product abc of three incommensurable lengths a, b, c. The inequalities (8) multiplied member by member yield a double inequality for this product:

$$mnp/N^3 < abc < (m+1)(n+1)(p+1)/N^3. \tag{10}$$

The results (9) and (10) allow us to evaluate the upper and lower bounds of the difference $V - abc$: increasing the first term and decreasing the second term of this difference, we form its upper bound

$$V - abc < (m+1)(n+1)(p+1)/N^3 - mnp/N^3$$

$$= (mn + np + pm + m + n + p + 1)/N^3;$$

increasing the second and decreasing the first term, we obtain the lower bound

$$V - abc > mnp/N^3 - (m+1)(n+1)(p+1)/N^3$$

$$= -(mp + pn + mn + m + n + p + 1)/N^3.$$

Thus, the lower bound is equal to the upper bound in absolute value but is negative, so that the absolute value of the difference $V - abc$ is shown to be less than its upper bound. Now this upper bound can be written as follows:

$$\{(m/N)(n/N) + (n/N)(p/N) + (p/N)(m/N)$$

$$+ [(m/N) + (n/N) + (p/N)]/N + 1/N^2\}/N,$$

where $m/N < a$, $n/N < b$ and $p/N < c$. Therefore the upper bound of the absolute value $|V - abc|$ is itself less than the expression $[ab + bc + ca + (b + c + a)/N + 1/N^2]/N$ and thus less than $(ab + bc + ca + a + b + c + 1)/N$:

$$|V - abc| < \alpha/N, \tag{11}$$

where the constant α in the righthand member is equal to: $\alpha = ab + bc + ca + a + b + c + 1$.

The inequality (11) involves an arbitrary integer N which can be chosen as large as we want. This means that a constant number $V - abc$ is less in absolute value than any arbitrarily small number α/N. Should it differ from zero, this constant number $V - abc$ could not verify the condition (11) for all possible choices of the arbitrary integer N.

Increasing N (that is, repeating our reasoning for $N = N_1$, then for $N = N_2$, then for $N = N_3$, $N = N_4$, ... etc. where $N_1 < N_2 < N_3$ and in general $N_k < N_{k+1}$, the different choices of integers N_k forming an infinite increasing sequence $N_1 < N_2 < N_3 < \cdots < N_k < N_{k+1} < \cdots$ with $\lim_{k=\infty} N_k = \infty$), and passing to the limit in the inequality $|V - abc| < \alpha/N_k$, we obtain at the limit, for $k = \infty$, $|V - abc| = 0$.

The proof of the formula $V = abc$ just given is more elaborate and much longer than the proof based on the principle of Cavalieri. Both proofs are based on the concept of absolute infinity, but the types of infinity used are different: Cavalieri's Principle states that a volume consists of a *continuum* of plane and parallel areas obtained as parallel sections of the volume and thus uses the more powerful kind of absolute infinity than the aleph-null, on the use of which is based the passage to the limit. This explains the conciseness and elegance of the proof based on the concept of continuum as compared with the proof using the passage to the limit.

The Cavalieri's concept of volume as a sum of areas is a very powerful tool which enables us to prove the equality of volumes of two solids of completely different shape provided their corresponding sections by parallel planes have for each secant plane equal areas. This condition presupposes that both solids are comprised between the same two parallel planes, so that corresponding sections which by definition are cut in these solids by the same secant plane are at the same distance from the base-plane. It is important to emphasize that the corresponding sections need not be of the same shape as long as their areas are equal:

CAVALIERI'S THEOREM: *Two solids of equal altitude have equal volumes if their sections, made by planes parallel to and at the same distance from their common base-plane, are for each secant plane equal in area.*

To illustrate this important theorem let us consider two piles of sheets of finite thickness, the number of sheets in each pile being the same. Denoting the area of the nth sheet in the first pile by S_n and the area of the nth sheet in the second pile by s_n, the sheets in both piles being counted from the base towards the top, it is sufficient to assume that for all values of n we have

$S_n = s_n$, to conclude that the volume of both piles (measured, for instance, by their weight) is equal. Now nothing is said about the *shape* of an individual sheet, so that the sheets may have any shapes.

The fact that $V = abc$ proves that the volume of a right rectangular parallelepiped is proportional to each one of its three dimensions. Thus, if v and V denote the volumes of two similar right rectangular parallelepipeds with a ratio r of corresponding segments, their edges being a, b, c for the smaller one of volume v and ra, rb, rc ($r > 1$) for the larger, then we have

$$V/v = ra \cdot rb \cdot rc/(abc) = r^3 abc/(abc) = r^3.$$

Therefore, *the ratio of volumes of two similar solids is equal to the cube of the ratio of their linear parts.*

Volume of a Tetrahedron

We observe that the expression $V = abc$ for the volume of a rectangular parallelepiped can be also written as $V = B \cdot h$, where $B = ab$ is the area of its base while $h = c$ is the altitude of the parallelepiped. Thus, its volume V is equal to the product of base-area by altitude. But for a tetrahedron we have $V = Bh/3$.

THEOREM: *The volume of a tetrahedron is equal to one third the product of its base-area by its altitude.*

The proof of this theorem is based on many lemmas and we begin by deducing these lemmas.

LEMMA I. If a tetrahedron is cut by a plane parallel to the base, the section is a triangle similar to the base-triangle and the lateral edges as well as the altitude are divided proportionally (Fig. 7).

PROOF: Denoting by OD the altitude of the tetrahedron OABC with the base ABC in the plane p, we cut OABC by a plane q which is parallel to the base, $q \parallel p$. The plane q cuts the edges and the altitude in E, F, G, H and the segments EF, FG, GE are parallel to AB, BC, CA respectively so that the triangles OEF, OFG, OGE are similar to those OAB, OBC, OCA respectively. Therefore OE/OA = EF/AB = OF/OB = FG/BC = OG/OC = GE/CA which proves that the triangle EFG is similar to that ABC. Moreover, considering the plane OEADH, we conclude that EH is parallel to AD, triangles OEH and OAD are similar and the ratio OE/OA is equal to that OH/OD.

Thus, because on the other hand EF/AB = OE/OA, we obtain the following result:

$$EF/AB = FG/BC = GE/CA = OH/OD.$$

Since the ratio of areas of two similar triangles is equal to the square of the ratio of their corresponding sides, we also have

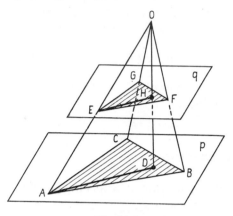

Fig. 21.7

LEMMA II. The area of a tetrahedron's section by a plane parallel to the base is equal to the product of the base-area times the square of ratio of the plane's distance from the vertex to the altitude of the tetrahedron.

PROOF: Since the ratio of corresponding sides of similar triangles EFG and ABC is equal to OH/OD, we have indeed

$$\text{area EFG/area ABC} = (OH/OD)^2$$

which is Lemma II.

We consider now two tetrahedrons of equal altitude, having their bases in the same plane p (Fig. 8) and such that the areas of their bases ABC and DEF are equal, the triangles ABC and DEF themselves being different in shape.

The vertices O and G are equidistant from the plane p and their distance H is the common altitude of both tetrahedrons. By hypothesis, area ABC = area DEF. If now a plane q parallel to the plane p and at a distance h from the vertices O, G cuts both tetrahedrons in triangles KLM and PQR, we can easily prove that these triangles have the same area.

We have indeed area KLM = (area ABC) · $(h/H)^2$ as well as area PQR = (area DEF) · $(h/H)^2$, so that the two sections are equal. Therefore, all sections by planes parallel to bases are equal and the tetrahedrons have equal volumes. This proves

LEMMA III. Two tetrahedrons have equal volumes if they have equal altitudes and equal base-areas.

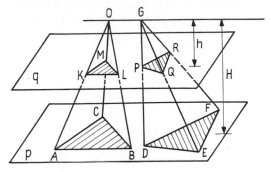

Fig. 21.8

LEMMA IV. A diagonal plane cuts a rectangular parallelepiped into two equal right triangular prisms.

A solid bounded by planes is called a polyhedron. If a polyhedron has two equal polygonal faces lying in two parallel planes, while the other faces comprised between the first two parallel and congruent faces are parallelograms, then it is called prism. The congruent and parallel faces are the bases and the parallelograms are the lateral faces of the prism. A triangular prism has triangles as its two congruent bases. A prism is called *right* if the dihedral angles of lateral faces with the bases are right dihedral angles.

A general parallelepiped is a prism whose bases are parallelograms. Thus, it has any dihedral (not necessarily right) angles and three sets of four parallel and equal edges. A plane through two parallel and opposite edges is called diagonal plane of the parallelepiped. Such is the plane ACGE in Fig. 9, the parallelepiped ABCDEFGH being rectangular.

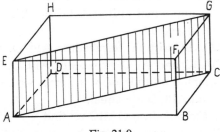

Fig. 21.9

The two triangular prisms ABCEFG and ACDEGH are congruent and their volumes are equal to one half the product of dimensions, that is, to $\frac{1}{2}AB \cdot AD \cdot AE = \frac{1}{2}AB \cdot BC \cdot BF$.

Now we can prove that the volume of a *right* tetrahedron is equal to one sixth the product *abc*, where *a*, *b*, *c* are lengths of edges of the right trihedral angle. On the Fig. 10 the right tetrahedron OABC is drawn in a position such that one of the three faces, OAB, of its right trihedral angle at O

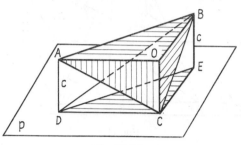

Fig. 21.10

is horizontal, the two other faces, AOC and BOC, being vertical. AD = OC = c and BE = c are perpendiculars dropped from the vertices A and B on the plane *p* through C and parallel to AOB, so that AOBCDE is a right triangular prism which includes the tetrahedron OABC in its interior.

The plane BCD decomposes the part of the volume of this prism unoccupied by the tetrahedron OABC into two other tetrahedrons ABCD and BCDE. Thus, the volume of this right triangular prism of dimensions OA = *a*, OB = *b*, OC = *c* is filled up by three tetrahedrons OABC, ABCD and BCDE. We know that the volume of the prism is equal to $\frac{1}{2}abc$ because it is exactly one half of a rectangular parallelepiped of same dimensions *a*, *b*, *c*. To prove that the volume of the tetrahedron OABC is equal to one sixth the product *abc* it is sufficient to establish that the three tetrahedrons contained within the prism have equal volumes. This can be done with the aid of Lemma III.

We first compare the tetrahedrons OABC and BCDE. They have equal bases, AOB = CDE, and equal altitudes, OC = BE. Therefore, by Lemma III, their volumes are equal.

Comparing now OABC with the tetrahedron ABCD, we consider the face AOC as base of OABC and ACD as base of ABCD. These triangles are equal and OB is common altitude of both tetrahedrons, so that again the volumes of OABC and ABCD are equal.

Thus, for the right tetrahedron OABC we find V = *abc*/6 which can also be written as one third the product of its base-area by the altitude. Finally, we consider any tetrahedron ACDE with base-area CDE and altitude $h = AF$ (Fig. 11) and compare it with another tetrahedron CDEG with the base CDE and the same altitude h, but having two right dihedral angles at edges CD and CE, so that its altitude is one of its edges, namely $GC = h = AF$. The volumes of these two tetrahedrons are equal (Lemma III).

On the same Fig. 11 we have a third tetrahedron CEGH whose base-area CEH is equal to that of the tetrahedron CDEG and therefore to the base-area of the first tetrahedron CDE because the straight line DH by construction is parallel to the line CE. The point H is defined, therefore, as the intersection point of a parallel to the line CE through the point D with the perpendicular CH to CE. We see thus that the third tetrahedron is a right tetrahedron with a right trihedral angle at the vertex C. The volumes of all three tetrahedrons being equal, we see that the volume of the first tetrahedron is equal to one third of its base-area by the altitude: $V = (\text{area CDE}) \cdot AF/3$.

This result is a particular case of a general theorem which includes also the formula for the area of a triangle, namely $\frac{1}{2}Bh$, where B is the length of the base of triangle and h its altitude. Comparing the two formulas $\frac{1}{2}Bh$ and $Bh/3$, we note the striking similarity of structure of these two formulas: the first expresses the measure of that part of two-dimensional space which is within a triangle, while the second one gives the measure of the part of three-dimensional space interior to a tetrahedron. The coefficients $\frac{1}{2}$ and $\frac{1}{3}$ are related to dimensionalities 2 and 3 of corresponding spaces, so that the

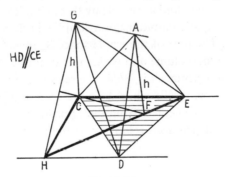

Fig. 21.11

formulas $\frac{1}{2}Bh$ and $Bh/3$ suggest, for a N-dimensional space, a generalization, namely the formula Bh/N where B is the measure of the base.

Let us check this suggestion for the case of a four-dimensional figure which is, in its space S_4, the analogue of triangle in S_2 and tetrahedron in S_3. First of all we must describe this *simplex* in S_4, as it is called in geometry. A simplex in S_N is the analogue of triangle in S_2 and it is the simplest configuration bounded by flat boundaries and closed. Thus, it divides the whole S_N into two parts, one interior to the simplex, and the other exterior to it, the latter part having an infinite extent, while the interior of a simplex is finite. Let us study how a simplex is built. To build a triangle in S_2 we use three straight lines. In an S_3 four planes form a tetrahedron. To delimit a finite part of S_4 bounded by three-dimensional spaces we need five of them because four three-dimensional spaces define only a point, that is, they form an open tetrahedral (four-faced) angle with the vertex at this point, and to close it we need a fifth space s_3 non-incident with the vertex of the tetrahedral angle. A general rule manifests itself in these constructions: the flat boundaries of a simplex in an N-dimensional space S_N are $N + 1$ flat $(N - 1)$-dimensional spaces immersed in S_N and so located that all of them except one intersect in a common point (defined precisely as their intersection-point), while the $(N + 1)$-th space s_{N-1}, non-incident with this point, closes the interior of the simplex separating it from the remainder of S_N. Thus, vertices and faces of a simplex form pairs of opposite elements. As particular cases we single out three one-dimensional boundaries of triangle in S_2, four two-dimensional faces of a tetrahedron in S_3 and five three-dimensional boundaries (volumes) of a simplex in S_4. We will call this simplex in S_4 a *pentacell* (Greek penta = five, latin cella = small room). A pentacell is bounded by five solids, namely by five tetrahedrons, as a tetrahedron is bounded by four triangles and a triangle by three simplexes (linear segments) of S_1. Thus, the complete boundary of a simplex in S_N is formed by $N + 1$ simplexes of S_{N-1}. The part of the whole space S_4 included within a pentacell may be called hypervolume and we set out to prove that the measure of the hypervolume of a pentacell is $Bh/4$, where B is the volume of the base-tetrahedron of this pentacell, while h is the length of the perpendicular dropped on the base-tetrahedron from the opposite vertex of pentacell; that is, h is the altitude of pentacell relatively to the tetrahedron chosen as the base.

Hypervolume of a Pentacell

Before proceeding to the evaluation of hypervolume of a pentacell we illustrate the method adopted for this evaluation on the examples of area of a triangle and volume of a tetrahedron.

We can build with a segment of straight line (simplex in S_1) a triangle (simplex in S_2) as follows (Fig. 12): suppose the point C is non-incident with the straight line to which belongs the segment AB; move the endpoints A, B of this segment towards C along the straight lines AC, BC in such a way that the segment approaches the point C remaining parallel to its initial position AB.

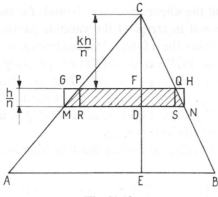

Fig. 21.12

Denoting this variable segment by MN, we observe that its length depends on the distance CD from the point C: triangles ABC and MNC are similar and therefore MN/AB = CD/CE, where AB and CE are base and altitude of the triangle ABC. The set of all positions of the variable segment MN during its motion toward the point C fills up the area of the triangle ABC.

Dividing the altitude $h = $ CE in n equal parts of length h/n and considering two adjacent points of this division D and F, so that DF $ = h/n$, we draw two segments through D, F parallel to AB. These segments MN and PQ have the following length:

$$MN = AB \cdot CD/h; \quad PQ = AB \cdot CF/h.$$

Suppose that F is the kth point in the division of the altitude, counting the points from C towards E, and therefore D is the $(k + 1)$th point. Then CF $= k \cdot (h/n)$ and CD $= (k + 1) \cdot (h/n)$.

Denoting the length of the base AB by B (abbreviation for the word base), we have the following expressions for the lengths MN and PQ: PQ $= kB/n$ and MN $= (k + 1) B/n$. The area MNPQ contains the rectangle PQRS and is itself contained within the larger rectangle GMNH. We denote the area MNPQ by A_{k+1} which is consistent with the fact that the total area of the triangle ABC is subdivided into n areas of the type A_k by parallels to AB drawn through the points of division of altitude into n equal parts. The area

MNPQ is the $(k + 1)$th partial area, if these partial areas are counted from the vertex C towards the base AB. Thus, the area ABC is a sum of n partial areas:

$$\text{area ABC} = A_1 + A_2 + A_3 + \cdots + A_{k+1} + \cdots + A_{n-1} + A_n. \quad (12)$$

We can easily find the upper and lower bounds for the area A_{k+1}, these bounds being expressed in terms of the variable parameter k, which—for different areas A_k—takes the n integral values from $k = 1$ up to $k = n$. We observe that the areas PQRS and GMNH are precisely the lower and the upper bound for the area $A_{k+1} = $ MNPQ. They are equal to PQ $\cdot$ MG and MN $\cdot$ MG respectively. But MG $= h/n$, PQ $= kB/n$ and MN $= (k + 1) B/n$, so that the inequality area PQRS $<$ area MNPQ $<$ area GMNH gives $(Bh/n^2) \cdot k < A_{k+1} < (Bh/n^2) \cdot (k + 1)$.

Using this result in (12), we deduce the following inequality for the triangle s area ABC:

$$(Bh/n^2) \cdot [0 + 1 + 2 + \cdots + (n - 1)] < \text{area ABC}$$
$$< (Bh/n^2) \cdot [1 + 2 + 3 + \cdots + (n - 1) + n].$$

Replacing the sums of first $(n - 1)$ and n integers by their values

$$1 + 2 + \cdots + (n - 1) = (n - 1) \, n/2;$$
$$1 + 2 + \cdots + (n - 1) + n = n(n + 1)/2,$$

we obtain a double inequality for the triangle's area ABC:

$$\tfrac{1}{2}Bh \cdot (1 - 1/n) < \text{area ABC} < \tfrac{1}{2}Bh \cdot (1 + 1/n). \quad (13)$$

Now the choice of the integer n being completely free of any limitations, we can pass to the limit increasing n to infinity. At the limit, for $n = \infty$, the inequalities (13) are transformed into an equality, namely area ABC $= \tfrac{1}{2}Bh$.

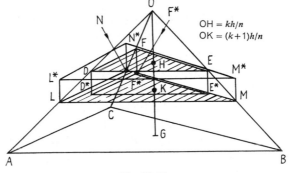

Fig. 21.13

We now unfold a triangle ABC into a tetrahedron OABC as follows. Suppose, the point O to be non-incident with the plane of the triangle ABC (Fig. 13) and move the points A, B, C towards O along the lines AO, BO, CO in such a way that their plane DEF remains parallel to its initial position ABC. If the altitude OG = h of tetrahedron pierces this plane DEF in the point H, then we have DE/AB = EF/BC = DF/AC = OH/OG, the small tetrahedron ODEF being similar to that OABC. Therefore, the area of the base DEF is equal to the base-area ABC of the original tetrahedron OABC multiplied by the square of the ratio OH/OG of the altitudes of two similar tetrahedrons. Denoting the base-area of OABC by B, we have area DEF = B · (OH/h)^2, where h = OG is the altitude of the tetrahedron OABC.

Dividing this altitude h in n equal parts of length h/n and considering two successive points of this division H and K, so that KH = h/n, we draw a plane LMN through the point K parallel to the base ABC. If H is the kth point in the division of the altitude, then the area DEF is equal to B $(k/n)^2$ since OH/h = k/n. Likewise the area LMN is equal to B $(k + 1)^2/n^2$.

Consider now the part LMNDEF of the tetrahedron's volume included between two planes through H, K and parallel to ABC. This horizontal slice of the tetrahedron's volume contains the right triangular prism DEFD*E*F* and itself is contained within the right triangular prism LMNL*M*N*. Computing the volumes of these two right triangular prisms, we find for the volume LMNDEF the following double inequality

$$\text{DNFD*F*N*} = B \cdot (k/n)^2 \, (h/n) = (Bh/n^3) \cdot k^2 < V_{k+1} = \text{LMNDEF}$$

$$< (Bh/n^3) \, (k + 1)^2 = \text{LMNL*M*N*}.$$

This result $(Bh/n^3) \, k^2 < V_{k+1} < Bh/n^3) \cdot (k + 1)^2$, where V_{k+1} denotes the part of the tetrahedron's volume included between the kth and the $(k + 1)$th planes parallel to ABC, will allow us to find another proof of the formula Bh/3 for the volume of a tetrahedron. Drawing planes parallel to ABC through all the points of the division of altitude by equidistant points we divide the volume of the tetrahedron into n horizontal slices of the type V_k, so that

$$\text{volume OABC} = V_1 + V_2 + V_3 + \cdots + V_{k+1} + \cdots + V_n. \quad (14)$$

Applying now to each term of the sum in (14) the inequality

$$(Bh/n^3) \cdot k^2 < V_{k+1} < (Bh/n^3) \, (k + 1)^2,$$

we deduce an inequality for the volume V of the tetrahedron OABC:

$$(Bh/n^3) [0^2 + 1^2 + 2^2 + \cdots + (n - 1)^2]$$
$$< V < (Bh/n^3) [1^2 + 2^2 + \cdots + n^2].$$

Now we know the following expression for the sum of squares of first n integers

$$1^2 + 2^2 + 3^2 + \cdots + n^2 = n (n + 1) (2n + 1)/6,$$

so that finally we obtain

$$(1 - 1/n) (2 - 1/n) Bh/6 < V < Bh (1 + 1/n) (2 + 1/n)/6. \qquad (15)$$

Passing to the limit for $n = \infty$, we prove the formula $V = Bh/3$.

We apply now the same method to the computation of the hypervolume of a pentacell whose base-tetrahedron ABCD has a volume denoted by B (measure of the *base*) and whose altitude is the length h of the perpendicular dropped from the vertex O, opposite to the base ABCD, on the tetrahedron OABC.

First of all we describe the pentacell as generated by a continuous motion of a tetrahedron, just as the tetrahedron was obtained by unfolding a triangle, and the triangle by unfolding a segment. We observe that the motion of a segment shrinking to a point was characterized by the fact that the direction of this motion was perpendicular to the segment. Likewise, the unfolding of a triangle into a tetrahedron was performed by the motion of a triangle shrinking to a point in the direction perpendicular to the plane of this triangle. In the first case the *area* of the triangle was obtained as a sum of all positions of a moving segment, so that a moving (and shrinking) *length* spanned an *area* during its motion. In the second case the *area* of a moving triangle generated a *volume* as a sum of all positions occupied by this area during its motion.

Generalizing these remarks, we consider in a four-dimensional universe S_4 a point O and a three-dimensional space s_3 *non-incident* with the point O, and locate in the space s_3 a tetrahedron ABCD. Joining the vertices of tetrahedron to the point O, we construct a pentacell whose five solid boundaries are formed by five tetrahedrons ABCD (considered as the *base* of pentacell), ABCO, BCDO, CDAO and DABO. The hypervolume contained within this pentacell OABCD may be generated as follows. Suppose that a variable three-dimensional space t_3 moves remaining parallel to the fixed space s_3 through the pentacell in such a way that in its initial position t_3 coincides with s_3 and then approaches the point O. The direction of its motion is perpendicular to the whole space s_3 and therefore perpendicular to the base-tetrahedron ABCD immersed in s_3.

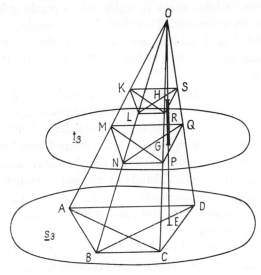

Fig. 21.14

The four three-dimensional spaces (fixed) defined by the sets of four points ABCO, BCDO, CDAO, DABO are boundaries of a tetrahedral angle with vertex at the point O. This tetrahedral angle is open and the fifth three-dimensional space t_3 closes it, forming a pentacell similar to OABCD, having the same vertex O and the same four lateral spaces ABCO, BCDO, CDAO, DABO but a different base. This base is a tetrahedron MNPQ whose vertices M, N, P, Q belong to straight lines AO, BO, CO, DO respectively and the altitude OG of the pentacell OMNPQ is the distance of the tetrahedron MNPQ, base of the pentacell OMNPQ, from the vertex O (see Fig. 14). The similarity of two pentacells entails the equality of the following ratios:

$$OM/OA = ON/OB = OP/OC = OQ/OD = OG/OE = OG/h,$$

where $OE = h$ is the altitude of the pentacell OABCD.

During the motion of the space t_3 towards the point O the variable tetrahedron MNPQ moves from the initial position ABCD towards O, shrinking to a point and vanishing at the moment when it reaches O. The hypervolume of the pentacell is generated by the moving volume of the variable tetrahedron MNPQ. This volume sweeps up the hypervolume OABCD and this last can be considered as a sum of all positions occupied by the variable volume MNPQ during its motion from ABCD towards O.

The altitude OE of pentacell is perpendicular to the space s_3 as well as to all positions of the variable space t_3 which moves precisely in the direction perpendicular to its extension. Therefore, if two positions of the moving tetrahedron MNPQ and KLRS, are considered, the segment GH of the altitude comprized between two volumes MNPQ and KLRS is perpendicular to both volumes.

Subdividing the altitude OE into n equal parts of length h/n and considering all three-dimensional spaces parallel to the space s_3 of the base-tetrahedron ABCD and passing through the points of the division, we cut the hypervolume of the pentacell in parallel slices (four-dimensional, of course) which are bounded by six volumes each: the four lateral tetrahedrons (walls of the tetrahedral angle at the point O) and two tetrahedrons (such as for example MNPQ and KLRS) which are sections of the hypervolume by two three-dimensional spaces parallel to s_3 and passing through two successive points (G and H) of the division.

Let us denote the volume of the kth tetrahedron by V_k and the measure of the kth slice of total hypervolume (which is comprised between the $(k-1)$th and the kth tetrahedron) by W_k, so that the total hypervolume W is the sum of n hypervolumes of slices W_k the subscript k taking integer values from $k = 1$ up to $k = n$ included:

$$\text{Hypervolume OABCD} = W = W_1 + W_2 + \cdots + W_k + \cdots + W_n.$$

Since the tetrahedrons, sections of the pentacell by spaces parallel to s_3, shrink towards the point O, the volume V_k of the kth tetrahedron MNPQ is greater than the volume V_{k-1} of the tetrahedron KLRS, $V_{k-1} < V_k$. We have OH $= (k-1)\,h/n$ and OG $= kh/n$, so that, using the fact that the ratio of similar volumes is equal to the cube of the ratio of their linear parts, we have

$$\text{vol MNPQ/vol ABCD} = (k/n)^3;$$

$$\text{vol KLRS/vol ABCD} = [(k-1)/n]^3.$$

Denoting the volume ABCD of the *base*-tetrahedron by B, we write therefore

$$\text{vol MNPQ} = V_k = B\,(k/n)^3; \quad \text{vol KLRS} = V_{k-1} = B\,[(k-1)/n]^3.$$

We can now evaluate the upper and lower bounds of the hypervolume W_k included between two tetrahedrons MNPQ and KLRS. Since the distance between the volumes of MNPQ and KLRS is equal to h/n and because the altitude of the hypervolume W_k is GH $= h/n$, we conclude that this hypervolume is interior to a right hyperprism based on the tetrahedron MNPQ and contains within itself another right hyperprism based on the tetrahedron KLRS. Thus, we obtain for its measure W_k the following inequalities:

$$V_{k-1} \cdot h/n = (Bh/n^4) \cdot (k-1)^3 < W_k < (Bh/n^4) \cdot k^3 = V_k \cdot h/n.$$

Summing up these inequalities from $k = 1$ to $k = n$, we deduce the upper and lower bounds for the total hypervolume W of the pentacell OABCD:

$$(Bh/n^4) [0^3 + 1^3 + 2^3 + \cdots + (n-1)^3]$$
$$< W < (Bh/n^4) \cdot (1^3 + 2^3 + \cdots + n^3). \tag{16}$$

We need now the expression of the sum of cubes of first n integers. This expression is suggested by the facts that $1^3 + 2^3 = 9 = 3^2 = (1+2)^2$; $1^3 + 2^3 + 3^3 = 9 + 27 = 36 = 6^2 = (1 + 2 + 3)^2$ etc., so that a natural guess is

$$1^3 + 2^3 + 3^3 + \cdots + (n-1)^3 = [(n-1)\,n/2]^2. \tag{17}$$

This guess is justified by mathematical induction. Suppose that (17) holds and form the sum of first n integers cubed

$$1^3 + 2^3 + \cdots + (n-1)^3 + n^3 = (n-1)^2 n^2/4 + n^3$$
$$= (n^2/4) \cdot (n^2 - 2n + 1 + 4n).$$

Computing the righthand member, it is found that this sum is indeed equal to the square of the sum of first powers of first n integers:

$$1^3 + 2^3 + \cdots + n^3 = (n^2/4) \cdot (n^2 + 2n + 1) = [n\,(n+1)/2]^2. \tag{18}$$

Using the formulae (17), (18) in the inequalities (16), we rewrite them as follows

$$(Bh/4)\,(1 - 1/n)^4 < W < (Bh/4)\,(1 + 1/n)^4. \tag{19}$$

A simple passage to the limit yields now the result $W = Bh/4$ and thus proves for the particular case $N = 4$ of four-dimensional space the general rule:

The hypervolume of a simplex in S_N *is obtained multiplying the measure* B *of its* (N − 1)-*dimensional base by the length of the altitude h and dividing the product by the dimension-number* N *of the space* S_N.

Changing our notations, we will now denote the base B and the altitude h of the simplex in S_N by B_N and h_N respectively, so that its hypervolume becomes $B_N \cdot h_N/N$. But the base of a simplex in S_N is itself a simplex in S_{N-1}, so that its measure B_N may be found applying the same general rule: $B_N = B_{N-1} \cdot h_{N-1}/(N-1)$, where B_{N-1} is the measure of the $(N-2)$-dimensional base of the simplex in S_{N-1} and h_{N-1} is its altitude. This reasoning can be applied successively to all simplexes of decreasing dimensions-number with measures B_N, B_{N-1}, B_{N-2}, ..., B_3, B_2, where the last one, B_2, is simply a rectilinear segment-base of the triangle B_3, so that we can replace B_2 by h_1, $B_2 = h_1$ Thus, we obtain a chain of relations

$$B_2 = h_1/1, \ B_3 = B_2 h_2/2, \ B_4 = B_3 h_3/3, \ ... \ B_N = B_{N-1}h_{N-1}/(N-1) \ ...,$$

which yield for the hypervolume of a simplex in S_N the following expression

$$h_1 h_2 h_3 \ ... \ h_{N-1} h_N/N!$$

We now want to apply this formula to a right simplex in S_4. A simplex in S_4 is called a right simplex if four edges concurrent at a vertex are mutually perpendicular lines, so that the tetrahedral angle formed at this vertex by four spaces s_3 concurrent at it is a right tetrahedral angle (the four spaces s_3 are perpendicular to each other). Denoting the lengths of edges of the right tetrahedral angle by a, b, c, d, we obtain for the hypervolume of a right pentacell the following expression: $abcd/24$. This expression is analogous to the formulas for the area of a right triangle, $ab/2$, and for the volume of a right tetrahedron, $abc/6$

The denominator 2 in the expression $ab/2$ of the area of a right triangle is related to the fact that a rectangle of same dimensions a and b can be divided into two equal right triangles. Likewise, in $abc/6$ the denominator 6 indicates that a rectangular parallelepiped contains six equal right tetrahedrons of same dimensions a, b, c as those of parallelepiped.

Consider now a rectangular octacell bounded by four pairs of parallel and congruent rectangular parallelepipeds, so that all tetrahedral angles of this octacell are right tetrahedral angles, the spaces forming them being perpendicular to each other. Denoting the four dimensions of this right octacell by a, b, c, d we obtain for its hypervolume the expression $abcd$. Comparing it with the corresponding expression $abcd/24$ for the hypervolume of a right pentacell, we come to the conclusion that a right octacell in S_4 contains 24 right and equal pentacells which fill out its hypervolume.

Volume of a Pyramid

A solid bounded by planes is called polyhedron. If all the faces of a poly-hedron except the base are triangles, the solid is a *pyramid*. The base of a pyramid is a polygon with any number of sides, so that we distinguish differ-ent kinds of pyramid according to the shape of the base: triangular (which is a tetrahedron), quadrangular, pentagonal, hexagonal, etc. A pyramid whose base is a *regular* polygon and which, moreover, verifies the condition that the foot of the altitude coincides with the center of the base, is called a *regular* pyramid.

Joining the foot F of the altitude OF of the pyramid (Fig. 15) to vertices of the base, we divide the volume of the pyramid into as many parts as many sides has the base. Each part thus obtained is a tetrahedron of the same altitude OF because OF is a common edge of all tetrahedrons composing the pyramid.

The volume of pyramid is the sum of volumes of these tetrahedrons. If B_1, B_2, ... denote the areas of bases of tetrahedrons, then their volumes are equal to $B_1 h/3$, $B_2 h/3$, ..., etc. Adding these products and picking out their common factor $h/3$, we obtain $h (B_1 + B_2 + + \cdots)/3$, where the sum of terms in the parentheses represents the total area B of the pyramid's base. Therefore, the law $Bh/3$ is now extended to all pyramids.

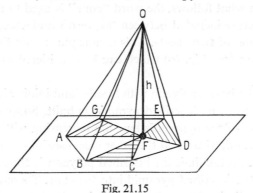

Fig. 21.15

Volume of a Cone

A *cone* is bounded by a curved surface called *conical* and which is generated by a moving straight line, if this line during its motion passes through a *fixed* point (called *vertex* of the cone) and through a variable point, this second point describing a plane closed curve. Thus, the moving straight line, often called *generatrix*, constantly intersects the plane curve which is the *base* of the cone. The perpendicular from the vertex to the plane of the base is the *altitude* of a cone.

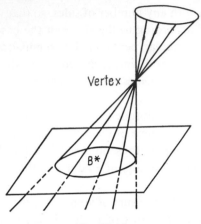

Fig. 21.16

Since a straight line is infinite, a cone extends into infinity in two opposite directions; it consists of two parts, the upper and the lower *sheet*, separated by the vertex. In what follows, the word "cone" is used to denote a part of this infinite structure included between the vertex and a secant plane which intersects only one of two sheets. This secant plane cuts the sheet along a plane closed curve (see Fig. 16) which can be considered as the base of the cone.

Inscribing in the base a polygon with N sides and joining its vertices to the vertex O of the cone, an inscribed pyramid is built. Suppose now that the number N of sides of the pyramid's base are increasing without limit; while the longest side (and, with it, all the other sides) shrinks to a point when N becomes infinite. At the limit the inscribed polygon is transformed into the base-curve and the inscribed pyramid into the cone. Therefore, the volume of the cone is the limit of the volume of the inscribed pyramid. But at every step of the passage to the limit for $N = \infty$, the volume of the inscribed pyramid was expressed by the product $Bh/3$, where h is the cone's altitude and B denotes the variable area of the pyramid's base. Therefore, the variable area B tends to the area of the base-curve of our cone and, at the limit for $N = \infty$, the cone's volume is obtained in the same form $B^*h/3$, where $B^* = \lim B$ is the base-area. Thus, the same rule which was obtained first for the tetrahedron's volume, then extended to the volume of a pyramid is proved now to hold for all cones:

The volume of a cone is equal to one third the product of its base-area by the altitude.

Generalizing this result to the four-dimensional structures in S_4, we build first a *hyperpyramid*, joining the vertices of a polyhedron in s_3 to a point of S_4 non-incident with the space s_3 and which becomes the vertex of this hyperpyramid. The perpendicular dropped from the vertex on the space s_3 is the altitude of a hyperpyramid and its hypervolume is equal to one fourth the product of the base-polyhedron's volume by the altitude of the hyper-pyramid because, by joining the foot of the altitude to the vertices of the base-polyhedrons, a decomposition of the hyperpyramid into pentacells is achieved. We assume that the base-polyhedron was, if needed, itself decom-posed into tetrahedrons. The fundamental fact is again the circumstance that the hyperpyramid's altitude is also the altitude of all these pentacells since it is perpendicular to their bases.

Given a volume bounded by a closed surface, a *hypercone* is built by join-ing every point of this closed surface in s_3 to a point of S_4 non-incident with s_3. Since a closed surface can be approximated by a sequence of in-scribed polyhedrons in such a way that the volume enclosed by this surface is the limit of volumes of polyhedrons when the number of faces tends to infinity (each face shrinking to a point), the hypervolume of the hypercone appears as limit of hypervolumes of inscribed hyperpyramids. Therefore, it is expressed by the same formula $V^* \cdot h/4$, where V^* and h are the base-volume and the altitude of the hypercone.

Frustrum of a Pyramid and of a Cone

The part of a pyramid or of a cone contained between its base and a secant plane parallel to the base is called a *frustrum*. The volume of a frustrum is the difference of volumes of two whole pyramids or cones: $V = BH/3 - bh/3$, where (Fig. 17) B, H and b, h are the base-area and the altitude of pyramids (or cones) whose difference is the given frustrum. The altitude of the frustrum is equal to $H - h$ and the expression of the volume $(BH - bh)/3$ can be transformed in such a way that the altitude of the frustrum becomes the common factor of three terms whose sum expresses the volume.

The similarity of two whole pyramids (or cones) entails the proportion $b/B = h^2/H^2$ since the ratio of corresponding areas is equal to the square of the ratio of corresponding segments. We write this proportion as follows:

$$H/h = B^{1/2}/b^{1/2},$$

so that

$$(H - h)/h = (B^{1/2} - b^{1/2})/b^{1/2}; \quad (H - h)/H = (B^{1/2} - b^{1/2})/B^{1/2}.$$

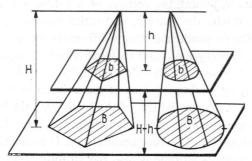

Fig. 21.17

Therefore, solving for H and h, we find

$$H = (H - h) B^{1/2}/(B^{1/2} - b^{1/2}); \quad h = (H - h) b^{1/2}/(B^{1/2} - b^{1/2}).$$

Now the expression of the volume can be written

$$3V = BH - bh = B(H - h) + b(H - h) + (Bh - bH)$$

and the last term $Bh - bH$ can be shown to contain the factor $H - h$:

$$Bh - bH = (H - h) B \cdot b^{1/2}/(B^{1/2} - b^{1/2}) - (H - h) b \cdot B^{1/2}/(B^{1/2} - b^{1/2})$$

$$= (H - h)(Bb)^{1/2}.$$

Thus, the final expression of the volume V of a frustrum (of a pyramid or of a cone) is as follows

$$V = (H - h)[B + (Bb)^{1/2} + b]/3.$$

This result is often expressed in the geometrical form:

The volume of a frustrum of a pyramid (cone) is equal to the sum of volumes of three pyramids (cones) of the altitude of the frustrum and whose base-areas are equal to those of the upper base, the lower base of the frustrum and of the mean proportional between them.

Generalization of Sine and Cosine Laws for Spherical Triangles

The metric properties of solid figures are studied with the aid of metric properties of the tetrahedron just as plane configurations are studied with the aid of triangles. The lengths of edges of a tetrahedron are directly related to plane angles of its four triangular faces, thus the essential problem in the study of the metric properties of the tetrahedron is the relation between its plane angles on one hand and the six dihedral angles on the other hand. There are also trihedral angles, but—as we shall see—these angles are directly related to dihedral angles, so that the interdependence of plane and dihedral angles is the central problem. The study of this problem makes up the content of so-called spherical trigonometry because a spherical triangle is related to a trihedral angle as follows.

Given a trihedral angle OABC (Fig. 18) with its vertex at O, we associate with it a unit sphere whose center is at the vertex O and whose radius is equal to one. The three planes of the trihedral angle AOB, BOC, COA intersect the unit-sphere along great circles and their arcs $\overset{\smile}{AB}$, $\overset{\smile}{BC}$, $\overset{\smile}{CA}$ form on the surface of the unit-sphere a spherical triangle ABC. The dihedral angles formed by three faces of the trihedral angle become angles of the spherical triangle which we will denote simply by capital letters A, B, C instead of $\widehat{BAC}$, $\widehat{CBA}$ and $\widehat{ACB}$ respectively. The sides of the spherical triangle AB,

$$\overset{\smile}{AB} = \gamma$$
$$\overset{\smile}{BC} = \alpha$$
$$\overset{\smile}{CA} = \beta$$
$$\widehat{FOE} = A$$

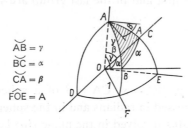

Fig. 21.18

BC, CA (arcs of great circles of the unit-sphere) are equal to the central angles they subtend: that is, to plane angles at the vertex O of the trihedral angle.

Therefore, the study of the interdependence of plane and dihedral angles of a tetrahedron, that is, of a given trihedral angle, can be made under the form of study of spherical triangles which is a very convenient form because of the very close analogy between plane and spherical trigonometry.

First of all we show that the trihedral angle OABC at O is equal to the excess of the sum A + B + C of its three dihedral angles over two right angles, that is, equal to $A + B + C - \pi$. The area of the spherical triangle ABC cut out on the surface of the sphere by the faces of the trihedral angle is directly proportional to the measure of this angle and to the square of the radius R. A right trihedral angle corresponds to an eighth part of the spherical surface, that is, to the area of the spherical triangle ADE, and this area is equal to $\frac{1}{2}\pi R^2$. Thus, *a right trihedral angle is equal to $\frac{1}{2}\pi$*. Now, it was shown in Chapter 17 that the area of a spherical triangle is equal to the product of its *spherical excess* by the square R^2 of the sphere's radius. Therefore, the spherical excess $A + B + C - \pi$ gives the measure of the trihedral angle OABC.

There are a great number of different formulas between the six elements of a spherical triangle, but important among them are formulas involving only *four* elements because any three given elements determine a spherical triangle completely. There are only four groups of such fundamental formulas and fifteen formulas in all: the first group contains three relations involving two sides and two opposite angles each; the second group of three formulas correlates three sides and one angle; its dual transform is the third group of three formulas containing three angles and one side each; finally, there are six formulas of the fourth group called *cotangent formulas* in which two sides are correlated to two angles, one of which is *included* between them. The formulas of the first and of the last group are selfdual.

Sine Law

The sides $\overset{\frown}{AB} = \gamma$, $\overset{\frown}{BC} = \alpha$, $\overset{\frown}{CA} = \beta$ of a spherical triangle ABC are angles (central) expressed in radians and in the spherical sine law their sines replace the side lengths involved in the plane sine law:

$$\text{Sin } \alpha/\text{Sin A} = \text{Sin } \beta/\text{Sin B} = \text{Sin } \gamma/\text{Sin C}$$

$$= 2\text{Cos}\,(\alpha/2)\,\text{Cos}\,(\beta/2)\,\text{Cos}\,(\gamma/2)\,\text{Tan}\,\varrho \tag{20}$$

where ϱ denotes the radius of the circumscribed circle expressed, as sides, in *radians*.

We prove first the equality of the three ratios Sin (side)/Sin (opposite angle); the value of these equal ratios will be computed at the end of this chapter. Taking any point P on the radius OC = R of the sphere (we consider the sphere of any radius R), drop the perpendicular PQ onto the plane OAB and, from the point Q, drop perpendiculars QM and QN onto radii OA and OB respectively. They form two right triangles PQM, PQN with right angles at the vertex Q, and $\widehat{PMQ}$ = A, $\widehat{PNQ}$ = B. Two other right

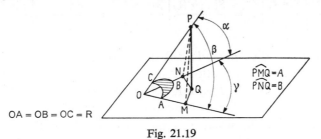

OA = OB = OC = R

Fig. 21.19

triangles are POM and PON with right angles at M and N. Their angles at O are β and α, so that OP · Sin α = NP and OP · Sin β = MP. Multiplying the first relation by Sin B, we obtain OP · Sin α · Sin B = NP · Sin B = PQ because in the triangle PQN the plane angle at N is equal to the dihedral angle between the planes OAB, OBC that is, to the angle B of the spherical triangle, the plane NPQ being perpendicular to the edge OB of this dihedral angle. Thus, the segment PQ is shown to be equal to OP · Sin α · Sin B.

On the other hand, multiplying the relation OP · Sin β = MP by Sin A, we obtain also OP · Sin β · Sin A = MP · Sin A = PQ for the same reason as for NP · Sin B. Thus, the segment PQ is also equal to OP · Sin β · Sin A. Comparing these two expressions of PQ, we have the equality Sin α · Sin B = Sin β · Sin A which gives the equality of two ratios Sinα/Sin A and Sin β/Sin B, thus proving the sine law (20).

It is important to verify that this law (20) is a generalization of the corresponding law in plane trigonometry. If so, the sine law a/Sin A = b/Sin B = c/Sin C for a plane triangle must be deducible from (20) as its particular case. A spherical triangle with fixed *lengths* a = Rα, b = Rβ, c = Rγ of its sides (length of an arc of great circle is equal to the product of the sphere's radius by the central angle) may be transformed into a plane triangle, increasing the radius R of the sphere without limit. Therefore, rewriting the sine law (20) in such a form that the radius R is involved explicitly

$$\text{Sin } (a/\text{R})/\text{Sin A} = \text{Sin } (b/\text{R})/\text{Sin B} = \text{Sin } (c/\text{R})/\text{Sin C}, \qquad (21)$$

we will study what becomes of it for R tending to infinity. The form (21) is obtained from (20), replacing the central angles α, β, γ by the ratios a/R,

b/R, c/R respectively, where a, b, c denote the lengths of arcs $\overset{\frown}{BC}$, $\overset{\frown}{CA}$, $\overset{\frown}{AB}$. Before passing to the limit for $R = \infty$, we multiply each member of (20) by R and write it as follows

$$\frac{\text{Sin } (a/R)}{a/R}\left[\frac{\text{Sin } A}{a}\right]^{-1} = \frac{\text{Sin } (b/R)}{b/R}\left[\frac{\text{Sin } B}{b}\right]^{-1} = \frac{\text{Sin } (c/R)}{c/R}\left[\frac{\text{Sin } C}{c}\right]^{-1}$$

Observing that the ratios a/R, b/R, c/R vanish for $R = \infty$, we conclude that at the limit, for $R = \infty$, the ratios of sines Sin (a/R), Sin (b/R), Sin (c/R) to their vanishing angles a/R, b/R, c/R become equal to one, so that (20) is transformed into the sine law of plane trigonometry as it must be.

The common value $2r$, where r is the *length* of the radius of circumscribed circle, is also the limit of the product of the common value of equal ratios in (20), namely $2 \text{ Cos } (\alpha/2) \cdot \text{Cos } (\beta/2) \cdot \text{Cos } (\gamma/2) \cdot \text{Tan } (r/R)$ since $\text{Cos } 0 = 1$ and, for $R = \infty$, the limit of the product $2R \text{ Tan } (r/R)$ is indeed $2r$.

Duality on the Spherical Surface

The duality on a plane relates straight lines and points. Its generalization correlates, on a spherical survace, great circles and points; the simplest way of realizing spherical duality consists in the replacement of a great circle by its pole and of a point by a great circle perpendicular to all great circles passing through this point.

Applying this dual transformation to a spherical triangle, we replace each vertex by a great circle and each great circle of a side by a point which is the pole of this great circle. Thus, another spherical triangle is formed, whose sides correspond to sides of the original triangle and whose vertices are dual images of great circles of the first triangle.

The dual image of a spherical triangle is called its *polar* triangle. The dual transformation applied to a polar triangle brings us back to the original triangle: if one sphericl triangle is the polar of another, then the second triangle is also the polar of the first. The following theorem is important as source of formulas in spherical trigonometry:

In two polar triangles each angle of the one is the supplement to 180° of a side of the other of which it is the dual image and vice versa each side of the one is the supplement to 180° of an angle of the other of which it is the dual image.

Let us call α', β', γ', A', B', C' the elements of the polar triangle which correspond to those A, B, C, α, β, γ of a given triangle ABC (Fig. 20). Denoting by M and N the intersections of arcs $\overset{\frown}{AC}$, $\overset{\frown}{BC}$ with the arc $\overset{\frown}{A'B'}$, we have $\overset{\frown}{A'N} = \overset{\frown}{MB'} = 90°$, as well as $\overset{\frown}{MN} = C$ because $A'C'$, $B'C'$, $A'B'$ are the equators of poles B, A, C respectively.

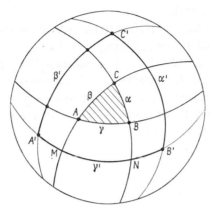

Fig. 21.20

Therefore, evaluating the side γ' of the polar triangle $A'B'C'$, we obtain:

$$\gamma' = \overset{\frown}{A'N} + \overset{\frown}{MB'} - \overset{\frown}{MN} = 180° - C.$$

This yields the proof of our theorem since in the relation $C + \gamma' = 180°$ we can replace C and γ' by C' and γ respectively and thus $C' = 180° - \gamma$.

Applying any formula of spherical trigonometry proved for a triangle whose elements are α, β, γ, A, B, C to its polar triangle, we have the right to replace the elements α, β, γ of the first triangle by $\pi - A, \pi - B, \pi - C$ considered as sides and A, B, C by $\pi - \alpha, \pi - \beta, \pi - \gamma$ considered as angles of another triangle without destroying the validity of the formula. The new formula thus obtained is the dual transform of the first and it may be called its dual companion.

The existence of polar triangle yields an easy proof of the fact that the sum of angles of a spherical triangle exceeds 180°. Moreover, it also gives an upper bound for the same sum. We observe that the sum of sides of a spherical triangle is positive and cannot exceed 360° because it also represents the sum of three plane angles of a trihedral angle (with its vertex at the center of the sphere) and this last sum is necessarily less than 360°. Thus, the sum

28 Kogbetliantz

$(\pi - A) + (\pi - B) + (\pi - C)$ of three sides of the polar triangle verifies the inequalities $0° < 540° - (A + B + C) < 360°$ which is equivalent to $180°$ $< A + B + C < 540°$. If the sum of angles reaches its maximum $540°$ then the triangle degenerates into a great circle, all three sides being arcs of this circle and each angle being equal to $180°$. Such a degenerated triangle makes an exception to the theorem which states that an equiangular triangle is at the same time equilateral.

Applying the dual transformation to the sine law we obtain again the same group of three equal ratios (20) since $\operatorname{Sin}(180° - A) = \operatorname{Sin} A$. Thus, the first group of formulas—the sine law—is selfdual. We pass now to the second group of three formulas forming the so-called cosine-law of spherical trigonometry which is also a generalization of the cosine-law of plane trigonometry, generalization quite different from cosine-law for tetrahedron we considered at the beginning of this chapter.

Cosine Law

Given a spherical triangle ABC on a sphere of radius R, so that the angular measures (in radians) of its sides are equal to the ratios of lengths a, b, c of sides to the radius R of the sphere, $\alpha = a/R$, $\beta = b/R$, $\gamma = c/R$, we draw a plane through the vertex C and tangent to the sphere so that the straight lines CD and CE are tangent to the sides $\overset{\smile}{AC}$ and $\overset{\smile}{BC}$. The line DE belongs to the intersection-line of this plane with the plane OAB, and it is a common side of two triangles CDE and DEO.

Applying the cosine-law of plane trigonometry to these two triangles, we express the square of their common side DE in two different ways. Comparing the two expressions thus obtained for DE^2, cosine-law of spherical trigonometry is deduced.

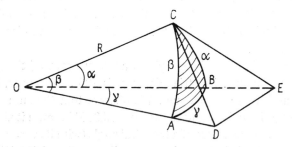

Fig. 21.21

We have indeed from the triangle CDE (Fig. 23)

$$DE^2 = CD^2 + CE^2 - 2CD \cdot CE \cdot Cos\, C,$$

where, from right triangles OCD and OCE, we have $CD = OC \tan \beta$ and $CE = OC \tan \alpha$. But $OC = R$ (radius of the sphere) and thus

$$DE^2/R^2 = Tan^2\beta + Tan^2\alpha - 2\, Tan\, \alpha \cdot Tan\, \beta \cdot Cos\, C.$$

On the other hand, from the triangle ODE, we find that

$$DE^2 = OD^2 + OE^2 - 2 \cdot OD \cdot OE \cdot Cos\, \gamma$$

$$= R^2(Sec^2\beta + Sec^2\alpha - 2\, Sec\, \alpha \cdot Sec\, \beta \cdot Cos\, \gamma)$$

because $R = OC = OD \cdot Cos\, \beta = OE \cdot Cos\, \alpha$, so that $OD = R \cdot Sec\, \beta$ and $OE = R \cdot Sec\, \alpha$. Dividing both members by R^2 and comparing the second expression for DE^2/R^2 thus obtained

$$DE^2/R^2 = Sec^2\beta + Sec^2\alpha - 2\, Sec\, \alpha \cdot Sec\, \beta \cdot Cos\, \gamma$$

with the first, we deduce the relation

$$Tan^2\beta + Tan^2\alpha - 2\, Tan\, \alpha \cdot Tan\, \beta \cdot Cos\, C$$

$$= Sec^2\beta + Sec^2\alpha - 2\, Sec\, \alpha \cdot Sec\, \beta \cdot Cos\, \gamma.$$

Replacing $Sec^2\beta$ and $Sec^2\alpha$ by their values $1 + Tan^2\beta$, $1 + Tan^2\alpha$ and dividing both sides by 2, we have: $Sec\, \alpha \cdot Sec\, \beta \cdot Cos\, \gamma = 1 + Tan\, \alpha \cdot Tan\beta \times Cos\, C$. A multiplication by $Cos\, \alpha \cdot Cos\, \beta$ transforms this relation into the usual form of the cosine law, namely

$$Cos\, \gamma = Cos\, \alpha \cdot Cos\, \beta + Sin\, \alpha \cdot Sin\, \beta \cdot Cos\, C. \qquad (22)$$

There are two other formulas of the same group which express $Cos\, \alpha$ and $Cos\, \beta$ in terms of functions of two other sides and of the cosine of the opposite angle. They are deduced by the same reasoning, using planes tangent to the sphere at points A and B. To write them down the so-called circular substitution may be applied. It consists in the simultaneous substitution of sides and angles in the following order: $A \rightarrow B \rightarrow C \rightarrow A$ and $\alpha \rightarrow \beta \rightarrow \gamma \rightarrow \alpha$. Thus,

$$Cos\, \alpha = Cos\, \beta \cdot Cos\, \gamma + Sin\, \beta \cdot Sin\, \gamma \cdot Cos\, A$$

$$Cos\, \beta = Cos\, \gamma \cdot Cos\, \alpha + Sin\, \gamma \cdot Sin\, \alpha \cdot Cos\, B. \qquad (23)$$

We now show that the spherical cosine-law reduces to the plane cosine-law when the radius R of the sphere becomes infinite. To verify this we rewrite the cosine-law (22) replacing α, β, γ by a/R, b/R, c/R and the three cosines Cos (a/R), Cos (b/R), Cos (c/R) by $1 - 2$ Sin$^2 (a/2R)$, $1 - 2$ Sin$^2 (b/2R)$ and $1 - 2$ Sin$^2 (c/2R)$ respectively:

$$1 - 2 \text{ Sin}^2 (c/2R) = 1 - 2 \text{ Sin}^2 (a/2R) - 2 \text{ Sin}^2 (b/2R) + 4 \text{ Sin}^2 (a/2R) \times$$

$$\times \text{ Sin}^2 (b/2R) + \text{ Sin } (a/R) \cdot \text{ Sin } (b/R) \cdot \text{ Cos } C.$$

Cancelling the term 1 on both sides, dividing by -2 and multiplying by R^2, we obtain the relation

$$[R \cdot \text{ Sin } (c/2R)]^2 = [R \cdot \text{ Sin } (a/2R)]^2 + [R \cdot \text{ Sin } (b/2R)^2$$

$$- \tfrac{1}{2} (R \text{ Sin } (a/R)) \cdot [R \text{ Sin } (b/R)] \cdot \text{ Coc } C$$

$$- 2 [R \text{ Sin } (a/2R) \text{ Sin } (b/2R)]^2 \tag{24}$$

which is another form of the cosine-law (22).

Now the passage to the limit for $R = \infty$ is prepared because in (24) we have only products of the general type $R \cdot$ Sin (k/R) whose limits are obtained as follows:

$$\lim_{R = \infty} [R \cdot \text{ Sin } (k/R)] = k \cdot \lim_{R = \infty} [\text{Sin } (k/R)/(k/R) = k.$$

Thus, passing to the limit for $R = \infty$ in (24), we obtain

$$(c/2)^2 = (a/2)^2 + (b/2)^2 - \tfrac{1}{2} ab \cdot \text{ Cos } C,$$

because the term 2 [R Sin $(a/2R)$ Sin $(b/2R)]^2$ vanishes for $R = \infty$. Multiplying the result of the passage to the limit by 4, the plane cosine-law is obtained.

Third Group of Formulas

We deduce now the three formulas of the third group, transforming the cosine-law by duality. Substituting in (22) $\pi - A$, $\pi - B$, $\pi - C$ for α, β, γ and $\pi - \gamma$ for C and applying the relation Cos $(180° - z) = -$Cos z, we have $-$Cos $C =$ Cos $A \cdot$ Cos $B -$ Sin $A \cdot$ Sin $B \cdot$ Cos γ, that is, changing the signs and using the circular substitution

$$\left. \begin{aligned} \text{Cos } C &= -\text{Cos } A \cdot \text{Cos } B + \text{Sin } A \cdot \text{Sin } B \cdot \text{Cos } \gamma \\ \text{Cos } A &= -\text{Cos } B \cdot \text{Cos } C + \text{Sin } B \cdot \text{Sin } C \cdot \text{Cos } \alpha \\ \text{Cos } B &= -\text{Cos } C \cdot \text{Cos } A + \text{Sin } C \cdot \text{Sin } A \cdot \text{Cos } \beta. \end{aligned} \right\} \tag{25}$$

This third group of formulae is a special feature of the spherical trigonometry. It is impossible in Euclidean geometry to find the three sides of a plane triangle whose three angles are known: the existence of similar triangles proves that the *shape* of a triangle (values of its angles) does not determine its *size* (lengths of its sides). We know that this is due to the Fifth Postulate which does not hold on the surface of a sphere.

Therefore, there is nothing surprising in the fact that formulas (25) allow us to find the sides of a spherical triangle, if its three angles are known. To compute the lengths $a = R\alpha$, $b = R\beta$, $c = R\gamma$ of the sides it is sufficient to know their angular measures α, β, γ and these angles are easy to find solving the relations (25) with respect to $\text{Cos}\,\alpha$, $\text{Cos}\,\beta$, $\text{Cos}\,\gamma$. It is of interest to study what is the final form of the expressions of sides in terms of angles obtained by the solution of (25).

Before performing this solution we observe that the same algebraical operations can be applied to the formulas of the second group, but it is sufficient to apply them to the formulas of the one of two groups because the dual transformation of the result will give the solution of the parallel problem for the other group. We choose the third group and express the cosines of sides in terms of functions of angles as follows. The product $\text{Sin}\,A \times \text{Sin}\,B \cdot \text{Cos}\,\gamma$ is equal to the sum of two terms $\text{Cos}\,C + \text{Cos}\,A \cdot \text{Cos}\,B$, so that, adding and subtracting $\text{Sin}\,A \cdot \text{Sin}\,B$, we form the expressions

$$\text{Sin}\,A.\,\text{Sin}\,B\,(1 + \text{Cos}\,\gamma) = \text{Cos}\,(A - B) + \text{Cos}\,C$$

$$= 2\,\text{Cos}\,[\tfrac{1}{2}\,(A - B + C)].\,\text{Cos}\,[\tfrac{1}{2}\,(-A + B + C)]$$

$$-\,\text{Sin}\,A.\,\text{Sin}\,B\,(1 - \text{Cos}\,\gamma) = \text{Cos}\,(A + B) + \text{Cos}\,C$$

$$= 2\,\text{Cos}\,[\tfrac{1}{2}\,(A + B + C)].\,\text{Cos}\,[\tfrac{1}{2}\,(A + B - C)].$$

Now, denoting the spherical excess of the triangle by $2t$, so that $A + B + C = \pi + 2t$, we write the arguments of cosines in the righthand members as follows: $\tfrac{1}{2}\,(A - B + C) = 90° + t - B$, $\tfrac{1}{2}\,(-A + B + C) = 90° + t - A$, $\tfrac{1}{2}\,(A + B + C) = 90° + t$ and $\tfrac{1}{2}\,(A + B - C) = 90° + t - C$. Therefore, the righthand members can be written as $2\,\text{Cos}\,(90 + t - B)\,\text{Cos}\,(90° + t - A) = 2\,\text{Sin}\,(A - t)\,\text{Sin}\,(B - t)$ and $-2\,\text{Sin}\,t \cdot \text{Sin}\,(C - t)$ respectively.

On the other hand, $1 + \text{Cos}\,\gamma = 2 \cdot \text{Cos}^2(\gamma/2)$ and $1 - \text{Cos}\,\gamma = 2\,\text{Sin}^2(\gamma/2)$. Thus, we obtain

$$2\,\text{Sin}\,A \cdot \text{Sin}\,B \cdot \text{Cos}^2(\gamma/2) = 2\,\text{Sin}\,(A - t)\,\text{Sin}\,(B - t)$$

$$2\,\text{Sin}\,A \cdot \text{Sin}\,B \cdot \text{Sin}^2(\gamma/2) = 2\,\text{Sin}\,(C - t)\,\text{Sin}\,t.$$

Dividing member by member and extracting the square root, we finally obtain the expressions of cotangents of half-angles $\alpha/2$, $\beta/2$, $\gamma/2$:

$$\text{Cotan} (\gamma/2) = [\text{Sin} (A - t) \, \text{Sin} (B - t)/\text{Sin} (C - t) \, \text{Sin} \, t]^{1/2}$$

$$\text{Cotan} (\alpha/2) = [\text{Sin} (B - t) \, \text{Sin} (C - t)/\text{Sin} (A - t) \, \text{Sin} \, t]^{1/2} \qquad (26)$$

$$\text{Cotan} (\beta/2) = [\text{Sin} (C - t) \, \text{Sin} (A - t)/\text{Sin} (B - t) \, \text{Sin} \, t]^{1/2}.$$

The dual transforms of the formulas (26) are obtained, observing that $A + B + C = 180° + 2t$ must be replaced by $540° - 2s$ (where $2s = \alpha + \beta + \gamma$), so that $180° + 2t$ becomes $540° - 2s$ and therefore t is to be replaced by $180° - s$. This entails the transformation of the difference $A - t$ into $(180° - \alpha) - (180° - s) = s - \alpha$, and likewise of $B - t$ and $C - t$ into $s - \beta$ and $s - \gamma$ respectively. Thus, the formulas (26), when transformed by duality, become

$$\text{Tan} \tfrac{1}{2}C = [\text{Sin} (s - \alpha) \cdot \text{Sin} (s - \beta)/\text{Sin} (s - \gamma) \, \text{Sin} \, s]^{1/2}$$

$$\text{Tan} \tfrac{1}{2}A = [\text{Sin} (s - \beta) \cdot \text{Sin} (s - \gamma)/\text{Sin} (s - \alpha) \, \text{Sin} \, s]^{1/2} \qquad (27)$$

$$\text{Tan} \tfrac{1}{2}B = [\text{Sin} (s - \gamma) \cdot \text{Sin} (s - \alpha)/\text{Sin} (s - \beta) \, \text{Sin} \, s]^{1/2}$$

$$\left(s = \frac{\alpha + \beta + \gamma}{2} \right).$$

With the aid of (27) it is easy to compute the angles of a spherical triangle whose sides are known. We do not perform the passage to the limit for $R = \infty$ in the formulas (26), (27), but simply state that this passage to the limit yields, as particular cases of spherical formulas (26) and (27), the following relations of the plane trigonometry:

$$2/c = [2 \, \text{Sin} \, A \cdot \text{Sin} \, B/(S \cdot \text{Sin} \, C)]^{1/2},$$

where S denotes the area of the plane triangle obtained at the limit, and

$$\text{Tan} \tfrac{1}{2}C = [(p - a)(p - b)/(p - c) \, p]^{1/2},$$

$p = \tfrac{1}{2} (a + b + c)$ being half the perimeter of the plane triangle.

It is of interest to show that the third group of formulas, (25), gives, at the limit for $R = \infty$, the proof that the sum of angles of a plane triangle is equal to 180°. We have indeed, if the length c of a side remains finite while R increases without limit, $\lim_{R = \infty} \gamma = \lim_{R = \infty} (c/R) = 0$ and therefore $\lim_{R = \infty} \text{Cos} \, \gamma = 1$. Thus, the first formula (25) becomes at the limit for $R = \infty$, $\text{Cos} \, C + \text{Cos} \, A \, \text{Cos} \, B - \text{Sin} \, A \cdot \text{Sin} \, B = 0$; that is, $\text{Cos} \, C + \text{Cos} (A + B) = 0$.

This can be written Cos $[\frac{1}{2}(A + B + C)] \cdot$ Cos $[\frac{1}{2}(A + B - C)] = 0$. The second factor cannot vanish because the absolute value of the angle $\frac{1}{2}(A + B - C)$ is less than 90°. Therefore, it is the first factor, Cos $[\frac{1}{2}(A + B + C)]$, which vanishes and this proves that the angle $\frac{1}{2}(A + B + C)$ is equal to 90°, so that $A + B + C = 180°$.

Cotangent Formulas

We now describe the structure of six formulas forming the fourth group. The lefthand member of a cotangent formula is a product of two cosines one of which is cosine of a side, while the other is cosine of an adjacent angle. Thus, there are two formulas with Cos α: the lefthand member of the one is Cos $\alpha \cdot$ Cos B while that of the other is Cos $\alpha \cdot$ Cos C. This explains the total number six of formulas of the fourth group.

The righthand member is a difference of two products. The first term involves the sine of the same side whose cosine is one of factors of the lefthand member; this sine is multiplied by the cotangent of another side also, the side being *adjacent* to the angle whose cosine is factor in the lefthand member. Finally, the second term is also a product of a sine by a cotangent, their arguments being angles: the argument of the sine is the same angle whose cosine stands in the lefthand member, while the argument of the cotangent is the angle opposite to the side whose cotangent stands in the first, positive, term of the righthand member.

Therefore, in each formula of the fourth group six trigonometric functions are involved: two sines, two cosines and two cotangents. Two of six elements of a spherical triangle are absent in each formula: one angle and one side adjacent to this angle. The lefthand member is the product of cosines of elements opposite to those not present in this formula. Thus, if γ and A are absent, then the lefthand member must be the product Cos $\alpha \cdot$ Cos C. The first term in the righthand member is Sin $\alpha \cdot$ Cotan β and the second —Sin C $\cdot$ Cotan B:

$$\text{Cos } \alpha \cdot \text{Cos C} = \text{Sin } \alpha \cdot \text{Cotan } \beta - \text{Sin C} \cdot \text{Cotan B}. \qquad (28)$$

PROOF. Consider two formulas of the second group

$$\text{Cos } \gamma = \text{Cos } \alpha \cdot \text{Cos } \beta + \text{Sin } \alpha \cdot \text{Sin } \beta \cdot \text{Cos C}$$

$$\text{Cos } \beta = \text{Cos } \gamma \cdot \text{Cos } \alpha + \text{Sin } \gamma \cdot \text{Sin } \alpha \cdot \text{Cos B}$$

and substitute in the first term of the righthand member of second formula for Cos γ its expression given by the first formula:

$$\text{Cos } \beta = \text{Cos}^2\alpha \cdot \text{Cos } \beta + \text{Sin } \alpha \cdot \text{Sin } \beta \cdot \text{Cos } \alpha \cdot \text{Cos C}$$

$$+ \text{Sin } \gamma \cdot \text{Sin } \alpha \cdot \text{Cos B.}$$

Transposing the term $\text{Cos}^2\alpha \cdot \text{Cos } \beta$ to the left and performing its subtraction from Cos β, we obtain $\text{Cos } \beta \cdot (1 - \text{Cos}^2\alpha) = \text{Cos } \beta \cdot \text{Sin}^2\alpha$, so that Sin α appears as common factor in all the terms of our relation. Dividing by it, we obtain

$$\text{Sin } \alpha \cdot \text{Cos } \beta = \text{Sin } \beta \cdot \text{Cos } \alpha \cdot \text{Cos C} + \text{Sin } \gamma \cdot \text{Cos B.}$$

Transposing the term Sin $\gamma \cdot$ Cos B to the left and dividing by Sin β, we obtain

$$\text{Sin } \alpha \cdot \text{Cotan } \beta - \text{Cotan B} \cdot \text{Sin B} \cdot \text{Sin } \gamma/\text{Sin } \beta = \text{Cos } \alpha \cdot \text{Cos C}$$

which is the formula (28) because the sine-law gives the relation Sin B $\times$ (Sin γ/Sin β) = Sin B $\cdot$ (Sin C/Sin B) = Sin C and the second term is therefore equal to Cotan B $\cdot$ Sin B (Sin γ/Sin β) = Cotan B $\cdot$ Sin C.

Substituting in the first term of the righthand member of the first formula for Cos β its expression given by the second formula, we deduce in the same way the cotangent formula for the product Cos $\alpha \cdot$ Cos B, namely

$$\text{Cos } \alpha \cdot \text{Cos B} = \text{Sin } \alpha \cdot \text{Cotan } \gamma - \text{Sin B} \cdot \text{Cotan C.} \qquad (29)$$

The four other cotangent formulas are obtained from (28) and (29) with the aid of circular substitution. They are not written down since the structure of such a formula is now completely clear.

The passage to the limit for R $= \infty$ in (28) is prepared multiplying this formula by R $\cdot$ Sin β:

$$\text{R Sin } \beta \cdot \text{Cos } \alpha \cdot \text{Cos C} = \text{R Sin } \alpha \cdot \text{Cos } \beta - \text{R Sin } \beta \cdot \text{Sin C} \cdot \text{Cotan B.}$$

Since $\lim_{R=\infty} (\text{R} \cdot \text{Sin } \alpha) = a$ and $\lim_{R=\infty} (\text{R} \cdot \text{Sin } \beta) = b$, while $\lim_{R=\infty} \text{Cos } \alpha = \lim_{R=\infty} \text{Cos} \beta$ $= 1$, at the limit for R $= \infty$ the relation (29) is transformed into

$$b \cdot \text{Cos C} = a \cdot - b \cdot \text{Sin C} \cdot \text{Cotan B}$$

which gives $a = b \cdot \text{Cos C} + c \cdot \text{Cos B}$ because $b \cdot \text{Sin C} \cdot \text{Cotan B} = c$ $\times$ Cos B (sine-law). Therefore, the cotangent formulas of spherical trigonometry generalize the projectiou's relations in a plane triangle.

Radius of Inscribed Circle

Three bisectors of the angles of a spherical triangle meet at the center of inscribed circle (Fig. 22) O and the contact points A*, B*, C* divide the sides $\alpha = \overset{\frown}{BC}$, $\beta = \overset{\frown}{CA}$, $\gamma = \overset{\frown}{AB}$ in segments v and w, w and u, u and v respectively, so that $u + v = \gamma$, $v + w = \alpha$, $w + u = \beta$. Adding, we find that $u + v + w = s = \frac{1}{2}(\alpha + \beta + \gamma)$ and therefore $u = s - \alpha$, $v = s - \beta$, $w = s - \gamma$. Consider now the right triangle AC*O. Applying to it the cotangent formula, we express the product $\mathrm{Cos}\,(s - \alpha) \cdot \mathrm{Cos}\,C^*$:

$$\mathrm{Cos}\,(s - \alpha) \cdot \mathrm{Cos}\,C^* = \mathrm{Sin}\,(s - \alpha) \cdot \mathrm{Cotan}\,(r/R) - \mathrm{Sin}\,C^*\,\mathrm{Cotan}\,(A/2),$$

where r/R denotes the radius of the inscribed circle. But in this relation the angle C* is a right angle and therefore $\mathrm{Cos}\,C^* = 0$, $\mathrm{Sin}\,C^* = 1$. Thus, we have $\mathrm{Sin}\,(s - \alpha) \cdot \mathrm{Cotan}\,(r/R) = \mathrm{Cotan}\,(A/2)$; that is,

$$\mathrm{Tan}\,(r/R) = \mathrm{Tan}\,(A/2) \cdot \mathrm{Sin}\,(s - \alpha). \tag{30}$$

On the other hand, $\mathrm{Tan}\,(A/2) = [\mathrm{Sin}\,(s - \beta)\,\mathrm{Sin}\,(s - \gamma)/\mathrm{Sin}\,(s - \alpha)\,\mathrm{Sin}\,s]^{1/2}$ (see formula 27) and therefore

$$\mathrm{Tan}\,(r/R) = [\mathrm{Sin}\,(s - \alpha)\,\mathrm{Sin}\,(s - \beta)\,\mathrm{Sin}\,(s - \gamma)\,\mathrm{Sin}\,s]^{1/2}/\mathrm{Sin}\,s.$$

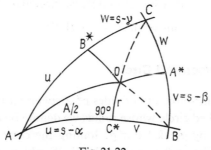

Fig. 21.22

The product of four sines standing under the radical plays important role in spherical trigonometry and for this reason we will denote it by a special symbol G: $G = \mathrm{Sin}\,(s - \alpha)\,\mathrm{Sin}\,(s - \beta)\,\mathrm{Sin}\,(s - \gamma)\,\mathrm{Sin}\,s$, so that

$$\mathrm{Tan}\,(r/R) = G^{1/2}/\mathrm{Sin}\,s. \tag{31}$$

Solving the relations (25) for cosines of sides, we deduced two results:

$$\mathrm{Sin}\,A \cdot \mathrm{Sin}\,B \cdot 2\mathrm{Cos}^2\,\tfrac{1}{2}\gamma = 2 \cdot \mathrm{Sin}\,(A - t)\,\mathrm{Sin}\,(B - t)$$
$$\mathrm{Sin}\,A \cdot \mathrm{Sin}\,B \cdot 2\mathrm{Sin}^2\,\tfrac{1}{2}\gamma = 2 \cdot \mathrm{Sin}\,(C - t)\,\mathrm{Sin}\,t, \tag{32}$$

where $2t = A + B + C - \pi$ denotes the spherical excess. Multiplying these relations member by member and observing that $4 \cdot \mathrm{Sin}^2(\tfrac{1}{2}\gamma)\,\mathrm{Cos}^2(\tfrac{1}{2}\gamma)$

$= \mathrm{Sin}^2 \gamma$, we find that

$\mathrm{Sin}^2 A \cdot \mathrm{Sin}^2 B \cdot \mathrm{Sin}^2 \gamma = 4\,\mathrm{Sin}\,(A - t)\,\mathrm{Sin}\,(B - t)\,\mathrm{Sin}\,(C - t)\,\mathrm{Sin}\,t = 4H$,

introducing a special symbol H for the product $\mathrm{Sin}\,(A - t)\,\mathrm{Sin}\,(B - t)$ $\times \mathrm{Sin}\,(C - t)\,\mathrm{Sin}\,t$. Therefore, dividing by $(\mathrm{Sin}\,A \cdot \mathrm{Sin}\,B \cdot \mathrm{Sin}\,C)^2$ and extracting the square root, we find the common value of equal ratios in the expression (20) of the sine-law

$$\mathrm{Sin}\,\alpha/\mathrm{Sin}\,A = \mathrm{Sin}\,\beta/\mathrm{Sin}\,B = \mathrm{Sin}\,\gamma/\mathrm{Sin}\,C = 2H^{1/2}/(\mathrm{Sin}\,A \cdot \mathrm{Sin}\,B \cdot \mathrm{Sin}\,C). \quad (33)$$

Transforming these results by duality, we find also

$$\mathrm{Sin}\,A/\mathrm{Sin}\,\alpha = \mathrm{Sin}\,B/\mathrm{Sin}\,\beta = \mathrm{Sin}\,C/\mathrm{Sin}\,\gamma = 2G^{1/2}/(\mathrm{Sin}\,\alpha \cdot \mathrm{Sin}\,\beta \cdot \mathrm{Sin}\,\gamma) \quad (34)$$

because the dual transform of H is $G = \mathrm{Sin}\,(s - \alpha)\,\mathrm{Sin}\,(s - \beta)\,\mathrm{Sin}\,(s - \gamma)$ $\times \mathrm{Sin}\,s$.

Dividing (33) member by member by (34), one finds

$$(\mathrm{Sin}\,\alpha/\mathrm{Sin}\,A)^2 = (H/G)^{1/2}\,(\mathrm{Sin}\,\alpha/\mathrm{Sin}\,A)^3, \quad (35)$$

because the sine-law shows that

$$\mathrm{Sin}\,\alpha \cdot \mathrm{Sin}\,\beta \cdot \mathrm{Sin}\,\gamma/\mathrm{Sin}\,A \cdot \mathrm{Sin}\,B \cdot \mathrm{Sin}\,C = (\mathrm{Sin}\,\alpha/\mathrm{Sin}\,A)^3.$$

Therefore, dividing (35) by $(\mathrm{Sin}\,\alpha/\mathrm{Sin}\,A)^2$, we find also that

$$\mathrm{Sin}\,\alpha/\mathrm{Sin}\,A = (G/H)^{1/2}.$$

Radius of Circumscribed Circle

Three perpendicular bisectors of sides of a spherical triangle meet at the center of circumscribed circle whose radius we denote by r_c (length), the ratio r_c/R being denoted by greek letter ϱ. Joining the center O to the vertices A, B, C, we divide the angles in parts U, V, W which verify the equations $U + V = C$, $V + W = A$, $W + U = B$. Therefore, one finds that $U + V + W = \frac{1}{2}(A + B + C) = \frac{1}{2}(180° + 2t) = 90° + t$ and thus $U = 90° - (A - t)$, $V = 90° - (B - t)$ and $W = 90° - (C - t)$.

Consider now the triangle AOB* and apply to its four elements ϱ, V, $\beta/2$ and angle $B^* = 90°$ the cotangent formula expressing the product $\mathrm{Cos}\,V \times \mathrm{Cos}\,\frac{1}{2}\beta$:

$$\mathrm{Cos}\,V \cdot \mathrm{Cos}\,(\tfrac{1}{2}\beta) = \mathrm{Sin}\,(\tfrac{1}{2}\beta) \cdot \mathrm{Cotan}\,\varrho - \mathrm{Sin}\,V \cdot \mathrm{Cotan}\,B^*.$$

But $\mathrm{Cotan}\,90° = 0$ and therefore, dividing by $\mathrm{Sin}\,(\tfrac{1}{2}\beta)$, $\mathrm{Cotan}\,\varrho$ is found:

$$\mathrm{Cotan}\,\varrho = \mathrm{Cotan}\,(\tfrac{1}{2}\beta) \cdot \mathrm{Sin}\,(B - t)$$

since $\mathrm{Cos}\,V = \mathrm{Cos}\,[90° - (B - t)] = \mathrm{Sin}\,(B - t)$.

On the other hand, by (26) we have $\text{Cotan}\,(\tfrac{1}{2}\beta) = H^{1/2}/\text{Sin}\,(B - t)\cdot\text{Sin}\,t$. Therefore, the radius of circumscribed circle can be computed with the aid of

$$\text{Cotan}\,\varrho = H^{1/2}/\text{Sin}\,t. \tag{36}$$

It remains to prove that the common value of ratios in the expression (20) of the sine law is equal to $2\cdot\text{Cos}\,(\tfrac{1}{2}\alpha)\cdot\text{Cos}\,(\tfrac{1}{2}\beta)\,\text{Cos}\,(\tfrac{1}{2}\gamma)\,\text{Tan}\,\varrho$.

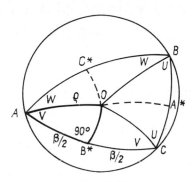

Fig. 21.23

Taking the first formula (32) and applying the circular substitution, we have:

$$\text{Cos}^2\,(\tfrac{1}{2}\alpha) = \text{Sin}\,(B - t)\,\text{Sin}\,(C - t)/\text{Sin}\,B\cdot\text{Sin}\,C;$$

$$\text{Cos}^2\,(\tfrac{1}{2}\beta) = \text{Sin}\,(C - t)\,\text{Sin}\,(A - t)/\text{Sin}\,C\cdot\text{Sin}\,A$$

$$\text{Cos}^2\,(\tfrac{1}{2}\gamma) = \text{Sin}\,(A - t)\,\text{Sin}\,(B - t)/\text{Sin}\,A\cdot\text{Sin}\,B.$$

Multiplying these squares of cosines and multiplying their product by $4\,\text{Sin}^2\,t$, we obtain using (33)

$$4\,\text{Sin}^2\,t\cdot\text{Cos}^2\,(\tfrac{1}{2}\alpha)\,\text{Cos}^2\,(\tfrac{1}{2}\beta)\,\text{Cos}^2\,(\tfrac{1}{2}\gamma) = 4H^2/(\text{Sin}^2\,A\cdot\text{Sin}^2\,B\cdot\text{Sin}^2\,C)$$

$$= H\cdot(\text{Sin}\,\alpha/\text{Sin}\,A)^2 \tag{37}$$

On the other hand, the expression (36) of the $\text{Cotan}\,\varrho$ shows that $\text{Sin}\,t = H^{1/2}\,\text{Tan}\,\varrho$, so that the relation (37), after the extraction of the square root, yields

$$H^{1/2}\,(\text{Sin}\,\alpha/\text{Sin}\,A) = 2\,\text{Sin}\,t\cdot\text{Cos}\,(\tfrac{1}{2}\alpha)\,\text{Cos}\,(\tfrac{1}{2}\beta)\,\text{Cos}\,(\tfrac{1}{2}\gamma)$$

$$= H^{1/2}\cdot2\,\text{Cos}\,(\tfrac{1}{2}\alpha)\,\text{Cos}\,(\tfrac{1}{2}\beta)\,\text{Cos}\,(\tfrac{1}{2}\gamma)\,\text{Tan}\,\varrho,$$

and thus justifies (20).

The application of fifteen fundamental formulas of spherical trigonometry to the solution of spherical triangles is discussed in the next chapter.

CHAPTER 22

Area and Volume of a Sphere.
Solution of Spherical Triangles

Among the curved surfaces, cylinders and cones are the simplest. Therefore, their study must precede the definition and computation of area and
volume of a sphere. The profound difference between cylinders and cones
on one hand, and spheres on the other hand, is due to the possibility of
developing a cylindrical or conical surface on a plane by cutting it along a
rectilinear element and rolling it out flat while this is impossible to do with
a spherical surface. This explains why the computation of area of a cylinder
or of a cone is easy and does not need a preliminary definition of the concept
of such an area: although a cylindrical or conical surface is a curved surface
and so is also its area, by rolling it out flat we transform such an area into an
equal *plane* area and can measure it as such.

Cylinders

Suppose that an infinite straight line moves through space, remaining
always parallel to a fixed direction and always intersecting a given fixed
curve (space curve or, in particular, a plane curve). It occupies at each
moment a definite position and the totality of all the positions occupied by
the moving line during its motion, considered altogether as an entity, forms
a surface called a *cylinder*. Thus, a cylinder is always parallel to some direction. The straight lines composing a cylindrical surface are called *rulings* of
this surface or, sometimes, *elements*. Any section of a cylinder by a plane
non-parallel to the direction of cylinder is a plane curve and may be considered
as the base of this cylinder. If the base of a cylinder is a normal section, its
plane being perpendicular to the direction of the cylinder, the cylinder is
called a *right* cylinder. A cylinder is open if its base is not a closed curve.
When the base of a cylinder is a closed curve, the cylinder extends into

infinity in two opposite directions only. An open cylinder may extend into infinity in a direction different from that of its rulings, for example, a parabolic cylinder is open. Another example is represented by a plane which belongs to cylinders: a cylinder whose base is a straight line is simply a plane.

Conical surfaces are particular cases of a more general class of *ruled* surfaces; that is, of surfaces formed with the aid of straight lines as their elements. Cylinders belong to conical surfaces and, to show it, we first define a conical surface. Suppose that a straight line rotates in such a way that it pivots around a fixed point, while its intersection-point with a given space curve moves on this curve. The totality of all the positions occupied in space by the moving line forms a surface. This surface, called *cone*, has a vertex V through which pass all the rulings of this cone. A cone has two parts, called *sheets*, connected only at the vertex. Thus, two fixed elements are involved in the definition of a conical surface: a point, vertex V, and a curve C lying on the cone and whose points are joined to the point V by the rulings.

Suppose now that the vertex V of a conical surface recedes along a certain straight line L and finally disappears, becoming the point at infinity of this straight line L. Since the vertex is at infinity, the rulings at the limit become parallel to the line L and therefore form a cylinder, defined by the curve C and the direction of the straight line L. When the vertex of a cone is rejected to infinity, one of two sheets also disappears, but the other becomes a cylinder.

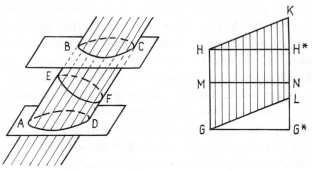

Fig. 22.1

The area ABCD (Fig. 1) of a cylinder bounded by two parallel planes which, in general, are not perpendicular to the rulings of the cylinder, is equivalent to that of a rectangle whose base is the length of a normal section EF of the cylinder by a plane perpendicular to the rulings and whose height is the length of equal segments intercepted on the rulings by two parallel planes. To prove this proposition we roll out flat the cylindrical surface ABCD on a plane, thus transforming it into an equivalent area of a parallelogram GHKL bounded by two pairs of parallel and equal segments GH = KL and HK = GL. Since the arc EF of the normal section is at each of its points perpendicular to the ruling through this point, rolling out the surface ABCD we transform EF into the rectilinear segment MN perpendicular to parallel lines GH and KL. Applying now the principle of Cavalieri, we consider the area GHKL as a sum of segments parallel and equal to the segment GH. Shifting them downward to the parallel GG* to the line MN, we do not change the magnitude of the area GHKL and at the same time we transform its shape into a rectangle GG*HH* with the base GG* = MN = EF and the height GH = AB, so that our proposition is proved.

If a cylinder is closed, then its section is a closed curve. Moreover, for a right closed cylinder the base curve is its normal section, so that the *lateral surface* of a closed cylinder is equal to the perimeter (length) of its base multiplied by the distance of its two bases, that is, by the height of the cylinder. In particular, the lateral surface of a right *circular* cylinder is equal to the product $2\pi r h$, where r is the radius of the circular cylinder and h is its height. Adding to the lateral surface the areas of two bases, that is, adding to $2\pi r h$ the doubled area $2\pi r^2$ of a circle with radius r, we obtain the total area $2\pi r (r + h)$ of a right circular cylinder of radius r and height h.

The volume enclosed within it is equal to the product $\pi r^2 h$ of the area πr^2 of its base and its height h. In Chapter 21 we saw that the volume of a right triangular prism whose base is a *right* triangle is equal to one half the product abc of its dimensions. The area of the base is equal to $\frac{1}{2}ab$, so that the volume of such a prism is obtained multiplying the area of its base $\frac{1}{2}ab$ by the height c of the prism. Any triangle can be divided into two right triangles and, therefore, any right triangular prism is a sum of two such prisms with right triangles as bases. Therefore, the volume of any right triangular prism is also equal to the product Bh, where B is the area of its triangular base and h is the altitude. A right prism may have any polygon as its base, but every polygon can be subdivided into a number of triangles. Therefore, any right prism is a sum of right triangular prisms and therefore the formula for the volume $V = Bh$ is extended to any right prism.

Applying Cavalieri's Principle, we can straighten out any inclined prism, shifting its sections parallel to the base, without changing its volume. Shifting of sections does not change the altitude either, so that the expression $V = Bh$ for the volume is now justified for *any* prism.

A prism is said to be inscribed in a cylinder, if the bases of the prism are inscribed in the bases of the cylinder, and the lateral edges of the prism coincide with the rulings of the cylinder, being parallel to its direction (Fig. 2).

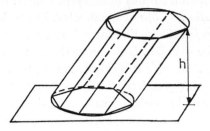

Fig. 22.2

If the number of sides of the inscribed prism's base increases without limit, each side shrinking to a point, at the limit the prism is transformed into the cylinder. Therefore, the volume of a cylinder is the limit of volumes of inscribed prisms, when the number of lateral parallelograms becomes infinite. Since these volumes are, at every step of the passage to the limit, expressed in the same way by the formula $V = Bh$ the volume of a cylinder is also equal to the product of the area B of its base by the height h of the cylinder.

Sections of a Circular Cone

If a plane intersects a given cone C along a circle, all the planes parallel to this plane and therefore perpendicular to the direction δ of its normal intersect the cone C in circles and the cone is called *circular*. A straight line parallel to the direction δ and passing through the vertex V of a circular cone is its axis of symmetry and, by abbreviation, is called simply *axis* of this cone. Every plane through the axis of a circular cone intersects it in two straight lines meeting at the vertex and is for the cone a plane of symmetry. Plane curves obtained as intersection-curves of a circular cone and of a plane are called *conical sections* or simply *conics*. Therefore, two intersecting straight lines form, considered as an entity, a conical section, or a particular conic. Since a cylinder is a cone with its vertex at infinity, a section of a circular cylinder by a secant plane is also a conic. Now, a plane parallel to the cylinder intersects it along two parallel lines and therefore two parallel lines form also a conic.

Two parallel or intersecting straight lines are exceptional conics: all the other conical sections are curves. Any section of a circular cylinder cut by a secant plane non-parallel to the cylinder is a closed regular oval (Fig. 3) called an *ellipse*. There are ellipses of different shapes: they are more or less elongated and the ratio $r = b/a$ of the shortest $2b$ and longest $2a$ diameters of an ellipse depends on the inclination of the secant plane with respect to the axis of the circular cylinder. If the angle the secant plane makes with the axis is a right angle, then this ratio is one, that is, the elliptical section is in fact a circle, circles being a variety of ellipses. When the angle decreases the ellipse becomes more and more elongated, the ratio r of shortest diameter to longest one decreasing and approaching zero when the secant plane tends to become parallel to the cylinder. The shape of an ellipse is characterized by its *eccentricity* which is related to the ratio r: the square root $(1 - r^2)^{1/2}$ is called the eccentricity. The circle's eccentricity is equal to zero. Two parallel lines are the limiting shape of an ellipse, when the ellipse's eccentricity reaches its maximum value one. For a proper ellipse the eccentricity is positive and less than one, and it increases when the elongation increases.

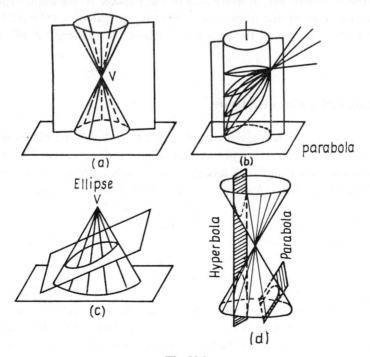

Fig. 22.3

An ellipse is obtained also by cutting a circular cone with a plane non-incident to the vertex of the cone, non-parallel to one of rulings and intersecting *one* sheet of the cone only. A conical section due to a secant plane non-incident with the vertex and cutting *both* sheets consists of two separate branches and is called a *hyperbola*. Finally, a section obtained by cutting a circular cone with a plane parallel to one of the rulings and non-incident with the vertex extends into infinity as does hyperbola, but in one direction only, the section having only one branch. This last type of conical sections is called a *parabola*.

A plane through the vertex of a cone can have only this single point in common with the cone, or can cut the cone along two straight lines, two rulings of this cone. If the cone is circular, a plane through its vertex intersects the cone in two rulings if the angle this secant plane makes with the axis of the cone is less than the angle of a ruling with the axis (all the rulings of a circular cone are equally inclined with respect to the axis).

If the angle of a plane through the vertex is greater than the cone's angle (that is, greater than the angle a ruling makes with the axis), then the plane and the cone have in common only the vertex. But, there is a third possibility: the angle of a plane through the vertex can be equal to the cone's angle and in this case the plane contains one of the rulings and only one. In this case the cone is tangent to the plane along this straight line they have in common and the plane is called a *tangent plane* to the cone. Thus, each tangent plane to a cone passes through its vertex. A plane tangent to a cylinder contains one and only one of its rulings and the cylinder and plane are tangent to each other along their common straight line.

Lateral Area of Frustrum of Circular Cone

The term *frustrum* denotes the part of a cone included between two sections of one of its two sheets and bounded by two parallel planes. A frustrum is often called a *truncated cone*, the part between the vertex and a plane section being called simply a *cone*. We study here the lateral surface of a frustrum of a circular cone, its volume having been discussed in Chapter 21. A truncated circular cone (frustrum) has two heights (Fig. 4). The height of its *lateral surface*, H = AB, is defined as the distance of the circumference of the upper base from the circumference of the lower base, and it is called *slant height*. Thus, the slant height of a cone is the distance VB of the vertex from the circumference of the base. A slant height is a segment of a ruling and thus lies on the conical surface.

A frustrum of a cone has also a height $h = $ CD which by definition is the distance between two parallel planes of both bases. For the frustrum of a circular cone its height is a segment intercepted on the axis by two bases. The height of a cone, therefore, is the length of the perpendicular dropped from its vertex onto the base.

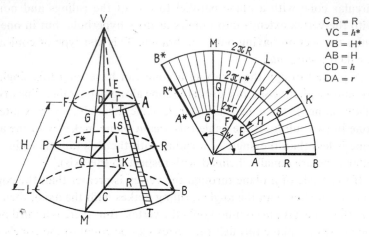

Fig. 22.4

Let us denote the radius CB of the base, the height VC and the slant height VB of a circular cone by R, h^* and H^* respectively. These three segments are related to each other by the Pythagorean relation $H^{*2} = R^* + h^{*2}$ because they form a right triangle VBC with VB $= H^*$ as hypotenuse. For a frustrum we must include also the radius DA of the upper base which is denoted by r, $r < R$. The four segments R, r, h, H in a frustrum of a circular cone satisfy the relation $H^2 = h^2 + (R - r)^2$. To evaluate the lateral surface of a frustrum we cut it along the ruling AB and roll it out onto a plane (Fig. 4). An equivalent plane area is thus obtained whose shape is that of a part of a circular ring bounded by two concentric circles of radii VA and VB and by lines AB and A*B* which form an angle $\widehat{BVB^*}$ denoted by $2w$. The circumferences of the lower and upper bases are transformed into arcs $\overgroup{BKLMB^*}$ and $\overgroup{AEFGA^*}$ of circles of radii VB and VA respectively, so that we obtain two equations: $\overgroup{BKLMB^*} = 2\pi R = 2w \cdot$ VB and $\overgroup{AEFGA^*} = 2\pi r = 2w \times$ VA. Adding them, we deduce the reaction

$$\pi\,(R + r) = w\,(VB + VA) = w\,(H^* - H)\,H^*$$

which we soon will need. The lateral area of the frustrum is equal to the difference of areas of two circular sectors VBLB*V and VAFA*V. The area of a circular sector is equal to the product of half the central angle and of the square of the radius, so that the area VBLB*V is equal to $w \cdot VB^2$ and that of VAFA*V to $w \cdot VA^2$. Therefore, the lateral area of the frustrum is expressed as a product:

$$wVB^2 - wVA^2 = w(VB^2 - VA^2)$$
$$= w(VB + VA)(VB - VA) = \pi(R + r)H$$

because the difference VB − VA is the slant height H of the frustrum. Thus,

The lateral area of a frustrum of a right circular cone is equal to the product of the slant height by the perimeter of the section lying halfway between the bases.

Indeed, the factor $\pi(R + r)$ can be written as $2\pi r^*$, where $r^* = \frac{1}{2}(R + r)$ is the radius of the circle PQRS halfway between the circles of radii r, R; thus the lateral area of the frustrum is equal to $\pi(R + r)H = 2\pi r^*H$. The product slant height times length of the midline reminds us of the same product expressing the area of a trapezoid. This likeness between the expressions of trapezoid's area and of the lateral area of a frustrum is not at all fortuitous. The lateral area of a frustrum can be considered as a sum of infinitesimal trapezoids TT of finite height equal to the slant height H and having their infinitely small bases on the circumferences of frustrum's bases. Such a trapezoid's area is equal to the product of its height H by the length of its midline and the addition of all such areas is performed by picking out their common factor H and adding the midlines of all the infinitesimal trapezoids. Since the sum of their midlines is the length of the midcircle PQRS of the lateral surface, the sum of areas of all trapezoids (that is, the area of the lateral surface) is equal to the product of the midcircle's circumference by the height H of trapezoids, that is, by the slant height.

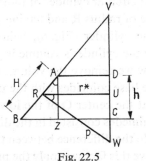

Fig. 22.5

The expression $2\pi r^* H$ for the lateral area of a frustrum of a circular right cone can be transformed into another form, namely $2\pi ph$, in which the slant height H is replaced by the height h of the frustrum, and the segment p is the length of the perpendicular RW to the ruling VAB from a point W of the axis and having its foot at the midpoint R of the segment AB (Fig. 5).

Draw two right triangles ABZ and RUW, the segments $AZ = h$ and $RU = r^*$ being perpendicular to BC and VC respectively. They are similar triangles. Indeed the acute angles $\widehat{BAZ}$ and $\widehat{URW}$ are equal because their side are perpendicular: $AZ \perp BC$ and thus $AZ \perp RU$ as well as $AB \perp RW$. Therefore, the corresponding sides are proportional and $AB/AZ = RW/RU$, that is, $H/h = p/r^*$. Therefore, we have two equal products $r^*H = ph$ which give the expression $2\pi ph$ for the lateral area of the frustrum we were looking for:

The lateral area of a frustrum of a circular right cone is equal to the product $2\pi ph$, where h and p denote the height of the frustrum and the segment of the perpendicular bisector of the slant height included between the axis and the slant height, respectively.

This result applies also to the area of the lateral surface of a right circular cone:

The lateral area of a right circular cone is equal to the product of the slant height by the perimeter of the section lying halfway between the base and the vertex.

Volume of a Sphere

We give here two direct proofs of the classical expression $4\pi R^3/3$ for the volume of a sphere found by Archimedes (287–212 B.C.). The first one based on the Cavalieri's Principle is remarkable by its simplicity and conciseness. *First proof.* Consider a right circular cylinder of radius R and height R equal to the radius. A hemisphere of radius R and having the same base as the cylinder is located within the cylinder (Fig. 6), being tangent to the upper base at its center J. Clearly the cylinder's volume is greater than the volume of the hemisphere. But now we remove the volume of a right circular cone OEFGH of height R whose base coincides with the upper base EFGH of the cylinder, the vertex being at the center O of the lower base.

The contribution of Archimedes consisted in the discovery that the volume of the hemisphere is equal to the difference between the volumes of the cylinder and of the cone. To prove this fact we apply the principle of Cavalieri and consider the horizontal sections of hemisphere, cylinder, and cone by planes parallel to the bases ABCD and EFGH. On Fig. 6 such a plane is drawn at a distance h from and above the lower base ABCD, so that OK = h. The cone OEFGH is characterized by equal height and base-radius, so that the similar cone of height h = OK has a circular base of equal radius KM = h also. Therefore, the areas of sections for the cylinder and for the cone are equal to πR^2 and πh^2 respectively and their difference is equal to $\pi (R^2 - h^2)$.

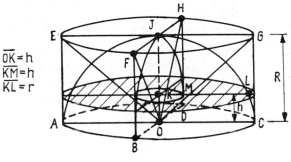

$$\overline{OK} = h$$
$$\overline{KM} = h$$
$$\overline{KL} = r$$

Fig. 22.6

We evaluate now the area of the corresponding section of the sphere. It is also a circular area of radius KL and therefore it is equal to πKL^2. But the right triangle OKL in which OL is hypotenuse gives the relation $KL^2 = OL^2 - OK^2$; that is, $KL^2 = R^2 - h^2$. Therefore, the area of the sphere's section is equal to $\pi (R^2 - h^2)$ and thus equal to the difference between the areas of cylinder's and cone's sections. The same conclusion holds for all sections of our three solids and therefore their volumes, which are sums of sections' areas, satisfy the same relation: the hemisphere's volume is equal to the difference between the volumes of the cylinder and of the cone.

The cylinder's volume is the product of the base-area by the height and the volume of the cone is one third of the same product because cylinder and cone possess equal heights and equal base-areas. Thus, the volume of the hemisphere is equal to two thirds of the product $\pi R^2 \cdot R$ (that is, to $2\pi R^3/3$) and the volume of the whole sphere is $4\pi R^3/3$.

Second proof. The use of the idea of continuum, implicitly contained in the formulation of the Principle of Cavalieri, and which allows us to find without difficulty the expression of the volume of a sphere, can be replaced by the use of passage to the limit, based on the concept of aleph-null.

Thus, both proofs involve the use of absolute infinity with an important difference insofar as the type of infinity involved is concerned. The continuum used in the first proof is actually a geometrical aspect of absolute infinity (continuum of points as a length, of segments as an area, of areas as a volume, etc.), while aleph-null related to the sequence of natural integers is an arithmetical concept. This explains why the second proof is more sophisticated than the first.

Again considering a hemisphere of radius R, subdivide its height OA into N equal parts of length R/N (Fig. 7) and cut the volume of the hemisphere into N horizontal slices by secant planes parallel to the base BCDE and passing through the points A_k of the height OA which divide OA into N equal parts. The point A_k is therefore at a distance equal to kR/N from the center $O = A_o$ of the base and the pole A of the equator BCDE is the end of the Nth part, so that $A = A_N$. The subscript k varies from $k = 0$ up to $k = N$. Denoting by V_k the volume of the kth slice bounded by planes through A_{k-1} and A_k, we have to study the sum $V_1 + V_2 + \cdots + V_N$, this sum representing the volume V of our hemisphere.

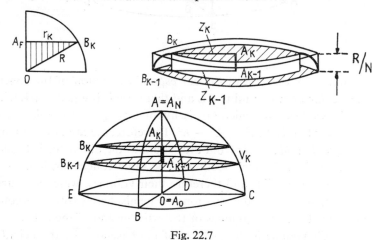

Fig. 22.7

The volume V_k of the kth slice cannot be computed directly because its lateral boundary is a curved surface. Therefore we estimate its upper and lower bounds and form an inequality verified by V_k. Consider the radii $A_{k-1}B_{k-1} = r_{k-1}$ and $A_kB_k = r_k$ of the lower and upper bases of the slice V_k. The right triangle OA_kB_k gives $OB_k^2 = OA_k^2 + A_kB_k^2$; that is, $R^2 = (kR/N)^2 + r_k^2$ and thus the radii of bases are:

$$r_{k-1}^2 = R^2 - (R/N)^2 \cdot (k-1)^2;$$
$$r_k^2 = R^2 - (R/N)^2 \cdot k^2.$$

Now the volume V_k is within a right circular cylinder of the same height R/N built on the lower base of V_k. Another right circular cylinder whose base is the upper base of the slice V_k and whose height is R/N is within V_k. Therefore, the volume V_k is greater than that of the second cylinder, but less than the volume of the first cylinder. Evaluating the volumes of these two cylinders, we obtain the inequalities

$$\pi r_k^2 (R/N) < V_k < \pi r_{k-1}^2 (R/N). \tag{1}$$

Replacing in (1) r_{k-1}^2, r_k^2 by their values, we have further

$$\pi R^3/N - (\pi R^3/N^3) \cdot k^2 < V_k < \pi R^3/N - (\pi R^3/N^3) \cdot (k-1)^2.$$

Giving to k the values 1, 2, 3, ..., $(N-1)$, N and summing member by member the N double inequalities thus obtained, we find a double inequality verified by the value V of the volume of our hemisphere

$$\pi R^3 - (\pi R^3/N^3) \sum_{k=1}^{N} k^2 < V = \sum_{k=1}^{N} V_k < \pi R^3 - (\pi R^3/N^3) \cdot \sum_{k=1}^{N} (k-1)^2. \tag{2}$$

The sum of squares of N successive integers is known and dividing by N^3, one finds

$$N^{-3} \cdot \sum_{1}^{N} (k-1)^2 = (N-1) \, N \, (2N-1)/6N^3$$
$$= \tfrac{1}{3} - \tfrac{1}{2}N^{-1} + \tfrac{1}{6}N^{-2} > \tfrac{1}{3} - \tfrac{2}{3}N^{-1}.$$

$$N^{-3} \cdot \sum_{1}^{N} k^2 = N \, (N+1) \, (2N+1)/6N^3$$
$$= \tfrac{1}{3} + \tfrac{1}{2}N^{-1} + \tfrac{1}{6}N^{-2} < \tfrac{1}{3} + \tfrac{2}{3}N^{-1}$$

Therefore, the inequality (2) becomes

$$\pi R^3 - \pi R^3(\tfrac{1}{3} + \tfrac{2}{3}N^{-1}) < V < \pi R^3 - \pi R^3(\tfrac{1}{3} - \tfrac{2}{3}N^{-1})$$

that is

$$(\tfrac{2}{3}) \pi R^3 (1 - 1/N) < V < (\tfrac{2}{3}) \pi R^3 (1 + 1/N). \tag{3}$$

This result proves that $V = 2\pi R^3/3$ because at the limit for $N = \infty$, the factors $1 - 1/N$ and $1 + 1/N$ become equal to one. This passage to the limit for $N = \infty$ is possible because the choice of the integer N is completely free of any limitations and therefore N can be as large as we want. Thus, the volume of the whole sphere is $4\pi R^3/3$, the expression $4\pi R^3/3$ being deduced this time with the aid of a passage to the limit.

Area of a Sphere

The expression $S = 4\pi R^2$ for the area S of a sphere of radius R can be easily deduced from the value $4\pi R^3/3$ of the sphere's volume and *vice versa*, but before discussing the interdependence of these two expressions $V = 4\pi R^3/3$ and $S = 4\pi R^2$ we shall prove the validity of the expression $S = 4\pi R^2$ by a direct evaluation of the area S with the aid of a passage to the limit.

A slice of the sphere bounded by two parallel secant planes is called *spherical zone*. The distance between these planes (represented by a segment of diameter perpendicular to them) is the altitude (or height) of the zone, the circular sections cut in the volume of the sphere by secant planes are bases. The lateral surface of a zone can be generated by rotating a circular arc about the diameter of the circle. Since the rotation of a semicircle about its diameter generates a sphere, the whole spherical surface can be considered as a particular case of lateral surface of a zone which covers the whole sphere and whose altitude H is equal to the diameter 2R of the sphere.

The expression $S = 4\pi R^2$ for the sphere's area is a particular case of the more general expression $S_H = 2\pi RH$ for the area of the lateral surface of a spherical zone of altitude $H: S = S_{2R} = 2\pi R \cdot 2R = 4\pi R^2$. Therefore, to find the area S of the whole sphere it is sufficient to establish that the area of a zone of altitude H is represented by the expression $S_H = 2\pi RH$.

Given a zone Z of altitude $H = AB$ generated by the rotation about the ine AB of an arc CD, we cut it by the plane ABCD and consider the right

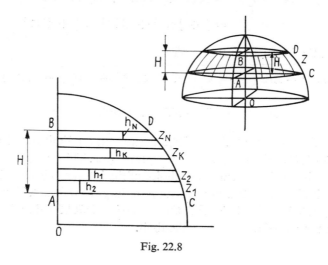

Fig. 22.8

half of the section obtained (Fig. 8). Dividing the arc $\overset{\frown}{CD}$ into N equal parts, we draw through the division-points planes parallel to the base of the zone Z, thus slicing it into N subzones $z_1, z_2, z_3, \ldots, z_N$ of the same arc $\overset{\frown}{CD}/N$, but of unequal altitudes $h_1, h_2, \ldots, h_{N-1}, h_N$ the sum of these altitudes being naturally equal to $H:h_1 + h_2 + h_3 + \cdots + h_N = H$. The area S_H of the zone Z is also the sum of areas $S_1, S_2, \ldots S_N$ of subzones, where S_k denotes the area of the kth subzone z_k of altitude h_k.

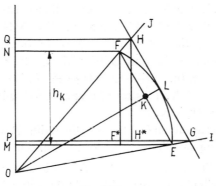

Fig. 22.9

The area S_k cannot be evaluated directly because all what we learned up to now is how to measure plane areas while the lateral surface of z_k is a curved surface. Therefore, we will compare the area S_k to areas we know how to measure and try to find the upper and the lower bound for S_k. Considering the k-th zone z_k separately (Fig. 9), we inscribe in it and circumscribe about it frustrums of right circular cones generated by rotation about OQ of the chord EF and of the segment GH, intercepted by the radii OEI and OFJ on the tangent to the arc $\overset{\frown}{ELF}$ at its midpoint L.

We know from plane geometry that the length of the circular arc $\overset{\frown}{ELF}$ is comprised between those of the chord EF and of the tangent GH: EF $< \overset{\frown}{ELF} < $ GH. Moreover, the elements of the arc ELF are farther from the rotation-axis OQ than the corresponding elements of the chord, but nearer to OQ than those of the tangent. Therefore, rotating about OQ the arc, the chord and the tangent, areas are generated which satisfy the same inequalities as those satisfied by the lengths, that is, the area S_k of the k-th zone is greater than the lateral area of the inscribed frustrum having the chord EF for this slant height, but S_k is smaller than the lateral area of the circumscribed frustrum with slant height GH.

Joining the midpoint L of the arc to the center O of the sphere and denoting by K the intersection-point of the radius OL $=$ R with the chord EF, we write down the expressions of lateral areas of both frustrums. The smaller one is equal to 2πOK $\cdot$ MN and the larger $-$ to 2πOL $\cdot$ PQ, where MN $= h_k$ and PQ are the altitudes of frustrums. Thus, the k-th zone's area S_k verifies the following double inequality:

$$2\pi \cdot OK \cdot h_k < S_k < 2\pi R \cdot PQ. \qquad (4)$$

To evaluate the altitude PQ of the circumscribed frustrum we consider similar triangles EFF* and GHH*, where FF*$|| =$ MN and HH*$|| =$ PQ. They yield the proportion PQ/MN $=$ HH*/FF* $=$ GH/EF. On the other hand, similar triangles OEF and OGH yield another proportion GH/EF $=$ OL/OK. Therefore, the ratio PQ/MN $=$ PQ/h_k is equal to that OL/OK $=$ R/OK; PQ/h_k $=$ R/OK. This result gives the following expression of the altitude PQ; PQ $=$ Rh_k/OK.

We know that the apothem OK tends to the radius R when the corresponding chord decreasing steadily shrinks to a point. Since we will increase the integer N without limit, the arc $\overset{\frown}{CD}$/N of the subzone z_k we are considering and its chord EF will ultimately vanish and thus at the limit, for N $= \infty$, the apothem OK becomes equal to R. Therefore, in expressing this apothem by a product R $(1 - e_N) =$ OK, the second factor $(1 - e_N)$ of this product will tend to one and at the limit, for N $= \infty$, will become equal to one: $\lim_{N=\infty} (1 - e_N) = 1$, that is, $\lim_{N=\infty} e_N = 0$. Substituting in (4) R $(1 - e_N)$ for OK and Rh_k/OK $= h_k/(1 - e_N)$ for PQ, we rewrite these inequalities as follows

$$2\pi R h_k (1 - e_N) < S_k < 2\pi R h_k (1 - e_N)^{-1}. \qquad (5)$$

It is important to observe that the infinitesimal e_N does not depend on the particular zone z_k and has the same value for all subzones because these subzones were obtained by dividing the arc $\overset{\frown}{CD}$ into equal parts with equal chords and therefore with equal apothems. Thus, applying the inequalities (5) to each term of the sum $S_H = S_1 + S_2 + S_3 + \cdots + S_N$ and observing that the common factors $2\pi R (1 - e_N)$ and $2\pi R (1 - e_N)^{-1}$ can be picked out, we have to sum up only the altitudes h_k of different subzones:

$$2\pi R (1 - e_N)(h_1 + h_2 + ... + h_N) < S_H < 2\pi R (1 - e_N)^{-1} \times$$
$$\times (h_1 + h_2 + ... + h_N).$$

The sum of altitudes of all subzones is the altitude of the zone Z, that is, the altitude denoted by H. Thus, for any integer N, upper and lower bounds of the area S_H are found and the inequalities

$$2\pi RH (1 - e_N) < S_N < 2\pi RH (1 - e_N)^{-1} \tag{6}$$

prove that $S_H = 2\pi RH$ because N can be chosen as large as we want and, on the other hand, the term e_N in the difference $1 - e_N$ vanishes for $N = \infty$:

The lateral area of a spherical zone of altitude H is equal to the product of the perimeter $2\pi R$ of a great circle by this altitude $H: S_H = 2\pi RH$.

Having justified the expression $4\pi R^2$ for the sphere's area, we compare it to the area of a circle of the same radius R as the sphere, that is, to πR^2. It can be stated that the area of a sphere is equal to four times the area of its great circle, so that if we cut the sphere into four equal parts by two perpendicular planes through a diameter, for each one of these four quarters of a sphere the sum of areas of its two flat faces is equal to the area of its third, curved face. The flat faces are half-circles of radius R, while the curved face is a lune with a right angle, the planes of flat faces being perpendicular. In other words, the area of a sphere is equal to the total area of all eight plane faces of four quarters of that sphere.

Denoting the area and the volume of a sphere by S and V, it can be said that, knowing one of these two quantities, the other can be computed because both are functions of radius R. Expressing this fact in algebraical terms, we say that the area S and the volume V of a sphere are related to each other by a formula. To find this formula it is sufficient to eliminate the radius R between, the two expressions $S = 4\pi R^2$ and $V = 4\pi R^3/3$. Raising the first one to a power with the exponent 3 and squaring the second expression, one obtains $S^3 = 64\pi^3 R^6$ and $V^2 = 16\pi^2 R^6/9$. Thus, multiplying V^2 by 36π, the same product $64\pi^3 R^6$ is obtained as for S^3. Therefore, the relation between S and V is as follows

$$36\pi V^2 = S^3. \tag{7}$$

This relation is exactly analogous to the relation $4\pi A = L^2$ between the area A and the length L of the circumference of a circle. The relation $4\pi A = L^2$ expresses a very important property of the flat Euclidean plane. It is true only for a circle and for any other closed curve whatever be its shape, the enclosed area A is always *less* than $L^2/4\pi$.

Likewise, given a closed surface of total area S, the volume enclosed by it is always *less* than $(S^3/36\pi)^{1/2}$ whatever be the shape of the closed surface, except the sphere for which the enclosed volume reaches its maximum, becoming equal to the square root $(S^3/36\pi)^{1/2}$. This maximum property of the sphere can be formulated also as a minimum property by inverting the statement: if it is known that a surface encloses a given volume V, then the total area of this closed surface is always *greater* than the cube root $(36\pi V^2)^{1/3}$, whatever be the shape of the enclosing surface, except the sphere for which the enclosing area reaches its minimum becoming equal to the cube root $(36\pi V^2)^{1/3}$.

Here are examples illustrating the extremum properties of the sphere. For a cube of edge length a we have $S = 6a^2$ and $V = a^3$, so that $36\pi V^2 = 36\pi a^6$, while $S^3 = 216a^6$. Since $\pi < 6$ we have for a cube the inequality $S^3 > 36\pi V^2$. For a cylinder of radius R and of altitude 2R the volume is $V = 2\pi R^3$ and the total area $S = 6\pi R^2$, so that again $S^3/(36\pi V^2) = \frac{3}{2}$ is greater than one.

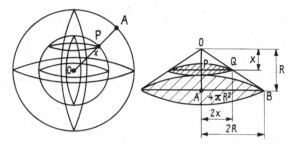

Fig. 22.10

Finally, we show how the expression for the volume of a sphere can be deduced from that $4\pi R^2$ for the area, using the principle of Cavalieri. A concentric sphere can be drawn through each point P on the radius OA of a sphere of a given radius R = OA. Applying the principle of Cavalieri, we state that the volume V of the sphere is a sum of areas of all these spheres whose radii vary from zero to R (Fig. 10). Now, denoting by x the radius OP of any interior concentric sphere through the point P, we state that the area of this sphere is equal to $4\pi x^2 = \pi(2x)^2$ and therefore can be represented as the area of a circle of radius $2x$. When $x = $ OP varies from $x = 0$ up to $x = $ R we obtain all the two-dimensional elements composing together the volume of the sphere.

Now these two-dimensional spherical elements can be replaced without changing their areas by circular areas which are plane areas and it is easy to show that the solid thus obtained is a right circular cone (Fig. 10) of altitude R and base-radius 2R. The volume of such a cone is indeed the sum of areas of its sections parallel to the base and through each point P of the cone's altitude OA = R passes one such section of area $\pi(2x)^2 = 4\pi x^2$, if the distance

OP of the center P of this circular section from the vertex O is equal to OP $= x$. To prove this assertion it is sufficient to observe that in two similar solids the ratio of corresponding areas is equal to the square of the ratio of corresponding segments. Considering the similar triangles OAB and OPQ, we conclude that the ratio of base-areas is equal to $(x/R)^2$, so that the area of the section through the point P is equal to that $4\pi R^2$ of the base multiplied by $(x/R)^2$; that is, to $4\pi x^2$.

Thus, the volume of the cone is composed of circular areas which are equal to corresponding spherical areas composing the volume of the sphere. Moreover, the two-dimensional elements of these two volumes are brought in one-to-one correspondence since the radius OP of the sphere and the altitude OP of the cone are identical segments and the corresponding elements of two volumes are equal. Applying the principle of Cavalieri, we conclude the equality of two volumes since sums of equals are equal. Using now for the volume of the cone the formula $V = Bh/3$, we find easily that the volume of a sphere of radius R is expressed by $V = 4\pi R^2 R/3 = (\frac{4}{3}) \pi R^3$.

Here is another variant of the same idea in which the principle of Cavalieri is replaced by the passage to the limit. In this variant the radius OA is divided into N equal parts and concentric interior spheres are drawn only through the division-points. They subdivide the volume V of the whole sphere into N spherical slices bounded by two concentric spheres whose radii differ by the Nth part of the radius R. Let us denote the volumes of these N spherical shells by V_k, $1 \leqslant k \leqslant N$, the kth shell of volume V_k being bounded by two interior spheres of radii $r_{k-1} = (k-1) R/N$ and $r_k = kR/N$, (Fig. 11).

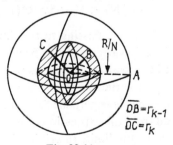

Fig. 22.11

The volume V_k bounded by two spheres of areas $4\pi r_{k-1}^2$ and $4\pi r_k^2$ has an uniform thickness R/N. Therefore, increasing the area of its lower base to $4\pi r_k^2$, we increase the volume so that the volume of the right circular cylinder thus obtained is greater than V_k. The altitude of this cylinder is equal to the thickness R/N of the spherical shell V_k. The area of its base is

$4\pi r_k^2 = 4\pi \, (kR/N)^2$, so that the volume of the cylinder is equal to $4\pi \, (R/N)^3 \times k^2$ and thus, $V_k < 4\pi \, (R/N)^3 \, k^2$.

On the other hand, decreasing the area of the upper spherical base of the shell V_k to $4\pi r_{k-1}^2$, we diminish the volume, so that the volume of another right circular cylinder thus obtained is less than V_k. This cylindrical volume is equal to $4\pi r_{k-1}^2 \cdot (R/N) = 4\pi \, (R/N)^3 \, (k-1)^2$, so that $V_k > 4\pi \, (R/N)^3 \times (k-1)^2$:

$$4\pi \, (R/N)^3 \, (k-1)^2 < V_k < 4\pi \, (R/N)^3 \, k^2 \qquad (1 \leqslant k \leqslant N).$$

Applying these inequalities to all the terms of the sum $V = \sum_1^N V_k$, we can pick out the common factor $4\pi \, (R/N)^3$, so that for the volume of the whole sphere V following inequalities are obtained

$$4\pi \, (R/N)^3 \cdot \sum_1^N (k-1)^2 < V < 4\pi \, (R/N)^3 \cdot \sum_1^N k^2.$$

But we know that the sums of squares of integers standing in both members can be easily evaluated:

$$\sum_1^N (k-1)^2 = N^3(1 - 1/N)\,(1 - \tfrac{1}{2}N)/3;$$

$$\sum_1^N k^2 = N^3(1 + 1/N)\,(1 + \tfrac{1}{2}N)/3,$$

so that finally

$$\tfrac{4}{3}\pi R^3(1 - 1/N)\,(1 - \tfrac{1}{2}N) < V < \tfrac{4}{3}\pi R^3(1 + 1/N)\,(1 + \tfrac{1}{2}N),$$

where N is an arbitrary integer. Passing to the limit for $N = \infty$, we prove that $V = \tfrac{4}{3}\pi R^3$ and in this variant of the proof the use of continuum is avoided. Since both variants are based on the use of the concept of absolute infinity it seems that the first variant is more elegant and easier to grasp.

We want now to show that inversely the formula $S = 4\pi R^2$ for the area of a sphere can be deduced from the expression of the volume. In this deduction we use also the passage to the limit. Inscribing in the sphere a polyhedron with N faces and denoting by D_N the length of the largest among the diagonals of all the faces of the polyhedron, we increase N without limit, imposing on the inscribed polyhedrons the following and very important limitation: when N increases, the length D_N approaches zero and $\lim\limits_{N=\infty} D_N = 0$ which means that, when the number of faces of the inscribed polyhedron increases and becomes infinite, *each face shrinks to a point*. The total area of all the faces of the inscribed polyhedron tends to the area S of the sphere and the volume enclosed by the polyhedron tends to the volume of the sphere. Denoting the area and the volume of the polyhedron by S_N and V_N, we have

$$\lim_{N=\infty} S_N = S, \qquad \lim_{N=\infty} V_N = V.$$

Dropping perpendiculars from the center of the sphere onto the polyhedron's faces and denoting them by h_k, $1 \leqslant k \leqslant N$, we have also $\lim\limits_{N=\infty} h_k = R$ (radius of the sphere). If the areas of faces are equal to B_k, $1 \leqslant k \leqslant N$, we can express the volume of the inscribed polyhedron as a sum of volumes of *pyramids* having their vertices at the center of the sphere and the faces B_k of the polyhedron as their bases. Applying the expression of the volume of a pyramid, we deduce for the volume of the polyhedron V_N the following expression

$$V_N = (B_1 h_1 + B_2 h_2 + B_3 h_3 + \cdots + B_N h_N)/3. \qquad (8)$$

Since the altitudes of pyramids h_k are less than the radius R of the sphere, the righthand member in (8) is less than the product of the sum of base-areas $\sum_1^N B_k$ by $R/3$, but the sum of base-areas is the total area of the polyhedron S_N and therefore its volume V_N is less than $RS_N/3$. The inequality $V_N < RS_N/3$ holds for any integer N and, passing to the limit for $N = \infty$, we deduce from it $V \leqslant RS/3$ because $\lim\limits_{N=\infty} V_N = V$ and $\lim\limits_{N=\infty} S_N = S$. Thus, the volume V and the area S of a sphere satisfy the relation

$$V \leqslant RS/3. \qquad (9)$$

We now set out to prove that they also satisfy another relation $V \geqslant RS/3$, so that (if this last relation is proved) $V = RS/3$. We shall use the fact that the altitudes h_k tend to R when N increases without limit. Choosing a positive number e, we are free to choose it as small as we want, so that the difference $1 - e$ is a fixed number less than one but as near to one as we want. Having thus chosen e, we can find another fixed number N* sufficiently large to have all the altitudes h_k greater than $R(1 - e)$, if N is chosen greater than N*. This is possible because when N increases the largest diagonal D_N of faces of our polyhedron tends to zero. Therefore each face becomes less in area than a circle of diameter D_N and the distance of this face from the center of the sphere is greater than the distance from the center of a circle of diameter D_N. But this last distance can be made greater than $R(1 - e)$ by choosing a sufficiently large N. Therefore, for any positive number e however small we have, for sufficiently large N, the N inequalities $h_k > R(1 - e)$ which entails with the aid of (8) the result

$$V_N > R(1 - e)(B_1 + B_2 + \cdots + B_N)/3 = RS_N(1 - e)/3$$

provided that $N > N^*$, the lower bound N^* for permissible values of N depending on e and increasing without limit when e approaches zero.

Therefore, if now we pass to the limit for $e = 0$, the inequality

$$V_N > RS_N(1 - e)/3$$

becomes at the limit

$$V \geqslant RS/3 \tag{10}$$

because $\lim_{e=0} V_N = \lim_{N=0} V_N = V$ as well as $\lim_{e=0} S_N = \lim_{N=0} S_N = S$ as result of the fact that $\lim_{e=0} N = \infty$.

The combined inequalities (9), (10) prove that $V = RS/3$ and therefore, if the volume V is known, $S = 3V/R = 3(\frac{4}{3})\pi R^3/R = 4\pi R^2$, so that indeed the area of the sphere can be deduced from the expression of its volume V. Of course, the same inequality (10) can be obtained using circumscribed polyhedron instead of inscribed.

Hypervolume of a Hypersphere in S_4

The sphere plays among closed surfaces of a three-dimensional space S_3 the same role as that played by circles in a plane (that is, in S_2) among closed curves. It can be said that both circles and spheres are solutions of the following problem: find the shape of the boundary whose measure is given (and, therefore, fixed), knowing that it encloses the largest portion of space. This problem can be considered in a space of any dimensionality. For a two-dimensional space its solution is a circle, while for a three-dimensional space it is a sphere. What about the solution of this problem for a four-dimensional space?

The circle and the sphere have in common a geometrical characteristic: they are both sets of points *(loci)* equidistant in their respective spaces from a fixed given point called center, the distance being called radius. Such a set of points equidistant from a center exists also in S_4 and it is called a *hypersphere*. The boundary of a circular area (circle as a line) is a locus of points equidistant from the center, so that if a circle is considered as an area, it must be defined as the set of points whose distances from the center do not exceed a maximum distance called the radius. Likewise, if a sphere is considered as a solid with its boundary surface, only the points forming the bound-ary-area of the sphere are equidistant from the center, so that sphere as a solid is a set of points whose distances form the center do not exceed the radius of the sphere. A hypersphere also has a boundary which is a volume and interior points, the set of interior points forming a finite portion of the four-dimensional space separated from the remaining infinite part of the space S_4 by the curved and closed *volume*, boundary of the hypersphere.

The fact that a volume, that is, a three-dimensional solid, can have a cur-vature when immersed in a four-dimensional space, and enclose in its inte-rior a portion of the four-dimensional space may seem incomprehensible to our mind with its three-dimensional mentality. The usual objection to this natural reaction of our mind, namely that we must not mix our physical ideas with the abstract constructions of a pure four-dimensional geometry, may be valid from a purely logical point of view, but it seems to miss the point: what is important is the desire to understand the instrinsic structure of four-dimensional space, to comprehend the structure of the hypersphere re-lating it to our experience, and this desire is simply neglected in the logical objection cited above.

Let us suppose for a moment that we know nothing about the existence of a third dimension and know only plane areas belonging to our two-dimen-sional world which is thus reduced to a plane. We can form the concept of a circle as a closed line—a set of points equidistant from a fixed point—and enclosing an arca, part of our universe. But, being two-dimensional, our mind can conceive no idea of volume and, moreover, our idea of area must differ from the usual concept of area in a very important way: being un-aware of a third dimension, the two-dimensional mind cannot imagine and understand that an area has no thickness in a direction perpendicular to it and that it can be bent, becoming curved. Therefore, if somebody wants to describe a sphere to our two-dimensional mind and tells us that an area may serve as a boundary to a volume and completely enclose it (thus being closed and nevertheless in some way empty inside), the feeling of uneasiness and incomprehensibility will be caused precisely by our too narrow concept of area. For a two-dimensional mentality, an area exists only in itself, can be studied only from inside, and cannot be perceived from outside because the outside does not exist other than in the form of an extension of area *in its own plane*. Moreover, for a two-dimensional being, an area cannot be seen in its totality but only explored point by point, penetrating inside the area through its boundary line, while a line can be seen as such with all its points perceived simultaneously.

We with our three-dimensional minds are in exactly the same position with the respect to a volume as the position of a two-dimensional being with respect to an area. We can see and perceive only the exterior boundary of a volume. To explore a volume we are obliged to make a hole through its boundary surface and penetrate inside as by a drill. A volume for us has a thickness in all directions and we do not realize that in the direction of the fourth dimension which is perpendicular to any direction lying within the volume, this volume has no thickness at all and is pierced in exactly one point by any straight line belonging to the fourth dimension. In other words, our three-dimensional mind cannot see a volume together with its interior from outside, cannot perceive all its points simultaneously, cannot locate it in a four-dimensional space. This weakness of our mind is due to its dependence on visual perceptions which are essentially three-dimensional and cannot be extended beyond three-dimensional space.

Nevertheless, we have at our disposal a precious faculty of our mind which is our imagination. Imagination was needed to form the idea of volume, to see mentally, not by our eyes, the interior of our globe and study its structure. If we want to explore the fourth dimension, we have only one way to comprehend its structure: we must imagine it. And first of all we have to imagine that a volume is analogous to an area in that respect that it has no thickness at all in a certain direction which can be called, for instance, "direction of the fourth dimension". To facilitate this first step towards the understanding of the four-dimensional geometry, time can be used as an illustration of relations in the four-dimensional space. Our perception of the existence of a volume is limited to a single moment in time: everything exists for us only now, at present, and the concept of a lasting, durable object is created by our mind. The idea of a volume which was there before we saw it and will be after we have seen it, is created by our imagination which uses the superposition in our memory of perceptions of this volume in different moments. What is given to us in reality is the sequence in time of different volumes perceived by us in different moments. There is no time element in the volume we perceive itself, *we* ascribe the duration in time to a volume, superposing in our imagination the eventual perceptions of it and correlating—in our imagination again—each moment of time with such an eventual (realized but exceptionally) perception. This superposition of volumes at different moments is possible only because each one of them taken separately has no "thickness" in time, time being completely exterior in our imagination to the three-dimensional space.

We can do the same in geometry, replacing time by the fourth dimension.

Since a volume has no extension at all along the fourth dimension we can imagine superposition along this fourth dimension of three-dimensional volumes, correlating with each point of a straight line belonging to the fourth dimension a volume. The totality (continuum) of volumes now extends along the fourth dimension exactly as a continuum of areas forming a volume has an extension along the third dimension not contained in any one of areas composing a volume. An area has no volume because it has no thickness in the direction of the third dimension, but the superposition of a continuum of areas is a volume. A volume has no extension in the fourth dimension, but their superposition creates a *hypervolume*; volumes thus superposed acquire a new quality which can be measured. The superposition of volumes along a fourth dimension can also be described as follows. Imagine that a solid, for instance a sphere of fixed radius, moves along a line belonging to the fourth dimension and therefore piercing the sphere in one point only, for example piercing the sphere in its *center*. If the solid moves remaining constantly in the same relative position with respect to the straight line we call its motion a *translation*. In a translation each point of the solid describes in the four-dimensional space a straight line, the rectilinear trajectories of all points being parallel. Considering now all the different positions the solid occupies in the four-dimensional space together, we superpose them in our imagination and the entity thus created is a four-dimensional body. The part of the four-dimensional space occupied by this body is called its hypervolume.

Thus, to give an example, if a segment of length a moves in a plane in a direction perpendicular to the segment, all the positions it occupies during its motion in the plane form an area and this area is a square, if the translation of the segment along the direction of motion is equal to a also. Suppose now that the square of area a^2 moves in space in a direction perpendicular to the square. The totality of all the positions it occupies in space during its motion forms a volume and this volume is a cube, if the measure of the square's translation is equal to a. Now—and here we must imagine a fourth direction which is perpendicular to the whole cube—let us move the cube of volume a^3 through the four-dimensional space in a direction which does not belong to the three-dimensional space of the cube and which is perpendicular to the cube. The solid cube describes a fourid-mensional body which can be defined as the totality of all the positions the cube occupies in the four-dimensional space during its translation. If the measure of this translation (that is, the common length of all parallel trajectories described by points of the cube) is equal to the length a of the cube's edge, a *hypercube* is obtained whose hypervolume is equal to a^4. The exterior boundary of this hypercube is formed by volumes which altogether form a closed volume, a polycell since each particular volume (cell) involved in the boundary is flat, the polycell being formed by intersecting three-dimensional spaces, as a polyhedron is formed by intersecting planes. The cells forming the boundary of a hypercube are all identical and for this reason the polycell is called a *regular polycell*. A cell is generated by the motion of a face of the cube and since this face is a square each cell itself is a cube identical to our original cube. Six cells are generated by six faces of the moving cube but the total number of cubical cells forming the polycell, that is, the closed boundary-volume of the hypercube, is *eight* because the initial, first, and the final, last, positions of the moving cube are also parts of the boundary. Therefore, this polycell could be named a *regular octocell* of the four-dimensional space. As for a polyhedron, the same name *hypercube* is used in two different senses: meaning a four-dimensional solid with its interior and thus having a hypervolume, or meaning the boundary-volume without including the interior hypervolume, that is, meaning the set of eight boundary cubes only. These eight cubes are joined to each other by their common faces, so that in the four-dimensional space they form a closed volume the interior of which (the hypervolume of measure a^4) is separated by these cubes from the exterior four-dimensional space. The volume of the boundary is equal to $8a^3$, so that a hypervolume a^4 is contained in a volume $8a^3$. The situation described is entirely analogous to the fact that in a cube a volume a^3 is contained within an area $6a^2$.

To justify the assertion that the hypervolume of a hypercube (another name often used for this four-dimensional solid is *tessaract*) is equal to a^4 it is sufficient to observe that sections of a tessaract made by three-dimensional spaces parallel to its cubical base are cubes of volume a^3. There are as many such cubical sections of volume a^3 as there are points in the altitude (along a fourth perpendicular to three edges of the base). The length of the altitude being a, the principle of Cavalieri states that the hypervolume is a sum of all sections' volumes. Thus, multiplying the volume of a section a^3 by the length a of the altitude which expresses the number of points (continuum) contained in the altitude, we obtain the measure of the hypervolume as sum of a continuum of volumes. The tessaract will be studied in details in the next chapter; we now return to the description of the hypersphere.

To explain the structure of a sphere to a two-dimensional mind it is necessary to insist on the possibility of bending areas in three-dimensional space. An area considered exclusively in its own plane cannot have a curvature, but an area immersed in a higher space can be curved and therefore can form a closed boundary of a part of this space. The same happens with volumes. If considered in its own space (as we are accustomed to do), a volume cannot have a curvature. But if, using the magic power of our imagination, we see it mentally as immersed in a four-dimensional space S_4 where it has no thickness in the direction perpendicular to it, we comprehend without effort that a volume can be curved in S_4 and therefore can be bent in such a way that it forms a closed structure *empty* (with respect to the four-dimensional space) *inside* and separating the exterior (and infinite) portion of the space S_4 from the hypervolume included within it. We define now the closed volume-boundary of a hypersphere as a set of points in S_4 equidistant from a given point O, center of the hypersphere, and give to their common distance from O the name of radius R. Points in S_4 whose distances from O exceed R are exterior to the hypersphere and do not belong to it. Points with distances from O less than R form the interior of the hypersphere and their totality is called hypervolume of the hypersphere. In what follows we use the abbreviation HS for the word "hypersphere".

Any section of a HS by a three-dimensional space s_3 passing through the center O is an ordinary sphere of radius R and it can be called a *great sphere* of this HS by analogy with great circles of a sphere. Sections by spaces non-incident with the center O are also spheres but of lesser radius whose precise value depends on the length of the perpendicular dropped from the center O on the secant space. Denoting this distance of the secant space s_3 from the center by h and passing a plane through h, we obtain a right triangle with legs h and r (where r is the radius of the sphere, intersection of the HS and of the secant space s_3) and the hypotenuse R, the radius of the HS. Therefore, the radius of the small sphere r satisfies the relation $r^2 + h^2 = R^2$, where the range of variation of the perpendicular h is the interval from zero up to R.

Suppose now that a HS approaches our three-dimensional space from the four-dimensional exterior, the distance x of its center from our space gradually decreasing. At the moment when this decreasing distance x reaches the value R equal to the radius of the moving HS, the HS becomes tangent to our space and a three-dimensional mind receives its first impression of it in the form of a point appearing in his three-dimensional world. If the HS moves with respect to this world s_3 in such a way that its center remains on the same perpendicular to s_3, the point develops into a solid sphere whose radius grows gradually when the center O of the HS approaches the three-dimensional world s_3. This radius at each moment is equal to $(R^2 - x^2)^{1/2}$, where x denotes the distance of the center of HS from the space s_3 in which is located our three-dimensional observer. When x vanishes (that is, when the center O penetrates into our three-dimensional world), the growing sphere reaches its maximum diameter 2R and immediately after it begins to shrink because the center of HS already disappeared from our universe and recedes from it after having traversed it through one point only (our three-dimensional universe has no thickness in s_4). Thus, the radius of the solid sphere—the form in which a three-dimensional mind perceives a HS traversing its universe—begins to decrease after its maximum R was reached and the solid sphere shrinks to a point which disappears also.

The birth of a sphere as a mere point, its gradual growth until the maximum is reached and then decay and death as a point also are analogous to the appearance of a point in the plane and flat universe of a two-dimensional mind, its gradual growth into a maximum circle, followed by the shrinking back of this circular area to a point which disappears completely, when a three-dimensional solid sphere traverses the plane of this two-dimensional being. This description of the structure of a HS as a set of its sections which are seen in their succession as a variable sphere, if a three-dimensional mind perceives them one after another, is incomplete if we omit to emphasize that a HS is a *static* concept which has nothing in common with motion. Therefore, a HS must be imagined as a simultaneous coexistence of all its spherical sections just described, exactly as a sphere is a set of its parallel circular sections considered altogether as an entity, but not in a succession in time, as they would necessarily appear to a two-dimensional mind.

Thus, a HS is a set (a continuum) of spherical volumes of different size piled upon one another in the four-dimensional space as circular areas of different size are piled upon one another in a three-dimensional space within an ordinary sphere. As for the continuum of circular sections of a sphere, this piling of spherical volumes proceeds in the direction along which the volumes have no thickness, that is, in the direction of that diameter of the HS which is perpendicular to parallel spaces s_3 of these parallel volumes.

This feature in the structure of an HS can be used in computing its hypervolume by the method analogous to the passage to the limit applied in the second proof of the expression for the volume V of a sphere. In this second proof, the volume $\frac{1}{2}V$, sliced by parallel planes into N parts V_k, was shown to satisfy a double inequality

$$\tfrac{2}{3}\pi R^3(1 - 1/N) < \tfrac{1}{2}V < \tfrac{2}{3}\pi R^3(1 + 1/N), \tag{3}$$

so that, by a passage to the limit for $N = \infty$, the result $\frac{1}{2}V = 2\pi R^3/3$ followed.

Let us consider half the hypervolume $\frac{1}{2}W$ of a HS of radius R as sliced into N hypervolumes W_k, $1 \leqslant k \leqslant N$, by parallel spaces drawn through the points of a division of radius R into N equal parts, these spaces being perpendicular to the radius R. Each part W_k extends in the direction of the radius only R/N because it is comprised between two adjacent and parallel secant spaces whose distance is equal to R/N. Therefore, all W_k have the same altitude equal to R/N. Each hypervolume W_k has two parallel bases which are solid spheres of radii r_{k-1} and r_k. Thus, the base volumes of a W_k are equal to $\frac{4}{3}\pi r_{k-1}^3$ (smaller upper base) and $\frac{4}{3}\pi r_k^3$ (larger lower base). We saw already that the radius r_k of a spherical solid section of an HS by a space whose distance from the center is equal to h_k is related to R and h_k by the Pythagorean Theorem: $r_k^2 + h_k^2 = R^2$. In our case the distance h_k of the secant space is equal to k parts of the subdivided radius so that $h_k = kR/N$ and thus $r_k = (R^2 - h_k^2)^{1/2} = R(N^2 - k^2)^{1/2}/N$. Therefore, the volumes of two bases of a W_k are equal to $\frac{4}{3}\pi \cdot (R/N)^3 [N^2 - (k-1)^2]^{3/2}$ and $\frac{4}{3}\pi \cdot (R/N)^3 (N^2 - k^2)^{3/2}$ respectively.

We now consider two auxiliary hypervolumes of the same altitude R/N as W_k and with spherical solid bases also, but one greater than W_k because both its bases are equal to the greater, lower base of W_k and the second one smaller than W_k because both its bases are equal to the upper, smaller base of W_k. These hypervolumes have a cylindrical shape because their both bases are identical solid spheres. Their altitude being at the same time the common length of their parallel edges, these auxiliary four-dimensional bodies may be called right spherical hypercylinders. The part W_k of the HS's hypervolume is contained within the larger hypercylinder and contains in its interior the smaller hypercylinder. The hypervolumes of hypercylinders are obtained multiplying their base-volumes by the length of the altitude, so that W_k satisfies the following double inequality

$$\tfrac{4}{3}\pi \cdot (R/N)^4 [N^2 - (k-1)^2]^{3/2} > W_k > \tfrac{4}{3}\pi \cdot (R/N)^4 (N^2 - k^2)^{3/2}. \quad (11)$$

Summing up the inequalities (11) for k varying from $k = 1$ up to $k = N$, we obtain for half the hypervolume $\tfrac{1}{2}W$ of the HS an inequality analogous to that (3) for half the volume of the sphere:

$$\tfrac{4}{3}\pi (R/N)^4 \cdot \sum_1^N [N^2 - (k-1)^2]^{3/2} > \tfrac{1}{2}W$$

$$> \tfrac{4}{3}\pi (R/N)^4 \cdot \sum_1^N (N^2 - k^2)^{3/2}. \quad (12)$$

The unique difference between (3) and (12) consists in the circumstance that in (12) the sums standing in the lefthand and righthand members are not yet evaluated. We omit the details of this evaluation and give only the final result which states that at the limit for N = ∞ both sums divided by N^4 become equal to the number $\frac{3}{16}$:

$$\lim_{N=\infty}\left\{N^{-4}\sum_1^N [N^2 - (k-1)^2]^{3/2}\right\} = \lim_{N=\infty}\left\{N^{-4}\sum_1^N (N^2 - k^2)^{3/2}\right\} = \tfrac{3}{16}.$$

Using this numerical result, we finally find the measure of half the hyper-volume $\frac{1}{2}$W of an HS and, doubling it, deduce the following expression for W

$$W = \pi^2 R^4/2. \tag{13}$$

The expression (13) for the hypervolume of an HS in S_4 together with the expressions πR^2 for the area of a circle in S_2 and $\frac{4}{3}\pi R^3$ for the volume of a sphere in S_3 can be considered as particular cases of a general formula expressing the measure of the portion of n-dimensional space S_n comprised within the locus of points of this S_n equidistant from a given point (center). This locus generalizes the sphere and represents in the space S_n the analogue of the spherical surface of our three-dimensional space. The measure of the interior n-dimensional space included within this locus is proportional to the nth power of the radius R of the locus and the coefficient of proportionality depends on the dimensionality n of the space S_n, so that its expression involves n. To express this measure in terms of n we introduce a special symbol for the integral part of the number $n/2$ and denote this largest integer contained in the number $n/2$ by $[n/2]$. If the dimensions' number n is even, then its half $n/2$ is an integer and therefore $[n/2] = n/2$, but if n is odd then $n/2$ is greater than $[n/2]$, and $[n/2] = n/2 - \frac{1}{2}$. Using this symbol, we have

$$\frac{(\pi/2)^{[n/2]}}{n(n-2)(n-4)(n-6)\cdots(n+2-2[n/2])}(2R)^n \tag{14}$$

and this measure of the n-dimensional content of the n-dimensional solid generalizing the sphere for the n-dimensional space S_n holds for all integral and positive values of n. Taking into consideration that all the factors in the denominator of (14) are positive and greater than zero, we conclude that the last factor is necessarily one or two. For instance in the one-dimensional space S_1 (straight line) the locus of points equidistant from a given center reduces to two points so that a segment of length 2R is the one-dimensional analogue of a circle in S_2 or of a sphere in S_3. The measure 2R of the content of an interval, as a part of S_1 included within the locus of points equidistant from a center, is indeed obtained as a particular case, for $n = 1$, of the general formula (14) because for $n = 1$ the coefficient is equal to one: $[\frac{1}{2}] = 0$ so that $(\pi/2)^{[1/2]} = 1$ and the denominator begins with the factor one and therefore has no other factors.

Substituting further $n = 2, 3, 4$ in the formula (14) we obtain the known expressions for the area of a circle in S_2, volume of a sphere in S_3, and hypervolume of an HS in S_4. It is interesting to observe that the coefficient $(\pi/2)^{[n/2]}$ $\times [n (n - 2) \cdots (n + 2 - 2 [n/2])]^{-1}$ of the general formula is a decreasing function of n: it is equal to $1; \pi/4 = 0.78 \cdots; \pi/6 = 0.52\cdots; \pi^2/32 = 0.30 \cdots$ for $n = 1, 2, 3, 4$ respectively. This coefficient represents the ratio of measures of space-contents of generalized sphere of diameter 2R and generalized cube of edge 2R, n-dimensional solids both of them. A generalized cube of edge 2R has a content equal to $(2R)^n$ and this cube is circumscribed to the generalized sphere of diameter 2R. Therefore, the generalized sphere inscribed into the generalized cube occupies within this circumscribed cube a fraction of its content, which is expressed by the coefficient of the formula (14) and thus decreases when the number of dimensions of space S_n, to which belong our generalized sphere and cube, increases. For example, in S_1 the same segment of length 2R corresponds to the "sphere" and to the "cube" of this one-dimensional space. In a plane, that is for $n = 2$, a circle occupies more than three quarters (namely, $\pi/4 = 0.78 \cdots$) of the square circumscribed about it. The volume of a sphere is only slightly greater than one-half $(\pi/6 = 0.52 \cdots)$ the volume of the circumscribed cube and, finally, the hypervolume of an HS is less than one third $(\pi^2/32 = 0.30 \cdots)$ of the hypervolume of the tessaract into which the HS is inscribed.

We want now to evaluate the boundary volume of a HS denoted in what follows by V*. This volume is related to the hypervolume W contained in it by a very simple relation $V* = 4W/R$, where R is the radius of the HS. With the aid of this relation one finds immediately that $V* = 4 (\pi^2 R^4/2)/R = 2\pi^2 R^3$, but first this relation must be established.

To prove the relation $W = RV*/4$ a new approach to the understanding of the structure of an HS is needed and this new approach is also analogous to the following description of an ordinary sphere, considered as a solid. Since through each point P on the radius OA of a sphere a concentric sphere of radius $r < R$ can be drawn, where r is equal to the distance OP of the point P from the center O of the sphere, a solid sphere can be defined and described as a set (a continuum) of concentric spherical surfaces packed closely together and filling up the interior of the sphere. Each one of them wraps tightly the spherical ball formed by all such surfaces contained within it, so tightly that there is no empty space between the ball and the spherical surface encasing the ball. The radii r of spherical surfaces composing the volume of the sphere of radius R vary from $r = 0$ up to and including $r = R$, so that the variable r takes every value contained in the interval extending from zero to R.

Describing a spherical volume as such a set of spherical surfaces, we in fact apply the principle of Cavalieri.

We apply now the same principle to the hypervolume of an HS. Through each point P of the radius OA = R of an HS a volume can be drawn which is similar to the boundary-volume V* of this HS and is also a locus of points in S_4 which are equidistant from the center O of the HS, their common distance from O being equal to r = OP. This volume through the point P can be considered as the boundary-volume of a smaller HS of radius r which is similar to and concentric with the given HS and is contained within it. Combining into an entity all such volumes which pass through all the points of the radius OA = R, a one-to-one correspondence relating the set of volumes and the set of points on OA, we obtain the whole four-dimensional solid hypersphere.

Thus, a hypersphere is also a set (a continuum) of concentric hyperspherical curved and closed volumes packed closely inside one another so that each one of them wraps in S_4 the hyperspherical ball formed by all such volumes contained in it so tightly that there remains no empty four-dimensional space between the ball and the hyperspherical volume surrounding this ball. Such is the structure of an HS as formed by nested hyperspherical volumes inserted into one other, the insertion in question being possible because volumes in S_4 have no thickness, can be bent and closed, encasing an empty four-dimensional hypervolume within a closed volume.

Using now this image of a hypersphere, we compute its hypervolume W applying the pattern with the aid of which was established the validity of the relation V = RS/3 between the volume V and the surface area S of a sphere of radius R. Thus, dividing the radius OA = R into N equal parts of length R/N, we draw within the hypervolume W of HS and through the division-points on OA hyperspherical volumes V_k of radii r_k = kR/N for all values of k from k = 1 up to k = N, the last Nth hyperspherical volume V_N being in fact the boundary-volume V* of the HS.

The volumes V_k and V* = V_N are similar because both are loci of points equidistant from the center O, the distances being equal to r_k and r_N = R for V_k and V* respectively. The ratio of two similar volumes is equal to the third power of the ratio of their corresponding segments. Therefore, the ratio V_k/V* of two similar hyperspherical volumes is equal to the cube of the ratio r_k/R = k/N of their radii. Thus, the relation

$$V_k = V^*(k/N)^3 \qquad (1 \leqslant k \leqslant N) \quad (15)$$

holds for all values of k.

Consider now the part W_k of the hypervolume of HS comprised between and bounded by two closed volumes V_{k-1} and V_k. This W_k extends along the radius OA (as well as along any radius of the HS) exactly R/N, this length R/N being the distance between two unequal and parallel bases V_{k-1} and V_k of W_k. Therefore, increasing the smaller base V_{k-1} and replacing it by V_k, we obtain a right hypercylinder of spherical base V_k containing within it the hypervolume W_k and having therefore a hypervolume which is greater than that of W_k. Now the hypervolume of a right hypercylinder is equal to the product of the volume of its base by the altitude and therefore W_k is less than $V_k(R/N)$; that is, less than $V^*R \cdot N^{-4}k^3$: $W_k < RV^*N^{-4}k^3$.

On the other hand, decreasing the larger base V_k of W_k and replacing it by V_{k-1}, another right spherical hypercylinder is obtained which is contained within W_k and whose hypervolume is less than W_k. This hypervolume being equal to $V_{k-1}(R/N) = RV^*N^{-4}(k-1)^3$, a lower bound for W_k is found and thus W_k verifies the inequality

$$(k-1)^3/N^4 < W_k/RV^* < k^3/N^4 \qquad (1 \leqslant k \leqslant N). \qquad (16)$$

Summing all these inequalities for $k = 1, 2, 3, \ldots, N-1, N$ and observing that the sum of cubes of first N integers is equal to

$$1^3 + 2^3 + 3^3 + \cdots + (N-1)^3 + N^3 = N^2(N+1)^2/4,$$

we deduce the following inequality for the hypervolume of an HS:

$$\tfrac{1}{4}(N-1)^2 N^2/N^4 < W/RV^* < \tfrac{1}{4}N^2(N+1)^2/N^4,$$

that is, multiplying by 4,

$$(1 - 1/N)^2 < 4W/RV^* < (1 + 1/N)^2.$$

This inequality holds for any integer N and, therefore, passing to the limit for $N = \infty$, we justify the relation $4W/RV^* = 1$ and with it the expression $V^* = 2\pi^2R^3$ given above for the hyperspherical boundary volume V^*

The expression $V^* = 2\pi^2R^3$, together with the expressions $4\pi R^2$ for the surface area of a sphere and $2\pi R$ for the length of the circumference of a circle, belongs to a general formula giving the measure of the boundary content of a generalized sphere in an S_n

$$2(\pi/2)^{[n/2]} \{(n-2)(n-4) \cdots (n+2-2[n/2])\}^{-1} \cdot (2R)^{n-1}, \qquad (17)$$

of which it is a particular case corresponding to $n = 4$. For $n = 1, 2, 3$ the denominator must be replaced by one.

The HS shares with the circle and the sphere their maximum-minimum properties. As a circle in S_2 and a sphere in S_3, an HS in S_4 is the exceptional body which realizes the maximum hypervolume contained in a given closed volume. On the other hand, for a given hypervolume the minimum volume containing this hypervolume must also have the shape of an HS. Here is the algebraical formulation of these facts. Eliminating the radius R from two relations $V^* = 2\pi^2 R^3$ and $R = 4W/V^*$, we find that $V^{*4} = 128\pi^2 W^3$ and this relation between the hypervolume and the closed boundary-volume of an HS is characteristic for this four-dimensional solid. For any other four-dimensional solid with a hypervolume w and the boundary-volume v^* a corresponding inequality holds:

$$v^{*4} > 128\pi^2 w^3. \tag{18}$$

Therefore, in the four-dimensional space S_4, the hypervolume and the boundary volume of any finite four-dimensional solid satisfy the limitation (18), except the hypersphere for which the sign of inequality must be replaced by the sign of equality. As an example, let us consider a tessaract of edge length a. The hypervolume of this hypercube is equal to a^4 and its boundary-volume is $8a^3$, eight ordinary cubes of same edge a and tangent to each other forming the boundary of a tessaract. The ratio of the fourth power of v^* $= 8a^3$ to the product $128\pi^2 w^3$, where $w = a^4$, is equal to $32/\pi^2$ and is greater than 3, thus amply justifying (18).

Solution of Right Spherical Triangles

At the end of this chapter we study the solution of spherical triangles, beginning first with the solution of right spherical triangles. A right spherical triangle can have one of its angles equal to $\pi/2$ and in this case it is called a *rightangular* spherical triangle, but it can also have one of its sides equal to $\pi/2$ and then it is called *rectilateral* spherical triangle. These two cases of right triangles are related to each other by the dual transformation. Therefore the same set of rules which serves for the solution of rightangular triangles, when transformed by duality, solves the rectilateral triangles. We add that very often rectilateral triangles. We add that very often rectilateral triangle is called *quadrantal*, the term *right* being then reserved for rightangular triangles.

Assuming the right angle of a spherical triangle is at the vertex A, so that $A = 90°$, we deduce from general formulas of spherical trigonometry studied in Chapter 21 a set of ten formulas which hold for a right triangle with right angle at A.

The first group (sine law), in which we substitute the value one for Sin A, yields two relations: $\text{Sin }\beta = \text{Sin }\alpha \cdot \text{Sin B}$; $\text{Sin }\gamma = \text{Sin }\alpha \cdot \text{Sin C}$. The cosine law (second group) gives $\text{Cos }\alpha = \text{Cos }\beta \cdot \text{Cos }\gamma$ because Cos A = 0. Using the same value zero for Cos A in the formulas of the third group, we obtain three formulas: $\text{Cos B} = \text{Sin A} \cdot \text{Sin C} \cdot \text{Cos }\beta = \text{Sin C} \cdot \text{Cos }\beta$, since Sin A = 1; also, $\text{Cos C} = \text{Sin B} \cdot \text{Cos }\gamma$ and $\text{Cos A} = 0 = -\text{Cos B} \cdot \text{Cos C} + \text{Sin B} \cdot \text{Sin C} \cdot \text{Cos }\alpha$, the last formula being written as $\text{Cos }\alpha = \text{Cotan B} \times \text{Cotan C}$. Finally, from six formulas of the fourth group (cotangent formulas) we retain the following four:

$$\text{Cos }\beta \cdot \text{Cos A} = \text{Sin }\beta\ \text{Cotan }\gamma - \text{Sin A} \cdot \text{Cotan C}$$

$$\text{Cos }\gamma \cdot \text{Cos B} = \text{Sin }\gamma\ \text{Cotan }\alpha - \text{Sin B} \cdot \text{Cotan A}$$

$$\text{Cos }\beta \cdot \text{Cos C} = \text{Sin }\beta\ \text{Cotan }\alpha - \text{Sin C} \cdot \text{Cotan A}$$

$$\text{Cos }\gamma \cdot \text{Cos A} = \text{Sin }\gamma\ \text{Cotan }\beta - \text{Sin A} \cdot \text{Cotan B},$$

obtained by applying circular substitution to formulas (28), (29) Chapter 21. If A = 90°, then Cos A = Cotan A = O and Sin A = 1, so that for a right triangle following four formulas are deduced:

$$\text{Sin }\beta - \text{Tan }\gamma \cdot \text{Cotan C}, \quad \text{Sin }\gamma = \text{Tan }\beta \cdot \text{Cotan B}$$

$$\text{Cos B} = \text{Tan }\gamma \cdot \text{Cotan }\alpha, \quad \text{Cos C} = \text{Tan }\beta \cdot \text{Cotan }\alpha.$$

We group these ten formulas in the following table which thus gives two expressions for the cosine of hypotenuse α, cosines of two angles B and C and for the sines of two legs β and γ:

$$\text{Cos }\alpha = \text{Cos }\beta\ \text{Cos }\gamma = \text{Cotan B} \cdot \text{Cotan C}$$

$$\text{Sin }\beta = \text{Sin }\alpha\ \text{Sin B} = \text{Tan }\gamma \cdot \text{Cotan C}$$

$$\text{Sin }\gamma = \text{Sin }\alpha\ \text{Sin C} = \text{Tan }\beta \cdot \text{Cotan B} \qquad (\text{A} = 90°) \quad (19)$$

$$\text{Cos B} = \text{Cos }\beta\ \text{Sin C} = \text{Tan }\gamma \cdot \text{Cotan }\alpha$$

$$\text{Cos C} = \text{Cos }\gamma\ \text{Sin B} = \text{Tan }\beta \cdot \text{Cotan }\alpha.$$

Now the dual transformation of these results yields a corresponding table of ten fundamental formulas for rectilateral ("quadrantal") spherical triangle with the side α equal to 90°:

$$\mathrm{Cos}\, A = -\mathrm{Cos}\, B \cdot \mathrm{Cos}\, C = -\mathrm{Cotan}\,\beta \cdot \mathrm{Cotan}\,\gamma$$

$$\mathrm{Sin}\, B = \mathrm{Sin}\,\beta \cdot \mathrm{Sin}\, A = \mathrm{Cotan}\,\gamma \cdot \mathrm{Tan}\, C$$

$$\mathrm{Sin}\, C = \mathrm{Sin}\,\gamma \cdot \mathrm{Sin}\, A = \mathrm{Cotan}\,\beta \cdot \mathrm{Tan}\, B \qquad (\alpha = 90°) \quad (20)$$

$$\mathrm{Cos}\,\beta = \mathrm{Sin}\,\gamma \cdot \mathrm{Cos}\, B = -\mathrm{Tan}\, C \cdot \mathrm{Cotan}\, A$$

$$\mathrm{Cos}\,\gamma = \mathrm{Sin}\,\beta \cdot \mathrm{Cos}\, C = -\mathrm{Tan}\, B \cdot \mathrm{Cotan}\, A.$$

Formulas (19) and (20) can be written down without errors by means of two rules devised by John Napier, the inventor of logarithms, and known as *Napier's Rules of five Parts*. To the five elements β, γ, α, B, C of a right triangle (the sixth element is the right angle A = 90°) correspond the five "parts" $\beta, \gamma, 90° - \alpha, 90° - B, 90° - C$ associated with five sides of *Napier's Pentagon* (Fig. 12). There are two parts contiguous to any given part and two parts that are not contiguous to it. Two contiguous parts are termed the *adjacent* parts, while two non-contiguous parts are called the *opposite* parts.

Napier's rules may now be stated as follows:

RULE I. The sine of a part is equal to the product of cosines of opposite parts.

RULE II. The sine of a part is equal to the product of tangents of adjacent parts.

Two expressions are thus formed for Sin β, Sin γ, Sin (90° − α) = Cos α, Cos B, Cos C and the ten formulae (19) are found.

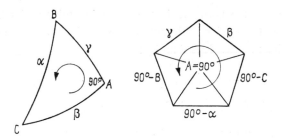

Fig. 22.12

The same mnemonic rules can be formulated for writing down the ten formulas (20). A second Napier's Pentagon is thus formed for a rectilateral triangle. To five elements A, B, C, β, γ of a rectilateral triangle (the sixth element is the side α equal to 90°) correspond the five parts A − 90°, 180° − B

$180° - C, \beta - 90°, \gamma - 90°$ associated with five sides of the second Napier's Pentagon (Fig. 13). The rules remain the same, so that the ten formulas (20) are obtained by applying Rule I and Rule II.

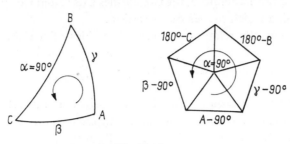

Fig. 22.13

The solution is obtained with the aid of formulas expressing the three unknown elements in terms of functions of two given elements. Six different cases are to be considered: two given elements may be (1) two legs; (2) one leg and the hypotenuse; (3) one leg and the adjacent angle; (4) one leg and the opposite angle; (5) the hypotenuse and one angle; (6) the two angles. Likewise, for a rectilateral (quadrantal) triangle we have the six dual cases: two given elements are (1) two angles adjacent to the side equal to 90°; (2) one angle adjacent and the other opposite to the side equal to 90°; (3) one adjacent angle and the side adjacent to this angle; (4) one adjacent angle and the side opposite to it; (5) the opposite angle and one side; (6) the two sides.

It is important to emphasize that the order in which the elements are arranged in the triangle must be observed in inscribing the parts on the sides of Napier's pentagons. Napier's rules I and II hold only if this condition of their validity is fulfilled. Moreover, if for an element the value of its sine is computed with the aid of Napier's rules, we must choose between two possible values of this element: to a known sine correspond two angles between 0° and 180°, one acute and the other obtuse. Therefore, a special rule must be indicated which fixes the choice of angle.

The following properties of right spherical triangles yield very convenient rules for the exact determination of elements given by their sines' values. An angle or a side will be said to be of the first quadrant if it is positive and acute; of the second quadrant if it is positive and obtuse. Using this terminology, we state that:

In a right triangle an oblique angle and the side opposite to it are always of the same quadrant; that is, both acute or both obtuse.

To prove this assertion, consider the formula $\text{Cos } C = \text{Cos } \gamma \cdot \text{Sin } B$ relating the cosines of opposite angle and side. The value of $\text{Sin } B$ is a positive number because we consider only the regular spherical triangles with angles not exceeding $180°$. Therefore, the two cosines $\text{Cos } C$ and $\text{Cos } \gamma$ are necessarily of same sign which proves our assertion.

Consider now the relation between three sides of a right triangle with $A = 90°$

$$\text{Cos } \alpha = \text{Cos } \gamma \cdot \text{Cos } \beta.$$

Thus, the sign of the product standing in the righthand member is the same as the sign of $\text{Cos } \alpha$. Suppose first that the hypotenuse α is an acute angle, so that its cosine $\text{Cos } \alpha$ has a positive value. Then the two cosines, $\text{Cos } \gamma$ and $\text{Cos } \gamma$, are of the same sign and therefore the two legs are of the same quadrant. But, if the hypotenuse is an obtuse angle α, then the legs belong to different quadrants, the product of their cosines being a negative number. Therefore:

The two legs of a right triangle are both acute or both obtuse if the hypotenuse α is less than $90°$. When the hypotenuse is greater than $90°$, then one of two legs is acute and the other is obtuse.

These two properties of right triangles are important and must be kept in mind in solving right triangles. The case when the hypotenuse of a right triangle is also equal to $90°$ so that the triangle is also rectilateral (or quadrantal) is simple: in this case $\text{Cos } \gamma \cdot \text{Cos } \beta = 0$, so that one of two legs, say γ, is also equal to $90°$ which entails also $C = 90°$ by the sine law. Therefore, the third vertex B is the pole of the great circle $\overset{\frown}{AC}$ and the triangle is half the lune of angle B. The side β opposite to this angle B is equal to B, $\beta = B$, their common value being in general any angle between $0°$ and $180°$.

Before discussing all the six cases of solution of right triangles, let us observe that the solution of a quadrantal triangle is reducible to that of a right triangle since applying the dual transformation to a quadrantal triangle, we obtain a right triangle whose solution yields the values of elements related to those of the original quadrantal triangle and from which the last ones are easily computed. Therefore, we do not discuss separately the solution of quadrantal triangles which of course follows exactly the same lines as that of right triangles.

FIRST CASE. Given the two legs β and γ, find the hypotenuse α and the angles B, C. In the Napier's Pentagon two sides β, γ are known. Taking the sine of their opposite side $90° - \alpha$, we find $\text{Cos } \alpha = \text{Cos } \beta \text{ Cos } \gamma$

and this formula yields the hypothenuse α. Further we can use again the pentagon or apply the sine law with Sin A = 1. The second way gives two proportions $1/\text{Sin}\,\alpha = \text{Sin B}/\text{Sin}\,\beta$ and $1/\text{Sin}\,\alpha = \text{Sin C}/\text{Sin}\,\gamma$, so that the two angles may be found with the aid of relations Sin B = Sin β/Sin α and Sin C = Sin γ/Sin α. Or, the pentagon can be used: the sines of its known sides β and γ are equal to the products of tangents of adjacent sides, so that Sin β = Tan γ · Cotan C, as well as Sin γ = Tan β · Cotan B. Solving for B and C, we have: Tan B = Tan β/Sin γ; Tan C = Tan γ/Sin β.

SECOND CASE. Given a leg β and the hypothenuse α, find the angles B, C and the second leg γ. The pentagon gives Cos γ = Cos α/Cos β and Cos C = Tan β · Cotan α, while the sine law yields Sin B = Sin β/Sin α.

THIRD CASE. Given a leg β and the adjacent angle C, find α, γ and B. Taking the sines of three sides of the pentagon, namely of 90° − B, 90° − C and of β, we obtain the three formulas Cos B = Cos β · Sin C, Cos C = Tan β · Cotan α which yields the value of Tan α = Tan β/Cos C, and Sin β = Tan γ · Cotan C from which we find Tan γ = Sin β · Tan C.

FOURTH (AMBIGUOUS) CASE. If a leg and the opposite angle are given, there are two right triangles with the same given elements and they form together a lune (Fig. 14). This is why the case we are discussing is called ambiguous.

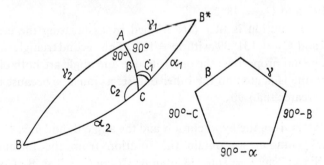

Fig. 22.14

In the figure the common (given) leg β belongs to both triangles BCA and B*CA, the angles at the common vertex A being right angles. From the figure we conclude that if the unknown elements are denoted by subscripts 1 and 2, so that for example $\overset{\frown}{AB^*} = \gamma_1$ and $\overset{\frown}{AB} = \gamma_2$, then we must have

$$C_1 + C_2 = \alpha_1 + \alpha_2 = \gamma_1 + \gamma_2 = 180°.$$

31 Kogbetliantz

The pentagon yields for all three unknown elements their sines expressed in terms of functions of known two elements:

$$\text{Sin } C = \text{Cos } B / \text{Cos } \beta; \quad \text{Sin } \alpha = \text{Sin } \beta / \text{Sin } B; \quad \text{Sin } \gamma = \text{Tan } \beta \cdot \text{Cotan } B,$$

so that indeed for each one of unknown elements we find two possible values, one acute and the other obtuse angle. The question how to associate them in two solutions is solved with the aid of two properties of right triangles formulated above.

Example of solution in an ambiguous case: given $\beta = 46°45'$ and B $= 59°12'$. The formula for the sine of the hypotenuse shows after the numerical computation that for the hypotenuse α we obtain two values $58°$ and $122°$. We will denote the acute angle $58°$ by α_1 and the obtuse by α_2. For two other elements numerical values are: $39°19'$ and $140°41'$ for the second leg and $48°21'$ and $131°39'$ for the angle C opposite to this leg γ.

Considering now the first triangle, whose hypotenuse $\alpha_1 = 58°$ is less than $90°$, we apply the rule which states that in such a right triangle the two legs are both acute or both obtuse. Since the given leg $\beta = 46°45'$ is acute we conclude that the acute angle $39°19'$ must be associated with the hypotenuse α_1 as the second leg: $\gamma_1 = 39°19'$. Now according to the first property of right triangles, the angle C_1 opposite to the side γ_1 must also be acute, so that $C_1 = 48°21'$. Thus, for the first triangle we have the three elements $\alpha_1 = 58°$, $\gamma_1 = 39°19'$, and $C_1 = 48°21'$.

The second solution is therefore formed by associating the elements $\gamma_2 = 140°41'$ and $C_2 = 131°39'$ with $\alpha_2 = 122°$. This second triangle satisfies the two fundamental properties: the opposite side and angle are both obtuse and of two legs one is acute and the other obtuse, as must be because the hypothenuse is greater than $90°$.

FIFTH CASE. Given the hypotenuse α and the angle B, find β, γ, C. With the aid of the pentagon we obtain the solution from the formulas $\text{Sin } \beta = \text{Sin } B \cdot \text{Sin } \alpha; \text{Tan } \gamma = \text{Tan } \alpha \cdot \text{Cotan } B; \text{Cotan } C = \text{Tan } B \cdot \text{Cos } \alpha.$

SIXTH CASE. Given two angles B, C, find the three sides. The solution is found with the aid of $\text{Cos } \alpha = \text{Cotan } B \cdot \text{Cotan } C, \text{Cos } \beta = \text{Cos } B / \text{Sin } C$ and $\text{Cos } \gamma = \text{Cos } C / \text{Sin } B.$

There are many relations between the elements of a right triangle which involve more than three elements and some of them are interesting in themselves, but they cannot be used in the solution of right triangles because they involve at least two unknown elements. The fundamental ten relations (19) can easily be transformed into other, but equivalent forms which sometimes can give more accurate results. As an example we cite the relation between the three sides

$$Tan^2(\gamma/2) = Tan\left[\tfrac{1}{2}(\alpha + \beta)\right] Tan\left[\tfrac{1}{2}(\alpha - \beta)\right]$$

which yields a more accurate evalution of the leg γ, when the other leg β and the hypotenuse α are known, than the formula $Cos\,\gamma = Cos\,\alpha/Cos\,\beta$.

Nevertheless the knowledge of the ten formulas (19) is completely sufficient to solve any one of six possible cases, as proves our discussion.

Solution of Oblique Spherical Triangles

The six cases of solution of *general* spherical triangles exhaust all possible combinations in which three given elements can be chosen among six elements of a triangle. They are:

(1) Given the three sides
(1*) Given the three angles
(2) Given two sides and the included angle
(2*) Given two angles and the included side
(3) Given two sides and an angle opposite to one of them
(3*) Given two angles and a side opposite to one of them.

The cases (1) and (1*) are easy to solve with the aid of formulas (26) and (27), Chapter 21, expressing the tangents of half-angles in terms of sides and the cotangents of half-sides in terms of angles. But the solution of cases (2) to (3*) becomes easy only, if the so-called *Napier's Analogies* are used. Therefore, first of all, we deduce these important formulas which generalize the tangent law of the plane trigonometry.

Napier's Analogies. There are four proportions known under this name:

$$Sin\left[\tfrac{1}{2}(A - B)\right]/Sin\left[\tfrac{1}{2}(A + B)\right] = Tan\left[\tfrac{1}{2}(\alpha - \beta)\right]/Tan\left(\tfrac{1}{2}\gamma\right)$$

$$Cos\left[\tfrac{1}{2}(A - B)\right]/Cos\left[\tfrac{1}{2}(A + B)\right] = Tan\left[\tfrac{1}{2}(\alpha + \beta)\right]/Tan\left(\tfrac{1}{2}\gamma\right) \qquad (21)$$

$$Sin\left[\tfrac{1}{2}(\alpha - \beta)\right]/Sin\left[\tfrac{1}{2}(\alpha + \beta)\right] = Tan\left[\tfrac{1}{2}(A - B)\right]/Cotan\left(\tfrac{1}{2}C\right)$$

$$Cos\left[\tfrac{1}{2}(\alpha - \beta)\right]/Cos\left[\tfrac{1}{2}(\alpha + \beta)\right] = Tan\left[\tfrac{1}{2}(A + B)\right]/Cotan\left(\tfrac{1}{2}C\right).$$

Dividing member by member the first by the second or the third by the fourth, the tangent law is obtained:

$$Tan\left[\tfrac{1}{2}(A - B)\right]/Tan\left[\tfrac{1}{2}(A + B)\right] = Tan\left[\tfrac{1}{2}(\alpha - \beta)\right]/Tan\left[\tfrac{1}{2}(\alpha + \beta)\right]. \qquad (22)$$

Let us begin by justifying the validity of the tangent law directly. Dividing Tan $[\frac{1}{2}(A - B)]$ = Sin $[\frac{1}{2}(A - B)]$/Cos $[\frac{1}{2}(A - B)]$ by Tan $[\frac{1}{2}(A + B)]$ = Sin $[\frac{1}{2}(A + B)]$/Cos $[\frac{1}{2}(A + B)$, we obtain

$$\frac{\text{Tan } [\frac{1}{2}(A - B)]}{\text{Tan } [\frac{1}{2}(A + B)]} = \frac{2 \text{ Sin } [\frac{1}{2}(A - B)] \cdot \text{Cos } [\frac{1}{2}(A + B)]}{2 \text{ Sin } [\frac{1}{2}(A + B)] \cdot \text{Cos } [\frac{1}{2}(A - B)]}.$$

But, the numerator and the denominator of the righthand member are equal to Sin A − Sin B and Sin A + Sin B respectively, so that

Tan $[\frac{1}{2}(A - B)]$/Tan $[\frac{1}{2}(A + B)]$ = (Sin A − Sin B)/(Sin A + Sin B). (23)

Replacing in this result the angles A, B by sides α, β, we obtain also:

Tan $[\frac{1}{2}(\alpha - \beta)]$/Tan $[\frac{1}{2}(\alpha + \beta)]$ = (Sin α − Sin β)/(Sin α + Sin β).   (24)

Now the sine law Sin A/Sin B = Sin α/Sin β entails also two other proportions

(Sin A − Sin B)/Sin B = (Sin α − Sin β)/Sin β

(Sin A + Sin B)/Sin B = (Sin α + Sin β)/Sin β;

and dividing them member by member, we prove that the righthand members in (23) and (24) are equal. Therefore the lefthand members are equal, too, and this completes the proof of the tangent law (22).

We set out now to prove the first of the four Napier's Analogies. The proof is based on the relation (30), Chapter 21

$$\text{Cotan } (\tfrac{1}{2}A) = \text{Sin } (s - \alpha) \cdot \text{Cotan } r,   (25)$$

where r is the radius of the inscribed circle. Using the expressions of sines of a sum and of a difference, we can write

Sin $[\frac{1}{2}(A - B)]$/Sin $[\frac{1}{2}A + B)]$

= (Sin $\frac{1}{2}$A · Cos $\frac{1}{2}$B − Cos $\frac{1}{2}$A · Sin $\frac{1}{2}$B) (Sin $\frac{1}{2}$A Cos $\frac{1}{2}$B + Cos $\frac{1}{2}$A Sin $\frac{1}{2}$B)$^{-1}$

Dividing the numerator and the denominator by the product Sin $\frac{1}{2}$A · Sin $\frac{1}{2}$B, we have

Sin $[\frac{1}{2}(A - B))]$/Sin $[\frac{1}{2}(A + B)]$

= (Cotan $\frac{1}{2}$B − Cotan $\frac{1}{2}$A) (Cotan $\frac{1}{2}$B + Cotan $\frac{1}{2}$A)$^{-1}$.

Replacing the cotangents by their expressions (25) and multiplying both terms of the fraction by Tan r we obtain

Sin $[\frac{1}{2}(A - B)]$/Sin $[\frac{1}{2}(A + B)]$

= {Sin $(s - \beta)$ − Sin $(s - \alpha)$}/{Sin $(s - \beta)$ + Sin $(s - \alpha)$}.

But the difference and the sum of two sines can be transformed into a product:

$$\text{Sin}\,(s - \beta) - \text{Sin}\,(s - \alpha) = 2\,\text{Sin}\,[\tfrac{1}{2}(\alpha - \beta)] \cdot \text{Cos}\,[\tfrac{1}{2}(2s - \alpha - \beta)]$$

$$\text{Sin}\,(s - \beta) + \text{Sin}\,(s - \alpha) = 2\,\text{Cos}\,[\tfrac{1}{2}(\alpha - \beta)] \cdot \text{Sin}\,[\tfrac{1}{2}(2s - \alpha - \beta)].$$

Dividing member by member the first of these two relations by the second, we obtain the second member of the first of Napier's Analogies because the meaning of the symbol s gives the expression $\tfrac{1}{2}(2s - \alpha - \beta)$ its value $\tfrac{1}{2}\gamma$.

Combining the first Napier's Analogy with the tangent law we deduce the second analogy. Applying the dual transformation to the first two analogies, we obtain the last two. In other words, applying the first two to the polar (dual) triangle, we deduce the last two analogies.

Now we can explain the solution of the cases (2) and its dual case (2*). Suppose that in the case (2) two sides α, β and the included angle C are given. The last two analogies solved for the tangents of $\tfrac{1}{2}(A \pm B)$ yield their values

$$\text{Tan}\,[\tfrac{1}{2}(A - B)] = \text{Tan}\,\tfrac{1}{2}C \cdot \text{Sin}\,[\tfrac{1}{2}(\alpha - \beta)]/\text{Sin}\,[\tfrac{1}{2}(\alpha + \beta)]$$

$$\text{Tan}\,[\tfrac{1}{2}(A + B)] = \text{Tan}\,\tfrac{1}{2}C \cdot \text{Cos}\,[\tfrac{1}{2}(\alpha - \beta)]/\text{Cos}\,[\tfrac{1}{2}(\alpha + \beta)],$$

which allow the computation of $\tfrac{1}{2}(A - B)$ and $\tfrac{1}{2}(A + B)$; that is, of A and B. To find γ the sine law is used and the choice between the acute and the obtuse angles having the same numerical value of Sin γ is fixed by the fact that *in a spherical triangle the order of magnitude of the sides is the same as that of their respective opposite angles.* In the dual case (2*), two first analogies yield the values of $\tfrac{1}{2}(\alpha + \beta)$ and $\tfrac{1}{2}(\alpha - \beta)$, that is, of α, β and then the sine law gives that of C.

In cases (3) and (3*), when two of the given elements are opposite, different types of solution are possible and perhaps even no solution at all. This is why the cases (3) and (3*) are called *ambiguous.* Three eventualities may be encountered: two different triangles having the same three given elements, one triangle and no triangle at all. As in the corresponding case of the plane trigonometry, the sine law yields the criterion which decides what of these three eventualities takes place in a given particular case.

Suppose that two sides α, β and the angle A are given. Then the sine law gives the value of the Sin B = Sin β · Sin A/Sin α. If the number Sin β · Sin A/Sin α happens to be greater than one, there cannot be a solution since the numerical value of the sine of a real angle does not exceed one. If this number is exactly equal to one, there is one and only one triangle having the given parts α, β, A; and in this triangle the angle B is a right angle because its sine is equal to one. Finally, if the numerical value of Sin B is less than one, then there may be two solutions and, if so, in the first triangle the angle B is an acute angle, while in the second triangle the angle B is obtuse.

When two values for the angle B are obtained it does not mean necessarily that there are two solutions. It may happen also that only one value is acceptable and then there will be only one solution; or perhaps both values obtained for B are not acceptable and there is no triangle with given parts α, β, A. Therefore, it is important to check if the values obtained for B are consistent with the fundamental property of a spherical triangle, namely: the order of magnitude of the sides is the same as that of their respective opposite angles. To fix our ideas suppose that the given sides α, β verify the inequality $\beta < \alpha$. Then the only acceptable values for B are those for which B < A and it is this criterion which decides, whether there are two or one or no solutions at all.

After the existence of one or two solutions was ensured and the corresponding values of B are computed, Napier's Analogies are used to find γ and C. They yield the expressions

$$\text{Tan } \tfrac{1}{2}\gamma = \text{Tan } \tfrac{1}{2}(\alpha - \beta) \cdot \text{Sin } [\tfrac{1}{2}(A + B)]/\text{Sin } [\tfrac{1}{2}(A - B)]$$

$$\text{Cotan } \tfrac{1}{2}C = \text{Tan } [\tfrac{1}{2}(A - B)] \cdot \text{Sin } [\tfrac{1}{2}(\alpha + \beta)]/\text{Sin } [\tfrac{1}{2}(\alpha - \beta)].$$

A similar discussion, with the roles of sides and angles interchanged, explains the solution of the dual case (3*) in which the given parts are two angles and a side opposite to one of these two angles. We omit this discussion because it is identical with the discussion of the case (3).

It is of interest to show how it can happen that the sine law gives two values for the angle B and nevertheless no solution exists. Suppose that the given parts are two obtuse angles A > B > 90° and a side α opposite to A and which is less than 90°: $\alpha < 90°$. Forming the expression Sin β = Sin B × Sin α/Sin A, we observe that in the righthand member the ratio Sin B/Sin A is greater than one because the angles A and B are both obtuse and B < A, so that Sin B > Sin A. Therefore, Sin β is greater than Sin α. On the other hand, for sufficiently small side α we will have Sin B · Sin α/Sin A < 1 since this inequality is satisfied, if Sin α < Sin A/Sin B. Therefore, three given parts A, B, α can be found such that $\alpha < 90°$, A > B > 90° and Sin α < Sin β < 1. Both values for the side β computed with the aid of sine law from the relation Sin β = Sin B · Sin α/Sin A are greater than the side (acute) α and therefore inacceptable since the sides α and β must verify the same inequality as that B < A verified by their respective opposite angles. Thus, for instance, there cannot be spherical triangle for which A = 150°, B = 120°,

$\alpha = 30°$ because the two values 60° and 120° obtained for the side β with the aid of the sine law are greater than 30°, while B < A.

The example just studied belongs to case (3*). Transforming it by duality, we obtain a corresponding example in the case (3). Suppose therefore that the three given elements are two sides $\alpha = 30°, \beta = 60°$ and the angle A $= 150°$. The second angle B opposite to the greater side $\beta = 60°$ must also exceed 150° since B > A, if there is a solution. But the computation of B with the aid of the relation Sin B = Sin β · Sin A/Sin α = Sin 60° gives for B two values 60° and 120° and both are less than A = 150°. Therefore, no triangle corresponds to data $\alpha = 30°, \beta = 60°$, A = 150° in spite of possibility of formal computation of the element B. If, disregarding the inacceptability of the values obtained for the angle B, the computation is continued and the numerical values for the tangents of half-angles $\gamma/2$ and C/2 are deduced, the nonexistence of solution is revealed in the negative signs obtained for the values of Tan $\frac{1}{2}\gamma$ and Cotan $\frac{1}{2}$C. These values are necessarily positive since the halfangles $\frac{1}{2}\gamma$ and $\frac{1}{2}$C are acute positive angles, so that if negative values for their tangents are obtained it becomes clear that there is no solution.

As an exercise let us discuss the proof of the following property of a particular spherical triangle:

EXERCISE. Prove that if the sum of angles of a triangle is 360°, then the sum of squares of cosines of its half-sides is equal to one:

$$\text{Cos}^2(\tfrac{1}{2}\alpha) + \text{Cos}^2(\tfrac{1}{2}\beta) + \text{Cos}^2(\tfrac{1}{2}\gamma) = 1. \tag{26}$$

Given A + B + C = 360°, so that the spherical excess is $2t = 360°$ $- 180° = 180°$ and $t = 90°$. The area of such a triangle is therefore equal to one quarter of the total area of the sphere. Turning to the formulas for tangents of half-sides, we have for Tan² $(\tfrac{1}{2}\alpha)$, for instance, [see (26), Chapter 21]

$$\text{Tan}^2(\tfrac{1}{2}\alpha) = \text{Cotan}^{-2}(\tfrac{1}{2}\alpha) = -\text{Sin}(90° - A)/[\text{Sin}(90° - B)\,\text{Sin}(90° - C)]$$

since $t = 90°$. Because A = 360° − (B + C), instead of Sin (90° − A) = Cos A we can write Cos (B + C) = Cos B · Cos C − Sin B · Sin C, which divided by Cos B · Cos C yields for Tan² $(\tfrac{1}{2}\alpha)$ + 1 the following expression

$$1 + \text{Tan}^2(\tfrac{1}{2}\alpha) = \text{Sec}^2(\tfrac{1}{2}\alpha) = \text{Sin B} \cdot \text{Sin C}/(\text{Cos B} \cdot \text{Cos C}) = \text{Tan B} \cdot \text{Tan C}.$$

Inverting and taking the reciprocals, we have further Cos² $(\tfrac{1}{2}\alpha)$ = Cotan B × Cotan C, so that the sum of the squares of cosines of half-sides is shown to be equal to the sum of three products of the type Cotan B · Cotan C:

$$\text{Cos}^2(\tfrac{1}{2}\alpha) + \text{Cos}^2(\tfrac{1}{2}\beta) + \text{Cos}^2(\tfrac{1}{2}\gamma)$$

$$= \text{Cotan B} \cdot \text{Cotan C} + \text{Cotan C} \cdot \text{Cotan A} + \text{Cotan A} \cdot \text{Cotan B}.$$

But the sum of the last two terms in the righthand member can be evaluated, because of $A + B + C = 360°$, as follows

$$\text{Cotan } A \cdot [\text{Cotan } B + \text{Cotan } C]$$

$$= -\text{Cotan } (B + C) \cdot [\text{Cos } B \cdot \text{Sin } C + \text{Cos } C \cdot \text{Sin } B]/(\text{Sin } B \cdot \text{Sin } C)$$

$$= -\text{Cos } (B + C)/(\text{Sin } B \cdot \text{Sin } C) = -\text{Cotan } B \cdot \text{Cotan } C + 1$$

and this yields the proof of relation (26).

The dual transform of the proposition just discussed is the following statement: If the sum of three sides of a spherical triangle is equal to 180°, then the sum of squares of cosines of its half-angles is equal to two

$$\text{Cos}^2(\tfrac{1}{2}A) + \text{Cos}^2(\tfrac{1}{2}B) + \text{Cos}^2(\tfrac{1}{2}C) = 2.$$

Ending the discussion of spherical triangles, we want to emphasize once more that the use of the sine law is a source of ambiguity even when there no doubts exist insofar as the number of solution is concerned. The ambiguity arises from the fact that to a numerical value of a sine always correspond two positive angles, one acute and the other obtuse. The choice between them, when one solution only is possible, must always be based on the fact that the order of magnitude of the sides is the same as that of their respective opposite angles and this fundamental property of spherical triangles must always be kept in mind, when a spherical triangle is to be determined from three given elements.

Hyperbolic Plane Trigonometry

Spherical trigonometry generalizes the metric relations between the elements of a plane Euclidean triangle, extending them to the triangles in a Riemannian plane. What about the metric relations between parts of a triangle in a hyperbolic Lobachevskian plane? Without attempting to give the proofs we will describe the content of so-called hyperbolic plane trigonometry the purpose of which is the study of triangles in a hyperbolic plane.

Formally speaking, any formula of the hyperbolic trigonometry can be deduced from the corresponding formula of spherical trigonometry replacing the sides α, β, γ of the spherical triangle by $i\alpha, i\beta, i\gamma$, where $i = (-1)^{1/2}$ is the imaginary unit, that is, the rotation factor through 90°. We know (Chapter 18) that the trigonometric functions of a purely imaginary argument are hyperbolic functions:

$$\text{Sin} \, (is) = i \, \text{Sinh} \, s; \quad \text{Cos} \, (is) = \text{Cosh} \, s; \quad \text{Tan} \, (is) = i \, \text{Tanh} \, s;$$
$$\text{Cotan} \, (is) = -i \, \text{Cotan} \, s.$$

Therefore, replacing the trigonometric functions by corresponding hyperbolic functions of sides α, β, γ we obtain the formulas of hyperbolic trigonometry with the aid of which any hyperbolic triangle in a Lobatchevskian plane can be completely determined, if three of its elements are given.

Thus, for example, ten fundamental formulas (19) for a right spherical triangle are transformed by this method into ten formulas for right hyperbolic triangles $(A = 90°)$:

$$\text{Cosh} \, \alpha = \text{Cosh} \, \beta \cdot \text{Cosh} \, \gamma = \text{Cotan} \, B \cdot \text{Cotan} \, C$$
$$\text{Sinh} \, \beta = \text{Sinh} \, \alpha \cdot \text{Sin} \, B = \text{Tanh} \, \gamma \cdot \text{Cotan} \, C$$
$$\text{Sinh} \, \gamma = \text{Sinh} \, \alpha \cdot \text{Sin} \, C = \text{Tanh} \, \beta \cdot \text{Cotan} \, B \qquad (27)$$
$$\text{Cos} \, B = \text{Cosh} \, \beta \cdot \text{Sin} \, C = \text{Tanh} \, \gamma \cdot \text{Cotanh} \, \alpha$$
$$\text{Cos} \, C = \text{Cosh} \, \gamma \cdot \text{Sin} \, B = \text{Tanh} \, \beta \cdot \text{Cotanh} \, \alpha.$$

As an example of the application of hyperbolic trigonometry we deduce the famous relation $\text{Tan} \, (\tfrac{1}{2}A) = e^{-\alpha}$ between the length OP of a perpendicular dropped from a point P on a straight line OQ and the angle of parallelism A corresponding to this length, that is, the angle $\overset{\frown}{OPX}$ formed with OP by a parallel PX to OQ through the point P. The dimensionless measure α of the distance OP from the point P to the line OQ is equal to the ratio OP/k, where k is an *absolute length* characterizing a hyperbolic plane in the same way as the length R of the radius characterizes a Riemannian plane represented by a spherical surface.

Let us consider the infinite hyperbolic triangle OPZ with two infinite sides OZ, PZ, the point Z being common point at infinity of two parallels, so that the angle at this point Z is zero, while the angle at the vertex P is the angle of parallelism $A = \overset{\frown}{OPZ}$, (Fig. 15).

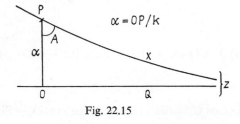

Fig. 22.15

Applying to this infinite triangle the seventh fundamental formula (27) $\text{Cos } \widehat{PZO} = \text{Cosh} (OP/k) \cdot \text{Sin } \widehat{OPZ}$, we find that the product $\text{Cosh } \alpha \cdot \text{Sin A}$ is equal to one because $\text{Cos } \widehat{PZO} = \text{Cos } 0 = 1$. Therefore $\text{Cosh } \alpha = 1/\text{Sin A}$ which gives $\text{Sinh}^2 \alpha = \text{Cosh}^2 \alpha - 1 = \text{Cosec}^2 A - 1 = \text{Cotan}^2 A$ and therefore $\text{Sinh } \alpha = \text{Cotan A}$. We form now the exponential $e^{-\alpha} = \text{Cosh } \alpha - \text{Sinh } \alpha = 1/\text{Sin A} - \text{Cos A}/\text{Sin A} = (1 - \text{Cos A})/\text{Sin A}$. But $1 - \text{Cos A} = 2 \text{Sin}^2 (\tfrac{1}{2}A)$ and $\text{Sin A} = 2 \text{Sin} (\tfrac{1}{2}A) \cdot \text{Cos} (\tfrac{1}{2}A)$ so that, finally,

$$e^{-\alpha} = \text{Tan} (\tfrac{1}{2}A). \tag{28}$$

Thus, Lobatchevsky's discovery is deduced. The relation (28) was mentioned in Chapter 17 without proof. The deduction just performed from the formulas (27) cannot be considered as a proof because we do not give the proof of (27). A proof of the important relation (28) based on the integration of a very simple differential equation can be found in the Appendices.

In all formulas of hyperbolic trigonometry the symbols α, β, γ for the sides of a hyperbolic triangle denote the ratios of their lengths to the absolute length k characterizing the particular hyperbolic plane to which these triangles belong. If k increases without limit the hyperbolic plane tends to become Euclidean and at the limit for $k = \infty$, the formulas of hyperbolic trigonometry are converted into those of ordinary plane trigonometry.

The sine law, cosine law and tangent law as well as Napier's analogies take in hyperbolic trigonometry the following form:

Sine Law

$$\text{Sinh} (a/k) : \text{Sinh} (b/k) : \text{Sinh} (c/k) = \text{Sin A} : \text{Sin B} : \text{Sin C}$$

Cosine Law

$$\text{Cosh} (a/k) = \text{Cosh} (b/k) \cdot \text{Cosh} (c/k) - \text{Sinh} (b/k) \cdot \text{Sinh} (c/k) \cdot \text{Cos A}$$

Cosine Law (Third group)

$$\text{Cos C} = -\text{Cos A} \cdot \text{Cos B} + \text{Sin A} \cdot \text{Sin B} \cdot \text{Cosh} (a/k)$$

Tangent Law

$$\text{Tan} [\tfrac{1}{2} (A - B)]/\text{Tan} [\tfrac{1}{2} (A + B)] = \text{Tanh} [(a - b)/2k]/\text{Tanh} [(a + b)/2k]$$

Cotangent Formulae

$$\text{Cosh} (a/k) \cdot \text{Cos C} = \text{Sinh} (a/k) \cdot \text{Cotanh} (b/k) - \text{Sin C} \cdot \text{Cotan B}$$

Napier's Analogies

$$\text{Sin } [\tfrac{1}{2} (A - B)]/\text{Sin } [\tfrac{1}{2} (A + B)] = \text{Tanh } [(a - b)/2k]/\text{Tanh } (c/2k)$$

$$\text{Cos } [\tfrac{1}{2} (A - B)]/\text{Cos } [\tfrac{1}{2} (A + B)] = \text{Tanh } [(a + b)/2k]/\text{Tanh } (c/2k)$$

$$\text{Sinh } [(a - b)/2k]/\text{Sinh } [(a + b)/2k] = \text{Tan } [\tfrac{1}{2} (A - B)]/\text{Cotan } (\tfrac{1}{2}C)$$

$$\text{Cosh } [(a - b)/2k]/\text{Cosh } [(a + b)/2k] = \text{Tan } [\tfrac{1}{2} (A + B)]/\text{Cotan } (\tfrac{1}{2}C).$$

The solution of hyperbolic triangles is omitted here because it does not differ essentially from that of spherical triangles, the unique difference consisting in the use of tables of hyperbolic functions together with the table of trigonometric functions.

CHAPTER 23

Regular Polyhedrons

Greek philosophers were always interested in the regular bodies. The proof of the fact that there are only five of them is ascribed to Plato. The last book of Euclid's *Elements* contains the theory of five regular polyhedrons.

We recall that a polygon is called regular if it has equal angles and equal sides. For instance, equilateral triangles and squares are regular polygons. By definition a polyhedron is regular if it has equal angles, equal edges and equal faces, so that its faces are regular and equal polygons. Thus, a regular polyhedron must be convex at every vertex if it is convex at one vertex, or concave at every vertex if it is concave at one vertex. Since a closed polyhedron cannot be concave at all its vertices, a regular polyhedron is necessarily a convex closed surface.

Before studying the theory of regular polyhedrons let us describe them.

Tetrahedron

Four equilateral and equal triangles form a regular tetrahedron with its four vertices, four trihedral angles, six edges with their six dihedral angles and the centroid which at the same time is incenter, circumcenter and ortho-center. A median is also an altitude so that the centroid is at three quarters of the altitude from the vertex. It bisects a midline whose length l can be easily deduced from theorem XXII, Chapter 15, which states that for any tetrahedron the sum of squares of its six edges is equal to four times the sum of squares of three midlines. Denoting the length of an edge by a, we have therefore $6a^2 = 12l^2$ and thus $l = a/\sqrt{2}$.

Now the radius R of the circumscribed circle is the hypotenuse in a right triangle OAE (Fig. 1) with legs $a/2$ and $a/2\sqrt{2}$ (half the length of the midline). Thus, $R^2 = a^2/4 + a^2/8 = 6a^2/16$ and $R = a\sqrt{6}/4$ which gives for the altitude $H = 4R/3$ the value $H = a(\frac{2}{3})^{1/2}$. The radius of the inscribed sphere r is equal to $R/3 = H/4$, so that $r = a\sqrt{6}/12$. To evaluate the dihedral angle we consider the right triangle EDK in which the hypotenuse DE is the altitude of the face ABD, the altitude $DK = H = a(\frac{2}{3})^{1/2}$ of the tetrahedron being the leg opposite to the angle at E which is the measure of the dihedral angle because the plane CDE is perpendicular to the edge AB. Thus, the sine of a dihedral angle is equal to $DK/DE = a(\frac{2}{3})^{1/2}/(\frac{1}{2}a\sqrt{3}) = 2\sqrt{2}/3$ and the dihedral angle is equal to Arcsin $(2\sqrt{2}/3) = 70°\ 31'\ 43''.65\cdots$

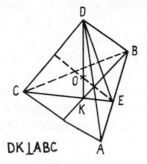

DK⊥ABC

Fig. 23.1

To compute the trihedral angle of the regular tetrahedron, describe a sphere of radius a (edge of the tetrahedron) about one of vertices taken as the center of this sphere. The trihedral angle at the center D cuts through the surface of the sphere and forms a spherical triangle ABC whose vertices are also vertices of the tetrahedron because the radius of the sphere is equal to the edge a (Fig. 2). Therefore the triangle ABC is regular and its angles are

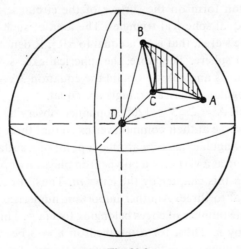

Fig. 23.2

equal to the dihedral angle of the tetrahedron; that is, to $70° 31' 43''.65$. The spherical excess of this triangle is thus equal to $211° 35' 11'' - 180° = 31° 35' 11'' = T$ and its area therefore is equal to Ta^2. The ratio T of this area Ta^2 to the square a^2 of the radius, is the measure (in radians) of the trihedral angle. Since a right trihedral angle (that is, a trihedral angle having three right dihedral angles) cuts out on the sphere's surface an equilateral spherical triangle EFG with three right angles, the measure of a right trihedral angle is $(3\pi/2 - \pi) a^2/a^2 = \pi/2 = 90°$ as for a plane right angle. The trihedral angle of a regular tetrahedron expressed in radians is equal to $\pi T/180° = 31° 35' 11'' \cdot \pi/180° = 0.1755 \cdot \pi = 0.551 \cdots$ radians.

It is of interest to emphasize that the sum of four trihedral angles of a tetrahedron is not constant but depends on the shape of the tetrahedron.

The dual transform of a regular tetrahedron T with respect to the circumscribed sphere S is again a regular tetrahedron T^* having the sphere S as its inscribed sphere because the vertices of T (which are lying on S) become by dual transformation tangent planes to S; thus the four faces of T^* are tangent to this sphere. The selfduality of regular tetrahedron is due to the fact that the number of its vertices is equal to that of faces: four vertices of T become four faces of T^* and four faces of T are transformed into four vertices of T^*. The vertices of T are centers of equilateral triangles, faces of T^*, and for this reason the first tetrahedron T is often said to be inscribed in the tetrahedron T^*.

As three vertices of a regular inscribed triangle divide the circumference of the circumscribed circle into three equal arcs, likewise the four vertices of a regular tetrahedron form on the surface of the circumscribed sphere four equilateral and equal spherical triangles. The area of such a triangle is one quarter the sphere's area, that is, it is equal to πR^2, R denoting the radius of the circumscribed sphere. Therefore, the spherical excess of this triangle is equal to π and for its angle A we obtain the equation $3A - \pi = \pi$ because the angles of a regular spherical triangle are equal.

The same result $A = 2\pi/3 = 120°$ is obtained observing that three spherical triangles converge at their common vertex so that three angles equal to A fill out the whole angular space 2π around a point of a surface. This number of faces converging at a vertex of a polyhedron plays an important role and it will be denoted in this chapter by the letter m. Thus, for a tetrahedron the number m is equal to three. Another important numerical characteristic of a polyhedron is the number of edges belonging to a face. This second number will be denoted by n. Thus, for a tetrahedron $n = 3$ because its faces are triangles, but for a cube whose faces are squares the number n is equal to four.

Since two contiguous faces of a polyhedron have in common one and only one edge the total number F of faces, the number n of sides in a face and the total number of edges E are related to each other:

$$2E = nF. \tag{1}$$

The product nF expresses the number of sides in all faces but in it each edge is counted twice because it belongs to two faces. Therefore, the value of the product nF is equal to twice the total number of edges of polyhedron that is equal to 2E. For instance, in a tetrahedron F $= 4$, E $= 6$, $n = 3$ and indeed we have $2E = 12 = 3 \cdot 4 = nF$.

On the other hand, the numbers m, E (number of edges) and the number V of vertices are related also. Each edge joins two vertices but around each vertex there are m edges terminating in this vertex. The number m is defined as number of faces around their common vertex but since two contiguous faces have also a common edge, m expresses also the number of edges radiating from a vertex. Therefore, from V vertices emanate in all mV edges and in this product each edge is counted twice because an edge joins two vertices:

$$2E = mV. \tag{2}$$

For a tetrahedron we have V $= 4$, $m = 3$ and E $= 6$: $2E = 12 = 3 \cdot 4 = mV$. It is important to emphasize that the relation $2E = mV = nF$ holds for all regular polyhedrons and remains valid also for irregular polyhedrons if they are formed in such a way that their faces have the same number of sides n, each vertex being surrounded by the same number of faces m.

Terminating the description of regular tetrahedron let us compute the side of a spherical triangle corresponding to a face of a regular tetrahedron inscribed in a sphere. This triangle is a regular one with angles equal to 120°. Denoting the angular measure of its side by $\pi - x$, we apply the cosine law of spherical trigonometry

$$\mathrm{Cos}\,(\pi - x) = \mathrm{Cos}^2(\pi - x) + \mathrm{Sin}^2(\pi - x)\,\mathrm{Cos}\,120° = \mathrm{Cos}^2 x - \tfrac{1}{2}\mathrm{Sin}^2 x$$

since $\mathrm{Cos}\,(\pi - x) = -\mathrm{Cos}\,x$ and $\mathrm{Sin}\,(\pi - x) = \mathrm{Sin}\,x$. Thus, for our unknown x we obtain the following equation

$$2\,\mathrm{Cos}^2 x - \mathrm{Sin}^2 x + 2\,\mathrm{Cos}\,x = 3\,\mathrm{Cos}^2 x + 2\,\mathrm{Cos}\,x - 1$$

$$= (3\,\mathrm{Cos}\,x - 1)\,(\mathrm{Cos}\,x + 1) = 0.$$

The root $\cos x = -1$ would give $x = -\pi$ and therefore $\pi - (-\pi) = 2\pi$ which cannot be the measure of the side we are looking for. Therefore, the answer is given by $3 \cos x - 1 = 0$, so that $\cos x = \frac{1}{3}$, $\sin x = 2\sqrt{2}/3$, Tan $x = 2\sqrt{2}$ and $x = 70° 31' 43'.65 \cdots$ and the angular measure of the side is found to be equal to $109° 28' 16''.34 \cdots$

Cube

The five characteristic numbers for a cube are: $V = 8$, $E = 12$, $F = 6$, $m = 3$, $n = 4$ since a cube has eight vertices belonging to six squares, faces of cube; three edges radiate from each vertex and in all there are twelve edges. The relation $2E = mV = nF$ is satisfied: $2E = 24 = 3 \cdot 8 = 4 \cdot 6$. Trihedral, dihedral and plane angles of a cube are all of them right angles. A cube is symmetrical in many senses: its center of symmetry O is located at the intersection of the four diagonals AH, BE, CF, DG joining the opposite vertices (Fig. 3); six pairs of equal and parallel opposite edges such as AB and EH define six planes of symmetry which are called diagonal planes;

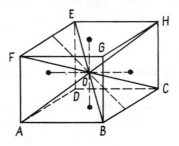

Fig. 23.3

these six diagonal planes intersect along four diagonals and pass through the center of symmetry O; sections of the cube by its diagonal planes are rectangles such as ABEH having $2^{1/2}$ as ratio of their sides; moreover there are three planes of symmetry parallel to faces and passing through O; these three planes intersect each other along three symmetry axes parallel to edges and joining the centers of opposite faces; there are thirteen axes of symmetry: four diagonals, three lines through centers of opposite faces and six lines through midpoints of opposite edges. The nine planes and thirteen axes of symmetry pass through the center of symmetry O.

Given a cube, inscribed and circumscribed spheres can be drawn. Their radii r and R expressed in terms of the length of edge a of cube are equal to $r = a/2$ and $R = \frac{1}{2}a\sqrt{3}$ respectively, $a\sqrt{3}$ being the length of a diagonal. The diagonal planes cut out on the surface of the circumscribed sphere six equal spherical squares of area $4\pi R^2/6$.

To find the angle A of these spherical squares we subdivide one of them into two spherical triangles drawing its diagonal (Fig. 4). The area of this spherical triangle is equal to $4\pi R^2/12 = \pi R^2/3$ so that its spherical excess is equal to $\pi/3$. Since its angles are A, A/2, A/2 where A denotes the angle of the square, we obtain for A the following equation: $2A = \pi + \pi/3 = 4\pi/3$ which gives $A = 2\pi/3 = 120°$.

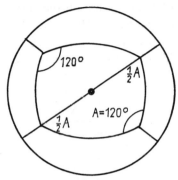

Fig. 23.4

Transforming a cube by duality we obtain another regular polyhedron: eight vertices of the cube become eight planes so that the dual transform has eight faces; the six faces of the cube generate six vertices and the number of

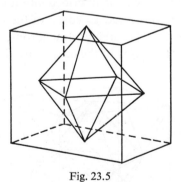

Fig. 23.5

edges remains unchanged. Therefore, the dual transform of a cube is a regular octahedron with its twelve edges and six vertices (Fig. 5). Since three edges are concurrent at a cube's vertex, while four edges belong to a face, in an octahedron three edges form a face and four edges radiate from a vertex. Thus,

the eight faces of an octahedron are regular triangles and they form tetrahedral angles at each of six vertices because four faces converge at each vertex.

This dual transformation of a cube into an octahedron can be performed
with respect to the sphere inscribed in the cube or with respect to the circumscribed sphere. In the first case, the inscribed sphere being tangent to the
cube's faces at their centers, the vertices of the resulting octahedron are
located at the centers of the cube's faces and the octahedron can be formed
by drawing straight lines joining the centers of contiguous faces. In the second case, the vertices of the cube are on the surface of the circumscribed
sphere and therefore the eight faces of the octahedron are formed by planes
tangent to the sphere at vertices of the cube (Fig. 6) so that by drawing straight
lines joining the centroids of contiguous faces of the octahedron a cube is
formed.

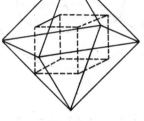

Fig. 23.6

Two regular tetrahedrons can be inscribed into a cube if the twelve diagonals of its six faces are considered as edges of these tetrahedrons (Fig. 7),
the eight vertices of the cube becoming tetrahedrons, vertices. The two tetrahedrons intersect along the edges of the octahedron inscribed in the cube.

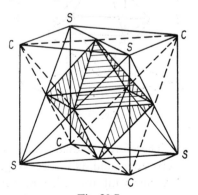

Fig. 23.7

The ordinary table salt (NaCl) crystallizes in the form of a cubical lattice, the atoms of sodium and chlorine being located at vertices of two tetrahedrons inscribed into a cube. In Fig. 7 they are denoted by letters S and C respectively. The distance between an atom of sodium and the adjacent atom of chlorine is equal to eight billionths ($8 \cdot 10^{-9}$) of an inch, such being the edge length of the unit-cube of a salt crystal. Two atoms of sodium belonging to a cube's face occupy the opposite vertices of the square face so that their distance is equal to $8\sqrt{2}$ billionths of an inch. Two other vertices are occupied by the atoms of chlorine whose distance is also equal to $8\sqrt{2}$ billionths of an inch.

Another example of regular polyhedron in the realm of crystals is the structure of diamond which is crystallized pure carbon. It is known to be harder than any other substance and this property of diamond is probably due to the geometrical arrangement of carbon atoms in the crystal. Each atom can be considered in its relative position to four neighbor atoms as located in the centroid (orthocenter, incenter, circumcenter) of a regular tetrahedron the vertices of which are occupied by four neighbor atoms. At the same time each atom can be considered as located at the common vertex of four regular tetrahedrons the centroids of which are occupied by the four neighbor atoms.

The carbon atom has four valencies and in such an arrangement into a tetrahedron lattice the carbon atoms of diamond use all their valencies, any two neighbor atoms being tied to each other by two valencies: one belonging to the first, and the other to the second of two neighbor atoms. The tetrahedron lattice is the most resistant lattice which can be built in a three-dimensional space because among regular polyhedrons the tetrahedron is the only one whose shape cannot be altered without varying the length of its four sides. These two features, use of all four valencies and of tetrahedron as unit structure, seem to explain the exceptional hardness of diamonds. The distance between any two neighbor atoms of diamond is equal to six billionths of an inch, more precisely to 6.1 billionths which yields for the length of tetrahedron's edge a $2R \left(\frac{2}{3}\right)^{1/2} = 2 \cdot 6.1 \cdot \left(\frac{2}{3}\right)^{1/2} = 10$ billionths $= 10^{-8}$ of an inch. The volume of so small a tetrahedron being equal to $a^3/6\sqrt{2}$ $= 10^{-24}/8.5$ of a cubic inch, there are $8.5 \cdot 10^{24}$ such tetrahedrons in a cubic inch of diamond.

Octahedron

The octahedron possesses—as its dual transform cube does—a center of symmetry through which pass nine axes of symmetry only (instead of thirteen axes of symmetry in a cube). Three of them join the opposite vertices;

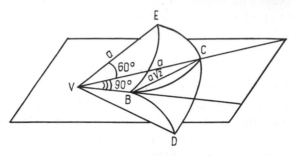

Fig. 23.8

six others pass through the midpoints of opposite (and parallel) edges. These nine axes are concurrent lines passing through the center of symmetry. There are also nine planes of symmetry: three diagonal planes dividing the octahedron into two equal quadrangular pyramids and six planes passing through the midpoints of parallel edges and two vertices which do not belong to these parallel edges. Each plane of the last six contains one diagonal and one midline; that is, the line through midpoints of parallel edges.

To find the value of dihedral angles of a regular octahedron let us draw a sphere of radius a equal to the edge-length with the center at a vertex V of the octahedron (Fig. 8). The four faces converging at V cut out on this sphere a spherical square BDCE whose vertices are also those of the octahedron because the radius of the sphere is equal to the octahedron's edge $a = $ VB. The diagonal $\overset{\frown}{BC}$ of this square is subtended by a chord BC of length $a \sqrt{2}$ because BC is also a diagonal of the plane square BDCE of side BD $= a$. Consider now a plane triangle VBC with sides VB $=$ VC $= a$ and BC $= a \sqrt{2}$. Since BC² $=$ VB² $+$ VC² this triangle is a right one with the right angle at V so that the side $\overset{\frown}{BC}$ of the spherical triangle BCD is equal to 90°: $\overset{\frown}{BC} = 90°$. The face BVE of the octahedron being a regular triangle, the angle $\overset{\frown}{BVE}$ is equal to 60° which gives also the same measure for the side $\overset{\frown}{BE} = 60°$. We can now apply the cosine law of spherical trigonometry to the spherical triangle BCE and express the cosine fo its side $\overset{\frown}{BC}$ = 90° as follows:

$$\text{Cos } \overset{\frown}{BC} = \text{Cos } \overset{\frown}{BE} \cdot \text{Cos } \overset{\frown}{CE} + \text{Sin } \overset{\frown}{BE} \cdot \text{Sin } \overset{\frown}{CE} \cdot \text{Cos } \overset{\frown}{BEC}$$

$$= \text{Cos}^2 60° + \text{Sin}^2 60° \cdot \text{Cos } \hat{E} = \text{Cos } \overset{\frown}{BC} = \text{Cos } 90° = 0.$$

But Cos 60° = $\frac{1}{2}$ and Sin 60° = $\sqrt{3}/2$, so that for the cosine of the dihedral angle $\hat{E}$ formed by two adjacent faces of the octahedron we find the equation $1 + 3 \text{ Cos } \hat{E} = 0$. Thus, Cos $\hat{E} = -\frac{1}{3}$, Sin $\hat{E} = 2\sqrt{2}/3$ and Tan $\hat{E} = -2\sqrt{2}$ which yields the value of $\hat{E}$ in degrees: $\hat{E} = 180° - 70° 31' 43''.65 \cdots = 109° 28' 16''.34 \cdots$

Knowing the dihedral angle we can easily compute the spherical excess of the square BCDE. It is equal to four times $\hat{E}$ minus 360°; that is, to 77° 53' 5''.4 $\cdots$ in spherical degrees. Comparing the value 77° 53' 5'' $\cdots$ of the tetrahedral angle of regular octahedron to those 31° 35' 11'' and 90° of trihedral angles of tetrahedron and cube, we see the reason why it is possible to fill all the space around a given point by eight juxtaposed cubes tangent to each other by their common faces while it cannot be done using tetrahedrons or octahedrons around a point as their common vertex. The total space around a point counts 720° spherical degrees (4π) and eight right trihedral angles make together exactly 90° $\cdot$ 8 = 720°, while the trihedral angles of regular tetrahedron and tetrahedral angle of regular octahedron are not aliquot parts of 720°.

There is, of course, another reason which explains why the cubes fill up the space. The eight cubes around their common vertex O (Fig. 9) have in

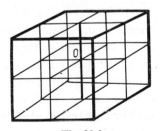

Fig. 23.9

common not only their faces but also edges: each one of these eight cubes is tangent to three neighbour-cubes by its three faces and has in common with three other cubes its three edges only, while with the last, eighth cube it shares only the common vertex O. In all, six edges radiate from O and around each one of these six edges are located four cubes. As their faces are tangent, each cube along this edge has two neighbors.

Since four dihedral angles surround an edge radiating from O, the sum of their measures must be equal to the whole angular space around this edge, that is, equal to 360°. And this is so because the dihedral angle of a cube is a right angle and has exactly 90°.

The dihedral angles of a regular tetrahedron or a regular octahedron are not aliquot parts of 360° and this is the second reason for the impossibility of filling up the space with them.

Dodecahedron and Icosahedron

We saw that a cube and an octahedron form a pair of dual regular polyhedrons. Another dual pair is formed by the so-called dodecahedron and icosahedron which transform into one other by duality. *Dodeca* and *icosa* are Greek words for *twelve* and *twenty*, so that these regular solids are polyhedrons with twelve and twenty faces respectively. Since in the dual transformation faces become vertices we conclude that the dodecahedron must have twenty vertices and the icosahedron only twelve. The number of edges is the same for both, namely thirty.

From these data we can determine the shape of the faces and the structure of the polyhedral angle at a vertex since the relations $2E = mV = nF$ yield for the unknown numbers m and n the following expressions

$$m = 2E/V, \quad n = 2E/F. \tag{3}$$

Thus, for a dodecahedron ($F = 12$, $V = 20$, $E = 30$) we obtain: $m = \frac{60}{20} = 3$, $n = \frac{60}{12} = 5$ which means that, n being equal to five, the faces are equilateral pentagons arranged by groups of three ($m = 3$) around each of twenty vertices (Fig. 10). Since by dual transformation V and F exchange their values, the formulas (3) prove that m and n also exchange their roles by dual transformation. Therefore, for an icosahedron we obtain $m = 5$ and $n = 3$: icosahedron is formed by twenty triangles arranged by groups of five around each of twelve vertices (Fig. 10).

We compute now the dihedral and trihedral angles of a dodecahedron. Choosing one of its vertices A as the center of the sphere with radius $a = AB$ (edge length) and drawing this sphere, we obtain (Fig. 11) on the spherical surface a triangle BCD whose sides are arcs of central angles equal to 108° because the angles of a regular pentagon are equal to 108° (subdividing it by diagonals into three triangles, we obtain the sum of angles 540° which is at the same time the sum of the five equal angles of the pentagon; thus we obtain for the pentagon's angle the value 540°/5 = 108°). Therefore, the sides of the spherical triangle BCD are also equal to 108° while its angles are equal to dihedral angles of the dodecahedron. Denoting the dodecahedron's dihedral angle by Â and applying the cosine law to the triangle BCD, we have Cos 108° = Cos² 108° + Sin² 108° · Cos Â.

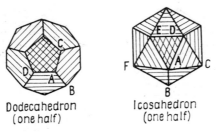

Dodecahedron   Icosahedron
(one half)   (one half)

Fig. 23.10

Replacing Cosine and Sine of 108° by their numerical values Cos 108° = −($\sqrt{5}$ − 1)/4 and Sin 108° = (10 + 2$\sqrt{5}$)$^{1/2}$/4, the numerical value of Cos Â is found to be equal to minus one divided by $5^{1/2}$, so that Sin Â = 2/$\sqrt{5}$ and Tan Â = −2. Thus, the dihedral angle of dodecahedron is equal to Â = Arctan (−2) = 116° 30′ 28″. The spherical excess of the same triangle BCD, that is, 3Â − 180° = 169° 31′ 24″, yields the value of the trihedral angle at the vertex Â expressed in spherical degrees.

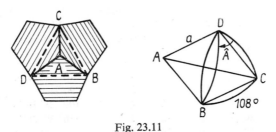

Fig. 23.11

Repeating the same computation for the icosahedron, we consider a sphere of radius a = AB, passing through five vertices A, B, C, D, E of a pentagon formed by five faces (triangles) of icosahedron converging at the vertex O, where the center of the sphere is located. A diagonal of the pentagon ABCDE, for instance AC (Fig 12), belongs to two equal triangles ABC and OAC. Therefore, the central angle at O subtended by the chord AC is equal to the angle ABC of the regular pentagon; that is, $\overset{\frown}{AOC}$ = 108°. In the spherical triangle ABC the angle at B is equal to the dihedral angle of the icosahedron.

It is included between two sides $\overset{\frown}{AB} = \overset{\frown}{BC} = 60°$ because the triangles OAB and OBC are regular and therefore their angles at O are equal to 60°. The side $\overset{\frown}{AC}$ opposite to the angle $\hat{B}$ was already found to be equal to 108°, so that, applying again the cosine law and expressing $\text{Cos } \overset{\frown}{AC} = \text{Cos } 108°$

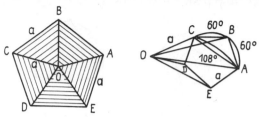

Fig. 23.12

$= -(\sqrt{5} - 1)/4$, we find the following equation for the cosine of the dihedral angle B:

$$-(\sqrt{5} - 1)/4 = (\tfrac{1}{2})^2 + (\sqrt{3}/2)^2 \cdot \text{Cos } \hat{B}.$$

Thus, $\text{Cos } \hat{B} = -\sqrt{5}/3$, $\text{Sin } \hat{B} = \tfrac{2}{3}$, $\text{Tan } \hat{B} = -2/\sqrt{5}$ and $\hat{B} = 180° - 41° 48' 23''.5 = 138° 11' 36''.5$.

The spherical excess of the pentagon ABCDE represents the value of the pentahedral angle at a vertex of icosahedron. It is equal to $5\hat{B} - 3 \cdot 180° = 150° 58' 02''.5$. The properties of five regular solids are summarized in the following table:

	Vertices	Edges	Faces	Edges at a vertex	Edges in a face	Angles dihedral (at an edge)	Angles polyhedral (at a vertex)
	V	E	F	m	n		
Tetrahedron	4	6	4	3	3	70° 31′ 43″6	31° 35′ 11″
Cube	8	12	6	3	4	90°	90°
Octahedron	6	12	8	4	3	109° 28′ 16″3	77° 43′ 05″
Dodecahedron	20	30	12	3	5	116° 30′ 28″	169° 31′ 24″
Icosahedron	12	30	20	5	3	138° 11′ 36″5	150° 58′ 02″5

Thus, there are at least five regular solids. Are there other regular solids than the five just studied? The answer is "no", and this fact was known already to Greek mathematicians. We now have to prove it. The first proof we will discuss is based on a theorem which concerns the sum of plane angles at the vertex of a polyhedral angle:

THEOREM. *The sum of face angles of a convex polyhedral angle is less than four right angles.*

The proof of this theorem is base on the following

LEMMA: The sum of two face angles of a trihedral angle is greater than the third face angle. To justify this lemma let $\overparen{ADB}$ denote in a trihedral angle ABCD with the vertex at D (Fig. 13) the face angle which is greater than either one of two other face angles $\overparen{ADC}$ and $\overparen{BDC}$. Therefore, it is possible to draw in the plane ADB and between DA and DB straight lines DE and DF which form the angles $\overparen{ADE} = \overparen{ADC}$ and $\overparen{BDF} = \overparen{BDC}$. Plotting three equal segments DK = DL = DR on the straight lines DC, DE, DF respectively and drawing through the three points K, L, R a plane intersecting DA and DB at points M and N, we build a triangle KMN. Now the triangles DMK and DML are equal by construction since they have equal angles included between two pairs of equal sides: $\triangle$ DMK = $\triangle$ DML. The same is true for two triangles DNK and DNR which are also equal: $\triangle$ DNK = $\triangle$ DNR. Therefore, we have ML = MK as well as NR = NK. Now, since MK + KN > MN, it is seen that ML + NR > MN which justifies the order of points R and L in the Figure 13. We have now

$$\overparen{ADE} + \overparen{BDF} = \overparen{ADB} + \overparen{FDE} > \overparen{ADB},$$

while on the other hand $\overparen{ADE} = \overparen{ADC}$ and $\overparen{BDF} = \overparen{BDC}$. Therefore, we conclude that

$$\overparen{ADB} < \overparen{ADC} + \overparen{BDC}$$

and the lemma is proved.

This fact, of course, is equivalent to the following property of a spherical triangle the sides of which do not exceed 180°: the sum of two sides of a spherical triangle is greater than the third side.

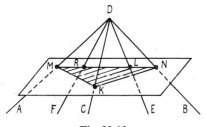

Fig. 23.13

If a sphere of radius one is drawn with the center at the vertex D, the lengths of sides of a spherical triangle cut out on the sphere's surface by the face planes of the trihedral angle are equal to face angles; and the same inequality is again justified because the sum of two sides of a spherical triangle is greater than the third, provided that triangles with sides exceeding 180° are discarded.

Now we can prove our lemma. A plane non-incident with the vertex P of a polyhedral angle cuts the edges of this angle at points A, B, C, ... etc. (Fig. 14) forming thus a polygon. Let us denote the sum of angles of this

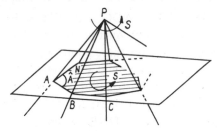

Fig. 23.14

polygon by s: $s = \hat{A} + \hat{B} + \hat{C} + \cdots = (n - 2) \cdot 180°$, if n is the number of faces of the polyhedral angle at P.

Consider the sum of angles of n triangles such as APB which belong to n faces of the polyhedral angle. This sum is equal to $n \cdot 180°$ and, on the other hand, it can be decomposed into the sum S of face angles at P and the sum T of angles adjacent to sides AB, BC, etc., of the polygon and lying in the faces of the polyhedral angle. Thus, if $S = \widehat{APB} + \widehat{BPC} + \cdots + \widehat{NPA}$ and $T = \widehat{ABP} + \widehat{PBC} + \widehat{BCP} + \cdots + \widehat{PNA} + \widehat{NAP} + \widehat{PAB}$, then $S + T = n \cdot 180°$.

The plane angles of trihedral angles located at the n vertices A, B, C, ..., etc., of the polygon satisfy the inequalities of the type $\widehat{ABP} + \widehat{CBP} > \widehat{ABC} = \hat{B}$, that is, the sum of two angles adjacent to two contiguous sides of the polygon and lying in the two contiguous faces is greater than the polygon's angle at their common vertex. Therefore, adding all these inequalities written down for all the n vertices of the polygon, we come to the conclusion that the sum T is greater than the sum s: $T > s = 180° (n - 2)$.

Therefore, the sum S of face angles of the polyhedral angle at P which is equal to $180° \cdot n - T$ is less than the difference $180° \cdot n - 180° (n - 2) = 360°$ which completes the proof of our lemma. We add that the total angular space around a point in a plane being equal to 360°, a polyhedral angle with a sum of face angles equal to 360° degenerates into a half-space, the planes of all its faces coinciding in one and the same plane. Therefore, the limitation $S < 360°$ is an essential condition for the existence of convex polyhedral angles.

The lemma just established is sufficient to prove that there are no more than five regular solids. The argument develops as follows. The faces of a regular polyhedron are regular polygons. The minimum number of faces converging at a vertex is three, so that $m \geqslant 3$. Suppose that the regular solid is bounded by triangles. Since a regular triangle's angle is equal to 60° there may be three, four or five triangular faces at a vertex, but m cannot exceed 5 because already for $m = 6$ the sum of face angles S does not verify the condition S < 360°. We have indeed 60° · 6 = 360°. Therefore, regular solids bounded by triangles can have only three, four or five faces around a vertex, all these three possible cases being realized: in a tetrahedron three triangles form its trihedral angles; in a octahedron there are four and in an icosahedron five triangles around each vertex.

Consider now the regular solid bounded by squares ($n = 4$). The angle of a square being equal to 90° there can be only one solid having three squares at each of its vertices and the cube realizes this possibility. Already for $m = 4$ we have S = 90° · 4 = 360° so that m cannot exceed 3.

If pentagons form the boundary of a regular solid there can be again only three of them around a vertex because the regular pentagon's angle equals 108° and therefore 108° · 4 exceeds 360°. We saw that this case is realized in a dodecahedron with its twelve pentagons.

Beginning with the regular hexagon the angles of regular polygons become so large that even three of them do not have a sum inferior to 360°. Thus, for instance, the angle of a regular hexagon is equal to 120° and if we try to form a trihedral angle with the aid of three regular hexagons grouped around a point as their common vertex we obtain a plane through this point because 120° · 3 = 360°. *A fortiori* regular polygons with seven, eight or more sides cannot form convex trihedral angle and cannot therefore be used as elements of boundary-surface of a regular polyhedron.

The argument just discussed was found by Greek mathematicians more than two thousand years ago. We will now study another proof of the same theorem based on the following relation between the three numbers F, m, n characterizing a regular polyhedron with F faces of n sides each and which meet by groups of m at their common vertices:

$$(m - 2)\, n \cdot F = 2m \cdot (F - 2). \tag{4}$$

With the aid of relations (1) and (2) 2E = nF = mV this relation (4) can be transformed into either of two equivalent forms

$$(n - 2)\, m \cdot V = 2n\, (V - 2) \quad \text{or} \quad (2 + E)\, mn = 2\, (m + n)\, E,$$

the first of which is the dual counterpart of (4) since F and V on the one hand, and m and n on the other, are exchanged by dual transformation applied to a regular solid.

To prove the relation (4) we circumscribe a sphere about a regular polyhedron whose F faces are polygons with n sides which converge by groups of m polygons at each of V vertices of the regular solid bounded by them. The surface $4\pi R^2$ of the circumscribed sphere is subdivided by diametral planes through the edges of the inscribed polyhedron into F *spherical* regular polygons with n sides of area $4\pi R^2/F$ each. These polygons encircle their common vertices and there are m polygons around each vertex. Let us denote the angle of these regular and equal polygons by $\hat{A}$. Since there are m such angles $\hat{A}$ around each vertex the value of $\hat{A}$ is equal to $2\pi/m$ (Fig. 15).

The area of a spherical polygon was found to be equal to $4\pi R^2/F$ because F of them fill up the total surface of the sphere. But the same area can be computed in terms of $\hat{A}$ and n, using the spherical excess of the polygon. To evaluate this spherical excess join the center of symmetry M to n vertices of the sperical polygon by arcs of great circles, subdividing thus its area into n

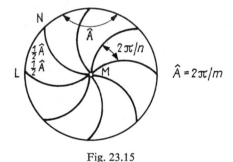

Fig. 23.15

isosceles spherical triangles of the type LMN (Fig. 15). The spherical excess of the whole polygon is equal to the sum of spherical excesses of n triangles. The angle $\overgroup{\text{LMN}}$ at the center of symmetry is equal to $2\pi/n$, while the equal angles $\overgroup{\text{MLN}}$ and $\overgroup{\text{MNL}}$ opposite to equal sides $\overgroup{\text{ML}}$, $\overgroup{\text{MN}}$ were constructed by bisecting the angle $\hat{A}$ of the polygons. Thus the sum of angles of a triangle is $2\pi/n + \hat{A}/2 + \hat{A}/2 = 2\pi/n + \hat{A}$ and its spherical excess is equal to $2\pi/n + \hat{A} - \pi$. Multiplying it by the number n of triangles we obtain the following expression for the spherical excess of the whole polygon

$$n\hat{A} - (n - 2)\pi.$$

Therefore, the area of a spherical polygon is equal to $[n\hat{A} - (n-2)\pi]\,R^2$. Comparing the two expressions of the same area we find the relation

$$4\pi R^2/F = [n\hat{A} - (n-2)\pi]\,R^2.$$

Dividing both members of this relation by R^2 and replacing in it $\hat{A}$ by its value $\hat{A} = 2\pi/m$, we obtain $4\pi/F = 2\pi n/m - (n-2)\pi$. Dividing by the common factor π, multiplying both members by mF and opening the parentheses, we have

$$4m = 2nF - mnF + 2mF$$

which yields (4), transposing the first two terms of the righthand member to the left and the unique term $4m$ of the lefthand member to the right.

To prove the uniqueness of five regular solids we solve (4) with respect to F

$$F = 4m\,[2n - m\,(n-2)]^{-1} \tag{5}$$

and discuss this expression of F taking into consideration following three points: 1) F must be an integer, 2) F cannot be less than 4 and 3) F cannot be negative.

The most important is the last point. Since F cannot be negative the denominator $2n - m(n-2) = 4 - (m-2)(n-2)$ must be positive. Being an integer it must exceed or at least be equal to one, so that our two unknown integers m and n must verify the inequality $4 - (m-2)(n-2) \geqslant 1$. Consider now the product $(m-2)(n-2)$. The inequality just written down gives $(m-2)(n-2) \leqslant 3$ and on the other hand, both m and n are at least equal to three so that $(m-2)(n-2) \geqslant 1$. The last observation is easy to justify: the number n of sides in a polygonal face is at least three since triangle is the simplest polygon possible, on the other hand at least three faces must meet at the vertex of a regular solid since trihedral angle is the simplest among polyhedral angles.

Thus, the product $(m-2)(n-2)$ of two integers $m-2$ and $n-2$ satisfies the condition

$$1 \leqslant (m-2)(n-2) \leqslant 3 \tag{6}$$

and only three integral values are possible in the interval $1-3$: the product $(m-2)(n-2)$ can take the values one, two or three and no other. We discuss these three possibilities separately.

(1) $(m-2)(n-2) = 1$. If the product of two positive integers is equal to one, both factors must be equal to one and this gives $m-2 = n-2 = 1$,

that is $m = n = 3$. Substituting $m = n = 3$ into (5) we find $F = \frac{12}{3} = 4$ which is possible since $F = 4$ fulfils the conditions 1) and 2). We know that the case $m = n = 3$, $F = 4$ is realized in the regular *tetrahedron*.

(2) $(m - 2)(n - 2) = 2$. Here we have two possible solutions: a) $m - 2 = 1$, $n - 2 = 2$ and b) $n - 2 = 1$, $m - 2 = 2$. They give: a) $m = 3$, $n = 4$ and b) $m = 4$, $n = 3$. The corresponding F is: in the case a) $F = 6$ and in the case b) $F = 8$, so that the *cube* and *octahedron* are obtained.

(3) $(m - 2)(n - 2) = 3$. Again two possible solutions: a) $m - 2 = 1$, $n - 2 = 3$ that is, $m = 3$, $n = 5$ with $F = 12$ *(dodecahedron)* and b) $m - 2 = 3$, $n - 2 = 1$ that is, $m = 5$, $n = 3$ with $F = 20$ *(icosahedron)*.

No other solution in integers of the double inequality (6) being possible, the theorem is proved.

The same conclusion could be reached with the aid of the equivalent relation $(2 + E) mn = 2(m + n) E$ which can be written as follows

$$1/m + 1/n = \tfrac{1}{2} + 1/E. \tag{7}$$

Since E is a finite positive integer its reciprocal $1/E$ is also a positive number and therefore the two unknown integers m and n satisfy the inequality

$$1/m + 1/n > \tfrac{1}{2}$$

the discussion of integral solutions of which yields again only five cases found above.

The relation (4) between three characteristics m, n, F of a regular solid can be transformed into an equivalent relation between the numbers V, E and F. Multiplying it by V

$$(mV - 2V) \cdot nF = 2mV (F - 2),$$

replacing mV and nF by 2E

$$(2E - 2V) \cdot 2E = 2 \cdot 2E (F - 2)$$

and dividing both members by 4E, the relation $E - V = F - 2$ is obtained, that is,

$$V - E + F = 2. \tag{8}$$

Thus, for all regular solids the number $V + F$ of its vertices and faces minus the number E of its edges is the same, namely 2. It is easy to check this result directly. For a tetrahedron $V = F = 4$ and $E = 6$, so that $4 - 6 + 4 = 2$. For a cube $V = 8$, $E = 12$, $F = 6$ and again $8 - 12 + 6 = 2$. For an octahedron the sum $V - E + F = 2$ because it is dual transform of a cube and therefore interchanging V and F in the same sum for a cube we do not change its value. A dodecahedron has $V = 20$, $E = 30$, $F = 12$ while its dual transform, icosahedron, is characterized by V = 12, E = 30, F = 20 and for both of them we obtain again 20 − 30 + 12 = 2.

This important fact is a particular case of the following general

EULER'S THEOREM. *The relation* V − E + F = 2 *holds for any simple polyhedron.*

Thus, Euler's Formula V − E + F = 2 deduced from the study of regular solids is not at all a special property of five regular polyhedrons and it is true for all solids bounded by planes provided that they are bounded by *simple* polyhedrons. To explain the meaning of this essential limitation without which the Euler's Theorem is no longer true, let us consider closed circuits drawn on the polyhedron's surface and consisting of edges exclusively, so that these broken and closed lines do not penetrate in the interior of a face. We will call such a sequence of contiguous edges a *closed cut*. By definition a polyhedron is *simple*, if any closed cut drawn on it separates its surface into two disconnected parts. The surface of a sphere is characterized by the same property and a simple polyhedron can be converted into a sphere by continuous bending and stretching of its surface.

There are polyhedrons which are not simple because they cannot be converted into a sphere by a continuous deformation of their surfaces. Such is for instance the polyhedron inscribed in or circumscribed to the surface of a tire (torus). It has a hole through it and Euler's Theorem does not hold for it.

In Fig. 16 are shown two polyhedrons with one and two holes. They are not simple. In the first one a right triangular prism ABCDEF is cut out from the solid formed by two truncated pyramids KLMDEF and GHJABC adjoined to another (exterior) right triangular prism GHJKLM. For this polyhedron V = 12, E = 24, F = 12 so that V − E + F = 0 instead of 2.

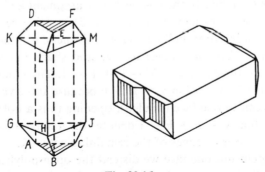

Fig. 23.16

For the other polyhedron with two holes we find by direct counting V = 28, E = 58, F = 28 and therefore V − E + F = −2.

It can be proved that for any polyhedron the value of the expression V − E + F depends on the number of closed cuts which can be drawn on its surface without dismembering it. More precisely V − E + F is equal to 2 − 2k where k denotes the greatest number of such closed cuts.

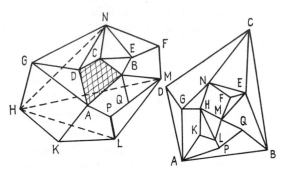

Fig. 23.17

Only one closed cut can be drawn, for instance ADKG or KLM, on the surface of the polyhedron ABCDEF (Fig. 16) without splitting it into separate parts and if to this first cut any other closed cut is added the surface falls into two disconnected pieces. Therefore for this polyhedron K = 1 and V − E + F = 2 − 2 = 0 as we found by direct counting.

But two closed cuts and no more than two can be drawn on the surface of the polyhedron with two holes through it without dismembering its surface and this explains the result V − E + F = −2 since for this polyhedron k = 2 and 2 − 2 · 2 = 2 − 4 = −2.

Returning to simple polyhedrons we set out to prove that the Euler's Theorem holds for them. In the course of our argument a given polyhedron with V vertices, E edges and F faces (Fig. 17), considered not as a solid but as a hollow polyhedral shell having no thickness, will undergo different transformations which will change its size and shape but will leave constant the value of the expression V − E + F − 1. The number one is subtracted from Euler's expression V − E + F because at the very beginning of our proof we remove one face (shaded), opening thus a hole ABCD in the polyhedron, so that V − E + F − 1 denotes the number of vertices and faces minus the number of edges of the remaining network.

After having cut out one face we distend the open polyhedron in such a way that it finally becomes a plane network of vertices and edges stretched out flat on a plane, that is, a polygonal area subdivided into smaller interior polygons. During this deformation of course the length of edges, the values of angles, the shape and areas of faces undergo variations, the contour ABCD of the hole becoming the perimeter of the final plane network. But the vertices, edges and faces remain as they are so that the number $V - E + F - 1$ does not change, the new meaning of $F - 1$ being now the number of areas into which the network of edges subdivides the total area.

The next step is the so-called triangulation of the plane network, that is, its transformation into a network of triangles only. This is done by drawing all the diagonals of interior polygons of more than three sides which decompose them into triangles. During this operation the number of vertices does not change but E and F increase: the subdivision of areas by diagonals increases the number F of areas and the diagonals become new edges, thus increasing also their number E. But—and this point is important for our proof—both E and F increase by the same number of units so that their difference $F - E$ does not change and after the triangulation it remains the same as before. To justify this it is sufficient to consider the effect of adding one diagonal to the network. A diagonal subdivides the area of the polygon into two parts so that the number F increases by one unit as does the number E, since this diagonal is added to the edges of the network. Thus, drawing a diagonal does not change the value of the expression $V - E + F - 1$.

Having performed the triangulation we begin now to remove gradually the exterior triangles of our network of triangles. A peripheral triangle can have only one side on the periphery of the network, its third vertex being interior, or it can have two such sides, all its three vertices belonging to the periphery of the network (Fig. 18). Removing a peripheral triangle of the second kind, for instance ABC, decreases the numbers V, E, F by one, two and one unit respectively because the network loses one vertex, two edges and one area. Therefore, again the expression $V - E + F - 1$ does not change and remains the same after the removal of a triangle.

We consider now the removal of a peripheral triangle of the first kind, for instance CDE. In this case it is sufficient to destroy the edge EC to remove the area CDE and with it the triangle. Thus, the effect of the removal of a triangle of the first kind is to decrease E and F by one unit without changing the number of vertices V. Therefore, this operation does not change the number $V - E + F - 1$ either.

Since all peripheral triangles are of the first or of the second kind we conclude that any peripheral triangle can be removed without changing the number $V - E + F - 1$. Now we transform our network of triangles remov-

33 Kogbetliantz

ing one after another all peripheral triangles. Since triangles which originally were in the interior of the network finally become peripheral and are removed, the operation stops only when the network shrinks to a single last triangle. During the operation the number $V - E + F - 1$ did not change. Therefore, it can be computed considering the last triangle with its elements, three

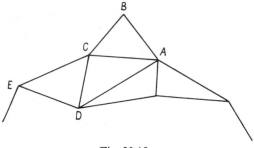

Fig. 23.18

vertices, three edges and one area, as our transformed network. For this triangle the expression $V - E + F - 1$ is equal to one because it represents for the transformed network the sum of number of vertices and areas minus the number of edges and a triangle has three vertices, one area and three edges. Thus, the expression $V - E + F - 1$ being equal to one, the original *complete* polyhedron is characterized by the relation $V - E + F = 2$ as it is stated in the theorem.

We can now extend the ancient Greek result related to the regular polyhedrons. A regular polyhedron is characterized by two essential features. The first one consists in the fact that its faces have all of them the same number of sides and therefore meet at their common vertices by groups of same number. We say therefore, because by dual transformation the same number of sides for all faces becomes same number of edges concurrent at a vertex and this last number is equal to the number of faces converging at a vertex. The second feature of a regular polyhedron is the equality of all edges and plane angles and this second feature can be dissociated from the first.

Thus, let us ask how many different polyhedrons can be found which are not regular but possess the first feature of regular polyhedrons, that is, have such a structure that their faces are polygons of same number of sides n and form groups of the same number m of faces around each of their V vertices? At first sight there should be many such irregular polyhedrons, the limitation of the number of regular polyhedrons to five only being caused by their regularity, that is, by the requirement to have equal sides and angles.

To study this question we observe that the relations (1) and (2) which require that 2E be equal to nF $= m$V are based exclusively on the first property of regular polyhedrons and therefore are independent from the equality of their sides or angles. The equality 2E $= n$F $= m$V holds therefore for the larger class of polyhedrons we are discussing now. Replacing in Euler's relation V $-$ E $+$ F $=$ 2 the numbers V and E by nF$/m$ and nF$/2$ we deduce from the Euler's Theorem the relation (4), that is, $(m - 2) n \cdot F = 2m(F - 2)$. Repeating word by word the reasoning we applied to regular polyhedrons we obtain the double inequality

$$1 \leqslant (m - 2)(n - 2) \leqslant 3$$

and conclude that there are only five irregular polyhedrons, whose faces are polygons of same number of sides which form groups of the same number of faces around each vertex: general tetrahedron, octahedron and icosahedron with triangular faces which are not equilateral triangles, general hexagon which is not a cube because its quadrangular faces are not squares but any quadrilaterals and general dodecahedron whose twelve pentagons are any irregular polygons of five sides.

It is plain that no further extension can be obtained because the number of polyhedrons with only triangular or only pentagonal faces is unlimited, the limitation to five only being due to the existence of *two* characteristic numbers m and n. Likewise there are countless polyhedrons whose faces form groups of same number of faces around each vertex without being polygons of same number of sides.

It is of interest to examine what becomes of Euler's Theorem in spaces other than the three-dimensional space? In a plane polygons are bounded by vertices and edges so that only two characteristic numbers V and E can be considered. Now it is plain that V $=$ E so that the Euler's Theorem for two-dimensional space takes the form V $-$ E $=$ 0. This suggests that the numbers of elements of different dimensions' number form an algebraic sum beginning with the number V of dimensionless elements (vertices $=$ points), the successive terms of which have alternating signs plus and minus and follow in the order of increasing dimensions' number. Thus, in a four-dimensional space S_4 the simplest shape of the boundary of a four-dimensional body is obtained if this body is bounded by flat three-dimensional spaces (hyperplanes). Such a four-dimensional object is called *polycell* because its boundary consists of a certain number of polyhedral *solids* which are its *cells*. A polycell in S_4 plays the same role as a polygon in S_2 (plane) and a polyhedron in S_3 (our usual three-dimensional space).

Each boundary cell of a polycell is a solid three-dimensional volume bounded by planes (faces), lines (edges) and points (vertices), so that the boundary of a polycell consists of four different kinds of elements: there are V vertices, E edges, F faces and S solid volumes. The structure of Euler's expressions in a plane $(V - E)$ and in a three-dimensional space $(V - E + F)$ suggests that for the numbers V, E, F, S of elements forming the boundary of a polycell in S_4, the combination $V - E + F - S$ must have the same numerical value for all *simple* polycells. And indeed generalizing Euler's Theorem for the four-dimensional space we can prove the

THEOREM. *The relation* $V - E + F - S = 0$ *holds for any simple polycell.*

Here again we meet the same limitation to *simple* polycells we encountered in Euler's Theorem. To define a simple polycell we consider closed polyhedrons formed within the boundary-volume of the polycell by the faces of different cells. A polycell which is not simple admits one or more closed polyhedrons along the surface of which it can be cut without being dismembered into disconnected parts. But if a cut along any closed polyhedron interior to the boundary-volume splits the polycell into two separate parts the polycell is called *simple*.

The proof of the theorem follows the same path as the proof of Euler's Theorem. Removing form the boundary volume the volume of one of peripheral cells, we open the access to the interior four-dimensional space of the polycell. Considering this interior space as empty we deform the boundary-volume of the polycell stretching it out flat in the three-dimensional space, where it becomes a network of solid polyhedrons. The number of vertices, edges, faces and solid volumes forming the boundary of the original polycell being V, E, F, S respectively, the removal of a volume diminishes S by one unit so that the expression $V - E + F - S$ becomes for our network of polyhedrons $V - E + F - (S - 1)$ where the new meaning of $S - 1$ is now the number of interior volumes into which the polyhedrons' faces subdivide the total volume occupied by the network.

The next step consists in the subdivision of polyhedrons with more than four faces into tetrahedrons. This subdivision is performed by drawing diagonal planes through the interior volumes of these polyhedrons. Each time one such diagonal plane is drawn one unit is added to the number $S - 1$ of volumes and one new face is created so that the number F also increases by one unit. Therefore, the operation does not change the number $V - E + F - S + 1$ which continues to represent the number of vertices and faces minus the number of edges and volumes of our network, which becomes now a network of tetrahedrons only.

In the total volume occupied by the network there are tetrahedrons of four different kinds. Some of them have no peripheral faces belonging to the exterior surface of the network. We call them interior tetrahedrons. All other are called exterior because they have at least one face which belongs to the exterior surface of the network. There are three different kinds of exterior tetrahedrons: with three, with two and with one exterior face. Let us consider the effect of the removal of an exterior tetrahedron on the numerical value of V − E + F − S + 1 in each of these three cases separately.

To remove an exterior tetrahedron with three exterior faces (Fig. 19) we must destroy three faces, three edges and cancel a vertex, so that all four numbers decrease: V and S by one and F and E by three units. Therefore, the differences V − S and F − E do not change and the value of the expression V − E + F − S + 1 remains what it was before the removal of the exterior tetrahedron with three exterior faces.

Suppose now that an exterior tetrahedron has two exterior faces ABC and ABD (Fig. 19). To remove it, it is sufficient to destroy the two faces ABC, ABD by cancelling one edge AB. No vertex is lost so that V does not change while E, F and S decrease one, two and one unit respectively. Therefore, again the expression V − E + F − S + 1 does not change.

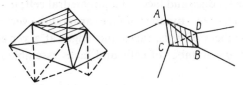

Fig. 23.19

Finally, to remove a peripheral tetrahedron with only one exterior face it is sufficient to destroy this face without changing the number of edges and vertices. Thus, F and S decrease by one unit and the removal of the tetrahedron does not change the numerical value of the expression V − E + F − S + 1.

Since after the removal of some peripheral tetrahedrons other tetrahedrons become peripheral this process can be continued until only one last tetrahedron remains. Because the expression V − E + F − S + 1 represents for this last tetrahedron the number of its vertices and faces minus the number of edges and volumes, it is equal to 4 + 4 − 6 − 1 = 1 which proves that for the original network V − E + F − S + 1 = 1 also. Therefore, we find that V − E + F − S = 0 which completes the proof of our theorem.

A polycell in general may have polyhedral cells of different number of faces being bounded by an assemblage of tetrahedrons, pentahedrons, hexahedrons etc. Moreover, the number of cells assembled around a common vertex varies from vertex to vertex as well as the number of cells surrounding a common edge. But in a polycell any two cells are tangent to each other along their common face. Let us now suppose that the different cells of a polycell, without being identical and equal in all their elements, are polyhedrons of same number of faces, edges and vertices. In other words, let us suppose that the boundary volume of a polycell is formed from irregular tetrahedrons, or octahedrons, or hexahedrons, or dodecahedrons, or finally icosahedrons, since—as we saw—there are only five possible classes of irregular polyhedrons the faces of which are polygons of same number of sides n and forming groups of same number m around each vertex. If their three characteristic numbers f, e, v are prescribed then the number m of faces assembled around a common vertex is equal to $m = 2e/v$, as well as $n = 2e/f$, where f, e, v denote us usual the number of faces, edges and vertices of a polyhedral cell.

The polycells just described are not regular because their polyhedral cells are not regular polyhedrons. Nevertheless, like regular polycells, they can be characterized by following thirteen numbers: V, E, F, S which denote as we know the numbers of vertices, edges, faces and cells respectively; v, e, f— numbers of vertices, edges and faces of a polyhedral cell; n – number of edges and vertices of a face; m – number of faces around the vertex of a polyhedral cell; p, η, φ – numbers of cells, faces and edges at a vertex of the polycell itself and, finally, q – number of cells and faces assembled around an edge of the polycell.

A dual transformation of a polycell characterized by these thirteen numbers generates another polycell the corresponding thirteen numbers of which are related to those of the original polycell in the following way. Let us denote the characteristic numbers of the transformed polycell by affixed asterisks, so that, for example, S* means the number of its cells. Using this notation we must have:

$$V^* = S; \quad E^* = F; \quad F^* = E; \quad S^* = V; \quad v^* = p; \quad e^* = \eta;$$

$$f^* = \varphi; \quad n^* = q; \quad p^* = v; \quad \eta^* = e; \quad \varphi^* = f; \quad q^* = n; \quad m^* = m.$$

In other words, there are six pairs of dually related numbers:

$$S \leftrightarrow V; \quad E \leftrightarrow F; \quad v \leftrightarrow p; \quad e \leftrightarrow \eta; \quad f \leftrightarrow \varphi; \quad n \leftrightarrow q,$$

while m is selfdual, these pairs being deduced by dual transformation of the definitions of these numbers. Thus, n denoting the number of edges and vertices of a face, its companion must denote the number of faces and cells assembled around an edge, that is, the number q^* and the same reasoning yields the other five pairs.

There are many relations between the characteristic numbers. Thus, we saw that $nf = 2e = mv$, where m is the number of edges and faces assembled around a vertex in a cell. This number is self-dual since the configuration formed by edges and faces of a polyhedron concurrent at one of its vertices is a polyhedral angle and the dual configuration of a polyhedral angle immersed in a four-dimensional space is again a polyhedral angle: its three-dimensional space to which it belongs becomes the vertex and its vertex is transformed into a three-dimensional space, edges become faces and faces—edges, so that the number m does not change: $m^* = m$.

Transforming now by duality the relation $mv = nf = 2e$, we obtain another relation $mp = q\varphi = 2\eta$. The Euler's relation $v - e + f = 2$ has also as its dual companion the relation $p - \eta + \varphi = 2$. Between the four numbers V, E, F, S and the eight numbers $v, e, f, n, p, \eta, \varphi, q$ we have five important relations

$$pV = vS; \quad fS = 2F; \quad \varphi V = 2E; \quad qE = eS; \quad nF = \eta V. \qquad (9)$$

The first one, $pV = vS$, is self-dual, while the third and the fifth are dual companions of the second and fourth respectively. Therefore, it will be sufficient to prove the first, second and fourth.

A cell has v vertices and there are S cells in a polycell. Therefore the total number of vertices in S cells is equal to vS. But these vS points are assembled by groups of p points in each one of V vertices of the polycell because p cells radiate from each vertex of a polycell. Thus, $pV = vS$.

A cell has f faces and in all there are fS faces in S cells of a polycell. But each face of the polycell contains two cell-faces because two adjacent cells have always a face in common. Therefore $2F = fS$ and also, by dual transformation, $2E = \varphi V$ which of course can be deduced directly without difficulty. The relation $qE = eS$ is justified as follows. The total number of edges in all S cells is equal to eS, but these eS edges are conciding by groups of q edges since each of E edges of the polycell is surrounded by q cells which have in common this polycell's edge. Therefore the product qE is equal to the total number of edges eS.

We will later transform the Euler's Formula $V - E + F - S = 0$ into an important self-dual relation between the four numbers η, n, e and q:

$$1/\eta + 1/n = 1/e + 1/q. \qquad (10)$$

In it $\eta \geqslant 4$ and $q \geqslant 3$ while two other numbers, n and e, depend on the choice of polyhedron-cell, this choice being only between the five polyhedrons: tetrahedron with $e = 6$ and $n = 3$, hexahedron for which $e = 12$ and $n = 4$, octahedron with $e = 12$ and $n = 3$, dodecahedron ($e = 30$ and $n = 5$) and, finally, icosahedron ($e = 30$ and $n = 3$).

Moreover, for regular polycells the number q—number of cells surrounding an edge of the polycell—is bounded from above because the sum of dihedral angles around an edge must remain less than $360°$. This condition is analogous to the fact that the sum of plane angles around a vertex of a polyhedron must be less than $360°$ otherwise the polyhedral angle at the vertex disappears (being flattened, if the sum is equal to $360°$) or becomes concave (if the sum exceeds $360°$). If the sum of dihedral angles around an edge of a polycell is equal to $360°$, the cells surrounding this edge do not form an angle in the four-dimensional space because their volumes fill up the whole three-dimensional space around the edge and therefore are flattened in the four-dimensional space. If this sum exceeds $360°$ the sense of the four-dimensional convexity of the angle is changed and this four-dimensional angle becomes concave which is not the case of regular polycells.

This important condition yields the following upper bounds for the value of the number q in the five possible cases: (1) if the regular polyhedral cell of a regular polycell is the tetrahedron whose dihedral angle is equal to D $= 70°31'43''$ the number q cannot exceed 5 since $6 \cdot D > 360°$; if the cell is a cube with D $= 90°$, then q must be less than 4 and the same upper bound 3 holds for octahedron- and dodecahedron-cell with D $= 109°28'$ and D $= 116°30'$ respectively; finally, if a regular icosahedron is chosen as cell of a regular polycell, the number q cannot reach 3 since the dihedral angle of an icosahedron is equal to D $= 138°11'$ and $3D = 414°33'$ which is greater than $360°$.

On the other hand, the number q cannot be less than 3 because in the dual transformation of a regular polycell into its dual companion, which is again a regular polycell, this number q becomes for the dual companion the number of sides in a face which cannot be less than three. Combining this lower bound $q \geqslant 3$ with the upper bound $q \leqslant 2$ for an icosahedron-cell, we come to the conclusion that *no regular polycell can be formed with icosahedrons*, the two conditions $q \geqslant 3$ and $q \leqslant 2$ being incompatible.

The choice of cube, octahedron and dodecahedron as cell of a regular polycell is possible and in all these three cases the number of cells surrounding an edge is equal to 3. If a regular tetrahedron is used as cell three values of q are possible because the upper bound for q is equal to 5 in this case. Therefore, with tetrahedron-cells there can be 3, 4 or 5 tetrahedrons around an edge.

The corresponding values for the number η of faces radiating from a vertex of the polycell are found with the aid of the relation (10) which we set out now to prove. We saw already that the total number of edges in all S cells is equal to $eS = qE$. On the other hand, in all F faces we have the same number of all edges expressed as a product nF because there are n sides in each polygonal face of a polycell and again we saw that $nF = \eta V$, so that the four products are equal: $\eta V = qE = nF = eS$. This result can be written as follows

$$V/(1/\eta) = E/(1/q) = F/(1/n) = S/(1/e) = r,$$

where r is the common value of these four equal ratios. Thus, we have

$$V = r/\eta; \quad E = r/q; \quad F = r/n; \quad S = r/e.$$

Substituting these expressions of V, E, F, S in the Euler's Formula $V - E + F - S = 0$ and dividing by the common factor r, we obtain precisely the relation (10) .

Regular Polycells from Tetrahedrons

The relation (10) applied to regular polytetrahedrons (as polycells formed with the aid of regular tetrahedrons can be called) becomes

$$1/\eta = 1/q - \tfrac{1}{6}$$

since for a tetrahedron $e = 6, n = 3$. Solving for η, we have $\eta = 6q/(6 - q)$. On the other hand, for a tetrahedron $v = 4, m = 2e/v = 3$ and $p = 2\eta/m = 2\eta/3 = 4q/(6 - q)$ as well as $\varphi = 2\eta/q = 12/(6 - q)$. Thus, the three cases $q = 3, 4, 5$ give for three different polytetrahedrons following characteristics: $v = f = 4, e = 6, n = m = 3$ and

Name	q	p	η	φ	V	E	F	S
Pentacell	3	4	6	4	5	10	10	5
16-Cell	4	8	12	6	8	24	32	16
600-Cell	5	20	30	12	120	720	1200	600

The first one, pentacell, is the simplest configuration formed by five three-dimensional spaces intersecting in five points by groups of four. It is also called simplex of the four-dimensional space. Let us use a common symbol

T for all regular simplexes of any space denoting the dimensions' number by a subscript, so that T_2 means regular triangle, T_3—regular tetrahedron, T_4—regular pentacell. Let us also call by analogy a segment T_1. To generate a triangle T_2 we move T_1 parallel to itself in a direction which is perpendicular to the flat space s_1 (straight line) to which T_1 belongs. We postulate moreover than T_1 shrinks gradually to a point and vanishes completely when the equal distances travelled by its two extremities become equal to the length of T_1.

Consider now a space s_2 (plane) and a regular triangle T_2 with three vertices A, B, C in it. To obtain the regular tetrahedron T_3 we move T_2 parallel to itself in a direction perpendicular to the plane s_2 and suppose moreover that T_2 gradually shrinks to a point D and vanishes completely when the segments AD, BD and CD described by three vertices of T_2 during the motion become equal to the common length AB = BC = CA of its three sides. Since the initial position of T_2 is a part of T_3 (which is a complete set of all positions T_2 occupied in the three-dimensional space s_3 during its motion), the number (3) of vertices is increased by one (point D, where T_2 vanishes) while the number of edges is increased by three because each of three vertices of T_2 describes a segment during the motion of T_2. The number of faces (one) is increased by the number of sides in T_2 because each side describes a face, so for example the side AB generates the face ABD. We can now say that, if the number of vertices and edges of T_2 is denoted by v_2 and e_2 while v_3, e_3, f_3 are the numbers of vertices, edges and faces of T_3, the process of generating T_3 by the motion of a shrinking T_2 yields the relations $v_3 = v_2 + 1$, $e_3 = e_2 + v_2, f_3 = 1 + e_2$ which indeed give $v_3 = 3 + 1 = 4$, $e_3 = 3 + 3 = 6$ and $f_3 = 1 + 3 = 4$ as it must be.

We apply now the same process to T_3 and move it parallel to itself, that is, in such a way that its space s_3 remains parallel to its initial position in the four-dimensional space s_4. The direction of motion of s_3 is naturally perpendicular to s_3. Moreover, we suppose that T_3 shrinks gradually to a point E where it vanishes completely. The point E is such that AE = BE = CE = DE = AB, the distances travelled by four vertices of T_3 in the space s_4 being equal to the common length AB of edges of T_3. Denoting the numbers of vertices, edges, faces and cells of T_4 by v_4, e_4, f_4, s_4, we have again the relations

$$v_4 = v_3 + 1, \quad e_4 = e_3 + v_3, \quad f_4 = f_3 + e_3, \quad s_4 = 1 + f_3$$

since the vertices generate edges, edges generate faces and faces generate cells during the motion. We saw indeed that T_1 generates T_2, T_2 becomes T_3 etc.

Substituting the values of v_3, e_3, f_3 we obtain the correct values for number of different elements composing a T_4: $v_4 = 4 + 1 = 5$, $e_4 = 6 + 4 = 10$, $f_4 = 4 + 6 = 10$ and $s_4 = 1 + 4 = 5$.

It is plain that this process of generating regular simplexes can be continued further: moving a T_4 immersed in a five-dimensional space s_5 in a direction perpendicular to the space s_4 to which belongs this T_4, a T_5 is generated, if T_4 gradually shrinks to a point its vertices describing segments equal to its edges.

Likewise, moving a T_5 immersed in a six-dimensional space s_6, a T_6 is generated if T_5 gradually shrinks to a point, etc. Therefore, it can be said that any space s_n of n dimensions possesses its simplex which, if regular, is a T_n. Thus, we have described a regular recurrent process for generating regular simplexes of any dimension-number n. It is of interest to show that their structure can be studied and described for any value of the dimension-number n. First we observe that a T_n is bounded by $n + 1$ spaces s_{n-1} whose intersections define as many, that is, $n + 1$ boundary simplexes T_{n-1}. Thus, a T_3 is bounded by four planes s_2 which define by their intersections four boundary triangles T_2. Likewise a regular pentacell T_4 is bounded by five regular tetrahedrons T_3, while a regular triangle T_2 has three sides T_1. To prove our assertion for T_n we use the mathematical induction. Suppose that this assertion is already justified for T_{n-1} so that we know that a T_{n-1} is bounded by n regular simplexes T_{n-2}. Moving T_{n-1} we generate T_n and during this process each boundary T_{n-2} generates a T_{n-1} so that n new boundary T_{n-1} are created. Adding to them the original T_{n-1} we obtain exactly $n + 1$ simplexes T_{n-1} as boundary for T_n.

This reasoning can be applied to all elements, that is, to elements of different dimensions of T_{n-1} which generate during the motion of T_{n-1} elements of T_n. Let us denote the number of elements of dimension k by E_k. To distinguish the number of elements of same dimension k in a T_n from numbers of elements in other simplexes T_m, $m \neq n$, we will use also the superscript n, so that finally the number of elements of dimension k in a T_n will be denoted by E_k^n. With this conventional notation we have for example, considering the regular tetrahedron T_3: $E_0^3 = 4$, $E_1^3 = 6$ and $E_2^3 = 4$, while—for the regular pentacell—$E_0^4 = 5$, $E_1^4 = 10$, $E_2^4 = 10$ and $E_3^4 = 5$.

To find general expression for the number E_k^n in terms of n and k we will prove that the numbers E_k^n verify the recurrent relation

$$E_k^{n+1} = E_k^n + E_{k-1}^n \qquad (0 \leqslant k \leqslant n), \qquad (11)$$

where E_n^n must be replaced by 1, if $k = n$. Moreover, the relation (11) holds also for $k = 0$, if E^n_{-1} is replaced by 1. To prove (11) in the case $k = 0$ it is sufficient to observe that the number of vertices E^n_0 in a T_n is increased by one when T_{n+1} is generated by the motion of a T_n shrinking to a point, so that indeed $E^{n+1}_0 = E^n_0 + 1$ which is (11) for $k = 0$. The case $k = n$ is that of the number of boundary simplexes E^{n+1}_n and we saw already that $E^{n+1}_n = E^n_{n-1} + 1$ which is (11) for $k = n$.

If k belongs to the range $1 \leqslant k \leqslant n - 1$, it can be said that each element of dimension $k - 1$ belonging to T_n generates an element of dimension k in T_{n+1} and therefore there will be E^n_{k-1} elements of dimension k in T_{n+1} generated by the motion of T_n. To them we must add E^n_k elements of dimension k belonging to T_n because the original position of T_n is to be included into T_{n+1} as its part. Thus, the number E^{n+1}_k of elements of dimension k in T_{n+1} is equal to the sum $E^n_{k-1} + E^n_k$ and the relation (11) is justified.

We emphasize that it is identical with the recurrent relation verified by the binomial coefficients C^n_k studied in all details in Chapter 9. Therefore, if the numbers E^n_k for some first values of the integer n can be expressed as binomial coefficients C^n_k, then they are equal to the binomial coefficients in general, for all values of the integral parameter n. It happens that it is so. Take for example $n = 2$ and consider the number of elements in a regular triangle T_2 with its three vertices, $E^2_0 = 3$, three sides, $E^2_1 = 3$, and one face (area), $E^2_2 = 1$. These numbers 3, 3, 1 are indeed binomial coefficients: $C^3_1 = C^3_2 = 3$ and $C^3_3 = 1$. The same holds for the elements of a regular tetrahedron T_3: $E^3_0 = C^4_1 = 4$, $E^3_1 = C^4_2 = 1$, $E^3_2 = C^4_3 = 4$, $E^3_3 = C^4_4 = 1$. If we take into consideration that, by definition, the symbol E^n_{-1} is equal to one, then in general, for all n, $E^n_{-1} = C^{n+1}_0 = 1$ and, in particular, $E^3_{-1} = C^4_0 = 1$, $E^2_{-1} = C^3_0 = 1$ so that, for triangle $(n = 2)$ and tetrahedron $(n = 3)$ we have the relation $E^n_k = C^{n+1}_{k+1}$. This relation then holds for all values of n as it can be shown by mathematical induction, using (11):

$$E^{n+1}_k = E^n_k + E^n_{k-1} = C^{n+1}_{k+1} = C^{n+1}_k = C^{n+2}_{k+1}.$$

Therefore, the number of elements of dimension k in a T_n is found:

$$E^n_k = C^{n+1}_{k+1} = (n+1)\, n\, (n-1) \cdots (n-k+1)/(k+1)\, k(k-1) \cdots 3 \cdot 2 \cdot 1 \tag{12}$$

and this explicit expression gives us the exact number of different elements composing a simplex T_n of any space s_n. Thus, the regular simplex T_{10} in the ten-dimensional space s_{10} has $E^{10}_1 = 55$ edges, $E^{10}_2 = 165$ faces, $E^{10}_3 = 330$ tetrahedrons, $E^{10}_4 = 462$ pentacells etc. It has also eleven vertices and is bounded by eleven T_9.

Thus, regular triangle, tetrahedron and pentacell belong to an infinite family of hypertetrahedrons (or hypertriangles) which are regular simplexes T_n existing in spaces of any dimension-number n, one T_n in each s_n. We can visualize only two first members of this infinite family, namely triangle and tetrahedron. Our mind is unable to see as a real body already the pentacell. Our perceptions are limited to three-dimensional objects only and this limitation of our space-sense is the unique cause of our belief that the exterior substratum of our perceptions—the physical universe—is also three-dimensional in itself, which is probably a wrong conception.

In spite of the fact that we cannot visualize a regular pentacell, we can imagine it because we know all the parts of which consists this four-dimensional regular body. To help our imagination we can also use the three-dimensional solids which are orthogonal projections of a pentacell upon a three-dimensional space. In one of these projections (see Fig. 20) the pentacell ABCDE is projected upon the space s_3 to which belongs one of its five boundary-tetrahedrons, namely the tetrahedron ABCD which therefore is not altered at all by the projection. The other four tetrahedrons clustered around their common vertex E are projected into tetrahedrons ABCE*, BCDE*, CDAE*, DABE*, where the point E* denotes the projection of the fifth vertex E of the pentacell upon the interior of the tetrahedron ABCD, this vertex E being exterior to the space s_3(ABCD) in the four-dimensional space to which belongs the pentacell.

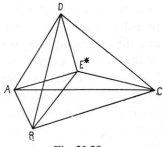

Fig. 23.20

Thus, in Fig. 20 we five tetrahedrons with their five vertices, ten triangular faces and ten edges composing together the exterior boundary of the hypervolume pentacell's, provided we read this figure as a three-dimensional solid tetrahedron ABCD whose interior volume is filled out by four other tetrahedrons around E*.

The structural features of the boundary volume of the pentacell are preserved in the projection: each one of five boundary-tetrahedrons is tangent to four others so that each face belongs to two adjacent tetrahedrons; around each of ten edges are assembled three tetrahedrons and three faces; from each one of five vertices radiate four tetrahedral cells. But the most essential feature—the finite portion of the hyperspace bounded by this continuous and closed boundary-volume, the interior of the pentacell—is naturally lost in

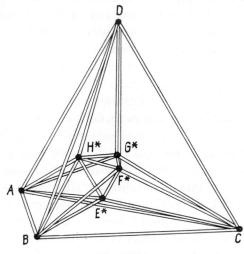

Fig. 23.21

the projection and it must be imagined, shifting in our imagination the fifth vertex E* into the four-dimensional space outside of the three-dimensional space $s_3(ABCD)$ and thus replacing it by the point E. We must also imagine that the shifting of the fifth vertex out of our space and into the four-dimensional space to which belongs the pentacell produces a kind of inflation of the volume, distending it in the four-dimensional space without destroying its continuity and the mutual disposition of its parts.

In Fig. 21 we give a similar projection upon our space of the 16-Cell with its eight vertices, twenty-four edges and thirty-two faces, the projection-space being that of the tetrahedron ABCD, so that the four other vertices E*, F*, G*, H* in Fig. 21 are projections of points E, F, G, H of the four-dimensional space to which belongs the 16-Cell. Here again all sixteen tetrahedrons forming the boundary volume of this regular hypersolid are tangent to each other so that every one is adjacent by its four faces to four neighbour-tetrahedrons, their volumes forming a single continuous and closed volume. On the figure we see clearly that there are four tetrahedral cells around each edge ($q = 4$), eight cells radiating from each vertex ($p = 8$), for example

D–ABC, D–F*G*H*, D–ABH*, D–BCF*, D–CAG*, D–AG*H*, D–BH*F*, D–CF*G* from the vertex D, twelve faces at each vertex ($\eta = 12$) as for example DF*B, DF*C, DBC; DG*C, DG*A, DCA; DH*A, DH*B, DAB; DF*G*, DG*H*, DH*F* at the vertex D, six edges at a vertex ($\varphi = 6$) etc.

It is possible to generate the 16-Cell by motion of a three-dimensional regular polyhedron in the four-dimensional space. This three-dimensional regular solid is the octahedron, so that the 16-Cell may be considered as a generalization of the octahedron. To begin with we will build up the square from a segment and the octahedron from a square.

We recall that a triangle is obtained if a segment moving parallel to itself shrinks to a point. Suppose now that a segment in motion and generating a regular triangle, is reflected in a linear mirror coinciding with the original position of this segment. Then the motion is doubled and performed in two opposite directions so that a rhombus is obtained. We change now the definition of this double motion and postulate that the segment AB (Fig. 22) moving in two opposite directions, perpendicularly to AB, shrinks to points C and D in such a way that a *square* ACBD is formed. This is the kind of motion we will now apply to the square ACBD itself, moving it in two opposite directions which both are perpendicular to the plane of the square. During this motion the diagonals AB and CD of the square generate tho squares AEBF and CEDF, the moving square shrinking to points E and F where it vanishes completely. The solid ABCDEF thus formed is the regular octahedron so that segment, square and regular octahedron belong to the same family of regular bodies which we will denote by O_n, the subscript n meaning the dimension-number of a member of this family. Thus, the segment is now O_1, while the square and the regular octahedron are O_2 and O_3.

Let us consider now a three-dimensional space s_3 with a regular octahedron O_3 in it immersed in a four-dimensional space s_4. In s_4 we have a certain direction which is perpendicular to s_3 so that through each point of O_3 passes a straight line parallel to this direction. All these straight lines pierce the three-dimensional solid O_3 in one point only since s_3 has no thickness in a direction perpendicular to it. We call these straight lines normals to O_3.

On each normal there are two opposite directions and in s_4 two motions of O_3 along the perpendicular to s_3 are possible. We impart now to O_3 a double motion in two opposite directions parallel to the normal to s_3 and moreover we suppose that O_3 gradually shrinks to a point during the motion so that it vanishes completely at two points G and H. These points lie on the straight line L perpendicular to s_3 and passing through the center of symmetry C of O_3. They are symmetrical with respect to C and the length CG = CH is fixed by the following condition: the common length of twelve equal segments AG = AH = BG = $\cdots$ = EH = FG = FH described by six vertices A, B, C, D, E, F of O_3 in their double motion is equal to the length of

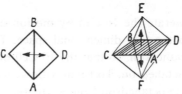

Fig. 23.22

edges of O_3. Thus, a regular four-dimensional polycell is generated by the motion of O_3 and this polycell O_4 can be defined as the totality of all positions occupied in s_4 by O_3 during its double motion.

The polycell O_4 happens to be precisely the 16-Cell bounded by sixteen regular tetrahedrons, and to prove this we shall count the elements of various dimensions composing together O_4. The cells of O_4 are tetrahedrons since they are generated by faces of O_3 shrinking to points G and H. Each face of O_3 generates two tetrahedrons-cells of O_4 and thus there are $E_3^4 = 2E_2^3$ $= 2 \cdot 8 = 16$ tetrahedrons in O_4. We observe that the initial position of the octahedron O_3 is not to be counted as a cell. Likewise, we have not counted the initial square O_2, whose double motion generates O_3, among the faces of O_3. Thus, we say that in O_3 we have $E_0^3 = 6$ vertices, $E_1^3 = 12$ edges and $E_2^3 = 8$ faces, but no volume: $E_3^3 = 0$. We will use also in what follows the symbol E_{-1}^3 whose value by definition is set equal to one, $E_{-1}^3 = 1$. Since $E_3^3 = 0$ we can also write the result just obtained $E_3^4 = 2E_2^3$ as follows:

$$E_3^4 = E_3^3 + 2E_2^3.$$

It is not difficult to justify the general relation

$$E_k^4 = E_k^3 + 2E_{k-1}^3 \qquad (k = 0, 1, 2, 3). \qquad (13)$$

For $k = 0, 1, 2$ a k-dimensional element in O_4 is generated by the motion of a $(k - 1)$-dimensional element of O_3 or belongs to O_3 considered in its initial position before it moves. Since O_3 undergoes a displacement in two opposite directions each element of O_3 generates two elements of O_4 and the number of k-dimensional elements in O_4 generated by the motion is thus equal to $2E_{k-1}^3$, while that in O_3 is E_k^3. Adding the numbers E_k^3 and $2E_{k-1}^3$ we obtain E_k^4 which justifies (13) for $k = 0, 1, 2$. The case $k = 0$ gives $E_0^4 = E_0^3$ $+ 2E_{-1}^3 = E_0^3 + 2$ since $E_{-1}^3 = 1$ and this agrees with the fact the double motion of O_3 generates two vertices G and H of O_4, the regular octahedron O_3 vanishing completely at these points.

Thus, the polycell O_4 has $E_0^3 + 2 = 6 + 2 = 8$ vertices, $E_1^3 + 2E_0^3 = 12 + 2 \cdot 6 = 24$ edges, $E_2^3 + 2E_1^3 = 8 + 2 \cdot 12 = 8 + 24 = 32$ faces and 16 cells which completes the proof that the 16-Cell is generated by the double motion of O_3 and is therefore an O_4. But we can continue the recurrent formation of regular polycells O_n which are in spaces of any dimension-number n, thus forming an infinite family of hyperoctahedrons $O_1, O_2, O_3, O_4, O_5, \ldots O_{n-1}, O_n, \ldots$ of which segment (O_1), square (O_2), regular octahedron (O_3) and regular 16-Cell (O_4) are the first four members.

Each O_n is obtained by double motion in two opposite directions of a O_{n-1} shrinking to a point in each of these two directions. The number E_k^n of its k-dimensional elements is obtained with the aid of the recurrent relations

$$E_k^{n+1} = E_k^n + 2E_{k-1}^n \qquad (14)$$

which is easily justified by observing that a k-dimensional element in O_{n+1} either is generated by the motion of a $(k-1)$-dimensional element in O_n or belongs to O_n considered in its initial position before it moves. Since the motion of O_n is a double motion, E_{k-1}^n $(k-1)$-dimensional elements of O_n generate $2E_{k-1}^n$ k-dimensional elements in O_{n+1} and (14) is justified. It holds for $k = 0, 1, \ldots, n-1, n$ if we define $E_{-1}^n = 1$ and $E_n^n = 0$ for all values of the integer n.

To solve the recurrent relations (14) and find thus an explicit expression for E_k^n in terms of n and k we first multiply (14) by 2^{-k} transforming it into

$$2^{-k}E_k^{n+1} = 2^{-k}E_k^n + 2^{1-k}E_{k-1}^n$$

and then observe that the product $2^{-k}E_k^n$ must be proportional to the binomial coefficient C_{k+1}^n because $C_{k+1}^{n+1} = C_{k+1}^n + C_k^n$. The factor of proportionality must be equal to 2 since for $n = 4$ we have $C_1^4 = 4$, while $2^0E_0^4 = E_0^4 = 8$. Checking for $n = 1, 2, 3, 4$ and various values of k we find indeed that $2^{-k} \cdot E_k^n = 2C_{k+1}^n$ and this solution holds also for $k = -1$ and $k = n$ since $2^{-(-1)}E_{-1}^n = 2E_{-1}^n = 2C_0^n = 2$ and thus $E_{-1}^n = 1$ as it must be, as well as $2^{-n}E_n^n = 2C_{n+1}^n = 0$, that is $E_n^n = 0$.

The explicit formula gives

$$E_k^n = 2^{k+1}C_{k+1}^n = 2^{k+1}n!/[(k+1)!\,(n-k-1)!] \qquad (0 \leqslant k \leqslant n-1)$$

Applying it for example to O_5, we have the following detailed description of the structural composition of the regular five-dimensional body bounded by regular 16-Cells. The O_5 has $E_4^5 = 2^5C_5^5 = 2^5 = 32$ boundary 16-Cells,

$E_3^5 = 2^4 C_4^5 = 80$ tetrahedrons, $E_2^5 = 2^3 C_3^5 = 8 \cdot 10 = 80$ triangular faces, $E_1^5 = 2^2 C_2^5 = 40$ edges and $E_0^5 = 2 \cdot C_1^5 = 10$ vertices, in all $242 = 3^5 - 1$ elements. In general, the total number of elements of various dimensions composing an O_n is equal to $3^n - 1$: 2 for a segment, 8 for a square, 26 in an octahedron, 80 in a 16-Cell.

Duality in S_n

In an n-dimensional geometry the fundamental elements of its n-dimensional world S_n are point, straight line, plane, three-dimensional space s_3 etc., their dimension-number k varying from $k = 0$ (point) up to $k = n - 1$ (hyperplane s_{n-1} of the n-dimensional geometry). Let us denote them by e_k with $k = 0, 1, 2, \ldots, n - 1$. Since in S_n n points define a perfectly determined s_{n-1} and, conversely, n hyperplanes intersect in a point defined by their intersection, the dual transformation replaces points by hyperplanes and hyperplanes by points. Therefore, in an S_n the elements e_k and e_h, k-dimensional and h-dimensional respectively, are dual if and only if $k + h = n - 1$. This is a generalization of the rules $k + h = 1, k + h = 2, k + h = 3$ which govern the dual transformations in the plane, three-dimensional and four-dimensional geometries respectively.

We will now apply this rule to regular polycells T_4, O_4 and the 600-Cell of the four-dimensional geometry. The regular pentacell T_4 has five vertices and as many cells and 10 edges and faces. Therefore, it is self-dual because its five vertices and cells are transformed dually into five cells and vertices, while ten faces and ten edges become ten edges and ten faces. What now about hypertetrahedron T_n in S_n? If we can prove that the number E_k^n of its k-dimensional elements is equal to that E_{n-k-1}^n of the $(n - k - 1)$-dimensional elements for all values of k in the range $0 \leqslant k \leqslant n - 1$, then it will show that T_n for any n is self-dual in the corresponding space S_n. Now we know that for a T_n the number E_k^n is equal to C_{k+1}^{n+1} while that E_{n-k-1}^n is equal to C_{n-k}^{n+1}. Applying the well known property of binomial coefficients to be equal, if equidistant from two ends of the binomial expansion, we have $C_{n+k}^{n+1} = C_{n+1-(n-k)}^{n+1} = C_{k+1}^{n+1}$. Thus, all the hypertetrahedrons T_n are self-dual in their spaces.

We pass now to hyperoctahedrons O_n. A square, O_2, is self-dual in the plane, but the regular octahedron O_3 is not because the number of its vertices, 6, is not equal to that of its faces, 8. And the dual transform of the regular octahedron is a cube with its eight vertices and six faces. The same holds for the 16-Cell O_4: transforming it dually we obtain another regular polycell in S_4 having sixteen vertices (as many as there are cells in O_4), thirty-two edges (number of faces in O_4), twenty-four faces (number of edges in O_4) and only eight cells (as many as there are vertices in O_4). For the 16-Cell we have found $p = 8$, $q = 4$, $\eta = 12$ and $\varphi = 6$, while $n = m = 3$, $v = f = 4$ and $e = 6$. Using the table of dually related characteristic numbers $v \leftrightarrow p$, $e \leftrightarrow \eta$, $f \leftrightarrow \varphi$, $n \leftrightarrow q$, $m \leftrightarrow m$, we conclude that the dual companion of the 16-Cell is characterized by the following values of its parameters: $p = 4$, $q = 3$, $\eta = 6$, $\varphi = 4$, $n = 4$, $m = 3$, $v = 8$, $f = 6$, $e = 12$. Interpreting these numerical values, we state that the dual companion of a 16-Cell is bounded by *eight cubes* since for it $v = 8$, $e = 12$, $f = 6$. These cubes are assembled by groups of four around a vertex and of three around an edge since $p = 4$ and $q = 3$. The regular polycell just found with the aid of the dual transformation is called *tessaract* and we denote it by the symbol C_4.

With the aid of the same dual transformation each member of the infinite family of hyperoctahedrons O_n generates its dual companion which we denote C_n. The family of regular bodies C_n is the third and thus, we have already three regular bodies T_n, O_n and C_n in the most general n-dimensional geometry of the n-dimensional world S_n. We will call C_n the *hypercube* of the n-dimensional space, so that C_1, C_2, C_3 and C_4 are a segment, a square, a cube and a tessaract in their respective spaces s_1 (line), s_2 (plane), s_3 (our familiar three-dimensional space) and s_4—four-dimensional space.

The relative location of the eight boundary cubes of a tessaract is shown in Fig. 23, which represents the projection of the tessaract in the three-dimensional space of its boundary-cube ABCDEFGH. Each of eight cubes is tangent to six other boundary cubes by its faces.

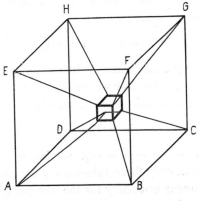

Fig. 23.23

We have not yet studied polycells bounded by cubes, octahedrons etc. and before discussing them we emphasize that the 600-Cell has also a dual companion among the regular polycells of S_4. It is not difficult to study this fifth regular polycell, applying to characteristic numbers of the 600-Cell the dual transformation. It was shown that for the 600-Cell $V = 120$, $E = 720$, $F = 1200$, $S = 600$, $p = 20$, $q = 5$, $\eta = 30$, $\varphi = 12$, $m = n = 3$, $v = f = 4$, $e = 6$. Therefore, the dual companion of the 600-Cell is characterized by:

$$V = 600, \ E = 1200, \ F = 720, \ S = 120, \ p = 4, \ q = 3, \ \eta = 6, \ \varphi = 4,$$

$$m = 3, \ n = 5, \ v = 20, \ f = 12, \ e = 30.$$

Interpreting these numerical values of characteristic numbers, we state that the dual companion of a 600-Cell is bounded by 120 dodecahedrons because $m = 3$, $n = 5$, $f = 12$, $v = 20$ and $e = 30$ characterize a dodecahedron and $S = 120$. These dodecahedrons are grouped by four around a vertex ($p = 4$) and by three around an edge ($q = 3$) of the polycell. The 120-Cell thus found has 600 vertices, 1200 edges and 720 faces. It does not belong to a family of regular bodies extending to all spaces and is particular to the four-dimensional space as is also the 600-Cell of which it is the dual companion. Thus, among five regular hypersolids in S_4 we know up to this moment, two, 120-Cell and 600-Cell, are particular to the four-dimensional space, while T_4 (pentacell), O_4 (16-Cell) and C_4 (tessaract) belong to three infinite families of regular hypersolids which have their analogues in spaces of any dimensions.

Family of Hypercubes C_n

The study of regular polycells formed with the aid of regular tetrahedrons was based on the general relation

$$1/\eta + 1/n = 1/e + 1/q \tag{15}$$

and we apply it now to the case when the boundary-cells are *cubes* for which $n = 4$ and $e = 12$. Thus, in the case we are studying now the general relation (15) is the same as for tetrahedrons-cells, namely

$$1/\eta = 1/q - \tfrac{1}{6}$$

since $1/e - 1/n = \tfrac{1}{12} - \tfrac{1}{4} = -\tfrac{2}{12} = -\tfrac{1}{6}$. Solving it for η, we have again $\eta = 6q/(6 - q)$, so that only three values for q are possible: $q = 3,4$ or 5.

But, this time the upper boundary for the number q of cells surrounding an edge is equal to 3 and thus, only *one* case remains possible, namely $q = 3$.

Therefore, $\eta = \frac{18}{3} = 6, p = 2\eta/m = 12/m = 4$ since for a cube the number m of faces or edges around a vertex is equal to 3. Further $\varphi = 2\eta/q$ $= \frac{12}{3} = 4$ and therefore the number of edges radiating from a vertex of the polycell is 4. The equalities $\eta V = qE = nF = eS$ become now $6V = 3E$ $= 4F = 12S$ and their common value is 96 so that $V = 16, E = 32, F = 24$ and $S = 8$. The polycell we are studying is therefore the tessaract C_4 and it is the unique regular polycell which can be formed with the aid of cubes as cells.

Moving a square the distance equal to the length of its edge and in a direction perpendicular to the square's plance, a cube of same edge is formed. In exactly same way a tessaract is obtained as the totality of all positions occupied in S_4 by a cube which moves the distance equal to the length of its edge in a direction perpendicular to the three-dimensional space s_3 to which this cube belongs. During this motion the number of vertices is doubled because each vertex of the cube C_3 describes an edge of the tessaract C_4 and thus yields two vertices of C_4 which are two ends of the edge generated by the vertex of C_3. Thus, denoting again by E_k^n the number of k-dimensional elements of a C_n, we have $E_0^4 = 2E_0^3$ and therefore $E_0^4 = 2.2^3 = 2^4 = V$. The edges of the tessaract either belong to the initial and final positions of C_3, which gives $2E_1^3$ edges of this type, or are formed during the motion of vertices which gives E_0^3 edges. Thus, for E_1^4 we obtain the expression $E_1^4 = 2E_1^3$ $+ E_0^3$, where $E_0^3 = 8$ and $E_1^3 = 12$ so that $E_1^4 = 2 \cdot 12 + 8 = 32 = E$. For the number of faces E_2^4 the same argument yields the analogous expression $E_2^4 = 2E_2^3 + E_1^3$ that is $E_2^4 = 2 \cdot 6 + 12 = 24 = F$. Finally, there are two cells C_3 representing the initial and final positions of the moving cube and six cells more are formed by the faces of C_3 during its motion the total number of cells being eight: $E_3^4 = 2E_3^3 + E_2^3$ because $E_3^3 = 1$, and $E_3^4 = 8 = S$.

Defining the symbol $E_{-1}^n = 0$, we can condense all these expressions into

$$E_k^{n+1} = 2E_k^n + E_{k-1}^n \qquad (0 \leqslant k \leqslant n)$$

where $n = 3$ for tessaract. But this recurrent relation holds for any n because, given a hypercube C_n of an n-dimensional space s_n, we can move it in a higher space s_{n+1} in a direction perpendicular to the space s_n to which it belongs and then stop its motion after a distance equal to the length of its edge is covered. Thus, C_{n+1} is generated and the number of its elements of various dimensionality verifies the recurrent relation $E_k^{n+1} = 2E_k^n + E_{k-1}^n$ because the initial and final positions of C_n are included in C_{n+1} as parts of its boundary. The solution of the relation $E_k^{n+1} = 2E_k^n + E_{k-1}^n$ is obtained by observing that the quotient $E_k^n/2^{n-k}$ verifies the corresponding recurrent relation

$$E_k^{n+1}/2^{n+1-k} = E_k^n/2^{n-k} + E_{k-1}^n/2^{n-(k-1)}$$

so that this quotient $E_k^n/2^{n-k}$ must be proportional to the binomial coefficient C_k^n. But comparing the numbers E_k^n to the product $2^{n-k}C_k^n$ for $n = 4$ we find that the coefficient of proportionality is simply equal to one because $E_0^4 = 16$ and $2^{4-0}C_0^4 = 2^4 = 16$, $E_1^4 = 32 = 2^{4-1}C_1^4$ etc.

Therefore, the number of elements of various dimensionality in a hypercube C_n of the n-dimensional space is given by the formula $E_k^n = 2^{n-k}C_k^n$, that is,

$$E_k^n = 2^{n-k}n(n-1) \cdots (n-k+1)/k! \qquad (0 \leqslant k \leqslant n-1) \qquad (16)$$

For example, the hypercube of five-dimensional space C_5 has $E_0^5 = 2^5 = 32$ vertices, since $C_0^n = 1$; $E_1^5 = 2^4 \cdot 5 = 80$ edges; $E_2^5 = 2^3 \cdot 10 = 80$ faces; $E_3^5 = 2^2 \cdot 10 = 40$ cells (cubes C_3) and $E_4^5 = 2 \cdot 5 = 10$ tessaracts. Comparing this result to numbers of elements of a hyperoctahedron O_5, we see clearly that C_5 and O_5 are mutually dual configurations in the five-dimensional space s_5. The general formula (16) shows in particular that a C_n has 2^n vertices and $2n$ boundary hypercubes C_{n-1}.

We pass now to polycells whose cells are regular octahedrons O_3 for which $v = 6$, $e = 12$, $f = 8$, $m = 4$, $n = 3$ so that $1/e - 1/n = \frac{1}{12} - \frac{1}{3} = -\frac{1}{4}$. In this case the relation (15) gives $1/\eta = 1/q - \frac{1}{4}$ and solving it for η, we obtain for η the expression $4q/(4 - q)$ This result shows again that the only value of q is three so that $\eta = 12$, $p = 2\eta/m = 6$ and $\varphi = 2\varphi/q = 8$. In this unique polycell bounded by regular octahedrons its octahedral cells are assembled by groups of six around each vertex, ($p = 6$). We state that $p = v$, $q = n$, $\eta = e$, $\varphi = f$ so that the relation $\eta V = qE = eS = nF$ gives $V = S$ and $E = F$: the polycell is *self-dual*. It has twenty-four vertices and cells as well as 96 edges and 96 faces. It is particular to four-dimensional space: in higher spaces S_n with $n \geqslant 5$ there is only one self-dual regular n-dimensional body – T_n, that is, hypertetrahedron. Thus, the 24-Cell does not belong to an infinite family of regular bodies and stands alone as the 600-Cell and its dual companion the 120-Cell. With this sixth regular polycell we have completed our study of regular polycells in the four-dimensional geometry and found that there is no more than six.

To prove this it remains to study the polycells formed with the aid of dodecahedrons. We saw indeed that no regular polycell can exist with icosahedric cells. For a dodecahedric cell we have $v = 20$, $e = 30$, $f = 12$, $n = 5$ so that $1/\eta = 1/q + 1/e - 1/n = 1/q + \frac{1}{30} - \frac{1}{5} = 1/q - \frac{1}{6}$ and

$\eta = 6q/(6 - q)$. On the other hand, it was established that the upper bound for q is equal to three so that there can be only one regular polycell bounded by dodecahedrons. For it $\eta = 6$, $p = 2\eta/m = 4$ because in a dodecahedron $m = 3$, $\varphi = 2\eta/q = 4$.

The relation $6V = 3E = 5F = 30S$ shows that this polycell is our 120-Cell since for $S = 120$ we obtain $6V = 3E = 5F = 3600$ and thus $V = 600$, $E = 1200$ and $F = 720$. Therefore, the number of regular bodies in the four-dimensional space is equal to six, one more than in the three-dimensional space, and three more than in all n-dimensional spaces with the dimension-number n exceeding four.

It is of interest to emphasize that the number of regular bodies which can be built in a given space depends for $n < 5$ upon the dimensionality of the given space: in the plane ($n = 2$) there are an infinite number of such flat two-dimensional bodies since a regular polygon of any number of sides can be constructed, in our three-dimensional space their number is five but for the four-dimensional space it again increases and takes the value six. But beginning with the space of five dimensions there are only three regular bodies hypertetrahedron, hypercube and hyperoctahedron in any space S_n, if $n \geqslant 5$.

This fact seems to indicate that the first four spaces (straight line, plane, our space and the four-dimensional space S_4) in some properties are unlike to other spaces with five and more dimensions. They seem to be very particular while the higher spaces are more homogeneous and similar insofar as their intrinsic structure is concerned.

Euler's Theorem holds also in higher spaces and we formulate it for a general n-dimensional space S_n omitting the proof. To generalize the concept of a polyhedron in S_3 we observe that it is bounded by flat spaces s_2 (planes) as a polycell is bounded by spaces s_3. Therefore, we will call hyperpoly-hedron in an S_n a configuration formed with the aid of a certain number of intersecting spaces s_{n-1} of $n - 1$ dimensions imbedded in S_n. Such a con-figuration cuts out and isolates a finite region of the n-dimensional space bounded by the intersecting $(n - 1)$-dimensional spaces s_{n-1}. Let us now denote the number of k-dimensional elements included in this hyperpoly-hedron by the symbol E_k^n, so that the number of its vertices is E_0^n, edges $-E_1^n$ etc. up to E_{n-1}^n which is the number of $(n - 1)$-dimensional spaces s_{n-1} form-ing the outer boundary of this hyperpolyhedron.

The n numbers E_k^n, $k = 0, 1, 2, ..., n - 1$, thus defined are not independent and Euler's Theorem establishes between them the following relation:

$$E_0^n - E_1^n + E_2^n - E_3^n + \cdots + (-1)^k E_k^n + \cdots + (-1)^{n-1} E_{n-1}^n = 1 - (-1)^n. \quad (17)$$

Thus, the expression with alternating signs standing in the lefthand member can have only two values: it is equal to 2 for spaces of odd dimension-number n and vanishes if this dimension-number n is even. We saw indeed that $V - E + F - S$ vanishes ($n = 4$) and we can add that in the plane geometry ($n = 2$) a polygon has as many sides as vertices so that again $V - E$ vanishes, while in the three-dimensional space $V - E + F = 2$.

It is easy to check Euler's Relation (17) on the example of regular hypertetrahedron T_n, hypercube C_n and hyperoctahedron O_n for which we have explicit expressions of the numbers E_k^n. Thus, for a T_n we have $E_k^n = C_{k+1}^{n+1}$ and therefore the lefthand member in (17) takes the form

$$C_1^{n+1} - C_2^{n+1} + \cdots + (-1)^k C_{k+1}^{n+1} + \cdots + (-1)^{n-1} C_n^{n+1}$$

$$= -(1 - 1)^{n+1} + 1 + (-1)^{n+1} = 1 - (-1)^n$$

which agrees well with (17).

Likewise, for a hypercube C_n, the numbers E_k^n are equal to $2^{n-k} C_k^n$ and computing the lefthand member in (17), we obtain

$$2^n C_0^n - 2^{n-1} C_1^n + 2^{n-2} C_2^n - \cdots + (-1)^k 2^{n-k} C_k^n + \cdots + (-1)^{n-1} 2 C_{n-1}^n$$

and this expression is equal to $(2 - 1)^n - (-1)^n$ because it is the binomial expansion of $(2 - 1)^n$ without its last term.

Finally, for a hyperoctahedron O_n we have $E_k^n = 2^{k+1} C_{k+1}^n$ wo that the value of the lefthand member in (17) is given by

$$2C_1^n - 2^2 C_2^n + \cdots + (-1)^k 2^{k+1} C_{k+1}^n + \cdots + (-1)^{n-1} 2^n C_n^n = -(1 - 2)^n + 1$$

as it must be. At the end of this chapter we give the table of six regular polycells of the four-dimensional space:

Characteristic Numbers

Name		V	E	F	S	p	q	η	φ	Bounded by	
Pentacell	T_4	5	10	10	5	4	3	6	4	Tetrahedrons	T_3
Tessaract	C_4	16	32	24	8	4	3	6	4	Cubes	C_3
16-Cell	O_4	8	24	32	16	8	4	12	6	Tetrahedrons	T_3
24-Cell		24	96	96	24	6	3	12	8	Octahedrons	O_3
120-Cell		600	1200	720	120	4	3	6	4	Dodecahedrons	
600-Cell		120	720	1200	600	20	5	30	12	Tetrahedrons	T_3

CHAPTER 24

Linear Transformations and Matrices

In Chapter 10, linear simultaneous equations were solved and studied from an algebraical point of view. In this chapter, based on Chapter 10, they are analyzed from the point of view of transformation of straight lines, planes and, in general, of spaces of any number of dimensions. Thus, a linear equation $ax = b$, when written as $y = ax$, establishes a one-to-one correspondence between points of two straight lines: to the origin O on the x-line (that is, to $x = 0$), corresponds $y = 0$, the origin O* on the y-line; in general, to any point P at the distance $x = $ OP from O corresponds one and only one point Q at the distance $y = $ O*Q $= ax$ from O*. Thus, $y = ax$ defines a mapping of x-line onto y-line and this mapping is called the linear transformation of x-line into y-line. If $a \neq 0$ this transformation admits an inverse transformation since $x = y/a$. An equivalent picture of a transformation is obtained if, instead of points, vectors are considered: a vector $x = $ OP on the x-line is transformed by $y = ax$ into a vector $y = $ O*Q on the y-line. If $a = 0$, the transformation degenerates and the null-vector $y = 0$ corresponds to *all* vectors x on the x-line. In other words, the whole of *line x* is transformed into a *point y* $= 0$. Such transformations as $y = 0$, in which dimensions are lost so that a space is mapped onto another space of lower dimensionality, are considered as singular transformations. Another example of a singular transformation is the system

$$a_{11}x_1 + a_{12}x_2 = y_1, \quad a_{21}x_1 + a_{22}x_2 = y_2 \tag{1}$$

when its determinant $D = a_{11}a_{22} - a_{12}a_{21}$ vanishes. If $D \neq 0$, the equations (1) transform a vector $x\,(x_1, x_2)$ with components x_1 and x_2 in the x-plane into the vector $y\,(y_1, y_2)$ in the plane of vectors y. As an example of a regular transformation (1) we have a rotation about the origin through an angle ω (Fig. 1)

$$y_1 = x_1 \operatorname{Cos} \omega - x_2 \operatorname{Sin} \omega, \quad y_2 = x_1 \operatorname{Sin} \omega + x_2 \operatorname{Cos} \omega \tag{1*}$$

which transforms a vector OP making an angle α with Ox_1 into a vector OQ making an angle $\alpha + \omega$ with O*y_1.

But, if $D = 0$ and equations (1) are compatible, then from $a_{11}a_{22} - a_{12}a_{21} = 0$ and from the criterion of compatibility $a_{11}y_2 - a_{21}y_1 = 0$ we deduce the proportion

$$a_{21}/a_{11} = a_{22}/a_{12} = y_2/y_1 = m = \text{constant}$$

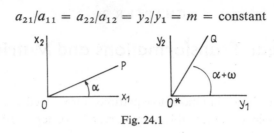

Fig. 24.1

and therefore $y_2 = my_1$ for *all* vectors in the *x*-plane. Thus, the *whole plane* x_1Ox_2 is mapped by (1) onto the *straight line* $y_2 = my_1$ in the plane $y_1O^*y_2$.

In general, a linear transformation expresses m variables $y_1, y_2, \ldots, y_m$ as linear functions of n variables $x_1, x_2, \ldots, x_n$

$$y_i = a_{i1}x_1 + a_{i2}x_2 + \cdots + a_{in}x_n = \sum_{j=1}^{n} a_{ij}x_j, \qquad (1 \leqslant i \leqslant m) \qquad (2)$$

so that the vector $x\,(x_1, \ldots, x_n)$ in an n-dimensional space S_n is transformed into a vector $y\,(y_1, \ldots, y_m)$ in an S_m. In (2) the matrix of coefficients

$$A = \begin{pmatrix} a_{11} & a_{12} & a_{13} & \cdots & a_{1n} \\ a_{21} & a_{22} & a_{23} & \cdots & a_{2n} \\ \cdots & \cdots & \cdots & \cdots & \cdots \\ a_{m1} & a_{m2} & a_{m3} & \cdots & a_{mn} \end{pmatrix} = (a_{ij}) \qquad (3)$$

which determines the transformation, can be considered as an operator A applied to the vector x, the effect of this operation being precisely the transformation of x into another vector y. There is a complete analogy between (2) and $y = ax$. For this reason the system (2) can be condensed in a single matricial equation $Ax = y$ and in this equation the operator A may be said to multiply the vector x, the product Ax being another vector y. We call a set of mn elements a_{ij}, $1 \leqslant i \leqslant m$ and $1 \leqslant j \leqslant n$, arranged as in (3), a matrix of order $m \times n$ and denote it (a_{ij}). The elements a_{ij} of (a_{ij}) are often called *entries* and sometimes *constituents*. The rows and columns of a matrix can be considered as vectors. Thus, a matrix of order $m \times 1$ which has only one column is a column-vector, while a matrix of order $1 \times n$ is a row-vector.

We use in the sequel square brackets for row-vectors and curled brackets for column-vectors: Thus, in

$$u = [u_1, u_2, \ldots, u_n] \quad \text{and} \quad v = \{v_1, v_2, \ldots, v_m\}$$

u is a row-vector, while v is a column-vector. A matrix of order 1×1 is a single number. Now any matrix is to be considered as an entity and we proceed to define the operations with these entities. First we define the addition of two matrices of same order by $(a_{ij}) + (b_{ij}) = (a_{ij} + b_{ij})$, so that the matrix (c_{ij}), sum of matrices (a_{ij}) and (b_{ij}), has as its elements the sums of corresponding elements of $A = (a_{ij})$ and $B = (b_{ij})$:

DEFINITION: $C = A + B$, if $c_{ij} = a_{ij} + b_{ij}$, provided A and B are of the same order.

Since the multiplication by an integer k reduces to addition of k equal terms, we see that $kA = (ka_{ij})$ and thus, to multiply a matrix by a fixed number it is sufficient to multiply *each element* of this matrix by this number. In particular, multiplying each element by (-1), $-A$ is obtained: $-A = (-a_{ij})$. Adding now A and $-A$, we obtain the so-called *zero-matrix* all the elements of which are zeros: $A + (-A) = (a_{ij} - a_{ij}) = (0)$. Two matrices are equal, if their difference is the zero-matrix. Therefore: $A = B$, if their order is the same and if they have same elements: $a_{ij} = b_{ij}$.

Matrix Multiplication

We can perform in succession two simple transformations $y = ax$ and $z = by$. The final result z can be considered as a direct transformation of vector x into z: $z = b(ax) = bax = cx$, where $c = ba$. Therefore, the succession of two transformations is reflected in the multiplication of their operators b and a and the operator c which defines a single equivalent transformation $z = cx$, is the *product* of operators b and a.

The same combination of two successive transformations can be built in the general case (2). Consider for instance that the mapping (2) of the n-dimensional space X (defined as the set of all possible vectors x with n components $x_1, x_2, \ldots, x_n$) onto the m-dimensional space Y of vectors y is followed by the mapping of the space Y onto a p-dimensional space Z which transforms vectors y $(y_1, y_2, \ldots, y_m)$ into vectors z $(z_1, z_2, \ldots, z_p)$:

$$z_k = b_{k1}y_1 + b_{k2}y_2 + \cdots + b_{km}y_m = \sum_{i=1}^{m} b_{ki}y_i \qquad (1 \leqslant k \leqslant p) \qquad (4)$$

Thus, the mapping $X \to Y \to Z$ transforms each vector x into a vector z and we can ask what is the algebraic expression of a *direct* transformation of x into z? To answer this question we eliminate the intermediary transformation (4) substituting in it the expressions of y_i in terms of x_j given by (2). The result is

$$z_k = \sum_{i=1}^{m} b_{ki} \sum_{j=1}^{n} a_{ij}x_j = \sum_{j=1}^{n} x_j \sum_{i=1}^{m} b_{ki}a_{ij} = \sum_{j=1}^{n} c_{kj}x_j, \qquad (1 \leqslant k \leqslant p) \quad (5)$$

where the coefficients of the direct transformation c_{kj} are defined by

$$c_{kj} = \sum_{i=1}^{n} b_{ki}a_{ij} \qquad (1 \leqslant j \leqslant n; \quad 1 \leqslant k \leqslant p) \qquad (6)$$

Denoting the transformations (2) and (4) by $y = Ax$ and $z = By$, we also denote the direct transformation (5) by $z = Cx$. Here A, B and C are matrices of transformations (2), (4), and (5) respectively. Now it can be stated that $z = By = B(Ax) = BAx = Cx$, so that the direct transformation's matrix C appears as the product of matrices A and B: $C = BA$. It is important to note that the rule of multiplication (6) is the same as the rule of multiplication of determinants: the element c_{ij} in the i-th row and the j-th column of the product matrix BA is the scalar product of the i-th *row*-vector of the *left* factor B and of the j-th *column*-vector of the *right* factor A. We stress the position of factors because—as we will see—the matrix multiplication is not commutative: the matrices BA and AB are different. Here is an example of this important property of matrix multiplication: we take first as factors square matrices of order 2×2

$$A = \begin{pmatrix} 7 & 1 \\ 2 & -1 \end{pmatrix} \qquad B = \begin{pmatrix} 2 & 3 \\ 5 & -4 \end{pmatrix}$$

and denote AB by $C = AB$, while $M = BA$. Computing their elements, one finds $c_{11} = [7, 1] \cdot \{2, 5\} = 19$, but $m_{11} = [2, 3] \cdot \{7, 2\} = 20$. Thus, already $c_{11} \neq m_{11}$ and this is sufficient to conclude that $C \neq M$. The two products are indeed:

$$C = AB = \begin{pmatrix} 19 & 17 \\ -1 & 10 \end{pmatrix} \neq \begin{pmatrix} 20 & -1 \\ 27 & 9 \end{pmatrix} = BA = M.$$

It is interesting to note that the sum of diagonal elements is the same:

$$c_{11} + c_{22} = m_{11} + m_{22} = 29.$$

Another example deals with the multiplication of rectangular matrices. In this case it is essential that in the product BA the number of *columns* in the *left* factor B is the same as the number of *rows* in the *right* factor A, other-wise the multiplication is not possible. We take B of order 2 × 3 and A of order 3 × 2, so that both multiplications BA and AB are possible:

$$B = \begin{pmatrix} 1 & -2 & 3 \\ -4 & 2 & 5 \end{pmatrix} \qquad A = \begin{pmatrix} 1 & 3 \\ -1 & 0 \\ 2 & 4 \end{pmatrix}.$$

Here we have

$$BA = \begin{pmatrix} 9 & 15 \\ 4 & 8 \end{pmatrix} \quad \text{and} \quad AB = \begin{pmatrix} -11 & 4 & 18 \\ -1 & 2 & -3 \\ -14 & 4 & 26 \end{pmatrix}.$$

This time the matrices BA and AB differ in order, but again the sums of their diagonal terms are the same, namely 17.

Though the determinant multiplication rule is identical to that of matrix multiplication, there are two important differences between the multiplica-tion of determinants and the multiplication of matrices: (1) the first one is commutative while the second one is not. Denoting the determinant of a square matrix A by det |A|, we have det |AB| = det |A| · det |B| = det |BA|, but AB ≠ BA. (2) Determinants are numbers and therefore a product of two determinants can vanish only when at least one of its two factors vanishes. But a matrix AB, product of two matrices A and B, may happen to be a zero-matrix without either of two factor-matrices being a zero-matrix.

EXAMPLE. Take

$$A = \begin{pmatrix} -6 & -4 & -2 \\ -9 & -6 & -3 \\ 3 & 2 & 1 \end{pmatrix} \quad \text{and} \quad B = \begin{pmatrix} 0 & 1 & -2 \\ -1 & 0 & 3 \\ 2 & -3 & 0 \end{pmatrix}$$

and compute the elements p_{ij} and q_{ij} of products P = AB and Q = BA. The result is: p_{ij} vanish, all of them, so that AB = $\emptyset$, where the symbol $\emptyset$ denotes zero-matrix (of any order), while $-q_{11} = q_{21} = q_{31} = 15$; $-q_{12} = q_{22} = q_{32} = 10$; $-q_{13} = q_{23} = q_{33} = 5$ and BA ≠ $\emptyset$, but det |BA| = 0. We conclude that a zero-matrix can be decomposed into a product of two non zero-matrices of which at least one has a vanishing determinant. Natur-ally, multiplying a matrix by zero-matrix produces a zero-matrix: A · $\emptyset$ = $\emptyset$ as well as $\emptyset$ · A = $\emptyset$.

The non-commutativity of matrix multiplication necessitates a distinction between two operations AB and BA, the multiplicand being as usual the right symbol and the multiplier the left symbol. When A is multiplied by B, as in BA, we say that the product BA is obtained by a *premultiplication of A by B*. The other product AB is said to be the result of a *postmultiplication of A by B*, despite the fact that in AB it is B which is multiplied by A. In both cases the elements of the product are scalar products of rows of the *left* factor and columns of the *right* factor.

It is important to study the exceptional cases when two factors of a matricial product commute, so that AB = BA. This is always so when one of two factor-matrices is the so-called *unit matrix*. A unit matrix, by definition, has all its diagonal elements equal to one and zeros as its off-diagonal elements. There are unit matrices of all orders and all of them are square matrices because in a rectangular matrix we cannot define its *diagonal* elements. A unit matrix is denoted I when its order is out of question. If we want to precise the order of a unit matrix we mark it as a subscript to I. Thus, I_3 denotes the unit matrix of order three: $\begin{pmatrix} 1 & 0 & 0 \\ 0 & 1 & 0 \\ 0 & 0 & 1 \end{pmatrix}$. The unit matrix commutes with all matrices. A matrix commutes with itself and this fact gives a meaning to integral powers A^n of a matrix A. But already the binomial theorem for matrices differs from the same theorem for numbers: since $AB + BA \neq 2AB$, we are obliged to consider in the square of a sum of two terms four (instead of three) different terms

$$(A + B)^2 = A^2 + AB + BA + B^2.$$

A matricial polynomial in *one* variable (matrix) A can be written without ambiguity as P(A), but to write down a polynomial of two variables, the arguments of which are matrices, we must write out each of its terms carefully preserving the order of matrices: a term of fifth degree in A and B, for instance, which has three factors A and two factors B may have many different meanings

$$A^3B^2, \quad A^2BAB, \quad A^2B^2A, \quad B^2A^3, \quad ABABA, \quad AB^2A^2 \quad \text{etc.}$$

There is an interesting class of matrices of second order which follow the rules of familiar algebra of complex numbers because they commute with each other: a matrix of this class is defined by two numbers a and b only, its off-diagonal elements are b (in the first row) and $-b$, while a stands in the diagonal. We have indeed

$$\begin{pmatrix} a & b \\ -b & a \end{pmatrix}\begin{pmatrix} c & d \\ -d & c \end{pmatrix} = \begin{pmatrix} ac - bd & ad + bc \\ -ad - bc & ac - bd \end{pmatrix} = \begin{pmatrix} c & d \\ -d & c \end{pmatrix}\begin{pmatrix} a & b \\ -b & a \end{pmatrix}$$

which is identical with the rule $(a + ib)(c + id) = ac - bd + i(ad + bc)$.

We see that the diagonal a plays the role of the real part of a complex number $a + ib$, while the off-diagonal b is analogous to the coefficient of $i = \sqrt{-1}$. We could define $i = \sqrt{-1}$ as the matrix $\begin{pmatrix} 0 & 1 \\ -1 & 0 \end{pmatrix}$, using *real* numbers 0 and 1 only. Then, defining one by the unit matrix, we could build the whole algebra of complex numbers as an algebra of real matrices since

$$a + ib = a \begin{pmatrix} 1 & 0 \\ 0 & 1 \end{pmatrix} + b \begin{pmatrix} 0 & 1 \\ -1 & 0 \end{pmatrix} = \begin{pmatrix} a & b \\ -b & a \end{pmatrix}.$$

A vector is a matrix of order $1 \times n$, if it is a row-vector, and of order $n \times 1$, if we have a column-vector. Thus, the product of a matrix and a vector is formed by the multiplication rule of matrices and we have to distinguish between pre- and post-multiplication of a vector x by a matrix M. In a premultiplication Mx, the vector x is of necessity a *column* vector; that is, a matrix of order $n \times 1$, the matrix M being of order $m \times n$. We know that the product PQ of matrices P of order $m \times n$ and Q of order $n \times p$ is a matrix of order $m \times p$. Therefore, the product Mx will be a matrix of order $m \times 1$, that is a column vector: *premultiplication of a vector by a matrix transforms it into another vector.*

In a postmultiplication of a vector y by a matrix M the product yM has a sense, if y is a row-vector only. If the order of M is $m \times n$, then the row-vector y must have m components, that is, considered as a matrix, it must be of order $1 \times m$. If so, then yM is of order $1 \times n$: *postmultiplication of a vector by a matrix also yields another vector.* The scalar multiplication of vectors is a particular case of matrix multiplication: in (x, y) the first factor, x, is a row-vector, the second one, y, is a column-vector and their product is a matrix of order 1×1, that is, a pure number (scalar) because the orders of factors are $1 \times n$ and $n \times 1$. But suppose that we form the product yx, premultiplying a row-vector x by a column-vector y. This is the case of matrix multiplication, when the factors are of orders $n \times 1$ and $1 \times n$ and in this order precisely. The result is a matrix of order $n \times n$:

$$[x_1, x_2, \ldots, x_n] \cdot \{y_1, y_2, \ldots, y_n\} = (x, y) = \text{pure number}$$

$$\{y_1, y_2, \ldots, y_n\} \cdot [x_1, x_2, \ldots, x_n] = \text{matrix A} = (a_{ij}),$$

where the elements of the matrix A are simply $a_{ij} = x_i y_j$, $1 \leqslant i, j \leqslant n$.

DEFINITION. The sum of diagonal elements in a square matrix A is called the *trace* of A. It is denoted by tr A.

We saw that despite the non-commutativity of matrix multiplication the determinant of a product AB is invariant under the permutation of factors: det AB = det BA. Another invariant is the trace of the product and we will prove that tr AB = tr BA. Here both factors are square matrices of same order $n \times n$. Denoting their entries by a_{ij} and b_{ij}, we have

$$\text{tr AB} = \text{tr C} = \sum_{i=1}^{n} c_{ii} = \sum_{1}^{n} \sum_{1}^{n} a_{ij}b_{ji} = T_1$$

$$\text{tr BA} = \text{tr D} = \sum_{j=1}^{n} d_{jj} = \sum_{1}^{n} \sum_{1}^{n} b_{ji}a_{ij} = T_2$$

and thus $T_1 = T_2$ which proves that the trace trAB = trBA.

Matrix Division. In the familiar algebra division by zero is impossible. We have to study now the matrix division and, from the beginning, state that insofar as matrices are concerned, division is impossible not only by zero-matrices, but also by matrices of a much larger class of *singular* matrices.

DEFINITION. A matrix the determinant of which vanishes is *singular*. This definition concerns square matrices only, rectangular ones having no determinants associated with them.

A division can be performed as a multiplication, multiplying the dividend by the reciprocal of the divisor. Therefore, the problem of division reduces to the problem of constructing the reciprocal of a regular matrix, that is of finding such a matrix X that the product AX or the product XA is the unit matrix I. We do not know whether a left reciprocal of A is the same matrix as the right reciprocal of A, but here is the proof that there is one reciprocal matrix only: Granted that LA = I and also AR = I, we have

$$L = LI = L(AR) = (LA)R = IR = R.$$

In this reasoning we used the associative law in replacing L (AR) by (LA) R. It is not difficult to verify that matrix multiplication, though not commutative, is associative. Denoting L (AR) = C = (c_{ij}) and (LA)R = M = (m_{ij}), we have by definition

$$c_{ij} = \sum_{k=1}^{n} 1_{ik} \sum_{s=1}^{n} a_{ks}r_{sj} = \sum_{s=1}^{n} r_{sj} \sum_{k=1}^{n} 1_{ik}a_{ks} = \sum_{s=1}^{n} \left(\sum_{k=1}^{n} 1_{ik}a_{ks} \right) r_{sj} = m_{ij}.$$

The matrices L (AR) and (LA)R are thus element for element identical and are usually denoted LAR, without using the parantheses.

The necessity of the condition det $|A| \neq 0$ for the inversion of A follows from the relation det $|A| \cdot$ det $|A^{-1}| =$ det $|I| = 1$, where A^{-1} is used to denote the reciprocal of A. A singular matrix has no reciprocal.

Reciprocal or Inverse Matrix

In Chapter 10 we proved that, given a non vanishing determinant det $|A|$ $= D \neq 0$, there is a reciprocal determinant the value of which is equal to D^{-1}. The (i, j)th element of D^{-1} was shown to be D_{ij}/D, where the symbol D_{ij} denotes the co-factor of the (j, i)th element in $D = \det |(a_{ij})|$.

The proof was based on the following property of co-factors:

"If cofactors of the elements of a row are multiplied by the elements of another row, the sum of such products vanishes" (Chapter 10). In exactly the same way we can prove that the matrix $B = (b_{ij})$, the elements of which are defined by $b_{ij} = D_{ji}/D$, is the reciprocal of $A = (a_{ij})$. It is sufficient to check that the product AB is the unit-matrix I. And, indeed, denoting the (i, j)th element of this product by $(AB)_{ij}$, we have:

$$(AB)_{ij} = \sum_{s=1}^{n} a_{is}b_{sj} = \sum_{s=1}^{n} a_{is}D_{js}/D = 0, \quad \text{if} \quad i \neq j \quad \text{and} \quad = 1, \quad \text{if} \quad i = j.$$

Thus, the product AB is the unit matrix I and $B = A^{-1}$.

Here again we have two divisions: to divide a matrix M by a regular matrix A it is sufficient to multiply M by A^{-1}. The premultiplication yields the quotient $A^{-1}M$ in the *left* division, while the quotient in a right division is MA^{-1}.

EXAMPLE: Let $A - \begin{pmatrix} 1 & 2 & 3 \\ 1 & 3 & 5 \\ 1 & 5 & 12 \end{pmatrix}$ and $B = \begin{pmatrix} 1 & 1 & 1 \\ 1 & 2 & 3 \\ 1 & 4 & 9 \end{pmatrix}$.

Then $A^{-1} = \begin{pmatrix} 11 & -9 & 1 \\ -7 & 9 & -2 \\ 2 & -3 & 1 \end{pmatrix} \cdot 3^{-1}$, so that

$$A^{-1}B = 3^{-1} \begin{pmatrix} 3 & -3 & -7 \\ 0 & 3 & 2 \\ 0 & 0 & 2 \end{pmatrix}, \quad \text{while} \quad BA^{-1} = 3^{-1} \begin{pmatrix} 6 & -3 & 0 \\ 3 & 0 & 0 \\ 1 & 0 & 2 \end{pmatrix}.$$

Here the two invariants are:

$$\det |A^{-1}B| = \det |BA^{-1}| = \tfrac{2}{3}, \quad \text{tr } A^{-1}B = \text{tr } BA^{-1} = \tfrac{8}{27}.$$

Transposition and Inversion of a Product

The operation of transposition defined in Chapter 10 for determinants consists in exchanging rows and columns of a matrix but preserving their order.

35 Kogbetliantz

Thus, a matrix A of order $m \times n$ when transposed becomes a new matrix of order $n \times m$. Denoting the transposed A by $\tilde{A}$ it is obvious that $\tilde{A} \neq A$. Even when A is a square matrix, so that the transposition does not change its order, its transpose $\tilde{A}$ is in general different from A.

DEFINITION. A matrix A such that its transpose $\tilde{A}$ is equal to it, $\tilde{A} = A$, is a symmetric matrix.

Denoting the elements of $\tilde{A}$ by $\tilde{a}_{ij}$, we can symbolize the operation of transposition as follows: if $A = (a_{ij})$, then $\tilde{A} = (\tilde{a}_{ij})$ is defined by $\tilde{a}_{ij} = a_{ji}$. Thus, in a symmetric matrix $a_{ji} = a_{ij}$. It is important to note that multiplication does not preserve the symmetry: the product of two symmetric matrices in general is not a symmetric matrix. Consider, for instance

$$\begin{pmatrix} 1 & 2 \\ 2 & -1 \end{pmatrix} \begin{pmatrix} 3 & 5 \\ 5 & 1 \end{pmatrix} = \begin{pmatrix} 13 & 7 \\ 1 & 9 \end{pmatrix} \quad \text{or} \quad \begin{pmatrix} 1 & i \\ i & 1 \end{pmatrix} \begin{pmatrix} i & 2 \\ 2 & 2i \end{pmatrix} = \begin{pmatrix} 3i & 0 \\ 1 & 4 \end{pmatrix}.$$

Transposing or inverting a product C of two square matrices A and B, $C = AB$, we obtain the product of their transposes or of their reciprocal matrices, but in these products the order of factors is inverted. Thus, we will prove that

$$\tilde{C} = \widetilde{AB} = \tilde{B} \cdot \tilde{A} \quad \text{and} \quad C^{-1} = (AB)^{-1} = B^{-1} \cdot A^{-1}. \tag{7}$$

We denote the elements of $\tilde{C}$ by $\tilde{c}_{ij}$, so that $\tilde{C} = (\tilde{c}_{ij}) = (c_{ji})$. Now, if $A = (a_{ij})$, $B = (b_{ij})$ then

$$\tilde{c}_{ij} = c_{ji} = \sum_{k=1}^{n} a_{jk} b_{ki} = \sum_{k=1}^{n} \tilde{a}_{kj} \tilde{b}_{ik} = \sum_{k=1}^{n} \tilde{b}_{ik} \tilde{a}_{kj} = (\tilde{B} \cdot \tilde{A})_{ij}$$

which proves that matrices $\tilde{C}$ and $\tilde{B} \cdot \tilde{A}$ are element for element identical.

To prove that $C^{-1} = B^{-1}A^{-1}$ we show that multiplying AB and $B^{-1}A^{-1}$, we obtain the unit matrix I. Indeed

$$C \cdot (B^{-1}A^{-1}) = AB \cdot B^{-1}A^{-1} = A(B \cdot B^{-1})A^{-1} = A \cdot I \cdot A^{-1} = AA^{-1} = I.$$

Thus, the reciprocal of AB is $B^{-1}A^{-1}$. Since there can be one reciprocal only, the product $(B^{-1}A^{-1})$ AB is equal to the unit matrix also.

The reversal rule in the inversion or transposition of products of two matrices is easily extended by mathematical induction to products of many matrices. The proof is the same in both cases and we give it for the transposition only. Granted that it holds for products of k matrices, we consider P, where $P = A_1 A_2 \cdots A_k B$ is a product of $k + 1$ matrices. Let $M = A_1 A_2 \cdots A_k$ so that $P = MB$ and $\tilde{M} = \tilde{A}_k \cdots \tilde{A}_2 \tilde{A}_1$. Then we have

$$\tilde{P} = (\widetilde{MB}) = \tilde{B} \cdot \tilde{M} = \tilde{B} \tilde{A}_k \tilde{A}_{k-1} \cdots \tilde{A}_2 \tilde{A}_1.$$

Naturally, the reversal rule in the transposition holds also for products of rectangular matrices. Let A and B be of orders $m \times n$ and $n \times p$ respectively. Then A and B are of orders $n \times m$ and $p \times n$, while C = AB is of order $m \times p$. Now $\tilde{B} \cdot \tilde{A}$ and $\tilde{C}$ will be of same order, namely $p \times m$, and they are element for element identical. The proof is the same as the proof above for square matrices.

Applying the reversal rule, it can be shown that inversion does not destroy the symmetry: the reciprocal of a symmetric matrix is also symmetric. Let S = $\tilde{S}$ be symmetric. Transposing the identity $SS^{-1} = I$ and noting that $\tilde{I} = I$, we conclude as follows:

$$\tilde{SS^{-1}} = \tilde{S}^{-1} \cdot \tilde{S} = \tilde{S^{-1}}S = I.$$

Multiplying the identity $\tilde{S^{-1}}S = I$ from the right by S^{-1}, we obtain the desired result:

$$\tilde{S^{-1}}SS^{-1} = \tilde{S^{-1}}(SS^{-1}) = \tilde{S^{-1}}I = \tilde{S}^{-1} = IS^{-1} = S^{-1}.$$

Matrices with Complex Elements

Up to this point we considered real matrices only. More important—especially for modern mathematical physics—are matrices the elements of which are complex numbers. Let A = (a_{hj}) and B = (b_{hj}) be of same order, their elements being real numbers. The matrix C = A + iB, where i denotes the imaginary unit $\sqrt{-1}$, has complex elements $c_{hj} = a_{hj} + ib_{hj}$ and the matrix C*, the elements c_{hj}^* of which are complex conjugates of elements c_{hj} of C, is called *conjugate* to C. Thus, to a complex matrix M we associate always its conjugate matrix M*.

DEFINITION. Either of two matrices M and $\tilde{M}$* is called *adjoint* of the other.

Thus, the adjoint of M is formed by taking complex conjugate of its transpose $\tilde{M}$. It is obvious that the transpose of transpose of M as well as the conjugate of conjugate of M is M itself and this explains the reciprocity of M and $\tilde{M}$* established in the definition.

EXAMPLE OF AN ADJOINT:

$$M = \begin{pmatrix} 3 + 2i & 4 - i \\ 1 - i & -3i \end{pmatrix} \quad \text{and} \quad \tilde{M}* = \begin{pmatrix} 3 - 2i & 1 + i \\ 4 + i & 3i \end{pmatrix}.$$

For a *real* matrix A its transpose is also its adjoint since A* = A, if A is real.

The concept of adjoint matrix serves to define the most important class of *Hermitian matrices*:

DEFINITION. A self-adjoint square matrix is a *hermitian* matrix: $\widetilde{H}^* = H$.

Thus, if $\widetilde{H}^* = H$, then H is hermitian. If a hermitian matrix is real, it is a symmetric matrix because, being self-adjoint, it is equal to its transpose. As we will see below, hermitian matrices share many common properties with symmetric matrices. Denoting the elements of a hermitian matrix H by $H_{ij} = a_{ij} + b_{ij}\sqrt{-1}$ with real a_{ij} and b_{ij}, we find for the elements of the adjoint matrix $H_{ij}^* = a_{ji} - b_{ji}\sqrt{-1}$. Therefore, $\widetilde{H}_{ij}^* = H_{ij}$ yields for the real and imaginary parts of H_{ij} the relations:

$$a_{ji} = a_{ij} \quad \text{and} \quad b_{ji} = -b_{ij}.$$

A real square matrix $B = (b_{ij})$ such that in it $b_{ji} = -b_{ij}$ is called *skew symmetric*. In a skew symmetric real matrix the diagonal terms vanish, while the off diagonal terms pairwise symmetric with respect to the main diagonal are equal in absolute value and have opposite signs. It can be said that a hermitian matrix is the sum of a real symmetric matrix and a real skew symmetric multiplied by $\sqrt{-1}$. It is seen that though the off diagonal elements of a hermitian matrix are complex, its diagonal terms and therefore its trace are real.

We know that multiplication does not preserve the symmetry. Likewise the multiplication does not preserve hermitian character of matrices-factors. It cannot, otherwise the symmetry would be preserved because the symmetrical character of real matrices is a particular case of hermitian character of complex matrices. Here is an example:

$$\begin{pmatrix} a & c+id \\ c-id & b \end{pmatrix}\begin{pmatrix} 1 & i \\ -i & 1 \end{pmatrix} = \begin{pmatrix} a+d-ic & c+i(a+d) \\ c-i(b+d) & b+d+ic. \end{pmatrix}$$

We saw that the inversion does not destroy the symmetry of a real matrix. Likewise the inversion preserves the hermitian character of a complex matrix. Let H be hermitian and denote by $G = H^{-1}$ the reciprocal of H. Taking the transpose conjugate of the identity $GH = I$ and using the fact that $\widetilde{H}^* = H$, we have $H\widetilde{G}^* = I$. Premultiplying this relation by $G = H^{-1}$, we conclude that $GH\widetilde{G}^* = \widetilde{G}^* = GI = G$ and this proves that the reciprocal of a hermitian matrix also belongs to the class of hermitian matrices: H^{-1} is self-adjoint, if H is.

Multiplying a hermitian matrix by $\sqrt{-1}$, a *skew hermitian* matrix is obtained. It can be defined as follows: a matrix G such that its adjoint $\widetilde{G}^*$ is equal to minus G, that is $\widetilde{G}^* = -G$, is called skew hermitian. It is clear that a *real* skew hermitian matrix is skew symmetric. To justify the definition, note that $-i$ is the complex conjugate of $i = \sqrt{-1}$ and therefore, if H is hermitian, the adjoint to iH is equal to $-i$H, because H is self-adjoint. Thus, $G = i$H is, indeed, skew hermitian.

Consider now a general complex matrix M which does not belong to hermitian matrices: $\widetilde{M}^* \neq M$, and form two products $M\widetilde{M}^*$ and $\widetilde{M}^*M$. They are not equal: in general, a matrix does not commute with its adjoint matrix. Take, for instance, $M = \begin{pmatrix} i & 1 \\ 1-i & 0 \end{pmatrix}$ with $\widetilde{M}^* = \begin{pmatrix} -i & 1+i \\ 1 & 0 \end{pmatrix}$. In this case

$$M\widetilde{M}^* = \begin{pmatrix} 2 & i-1 \\ -1-i & 2 \end{pmatrix}, \quad \text{while} \quad \widetilde{M}^*M = \begin{pmatrix} 3 & -i \\ i & 1 \end{pmatrix}.$$

Though $M\widetilde{M}^* \neq \widetilde{M}^*M$, it strikes us that both products are *hermitian*. This is a general rule: *a matrix* $N = M\widetilde{M}^*$ *which is the product of two mutually adjoint matrices is a hermitian matrix.* To prove this rule it is sufficient to note that $N^* = (M \cdot \widetilde{M}^*)^* = M^* \cdot \widetilde{M}$ and, thus, $\widetilde{N}^* = (\widetilde{M^*\widetilde{M}}) = \widetilde{M} \cdot \widetilde{M}^*$ $= M\widetilde{M}^* = N$: being self-adjoint, N is, indeed, hermitian.

A hermitian matrix commutes with its adjoint matrix because it is self-adjoint and commutes with itself. But the class of matrices which commute with their adjoint matrices, so that the two products $M \cdot \widetilde{M}^*$ and $\widetilde{M}^* \cdot M$ are identical: $M \cdot \widetilde{M}^* = \widetilde{M}^* \cdot M$, comprises also matrices which are not hermitian. This class has important properties and matrices which belong to it are called *normal* matrices. The example above proves that there are matrices which are not normal.

We terminate this short study of current terminology used in dealing with matrices, proving that the reversal rule applies also to the adjoint of a product of two matrices. We have, indeed, for $P = AB$:

$$\widetilde{P}^* = \overline{\widetilde{A^*B^*}} = \widetilde{B}^* \cdot \widetilde{A}^*.$$

Orthogonal and Unitary Matrices

Among linear transformations the rotations of orthogonal coordinate system are characterized by the conservation of distances, in particular by the invariance of lengths of vectors, provided the axes remain rectangular, that is, orthogonal. The formulas of transformation of coordinates and of components of vectors involve the cosines of angles formed by old and new axes. Let us fix our ideas discussing first the particular case of three-dimensional space. We choose our notations as follows: $Ox_1x_2x_3$ is the old system as it was before the rotation, while after the rotation it becomes $Oy_1y_2y_3$, so that the same vector x with components x_1, x_2, x_3 in the old system will be denoted y with components y_1, y_2, y_3 when considered in the new system. Since x and y denote one and the same vector in orthogonal systems $Ox_1x_2x_3$ and $Oy_1y_2y_3$ we have the condition

$$x_1^2 + x_2^2 + x_3^2 = y_1^2 + y_2^2 + y_3^2 \tag{8}$$

which holds identically, the vector $x\,(x_1x_2x_3)$ being arbitrary.

The cosine of the angle formed by a new axis Oy_j, $j = 1, 2, 3$, with an old axis Ox_i, $i = 1, 2, 3$, will be denoted by c_{ij} and the nine cosines c_{ij} form a matrix C of order 3×3:

$$Oy_1\ \ Oy_2\ \ Oy_3$$

$$\mathrm{C} = \begin{pmatrix} c_{11} & c_{12} & c_{13} \\ c_{21} & c_{22} & c_{23} \\ c_{31} & c_{32} & c_{33} \end{pmatrix} \begin{matrix} Ox_1 \\ Ox_2 \\ Ox_3 \end{matrix}$$

Projecting the x-components of our vector on the y-axes and the y-components on the x-axes, we obtain the formulae of linear transformation due to the rotation of coordinate system about the fixed origin:

$$y_j = \sum_{i=1}^{3} c_{ij}x_i; \quad x_i = \sum_{j=1}^{3} c_{ij}y_j. \tag{9}$$

Before using these relations in (8), we introduce a notation for the elements of the unit matrix of order $n \times n$. This notation, due to Kronecker, is as follows: the (i, j)th element of I which belongs to the ith row and the jth column is denoted δ_{ij}. Therefore, by definition of these new symbols, we have

$$\delta_{ij} = 0, \quad \text{if}\quad i \neq j,$$

but

$$\delta_{ij} = \delta_{ii} = 1, \quad \text{if}\quad i = j.$$

$$\tag{10}$$

Now we transform the lefthand member of (8) with the aid of (10):

$$x_1^2 + x_2^2 + x_3^2 = \sum_{i=1}^{3} \sum_{k=1}^{3} \delta_{ik}x_i x_k.$$

In the righthand member of (8) we substitute the expressions (9) of y_j in terms of x_i:

$$y_1^2 + y_2^2 + y_3^2 = \sum_{j=1}^3 y_j^2 = \sum_{j=1}^3 \left(\sum_{i=1}^3 c_{ij}x_j \right)^2 = \sum_{j=1}^3 \left(\sum_{i=1}^3 c_{ij}x_i \right) \left(\sum_{k=1}^3 c_{kj}x_k \right)$$

$$= \sum_{j=1}^3 \sum_{i=1}^3 \sum_{k=1}^3 c_{ij}c_{kj}x_ix_k = \sum_{i=1}^3 \sum_{k=1}^3 x_ix_k \left(\sum_{j=1}^3 c_{ij}c_{kj} \right).$$

Thus, the condition (8) takes now the form

$$\sum_{i=1}^3 \sum_{k=1}^3 \delta_{ik}x_ix_k = \sum_{i=1}^3 \sum_{k=1}^3 \left(\sum_{j=1}^3 c_{ij}c_{kj} \right) x_ix_k.$$

Or, transferring the lefthand member into the righthand member:

$$\sum_{i=1}^3 \sum_{k=1}^3 \left[\sum_{j=1}^3 c_{ij}c_{kj} - \delta_{ik} \right] \cdot x_ix_k = 0. \tag{11}$$

But the vector of components x_1, x_2, x_3 is arbitrary and the identity (11) can be true only when all the coefficients of x_ix_k vanish. Thus, the nine cosines c_{ij}, elements of the matrix C, satisfy six relations

$$\sum_{j=1}^3 c_{ij}c_{kj} = \delta_{ik}. \qquad (i, k = 1, 2, 3) \tag{12}$$

Three of them, obtained for $i = k = 1, 2, 3$, namely $c_{i1}^2 + c_{i2}^2 + c_{i3}^2 = 1$, prove that the row-vectors of C are unit vectors of length one. The three others of the type $c_{i1}c_{k1} + c_{i2}c_{k2} + c_{i3}c_{k3} = 0, i \neq k$, prove that these row-vectors are orthogonal to each other. But what about the column-vectors of C?

Substituting in the lefthand member of (8) the expressions (9) of x_i in terms of y_j and repeating our reasoning, we obtain six more relations similar to (12):

$$\sum_{i=1}^3 c_{ij}c_{ik} = \delta_{jk} \qquad (j, k = 1, 2, 3) \tag{13}$$

and these relations prove that the column-vectors of C are orthogonal to each other and are also unit vectors, as are the row-vectors.

We compute now the product $C \cdot \tilde{C}$. Denoting it by $Q = C \cdot \tilde{C} = (q_{ik})$ and observing that $\tilde{C} = (c_{ji}) = (\tilde{c}_{ij})$, we have thanks to (12)

$$q_{ik} = \sum_{j=1}^3 c_{ij} \cdot \tilde{c}_{jk} = \sum_{j=1}^3 c_{ij}c_{kj} = \delta_{ik}.$$

Thus, the product Q is the unit matrix I and our result $C \cdot \tilde{C} = I$ shows that the transpose of C is its reciprocal matrix $C^{-1}: \tilde{C} = C^{-1}$.

Now det $|C| = $ det $|\tilde{C}|$. Therefore we deduce from $C \cdot \tilde{C} = I$ that the square of det $|C|$ is equal to det $|I| = 1$. Extracting the square root, we have two possibilities: det $|C| = 1$ or det $|C| = -1$. Before the rotation C was the unit matrix and det $|C|$ was equal to 1. During the rotation cosines c_{ij} change continuously so that det $|C|$ could change only as a continuous function. It could not jump from plus one to minus one and therefore we conclude that the determinant of matrix C is equal to one.

The relation $\tilde{C} = C^{-1}$ implies a connection between the elements c_{ij} of C and their cofactors which we will denote by F_{ij}. These cofactors are elements of C^{-1}: the (i, j)th element of C^{-1} is indeed equal to $F_{ji}/$det $|C|$, but det $|C|$ $= 1$ and thus F_{ji} is the (i, j)th element of C^{-1}. But the (i, j)th element of $\tilde{C}$ is c_{ji} and it is seen from $\tilde{C} = C^{-1}$ that $c_{ji} = F_{ji}$; that is,

$$c_{ij} = F_{ij}. \qquad (i, j = 1, 2, 3) \qquad (14)$$

For instance, $c_{11} = F_{11} = c_{22}c_{33} - c_{23}c_{32}$.

In all, twenty-two relations (12, (13), (14), and det $|C| = 1$ are established between the nine cosines c_{ij}. Their matrix C belongs to the class of *orthogonal* matrices. There are orthogonal matrices of all orders and their properties— exemplified in the particular case of C—do not depend on the order.

DEFINITION. A real square matrix M is an orthogonal matrix if $M\tilde{M} = I$.

The transpose $\tilde{M}$ of an orthogonal matrix M is also its reciprocal: $\tilde{M}$ $= M^{-1}$, and this relation is sufficient to deduce all the properties of M, but first we will proceed as in the case of the orthogonal matrix C of order 3×3. Consider a rotation about the fixed origin of an orthogonal system of coordinates $Ox_1x_2 \cdots x_n$ in a n-dimensional space S_n and denote the final position of old axes Ox_k by $Oy_1y_2 \cdots y_n$. There are now n^2 cosines of as many angles formed by an old and a new axes of coordinates. Denote as before by c_{ij} the cosine of the angle $\widehat{x_iOy_j}$ and by M the matrix $M = (c_{ij})$, $1 \leqslant i$, $j \leqslant n$. We set out to prove that M is an orthogonal matrix.

The formulas of transformation of coordinates are given by (9), provided the summations are extended up to n instead of 3. The condition (8) becomes

$$x_1^2 + x_2^2 + \cdots + x_n^2 = y_1^2 + y_2^2 + \cdots + y_n^2$$

Nothing is changed in our proof of the relation $C\tilde{C} = I$ except the replacement of the upper limit of summations 3 by n and the final results (12) and

(13) are obtained in the form

$$\sum_{j=1}^{n} c_{ij}c_{kj} = \delta_{ik} \quad \text{and} \quad \sum_{i=1}^{n} c_{ij}c_{ik} = \delta_{jk}. \tag{15}$$

Thus, M is orthogonal, its rows and columns are unit vectors, row-vectors are pairwise orthogonal and so are column-vectors, and finally the determinant of M is equal to one.

All these properties follow from the definition. Let M satisfy it: $M\tilde{M} = I$, and denote its elements by m_{ij}. The relation $M\tilde{M} = I$ means, by definition of multiplication, that

$$\sum_{k=1}^{n} m_{ik}m_{jk} = 0, \quad \text{if} \quad i \neq j, \quad \text{and} \quad \sum_{k=1}^{n} m_{ik}m_{ik} = 1$$

which is, indeed, the first part of (15). Likewise the relation $\tilde{M} \cdot M = I$ gives the second part of (15). From (15) follow all the properties of an orthogonal matrix.

It is important to note that the product of two (or more) orthogonal matrices is also an orthogonal matrix: in $P = MN$ let the factors M and N be orthogonal matrices, so that $M \cdot \tilde{M} = N \cdot \tilde{N} = I$; then

$$P \cdot \tilde{P} = MN \cdot \widetilde{MN} = M \cdot N\tilde{N} \cdot \tilde{M} = MI\tilde{M} = M\tilde{M} = I.$$

As an example we consider the following problem: determine the most general orthogonal matrix of order 2×2. We use the property (14), that is $c_{ij} = F_{ij}$, where F_{ij} is cofactor of c_{ij} in the determinant (c_{ij}). For $n = 2$ we have $c_{22} = F_{22} = c_{11}$ and $c_{21} = F_{21} = -c_{12}$, so that already the matrix is defined by its two elements c_{11}, c_{12} of the first row. But this row is a unit vector and therefore $c_{11}^2 + c_{12}^2 = 1$. Defining an angle θ by its $\sin \theta = c_{12}$ and $\cos \theta = c_{11}$, we see that an orthogonal matrix of order 2×2 is always of the form $\begin{pmatrix} \cos \theta & \sin \theta \\ -\sin \theta & \cos \theta \end{pmatrix}$. Denoting this matrix by O_2, we can represent it as follows:

$$O_2 = I \cdot \cos \theta + J \cdot \sin \theta, \quad \text{where} \quad I = \begin{pmatrix} 1 & 0 \\ 0 & 1 \end{pmatrix} \quad \text{and} \quad J = \begin{pmatrix} 0 & 1 \\ -1 & 0 \end{pmatrix}.$$

But we saw that the algebra of matrices of this type is the same as the algebra of complex numbers, the matrix J playing the role of $\sqrt{-1}$. Therefore, the matrix O_2 behaves as the rotation factor $e^{i\theta}$. It cannot surprise us, since both $e^{i\theta}$ and O_2, represent in different languages a plane rotation through an angle θ.

As the symmetric matrices are the real case of hermitian, so the orthogonal matrices are real *unitary* matrices. The class of *unitary* matrices is defined as follows:

DEFINITION. A complex square matrix U is an unitary matrix, if $U \cdot \widetilde{U}^* = I$. The characteristic property of orthogonal matrices can be formulated as follows: a scalar product (x, y) of vectors x and y is invariant in a linear transformation the matrix of which is orthogonal. Let this matrix be O. Then, in symbols

$$(Ox, Oy) = (x, y). \tag{16}$$

From point of view of geometry, (16) is self-evident: the linear transformation being a rotation about the origin, lengths and angles are invariant and therefore so are the scalar products which are determined by them. But we give now a purely algebraical proof of (16) because when we will have to generalize it for unitary matrices the geometric intuition will be of no help.

We know that the square of length of a vector z, denoted $|z|^2$, is also equal to the scalar product (z, z) and this scalar square of z, in turn, is obtained by the rule of matrix multiplication as a product of a row-vector $\tilde{z}$ and a column-vector z

$$|z|^2 = (z, z) = \tilde{z} \cdot z.$$

Here—and from now on, in the sequel—we denote a column-vector simply by a letter. When the same vector is considered as a row-vector, we denote it as a *transposed* column-vector.

Let O be an orthogonal matrix and consider the vector Ox obtained from a vector x by a linear transformation with matrix O. We first prove that $|Ox|^2 = |x|^2$:

$$|Ox|^2 = \widetilde{Ox} \cdot Ox = \tilde{x}\widetilde{O}Ox = \tilde{x}Ix = \tilde{x} \cdot x = |x|^2.$$

Now

$$|Ox + Oy|^2 = (Ox + Oy, Ox + Oy) = (Ox, Ox) + 2(Ox, Oy) + (Oy, Oy),$$

as well as

$$|Ox + Oy|^2 = |x + y|^2 = (x + y, x + y) = (x, x) + 2(x, y) + (y, y).$$

But, $(Ox, Ox) = |Ox|^2 = |x|^2 = (x, x)$ and also $(Oy, Oy) = (y, y)$. Thus, comparing two expressions of $|Ox + Oy|^2$, we justify (16).

In the realm of vectors with complex components the definition of scalar product is framed in such a way that the scalar *square* of a complex vector is a *real and positive* number; if vectors x and y have complex components, the scalar product (x, y) is defined by:

$$(x, y) = \tilde{x} \cdot y^* = x_1 y_1^* + x_2 y_2^* + \cdots + x_n y_n^*,$$

the components of the *second* factor y being replaced by their complex conjugates. In particular, if the n components of x are $a_i + b_i \sqrt{-1}$, then

$$|x|^2 = (x, x) = \tilde{x} \cdot x^* = \sum_{i=1}^{n} (a_i^2 + b_i^2) > 0.$$

The positive number $|x|^2$ generalizes the square of length and $|x|$ is called *norm* of the vector x. The scalar product of two real vectors is symmetric: $(x, y) = (y, x)$, but when x and y have complex components, (y, x) is the complex conjugate of (x, y): $(y, x) = (x, y)^*$.

To prove the generalization $(Ux, Uy) = (x, y)$ of (16), where U denotes a unitary matrix, we note that $U \cdot \tilde{U}^* = I$ is equivalent to $U^* \cdot \tilde{U} = I$ since $I^* = I$. Therefore, the transpose $\tilde{U}$ of an unitary matrix is the reciprocal of its complex conjugate U^*, that is, $\tilde{U} = (U^*)^{-1}$. In other words, $\tilde{U} \cdot U^* = I$ is a corollary of the definition.

Now

$$(Ux, Uy) = (\tilde{U}x) \cdot (Uy)^* = \tilde{x} \cdot \tilde{U}U^* \cdot y^* = \tilde{x} \cdot I \cdot y^* = \tilde{x} \cdot y^* = (x, y).$$

Generalizing the concept of orthogonality in a real domain to the complex vectors, we call two complex vectors orthogonal to each other, if their scalar product vanishes. Analyzing the relations $U \cdot \tilde{U}^* = I$ and $\tilde{U}^* \cdot U = I$ in exactly the same way, as it was done for orthogonal matrices, we deduce from the definition of unitary matrices that their row- and column-vector are unit vector, rows are pairwise orthogonal and so are column-vectors. The determinant of a unitary matrix is a complex number. From the definition it follows that $\det |U| \cdot \det |\tilde{U}^*| = |\det |U||^2 = 1$. Thus, all what can be said about $\det |U|$ is that its modulus is equal to one. In other words, $\det |U| = e^{it}$, where t is real and indetermined. The product of unitary matrices U_1, U_2 is unitary: let $U_1 U_2 = N$, then

$$N \cdot \tilde{N}^* = U_1 U_2 \cdot \widetilde{U_1^* U_2^*} = U_1 \cdot U_2 \tilde{U}_2^* \cdot \tilde{U}_1^* = U_1 \cdot I \cdot \tilde{U}_1^* = U_1 \tilde{U}_1^* = I.$$

As an example, we solve the following

PROBLEM: Find the most general unitary matrix of order 2×2.

If U is unitary, so is $e^{it}U$. Indeed, letting $N = e^{it}U$, we have $N \cdot \tilde{N}^* = e^{it}U \cdot e^{-it}\tilde{U}^* = U\tilde{U}^* = I$. Therefore, it is sufficient to find the most general unitary matrix with determinant equal to one. Multiplying it by e^{it}, with an indetermined t, we obtain the solution of the problem. Consider now U $= \begin{pmatrix} a & b \\ c & d \end{pmatrix}$, where the four complex numbers a, b, c, d satisfy the condition $ad - bc = 1$, as a unitary matrix. Then, expressing that the first row and the second column are unit vectors, we have $aa^* + bb^* = 1$ and $bb^* + dd^* = 1$. Multiplying the relation $ab^* + cd^* = 0$ (it expresses that the columns are orthogonal) by bd and replacing dd^* by $1 - bb^*$, we obtain $(ad - bc) bb^* + bc = 0$. But $ad - bc = 1$ and thus $bc = -bb^*$ and $c = -b^*$. Substituting $-b^*$ for c in the relation $ad - bc = 1$ and replacing bb^* by $1 - aa^*$, we obtain $ad = aa^*$, so that $d = a^*$.

Our U is now $\begin{pmatrix} a & b \\ -b^* & a^* \end{pmatrix}$ with $aa^* + bb^* = 1$. Since $|a|^2 + |b|^2 = 1$, we can take $|a|$ and $|b|$ as Cos θ and Sin θ. Nothing more can be said about a and b and therefore $a =$ Cos $\theta \cdot e^{i\alpha}$ and $b =$ Sin $\theta \cdot e^{i\beta}$ with indetermined α and β. The general expression of a unitary matrix of order 2×2 contains four arbitrary parameters t, α, β and θ. The solution itself is

$$e^{it} \cdot \begin{pmatrix} e^{i\alpha} \text{ Cos } \theta & e^{i\beta} \text{ Sin } \theta \\ -e^{-i\beta} \text{ Sin } \theta & e^{-i\alpha} \text{ Cos } \theta \end{pmatrix}.$$

Eigenvalues and Eigenvectors of a Matrix

In a linear transformation $y =$ Ax the vector y, obtained by premultiplying a vector x by the matrix A of the transformation, differs from x not only in length, but also in direction. Are there such particular vectors x for which their transforms y have the *same direction* as x? If such exceptional vectors x can be found, we shall call them *eigenvectors* (or latent, proper, characteristic vectors).

If the vector Ax has the same direction as x, then it is proportional to x and, as such, can be expressed as λx, where the coefficient of proportionality λ is a constant, real if the matrix A and the vector x are both real, but complex in general. Thus, the eigenvectors x are solutions of equation A$x = \lambda x$, or of the equivalent equation

$$(\text{A} - \lambda \text{I}) x = 0. \tag{17}$$

The matricial equation (17) is another way of writing down a system of n homogeneous equations, the n unknowns $x_1, x_2, \ldots, x_n$ of which are the components of the vector x. Denoting the elements of A by a_{ij}, this system is as follows

$$(a_{11} - \lambda) x_1 + a_{12}x_2 + \cdots + a_{1n}x_n = 0$$

$$a_{21}x_1 + (a_{22} - \lambda) x_2 + \cdots + a_{2n}x_n = 0 \qquad (18)$$

$$\cdots \cdots \cdots \cdots \cdots \cdots \cdots \cdots$$

$$a_{n1}x_1 + a_{n2}x_2 + \cdots (a_{nn} - \lambda) x_n = 0$$

If the determinant of the system (18) does not vanish, this system has the trivial solution $x_1 = x_2 = \cdots = x_n = 0$ only.

This determinant det $|A - \lambda I| = D(\lambda)$ is a function of the unknown coefficient of proportionality λ, namely $D(\lambda)$ is a polynomial of nth degree in the variable λ. It becomes clear that to find eigenvectors of matrix A, we must first of all make the determinant $D(\lambda)$ vanish; that is, we must solve the ordinary algebraical equation of nth degree

$$D(\lambda) = \det |A - \lambda I| = 0. \qquad (19)$$

The system has non vanishing solutions only for those values of λ which satisfy equation (19). The roots of this equation are called *eigenvalues* of matrix A (also: latent roots, proper or characteristic values of A).

There are in general n roots of the equation (19) and they are denoted usually $\lambda_1, \lambda_2, \lambda_3, \ldots, \lambda_n$. To each eigenvalue λ_i corresponds an eigenvector $X^{(i)}$ the components of which $x_{1i}, x_{2i}, x_{3i}, \ldots, x_{ni}$ are determined solving the system (18) where the parameter λ was replaced by the number λ_i.

The case of multiple roots of (19) is much more complicated then the case of n simple and distinct eigenvalues $\lambda_i, 1 \leqslant i \leqslant n$. Omitting the study of eigenvectors in the case of multiple eigenvalues, we discuss here the case when $\lambda_i \neq \lambda_j, i \neq j$, only.

In the case when λ_i is a simple root of (19), the rank of the determinant $D(\lambda_i) = \det |A - \lambda_i I|$ is equal to $n - 1$. Therefore, among the n components $x_{1i}, x_{2i}, \ldots, x_{ni}$ of the eigenvector $X^{(i)}$ one is indetermined and the $n - 1$ other components are expressed in the solution as linear functions of the arbitrary component, of say x_{ni}. It is convenient—and is usually done—to choose the arbitrary component in such a way that the eigenvector becomes a *unit vector*.

EXAMPLE. We determine the eigenvalues and eigenvectors of a matrix A of order 3×3 with the elements: $a_{11} = a_{22} = -a_{33} = 2; a_{12} = a_{21} = 0;$

$a_{13} = a_{31} = -3$ and $a_{23} = a_{32} = \sqrt{3}$. Subtracting from its diagonal elements the parameter λ, we obtain the matrix $A - \lambda I$:

$$A - \lambda I = \begin{pmatrix} 2-\lambda & 0 & -3 \\ 0 & 2-\lambda & \sqrt{3} \\ -3 & \sqrt{3} & -2-\lambda \end{pmatrix}.$$

Computing the determinant of this matrix, $D(\lambda)$, we form the third degree equation: $D(\lambda) = -\lambda^3 + 2\lambda^2 + 16\lambda - 32 = 0$. Its three roots are simple and it is easy to check that they are: $\lambda_1 = 4$, $\lambda_2 = 2$ and $\lambda_3 = -4$. The system (18) in this case is as follows:

$$(2 - \lambda) x_1 - 3x_3 = 0, \quad (2 - \lambda) x_2 + x_3 \sqrt{3} = 0,$$

$$-3x_1 + x_2 \sqrt{3} - (2 + \lambda) x_3 = 0.$$

The first eigenvector is obtained for $\lambda = \lambda_1 = 4$ and for it we find two independent (principal) equations, namely $2x_1 + 3x_3 = 0$ and $-2x_2 + x_3 \sqrt{3} = 0$. We take arbitrarily $x_3 = 2$, so that $x_1 = -3$ and $x_2 = \sqrt{3}$. The sum of squares of these components is 16. Thus, to reduce the length of the vector to one unit we divide the components by four. Now the first eigenvector $X^{(1)}$ is a unit vector with components $x_{11} = -\frac{3}{4}$, $x_{21} = \sqrt{3}/4$ and $x_{31} = \frac{1}{2}$. Exactly in the same way we determine the two other vectors which correspond to $\lambda_2 = 2$ and to $\lambda_3 = -4$. The results can be summarized in the following table

Eigenvalue	$\lambda_1 = 4$	$\lambda_2 = 2$	$\lambda_3 = -4$	
Eigenvector	$X^{(1)}$	$X^{(2)}$	$X^{(3)}$	
1st Component	$-\frac{3}{4}$	$\frac{2}{4}$	$\sqrt{3}/4$	
2nd Component	$\sqrt{3}/4$	$2\sqrt{3}/4$	$-\frac{1}{4}$	$= M$
3rd Component	$\frac{2}{4}$	0	$2\sqrt{3}/4$	

The nine components of three eigenvectors form a matrix M of order 3×3. The columns of this matrix, called the *modal* matrix of A, are unit vectors because they are the eigenvectors of the matrix A. But analyzing the structure of M we find that its rows also are unit vectors, they are pairwise orthogonal and so are also columns. Moreover, the determinant of the modal matrix is equal to one. All this suggests that the matrix M is an orthogonal one. Forming the product $M \cdot \tilde{M}$, we obtain indeed I which confirms the suggestion. This fact is due to the symmetry of the matrix A and it is a particular case of the following

THEOREM. *Eigenvalues and eigenvectors of a real and symmetric matrix are real and its modal matrix is an orthogonal one.*

It is sufficient to prove that the eigenvalues are real: then the components of eigenvectors also are real as solutions of the system (18) with real coefficients. In general, the eigenvalues of A involved in the equation $Ax = \lambda x$ may be complex numbers. Taking the complex conjugate of this equation we obtain $Ax^* = \lambda^* x^*$ since A is real: $A^* = A$. Premultiplying the equations $Ax = \lambda x$ and $Ax^* = \lambda^* x^*$ by $\widetilde{x^*}$ and $\tilde{x}$ respectively and then subtracting the second one from the first, a purely numerical result is obtained:

$$\widetilde{x^*} \cdot Ax - \tilde{x} \cdot Ax^* = (\lambda - \lambda^*) \cdot |x|^2. \tag{20}$$

The lefthand member is a pure number because its terms are scalar products of two vectors. On the other hand, considered as a matricial product of three matrices, each of its two terms is a matrix of order 1×1 and therefore it is invariant under the transposition. Take, for instance, the first term $\widetilde{x^*} \cdot Ax$. Its three factors are matrices of orders $1 \times n$, $n \times n$, $n \times 1$. After the transposition it takes the same form as the second term:

$$\widetilde{x^*}Ax = \widetilde{\widetilde{x^*}Ax} = \widetilde{Ax} \cdot x^* = \tilde{x} \cdot \widetilde{A} \cdot x^* = \tilde{x} \cdot Ax^*$$

because $\widetilde{A} = A$, being a symmetric matrix. Thus, in (20) the lefthand member vanishes and therefore $(\lambda - \lambda^*) \cdot |x|^2 = 0$. The second factor $|x|^2$ of this vanishing product cannot vanish because the system (18) has non-trivial solutions. Therefore it is the difference $\lambda - \lambda^*$ which is equal to zero and this means that the eigenvalue λ is a real number.

To prove that the modal matrix of a real and symmetric matrix is orthogonal we first have to prove that its columns, that is the eigenvectors of A, are pairwise orthogonal. Let λ_k and λ_m be two eigenvalues ($\lambda_k \neq \lambda_m$) and $X^{(k)}$, $X^{(m)}$ the corresponding eigenvectors:

$$AX^{(k)} = \lambda_k \cdot X^{(k)} ; \quad AX^{(m)} = \lambda_m \cdot X^{(m)}. \tag{21}$$

Premultiplying the first equation (21) by $\widetilde{X^{(m)}}$ and the second one by $\widetilde{X^{(k)}}$ and subtracting the second from the first ,we construct the relation

$$\widetilde{X^{(m)}}AX^{(k)} - \widetilde{X^{(k)}}AX^{(m)} = \lambda_k\widetilde{X^{(m)}}X^{(k)} - \lambda_m\widetilde{X^{(k)}}X^{(m)} = (\lambda_k - \lambda_m)(X^{(k)}, X^{(m)}) \tag{22}$$

The scalar product $(X^{(k)}, X^{(m)})$ is symmetrical because the eigenvectors of a real symmetric matrix are real: $\widetilde{X^{(m)}} \cdot X^{(k)} = \widetilde{X^{(k)}} \cdot X^{(m)} = (X^{(k)}, X^{(m)})$.

In (22), as in (20), each term of its lefthand member is invariant under the transposition. Transposing one of them, the other is obtained and this proves —as for (20)—that the lefthand member of (22) is equal to zero. Therefore, the product standing in the righthand member vanishes also. Of its two factors the first one, $\lambda_k - \lambda_m$, does not vanish. Therefore, it is the second factor, namely the scalar product $(X^{(k)}, X^{(m)})$ of two columns of the modal matrix which vanishes and this proves the orthogonality of any two columns of the modal matrix.

It remains to prove that this matrix, let us call it M (m_{ij}), is an orthogonal one. Any two columns of M (the jth and the kth, for instance) are orthogonal, and this fact is expressed as follows

$$\sum_{i=1}^{n} m_{ij}m_{ik} = \sum_{i=1}^{n} \tilde{m}_{ji}m_{ik} = \delta_{jk} \qquad (j, k = 1, 2, ..., n). \qquad (23)$$

The equation (23) is nothing else than the rule of matrix multiplication and it gives the elements of the matricial product $\tilde{M} \cdot M$. These elements δ_{jk} are elements of I and therefore $\tilde{M} \cdot M = I$. Thus, M is indeed an orthogonal matrix.

The fact that n eigenvectors of a real symmetric matrix A are pairwise orthogonal and form therefore a system T_n of n mutually perpendicular axes of Cartesian coordinates in an n-dimensional space S_n was proved assuming that n eigenvalues of A are distinct, the equation (19) having *simple* roots only.

It is not difficult to eliminate this assumption. Imagine such a small variation of coefficients in the equation (19) that each of its multiple roots is dissociated into simple roots. Imagine moreover that this variation of coefficients depends on as many variable parameters as many multiple roots of (19) were present, so that for a set of special values of these parameters the variation disappears and the simple roots of (19) which resulted from dissociation of multiple roots recombine again, and *simultaneously*, into multiple roots of (19). Such a variation of the equation (19) naturally is due to a corresponding variation of the elements of A. Let us denote by a'_{ij} the elements modified by the variation, so that A now becomes a new matrix $A' = (a'_{ij})$. The equation (19) formed for A' has simple roots only and the eigenvectors of A' form a cartesian system T_n of n orthogonal axes in S_n. Now we can transform A' back into the original matrix A making the variation disappear *continuously*. During this transformation the system T_n of n mutually perpendicular eigenvectors can only turn in the n-dimensional space S_n because it remains always an orthogonal system. Therefore, its ultimate position in S_n, when the variation vanishes and the variable matrix A' becomes equal to A, is the limit of various positions taken by the solid system T_n during its motion in S_n. Therefore, in this ultimate position the n eigenvectors (this time they are eigenvectors of A) remain mutually orthogonal despite the fact that they belong to a matrix with multiple eigenvalues.

We were able to eliminate the assumption that all n eigenvalues of A are distinct, using the property of eigenvectors to be orthogonal. But this property is due to the symmetry of A as is shown in the following *Example*. That real asymmetric matrices have in general complex eigenvectors and complex eigenvalues, or—if these are real—non-orthogonal eigenvectors is confirmed on the example of matrices $J = \begin{pmatrix} 0 & 1 \\ -1 & 0 \end{pmatrix}$ and $N = \begin{pmatrix} 1 & 4 \\ 1 & 1 \end{pmatrix}$. The eigenvalues of J are $\pm i = \pm \sqrt{-1}$ and the eigenvectors are also complex: the components of $X^{(1)}$ are 1 and $i = \sqrt{-1}$, while those of $X^{(2)}$ are 1 and $-i$. The matrix N has eigenvalues -1 and 3 and its eigenvectors $X^{(1)}$, $X^{(2)}$ have as components $2/\sqrt{5}, -1/\sqrt{5}$ and $2/\sqrt{5}, 1/\sqrt{5}$ respectively. The modal matrix of N is not orthogonal since the scalar product $(X^{(1)}, X^{(2)})$ does not vanish. It is equal to $\frac{3}{5}$ and the eigenvectors form an *acute* angle.

A linear transformation $y = Az$ expresses a relation between vectors y and z. This relation is a geometric one and, as such, it is independent from the choice of system of coordinates. Therefore, the linear transformation which relates z to y, or transforms y into z, does not change when a system of co-ordinates is replaced by another system. But, in symbolizing the linear transformation in question by $y = Az$, where the matrix A is said to represent the linear transformation, we are using a system of coordinates because the equation $y = Az$, when written explicitly, involves the *components* of vectors y and z. To define the components of a vector, we must first fix the choice of coordinates. Moreover, if we change the system of coordinates in which our equation was written, it will change also. Thus, we see that, in general, the representation of a linear transformation by a matrix is always related to a particular system of coordinates. In other words, the same linear transformation can be, and indeed is, represented by many different matrices, when it is considered in as many different systems of coordinates. These matrices should have something in common because they are representations of the same transformation. They do, and for this reason they are grouped together in the concept of *class of similar matrices*:

DEFINITION. Two matrices A and B related by $B = T^{-1}AT$ are similar, provided the matrix T is a regular one ($\det |T| \neq 0$).

All the matrices which belong to a class of similar matrices have in common their eigenvalues, but not their eigenvectors: in general similar matrices have different sets of eigenvectors.

The origin of the concept of similar matrices is the transformation of coordinates in an S_n. Assume that the system $Ox_1x_2 \cdots x_n$ is replaced by a new system $O\xi_1\xi_2 \cdots \xi_n$ and that the two systems are related by the equations of transformation of coordinates

$$x = T\xi \quad \text{and} \quad \xi = T^{-1}x. \tag{24}$$

In (24) x is the radius vector of a point the old coordinates of which are $x_1, x_2, ..., x_n$ while ξ is the same radius vector of the same point in the new system of coordinates $\xi_1, \xi_2, ..., \xi_n$. The matrix T is of necessity a regular matrix and its determinant does not vanish because the transformation of coordinates (24) is reversible.

Consider now the linear transformation expressed in the old system by $y = Az$. The two vectors y and z will be denoted in the new system by η and ζ respectively and therefore $y = T\eta$ and $z = T\zeta$.

In the new system of coordinates the linear transformation is symbolized by $\eta = B\zeta$ and we want to find out how the matrix B, which represents in the new system the same transformation A represents in the old system, is related to A and T. Replacing in $y = Tz$ the vectors y and z by their expressions $y = T\eta$, $z = T\zeta$, we obtain $T\eta = AT\zeta$ and a premultiplication by the reciprocal T^{-1} yields the answer. From $\eta = T^{-1}T\eta = T^{-1}AT\zeta$ we conclude that B is *similar* to A, namely

$$B = T^{-1}AT. \quad (\det |T| \neq 0)$$

We now prove the important

Theorem: *Similar matrices have the same eigenvalues.*

We know that the eigenvalues of $B = T^{-1}AT$ are roots of an algebraical equation $\det |B - \lambda|I = 0$. Replacing in it B by $T^{-1}AT$ and also the unit matrix I by $T^{-1}IT$, we can write this equation as follows

$$\det |T^{-1}AT - \lambda T^{-1}IT| = \det |T^{-1}(A - \lambda I)T| = 0.$$

Since the multiplication rule for determinants is the same as for matrices, the determinant of a matricial product is equal to the product of determinants of factor-matrices. This allows us to write the equation of eigenvalues of B as follows

$$\det |B - \lambda I| = \det |T^{-1}| \cdot \det |A - \lambda I| \cdot \det |T| = \det |A - \lambda I| = 0,$$

Since $\det |T^{-1}| \cdot \det |T| = \det |T^{-1}T| = \det |I| = 1$.

Thus, the eigenvalues of B satisfy the equation for the eigenvalues of A and this proves the theorem. The eigenvectors of B are related to those of A: let u and v denote the eigenvectors of A and B which correspond to the same eigenvalue λ, then $Au = \lambda u$ and $Bv = \lambda v$. The last equation, premultiplied by T, takes the form

$$TBv = TT^{-1} \cdot ATv = A(Tv) = \lambda Tv$$

which proves that the vector Tv is the eigenvector of A corresponding to the eigenvalue λ, that is $Tv = u$ and $v = T^{-1}u$.

Returning to the case of a real symmetric matrix A, we consider the class of matrices similar to A and look for a member of this class which is a *diagonal* matrix. In other words, we want to find a special coordinate system in which the linear transformation represented in our coordinate system by A takes the simplest expression possible. Indeed, if D is a diagonal matrix with elements d_i on the main diagonal and zeros as its off diagonal elements, then the linear transformation $y = Dx$ reduces to n equations $y_i = d_i x_i$, $1 \leqslant i \leqslant n$. In such a case the transformation simply lengthens or shortens each component of x in a certain proportion without rotating it. In short, we will try to diagonalize A.

Diagonalization of a Real Symmetric Matrix

A diagonalization of a matrix—if it is possible—produces a matrix the diagonal elements of which are eigenvalues of the original matrix, provided that we define the meaning of the word diagonalization as above; that is, looking for a diagonal matrix *similar* to the original. Such a matrix of eigenvalues is called *spectral* matrix associated with the original matrix. We have already built an orthogonal matrix associated with a real and symmetric matrix A, namely its *modal* matrix U, the columns of which are eigenvectors of A. We call it U because being orthogonal it belongs to the class of unitary matrices. In our case U is a real matrix. We now compute and compare the elements of two products AU and UL, where L denotes the spectral matrix of A. Therefore L is a diagonal matrix and $L = (\lambda_j \delta_{ij})$. The elements of U are the components x_{ij} of eigenvectors $X^{(j)}$ of A, so that the (i, j)th element of AU, denoted by $(AU)_{ij}$, is given by

$$(AU)_{ij} = \sum_{s=1}^{n} a_{is} x_{sj}.$$

On the other hand, the corresponding element, $(UL)_{ij}$, of the product UL is equal to

$$(UL)_{ij} = \sum_{s=1}^{n} x_{is} \cdot \delta_{sj} \cdot \lambda_j = x_{ij}\lambda_j.$$

Now the components $x_{sj}, 1 \leqslant s \leqslant n$, of the jth eigenvector $X^{(J)}$ satisfy the system (18) which is equivalent to the matricial equation $AX^{(J)} = \lambda_j X^{(J)}$. The ith equation of this system tells us that the expressions of $(AU)_{ij}$ and of $(UL)_{ij}$ are identical because

$$\sum_{s=1}^{n} a_{is}x_{sj} = x_{ij}\lambda_j.$$

Thus, we see that AU = UL. Premultiplying this relation by U^{-1}, we have (25)

$$U^{-1}AU = L \tag{25}$$

Thus, with the aid of the modal matrix U it is possible to diagonalize a real symmetric matrix with the conservation of the set of eigenvalues or—as it is often used to say—of its *spectrum*.

EXAMPLE. Returning to the matrix A of order 3×3 with the eigenvalues 2, 4 and -4

$$A = \begin{pmatrix} 2 & 0 & -3 \\ 0 & 2 & \sqrt{3} \\ -3 & \sqrt{3} & -2 \end{pmatrix},$$

we consider its modal matrix

$$U = \frac{1}{4} \begin{pmatrix} 2 & -3 & \sqrt{3} \\ 2\sqrt{3} & \sqrt{3} & -1 \\ 0 & 2 & 2\sqrt{3} \end{pmatrix}$$

and its reciprocal U^{-1}. This reciprocal is equal to the transpose $\tilde{U}$ of U because the modal matrix of a real symmetric matrix is orthogonal: $U \cdot \tilde{U} = I$, and therefore

$$U^{-1} = \tilde{U} = \frac{1}{4} \begin{pmatrix} 2 & 2\sqrt{3} & 0 \\ -3 & \sqrt{3} & 2 \\ \sqrt{3} & -1 & 2\sqrt{3} \end{pmatrix}.$$

Forming first the product $U^{-1}A$, one finds the matrix

$$\begin{pmatrix} 1 & \sqrt{3} & 0 \\ -3 & \sqrt{3} & 2 \\ -\sqrt{3} & 1 & -2\sqrt{3} \end{pmatrix}.$$

Postmultiplying it by U, the spectral matrix

$$L = \begin{pmatrix} 2 & 0 & 0 \\ 0 & 4 & 0 \\ 0 & 0 & -4 \end{pmatrix}$$

is obtained.

The relation (25) can be used to prove that the eigenvalues of an integral and positive power A^n of A are corresponding powers of eigenvalues of A. Raising both members of (25) to the nth power and noting that $UU^{-1} = I$, one finds

$$(U^{-1}AU)^n = (U^{-1}AU) \cdot (U^{-1}AU) \cdots (U^{-1}AU) = U^{-1}A^nU = L^n = (\lambda_j^n \cdot \delta_{ij})$$

since to raise a diagonal matrix to the nth power it is sufficient to raise to the same power its diagonal elements. The relation $U^{-1}A^nU = L^n$ proves that A^n and L^n are similar matrices. Therefore, the eigenvalues of L^n (which are its diagonal elements because L is a diagonal matrix) are also those of A^n; that is, they are the nth powers of eigenvalues of A. Squaring, for instance, the matrix A in the example above, the matrix

$$A^2 = \begin{pmatrix} 13 & -3\sqrt{3} & 0 \\ -3\sqrt{3} & 7 & 0 \\ 0 & 0 & 16 \end{pmatrix}$$

is obtained. The characteristic equation $D(\lambda) = \det |A^2 - \lambda I| = 0$ is now $(\lambda^2 - 20\lambda + 64)(16 - \lambda) = 0$ and its roots—eigenvalues of A^2—are 4, 16 and 16. They are indeed squares of 2, 4 and -4.

If $\det |A| \neq 0$, then A has a reciprocal matrix A^{-1}. Again the eigenvalues of A^{-1} are reciprocals of those of A. Taking the reciprocals of both members in (25), we have indeed $U^{-1}A^{-1}U = L^{-1}$, which shows that A^{-1} and L^{-1} have same eigenvalues. Here again the elements of L^{-1} are reciprocals λ_j^{-1} of elements of L, so that raising A to an integral negative power also raises its eigenvalues to the same power, provided $\det |A| \neq 0$.

The property of eigenvalues just described was proved for real symmetry matrices only. But it is a general property and to prove it we premultiply the relation $Ax = \lambda x$ by A^{n-1}, where n is a positive integer:

$$A^n x = A^{n-1}(Ax) = \lambda \cdot A^{n-1}x = \lambda A^{n-2}(Ax) = \lambda^2 A^{n-3}(Ax) = \cdots$$

$$= \lambda^{n-1}Ax = \lambda^n x.$$

The result is $A^n x = \lambda^n x$ and it proves that λ^n is an eigenvalue of A^n, if λ is an eigenvalue of A, the eigenvector being the same for A and for A^n. If A is not singular (that is, $\det|A| \neq 0$), then dividing $Ax = \lambda x$ on both sides by λ and premultiplying by A^{-1}, the relation $A^{-1}x = \lambda^{-1}x$ is obtained. Thus, the property we are discussing is extended to the minus first power. Raising A^{-1} to the nth power, $n > 0$, we extend this property to all integral *negative* powers of A.

The property just proved is important because it allows an indirect determination of eigenvalues of many matrices defined as function of a matrix A the eigenvalues of which are known. Let $M = f(A)$ be defined by a polynomial or even by an infinite series the terms of which are powers of A

$$M = f(A) = c_0 I + c_1 A + c_2 A^2 + c_3 A^3 + \cdots + c_m A^m + \cdots = \sum_{m=0}^{\infty} c_m A^m.$$

Premultiplying an eigenvector x of A which corresponds to the eigenvalue λ of A, by the matrix M, using the relation $A^n x = \lambda^n x$ and observing that $f(\lambda) = c_0 + c_1\lambda + c_2\lambda^2 + \cdots + c_m\lambda^m + \cdots$, we have

$$Mx = \sum_0^{\infty} c_m A^m x = \left(\sum_0^{\infty} c_m \lambda^m \right) x = f(\lambda)\, x.$$

Thus, it is seen that the eigenvalues of $M = f(A)$ are $f(\lambda)$; that is, they are the same function of eigenvalues of A, as M is of A.

EXAMPLE. Let t denote a real angle and J the matrix $\begin{pmatrix} 0 & 1 \\ -1 & 0 \end{pmatrix} = J$. The exponential series

$$M = \sum_{n=0}^{\infty} t^n J^n / n! = I + tJ + t^2 J^2/2! + t^3 J^3/3! + \cdots + t^n J^n/n! + \cdots \quad (26)$$

defines the matrix $M = e^{tJ}$. We saw that the eigenvalues of J are $\pm \sqrt{-1} = \pm i$. Therefore, the eigenvalues of M are e^{it} and e^{-it}. We can check it as follows. Squaring the matrix J, we have $J^2 = -I$. Therefore, $J^{2n} = (-1)^n I$, while $J^{2n+1} = (-1)^n J$. Substituting for the powers of J in (26) their values, it is seen that

$$M = I \cdot \sum_0^\infty (-1)^n t^{2n}/(2n)! + J \cdot \sum_0^\infty (-1)^n t^{2n+1}/(2n + 1)!$$

$$= I \cdot \cos t + J \cdot \sin t.$$

Thus, computing M directly, we obtain

$$M = e^{tJ} = \begin{pmatrix} \cos t & 0 \\ 0 & \cos t \end{pmatrix} + \begin{pmatrix} 0 & \sin t \\ -\sin t & 0 \end{pmatrix} = \begin{pmatrix} \cos t & \sin t \\ -\sin t & \cos t \end{pmatrix}.$$

The eigenvalues of M are roots of the quadratic equation

$$D(\lambda) = \begin{vmatrix} \cos t - \lambda & \sin t \\ -\sin t & \cos t - \lambda \end{vmatrix} = \lambda^2 - 2\lambda \cdot \cos t + 1 = 0$$

which agrees with their values e^{it} and e^{-it} obtained above.

The matrix M is orthogonal and the result just obtained, namely the fact that its eigenvalues are rotation-factors (that is, complex numbers of modulus equal to one), $|\lambda_j| = 1$, holds not only for all orthogonal but also for all unitary matrices. To prove this important property of unitary matrices we consider the relation $Ux = \lambda x$, where U denotes a unitary matrix, as well as the complex conjugate equation $U^*x^* = \lambda^*x^*$. Transposing the conjugate relation and then multiplying it member by member by $Ux = \lambda x$, we form the numerical equation

$$\overline{\widetilde{U^*x^*}} \cdot Ux = \widetilde{x^*}\widetilde{U^*} \cdot Ux = \widetilde{x^*} \left(\widetilde{U^*}U \right) x = \widetilde{x^*}Ix = |x|^2 = \lambda^*\widetilde{x^*} \cdot \lambda x$$

$$= \lambda^*\lambda \cdot \widetilde{x^*}x = |\lambda|^2 \cdot |x|^2.$$

From the equation $|x|^2 = |\lambda|^2 \cdot |x|^2$ we conclude $|\lambda|^2 = 1$, so that indeed $|\lambda| = 1$.

Take, for instance, the most general unitary matrix of order 2×2. The equation

$$\begin{vmatrix} e^{i(t+\alpha)} \cdot \cos \theta - \lambda & e^{i(t+\beta)} \cdot \sin \theta \\ -e^{i(t-\beta)} \cdot \sin \theta & e^{i(t-\alpha)} \cdot \cos \theta - \lambda \end{vmatrix} = 0$$

yields its eigenvalues $\lambda_1 = e^{i(t+u)}$ and $\lambda_2 = e^{i(t-u)}$, where the auxiliary angle u is defined by $\cos u = \cos \theta \cdot \cos \alpha$.

We studied integral powers of a matrix, but what about extracting square roots? This question is related to the decomposition of a real matrix R into a product QS of an orthogonal matrix Q and a symmetric matrix S. This decomposition is possible in the general case of any real matrix R.

It is based on special properties of the product $\tilde{R}R = P$. The matrix P is not only a symmetrical one, but also its eigenvalues are, all of them, *positive* numbers. This is important because in the decomposition $R = QS$ the symmetric matrix S is obtained by extracting square root from the matrix P. The eigenvalues of P must be positive since otherwise those of $P^{1/2}$ which are—as we will prove—square roots of eigenvalues of P could not be real numbers, while the symmetric matrix S has real eigenvalues. We begin by studying the matrix $P = \tilde{R} \cdot R$. Its transpose $\tilde{P}$ is equal to $\widetilde{\tilde{R}R}$ $= \tilde{R} \cdot \tilde{\tilde{R}} = \tilde{R} \cdot R = P$ and this proves the symmetry of P. Therefore, the eigenvalues of P are real. To prove that they are positive we observe that from $Px = \lambda x$ we deduce $\tilde{x} \cdot Px = \lambda \tilde{x} \cdot x = \lambda |x|^2$, so that the eigenvalue λ is equal to a fraction $\tilde{x} \cdot Px/|x|^2$ the denominator of which is positive. But, the numerator of this fraction is also a positive number:

$$\tilde{x} \cdot Px = \tilde{x} \cdot \tilde{R}Rx = \tilde{x}\tilde{R} \cdot Rx = \widetilde{Rx} \cdot Rx = |Rx|^2 > 0,$$

which proves that P has positive eigenvalues d_i^2. Denoting the modal matrix of P by U, we have $P = ULU^{-1} = UL\tilde{U}$, where L—the spectral matrix of P—is a diagonal matrix with positive elements: $L = (d_i^2 \cdot \delta_{ij})$. It is easy to extract the square root from L and this square root is the matrix $L^{1/2}$ $= (d_j \cdot \delta_{ij})$, where d_j denotes positive square root $\sqrt{d_j^2}$. We have indeed $(d_j\delta_{ij})^2 = L$ since to multiply diagonal matrices it is sufficient to multiply their corresponding diagonal elements.

Now we can construct a matrix S defining it by $S = U \cdot L^{1/2} \cdot U^{-1}$. The new matrix S is a symmetrical one. We have indeed, using $U^{-1} = \tilde{U}$ (the modal matrix U of a symmetric matrix P is orthogonal)

$$\tilde{S} = \overline{U\widetilde{L^{1/2}}\tilde{U}} = \tilde{U}\widetilde{L^{1/2}}\tilde{U} = UL^{1/2}\tilde{U} = S.$$

The matrix S is the square root from P. To prove this point it is sufficient to show that $S^2 = P$

$$S^2 = UL^{1/2}U^{-1} \cdot UL^{1/2}U^{-1} = UL^{1/2} \cdot I \cdot L^{1/2}U^{-1} = ULU^{-1} = P.$$

The matrices S and $L^{1/2}$ are similar. They have same eigenvalues and this shows that all the eigenvalues of S (which are those of $L^{1/2}$) are positive. The determinant det $|S|$ does not vanish: det $|U| = $ det $|\tilde{U}| = 1$ gives

$$\det |S| = \det |U| \cdot \det |L^{1/2}| \cdot \det |\tilde{U}| = \det |L^{1/2}| = d_1 d_2 d_3 \cdots d_n > 0.$$

Therefore, the matrix S^{-1}, the reciprocal of S, does exist. Postmultiplying R by S^{-1} we can prove that the product $Q = RS^{-1}$ is an orthogonal matrix:

$$\tilde{Q} \cdot Q = \overline{\widetilde{RS^{-1}}} \cdot RS^{-1} = \widetilde{S^{-1}} \cdot \tilde{R}R \cdot S^{-1} = \widetilde{S^{-1}}PS^{-1} = \widetilde{S^{-1}}ULU^{-1} \cdot S^{-1}.$$

Now,

$$S^{-1} = (U \cdot L^{1/2}U^{-1})^{-1} = U \cdot L^{-1/2}U^{-1} = UL^{-1/2}\tilde{U} \text{ and } \widetilde{S^{-1}} = S^{-1}$$

because $\tilde{S} = S$.
Thus,

$$\tilde{Q}Q = (UL^{-1/2}U^{-1}) \cdot (ULU^{-1})(UL^{-1/2}\tilde{U}) = UL^{-1/2}LL^{-1/2}\tilde{U}$$

$$= U\tilde{U} = I.$$

Postmultiplying the relation $RS^{-1} = Q$ by S, we finally prove the decomposition $R = QS$ of a most general real matrix R into a product of an orthogonal and a symmetric matrix.

Since $S = UL^{1/2}\tilde{U}$ the relation $R = QS$ can be written $R = QU \cdot L^{1/2}\tilde{U}$. The product QU of two orthogonal matrices is orthogonal. Indeed, letting $QU = V$ and forming $V\tilde{V}$, we find that $V\tilde{V} = I$:

$$V\tilde{V} = QU \cdot \widetilde{QU} = QU \cdot \tilde{U}\tilde{Q} = Q(U\tilde{U})\,\tilde{Q} = QI\tilde{Q} = Q\tilde{Q} = I.$$

Therefore, $R = VL^{1/2}\tilde{U}$. Premultiplying by $\tilde{V}$ and postmultiplying by U,

$$\tilde{V}RU = L^{1/2}, \tag{27}$$

we prove that any real matrix can be transformed into a diagonal matrix pre- and postmultiplying it by two orthogonal matrices. This transformation does not preserve the eigenvalues: we saw that the elements of $L^{1/2}$ are related to the eigenvalues of $\tilde{R}R$, being their square roots, but they are not eigenvalues of R itself.

From (27) we deduce also the representation of R as a product of three matrices $R = V \cdot L^{1/2}U^{-1}$, two of which, V and U^{-1}, are orthogonal, while $L^{1/2}$ is a diagonal matrix. The geometrical meaning of this representation is as follows: a linear transformation consists in a rotation (U^{-1}), then a stretching or contraction of each component of a vector in different proportions ($L^{1/2}$) which is followed by another rotation (V).

EXAMPLE. To decompose the matrix $R = (r_{ij})$ of order 2×2 given by $r_{11} = 1, r_{12} = 0, r_{21} = \sqrt{3}$ and $r_{22} = -2$, we compute the product $P = \tilde{R}R$

$$P = \begin{pmatrix} 1 & \sqrt{3} \\ 0 & -2 \end{pmatrix}\begin{pmatrix} 1 & 0 \\ \sqrt{3} & -2 \end{pmatrix} = \begin{pmatrix} 4 & -2\sqrt{3} \\ -2\sqrt{3} & 4 \end{pmatrix}$$

and

$$L = \begin{pmatrix} 4 + 2\sqrt{3} & 0 \\ 0 & 4 - 2\sqrt{3} \end{pmatrix}.$$

The eigenvectors of P are $(1, -1)/\sqrt{2}$ and $(1, 1)/\sqrt{2}$, so that the modal matrix is

$$U = \frac{1}{\sqrt{2}} \begin{pmatrix} 1 & 1 \\ -1 & 1 \end{pmatrix} \quad \text{and} \quad U^{-1} = \tilde{U} = \frac{1}{\sqrt{2}} \begin{pmatrix} 1 & -1 \\ 1 & 1 \end{pmatrix}$$

Extracting square roots from $d_1^2 = 4 + 2\sqrt{3}$ and $d_2^2 = 4 - 2\sqrt{3}$, we have $d_1 = \sqrt{3} + 1$ and $d_2 = \sqrt{3} - 1$. Therefore

$$S = UL^{1/2}U^{-1} = \frac{1}{2} \begin{pmatrix} 1 & 1 \\ -1 & 1 \end{pmatrix} \begin{pmatrix} \sqrt{3}+1 & 0 \\ 0 & \sqrt{3}-1 \end{pmatrix} \begin{pmatrix} 1 & -1 \\ 1 & 1 \end{pmatrix} = \begin{pmatrix} \sqrt{3} & -1 \\ -1 & \sqrt{3} \end{pmatrix}$$

and

$$S^{-1} = \frac{1}{2} \begin{pmatrix} \sqrt{3} & 1 \\ 1 & \sqrt{3} \end{pmatrix}.$$

Forming the product $Q = RS^{-1}$, we finally have the decomposition

$$R = \begin{pmatrix} 1 & 0 \\ \sqrt{3} & -2 \end{pmatrix} = QS = \frac{1}{2} \begin{pmatrix} \sqrt{3} & 1 \\ 1 & -\sqrt{3} \end{pmatrix} \cdot \begin{pmatrix} \sqrt{3} & -1 \\ -1 & \sqrt{3} \end{pmatrix}$$

Hermitian Matrices

By definition a complex self-adjoint matrix is called hermitian. Thus, if H is hermitian $H^* = H$. Hermitian matrices generalize real symmetric matrices and share with them many of their properties. We set out to prove the reality of eigenvectors of a H and the unitary character of its modal matrix.

THEOREM. Eigenvalues of a hermitian matrix are *real* and its complex eigenvectors form a *unitary* modal matrix.

Let x and λ denote an eigenvector and the corresponding eigenvalue of a hermitian matrix H. Premultiplying by $\tilde{x}^*$ the relation $Hx = \lambda x$ and then subtracting form it the conjugate equation $H^*x^* = \lambda^*x^*$ premultiplied by $\tilde{x}$, we obtain

$$\tilde{x}^*Hx - \tilde{x}H^*x^* = (\lambda - \lambda^*) \cdot |x|^2. \tag{28}$$

Considering $\tilde{x}H^*x^*$ as a product of three matrices of orders $1 \times n$, $n \times n$ and $n \times 1$ respectively, we conclude that this product is a matrix of order 1×1; that is, a complex *number*. A number is not changed by a transposition. Therefore, transposing $\tilde{x}H^*x^*$ we cannot change its value:

$$\tilde{x}H^*x^* = \overline{\tilde{x}\widetilde{H^*x^*}} = \tilde{x}^*\widetilde{H}^*\tilde{\tilde{x}} = \tilde{x}^*Hx$$

which proves that the lefthand member of (28) vanishes. Thus, its righthand member is equal to zero. Since $|x|^2$ does not vanish we have $\lambda - \lambda^* = 0$ and this proves that λ is a real number.

COROLLARY: The scalar product $(x, Hx) = \tilde{x}H^*x^* = \lambda\tilde{x}x^* = \lambda |x|^2$ is always, for all real or complex vectors x, a real number. In general, if x and y are two complex vectors, interchanging the order of factors in their scalar product (x, y) changes its value: $(y, x) = (x, y)^*$. The fact that (x, Hx) has always a real value entails the relation

$$(x, Hx) = (Hx, x)$$

which is very important in the applications of hermitian matrices. It is a particular case of the general relation

$$(x, Hy) = (Hx, y) \qquad (29)$$

which is often taken as the definition of hermitian matrices. In the proof of (29) we use the definition $\tilde{H}^* = H$ of hermitian matrix in the transposed form $H^* = \tilde{H}$:

$$(x, Hy) = \tilde{x}H^*y^* = \tilde{x}\tilde{H}y^* = \widetilde{Hx} \cdot y^* = (Hx, y).$$

Consider now the scalar product (x_k, x_m), where x_k and x_m are two column-vectors of the modal matrix M of H, that is, two eigenvectors of H. To prove that M is unitary it is sufficient to show that (x_k, x_m) vanishes:

$$(\lambda_k - \lambda_m) \cdot (x_k, x_m) = (\lambda_k x_k, x_m) - (x_k, \lambda_m x_m) = (Hx_k, x_m) - (x_k, Hx_m) = 0,$$

by (29), so that the modal matrix of a hermitian matrix is unitary.

EXAMPLE. Let $H = \begin{pmatrix} 3 & 1+i \\ 1-i & 2 \end{pmatrix}$. To eigenvalues $\lambda_1 = 4$ and $\lambda_2 = 1$ correspond the eigenvectors with complex components $x_1 = (1 + i, 1)/\sqrt{3}$ and $x_2 = (-1, 1 - i)/\sqrt{3}$, and $3 (x_1, x_2) = 3\tilde{x}_1 x_2^* = (1 + i) [(-1) + 1] = 0$.

In diagonalizing a real symmetric matrix with the aid of its modal matrix we proved the relation $AU = UL$, where U and L are modal and spectral matrices of the symmetric matrix A. The same relation exists between a hermitian matrix H, its modal unitary matrix U and the diagonal matrix L the elements of which are eigenvalues of H.

We have, indeed, for H of the example above

$$HU = \begin{pmatrix} 3 & 1+i \\ 1-i & 2 \end{pmatrix} \frac{1}{\sqrt{3}} \begin{pmatrix} 1+i & -1 \\ 1 & 1-i \end{pmatrix} = \frac{1}{\sqrt{3}} \begin{pmatrix} 4+4i & -1 \\ 4 & 1-i \end{pmatrix}$$

$$= \frac{1}{\sqrt{3}} \begin{pmatrix} 1+i & -1 \\ 1 & 1-i \end{pmatrix} \begin{pmatrix} 4 & 0 \\ 0 & 1 \end{pmatrix} = UL$$

and therefore, premultiplying by U^{-1}, $U^{-1}HU = L$.

The proof of $HU = UL$ is the same as for real symmetric matrices: denoting the (i, j)th element of HU and UL by subscripts ij, and the elements of L and U by $\lambda_j \delta_{ij}$ and x_{ij},

$$(HU)_{ij} = \sum_{s=1}^{n} a_{is} x_{sj} = \lambda_j x_{ij} = \sum_{s=1}^{n} x_{is} \lambda_s \delta_{sj} = (UL)_{ij}.$$

From $HU = UL$ we deduce $U^{-1}HU = L$ and $H = ULU^{-1} = UL\widetilde{U}^*$.

Considering now the most general complex matrix G we discuss its decomposition into a product UH of a unitary and a hermitian matrices. This generalisation of the decomposition of a real matrix R into a product of orthogonal and symmetric matrices proceeds in exactly the same way as in the case of real matrices. First we have to prove that the product $\widetilde{G}^*G = P$ is hermitian:

$$\widetilde{P} = \widetilde{\widetilde{G}^*G} = \widetilde{G} \cdot \widetilde{\widetilde{G}}^* = \widetilde{G} \cdot G^* = P^*,$$

so that indeed $\widetilde{P}^* = P$ and P is hermitian. Diagonalizing it with the aid of its modal matrix M and denoting the spectral matrix of P by L

$$L = M^{-1}PM = \widetilde{M}^* \widetilde{G}^* GM = (\lambda_j \delta_{ij}),$$

we can prove that the eigenvalues of the hermitian matrix P are not only real but also positive. Taking the conjugate $P^* x^* = \lambda x^*$ of the relation $Px = \lambda x$ and premultiplying it by $\widetilde{x}$, we have

$$\widetilde{x}P^* x^* = \widetilde{x}(\widetilde{G}^*G)^* x^* = \widetilde{x}\widetilde{G} \cdot G^* x^* = \widetilde{Gx} \cdot (Gx)^* = |Gx|^2 = \lambda x x^* = \lambda |x|^2.$$

Thus, an eigenvalue λ is a fraction both terms of which are positive and in any case non-negative (it may happen that G is a singular matrix and in this case P may have vanishing eigenvalues). Since λ_j are, all of them, positive or zero we will denote them by $d_j^2 = \lambda_j$.

Extracting the square root from the matrix L, we obtain another diagonal matrix $L^{1/2} = (d_j \cdot \delta_{ij})$ with the aid of which we can build the product $H = ML^{1/2}\widetilde{M}^*$. To justify the notation H we now prove the hermitian character of this product:

$$\widetilde{H}^* = \left(\overline{ML^{1/2}\ \widetilde{M}^*}\right)^* = ML^{1/2}\ \widetilde{M}^* = H.$$

It is easily seen that $H = P^{1/2}$:

$$H^2 = ML^{1/2}\ \widetilde{M}^* \cdot ML^{1/2}\ \widetilde{M}^* = ML^{1/2}\left(\widetilde{M}^*M\right)L^{1/2}\ \widetilde{M}^* = ML\widetilde{M}^*$$

$$= P = \widetilde{G}^* \cdot G.$$

Defining now a matrix U by $U = GH^{-1}$, we have to prove that U is unitary:

$$\widetilde{U}^*U = \left(\widetilde{\overline{GH^{-1}}}\right)^* \cdot GH^{-1} = \left(\widetilde{H}^*\right)^{-1} \cdot \left(\widetilde{G}^*G\right) \cdot H^{-1} = H^{-1}H^2H^{-1} = I.$$

From $U = GH^{-1}$ follows the decomposition $G = UH$ of a general complex matrix into a product of a unitary, U, and hermitian, H, matrices. In our proof we used H^{-1}. The existence of a reciprocal to $H = ML^{1/2}\widetilde{M}^*$ follows from $\det |H| \neq 0$ in the general case, when G is not singular and $d_j \neq 0$ for $1 \leqslant j \leqslant n$:

$$\det |H| = \text{Det} |M| \cdot \det |L^{1/2}| \cdot \det \left|\widetilde{M}^*\right| \neq 0$$

since
$$|\det |M|| = |\det |M^*|| = 1 \quad \text{and} \quad \det |L^{1/2}| = d_1 d_2 \cdots d_n \neq 0.$$

If G is singular, the theorem holds, but its proof is different. We omit the discussion of this special case, as we did also for real case.

Using the definition of H by $ML^{1/2}\widetilde{M}^*$, we rewrite the decomposition $G = UH$ as follows: $G = UM \cdot L^{1/2}\widetilde{M}^*$. The product $N = UM$ of unitary matrices is also unitary. Therefore, the relation $G = NL^{1/2}\widetilde{M}^*$ proves that it is possible to find two unitary matrices, here N^{-1} and M, such that premultiplying and postmultiplying G by them, a general complex matrix G is transformed into a diagonal matrix: $N^{-1}GM = L^{1/2}$. As in the real case, the eigenvalues are not preserved in this transformation.

Characteristic Equation of a Matrix

We terminate our study of matrices by the proof of so-called Hamilton-Cayley theorem:

THEOREM. A matrix A of order $n \times n$ satisfies the matricial equation of nth degree $f(A) = \emptyset$, where $f(\lambda) = \det |A - \lambda I|$ is the characteristic polynomial of A the roots of which are eigenvalues of A.

The symbol $\emptyset$ denotes the zero matrix and the equation $f(A) = \emptyset$ expresses that all the elements of the matrix $f(A)$ vanish. We give first the proof for the case when all n roots of the equation $f(\lambda) = 0$ are distinct; that is, $\lambda_i \neq \lambda_j$, if $i \neq j$. The result holds for multiple roots also and it can be proved applying the same reasoning which was used to eliminate the assumption of distinct roots in the discussion of orthogonality of eigenvectors of a real symmetric matrix. A second, more complicated, proof is a general one in the sense that it is independent from the assumption of distinct roots.

FIRST PROOF. Denoting as usual the n distinct roots of the equation $f(\lambda) = 0$ by λ_j, $1 \leqslant j \leqslant n$, so that $f(\lambda_j) = 0$, we have n relations

$$Ax_j = \lambda_j x_j, \qquad\qquad (1 \leqslant j \leqslant n)$$

where x_j are the eigenvectors of the matrix A. These eigenvectors form a set of n independent vectors. They belong to an n-dimensional space S_n and an arbitrary vector y of this space can be expressed as a linear combination

$$y = \sum_{j=1}^{n} c_j x_j$$

of eigenvectors x_j because the set of $n+1$ vectors $x_1, x_2, \ldots, x_n, y$ in an n-dimensional space S_n cannot be a set of independent vectors (Chapter 10).

Writing the polynomial $f(\lambda)$ explicitly as $f(\lambda) = \det |\lambda I - A| = \lambda^n + a_1 \lambda^{n-1} + \cdots + a_{n-1}\lambda + a_n$, we form the matrix

$$M = f(A) = A^n + a_1 A^{n-1} + a_2 A^{n-2} + \cdots + a_{n-1}A + a_n I$$

and premultiply by M an *arbitrary* vector y:

$$My = M\left(\sum_{j=1}^{n} c_j x_j\right) = \sum_{j=1}^{n} c_j \cdot Mx_j.$$

Now the matrix M is a sum of matrices of the type $a_k A^{n-k}$, $k = 0, 1, \ldots, n$, and therefore $Mx_j = \sum_{k=0}^{n} a_k A^{n-k} x_j$, where $a_0 = 1$. But we saw already that $A^m x_j = \lambda^m x_j$ and this proves that

$$Mx_j = \sum_{k=0}^{n} a_k \lambda^{n-k} \cdot x_j = x_j \cdot \sum_{k=0}^{n} a_k \lambda^{n-k} = x_j \cdot f(\lambda_j) = x_j \cdot 0 = 0,$$

since $f(\lambda_j) = 0$ by definition of λ_j. Thus, it is seen that $My = 0$.

A matrix which annihilates *all the vectors* has all its elements equal to zero. Such is the case of M because it was shown that $My = 0$ for any vector y.

EXAMPLE. The matrix A of order 3×3 and its powers A^2 and A^3 given by

$$A = \begin{pmatrix} -2 & 2 & -3 \\ 2 & 1 & -6 \\ -1 & -2 & 0 \end{pmatrix}; \quad A^2 = \begin{pmatrix} 11 & 4 & -6 \\ 4 & 17 & -12 \\ -2 & -4 & 15 \end{pmatrix}; \quad A^3 = \begin{pmatrix} -8 & 38 & -57 \\ 38 & 49 & -114 \\ -19 & -38 & 30 \end{pmatrix}$$

satisfy the characteristic equation

$$f(A) = A^3 + A^2 - 21A - 45I = 0$$

which is obtained expanding the determinant

$$f(\lambda) = \det |\lambda I - A| = \begin{pmatrix} -2-\lambda & 2 & -3 \\ 2 & 1-\lambda & -6 \\ -1 & -2 & -\lambda \end{pmatrix} = \lambda^3 + \lambda^2 - 21\lambda - 45.$$

The proof just discussed is based on the independence of n eigenvectors of a matrix with distinct eigenvalues. It is short because the proof of this independence was not included. For a hermitian or real symmetric matrix the fact that their eigenvectors are independent is self-evident because they are orthogonal (Chapter 10). We add now a proof which holds for any complex matrix A.

THEOREM. If all the eigenvalues of a matrix A are distinct, its eigenvectors from a set of independent vectors.

Assuming they are dependent, we postulate the existence of n constants c_k such that firstly not all of them vanish, $\sum_1^n |c_2^2|^2 > 0$, and secondly

$$c_1 X_1 + c_2 X_2 + \cdots + c_n X_n = 0, \qquad \left(\sum_1^n |c^k|^2 > 0 \right) \tag{30}$$

where X_j is the jth eigenvector of A, its components being x_{ij}, $1 \leqslant i \leqslant n$.
Premultiplying (30) by A, A^2, ..., A^{n-1}, $n-1$ more relations are obtained:

$$\sum_{k=1}^n \lambda_k^s \cdot c_k X_k = \lambda_1^s \cdot c_1 X_1 + \lambda_2^s \cdot c_2 X_2 + \cdots + \lambda_n^s \cdot c_n X_n = 0 \quad (0 \leqslant s \leqslant n-1) \tag{31}$$

The system (31) of n *vectorial relations* is equivalent to n numerical systems, one for each determined component of vectors X_k. Taking, for instance, the system for the jth component, $(0 \leqslant s \leqslant n - 1)$:

$$\sum_{k=1}^n \lambda_k^s \cdot c_k x_{jk} = \lambda_1^s \cdot c_1 x_{j1} + \lambda_2^s \cdot c_2 x_{j2} + \cdots + \lambda_n^s \cdot c_n x_{jn} = 0, \tag{32}$$

and considering it as a system of n homogeneous equations for n unknowns $z_k = c_k x_{jk}$ with coefficients λ_k^s, we set out to prove that (32) has a non-trivial solution for at least one special value of j. We have indeed

$$\sum_{j=1}^n \sum_{k=1}^n |c_k|^2 \cdot |x_{jk}|^2 = \sum_{k=1}^n |c_k|^2 \cdot |X_k|^2 = \sum_{k=1}^n |c_k|^2 > 0,$$

the eigenvectors X_k being, as usual, unit vectors. This proves that not all the products $c_k x_{jk}$ vanish and therefore for some j we obtain a non-trivial solution of the homogeneous system (32) *as a corollary of our assumption* (30).

Now it is relatively easy to prove that the determinant of coefficients of the system (32) does not vanish and therefore this system *cannot* have non-trivial solutions. The contradiction thus deduced proves the falsity of our assumption (30) and the fact that eigenvectors are independent is established.

It remains to show that the determinant of (32) is not zero and it is here that the condition of distinct roots of characteristic equation plays its decisive role. The determinant in question is as follows

$$D = \begin{vmatrix} 1 & 1 & \ldots\ldots & 1 \\ \lambda_1 & \lambda_2 & \ldots\ldots & \lambda_n \\ \lambda_1^2 & \lambda_2^2 & \ldots\ldots & \lambda_n^2 \\ \cdot\cdot\cdot\cdot\cdot\cdot\cdot\cdot\cdot\cdot\cdot\cdot\cdot\cdot\cdot \\ \lambda_1^{n-1} & \lambda_2^{n-1} & \ldots\ldots & \lambda_n^{n-1} \end{vmatrix}$$

Expanding it, we find out that it is equal to the product of all $\frac{1}{2}n(n-1)$ differences $\lambda_j - \lambda_i$ for $1 \leqslant i < j \leqslant n$

$$D = \prod_{j=2}^{n} \prod_{i=1}^{j-1} (\lambda_j - \lambda_i)$$

It is obvious that D does not vanish when all n eigenvalues are distinct, while in the case of multiple eigenvalues $D = 0$.

The Hamilton-Cayley theorem has many various applications. One of them is the computation of the reciprocal matrix A^{-1}, provided A is not singular. The coefficient a_n of the last term in the Hamilton-Cayley equation

$$f(A) = A^n + a_1 A^{n-1} + \cdots + a_{n-1}A + a_n I = 0 \tag{33}$$

is equal to $(-1)^n \cdot \det |A|$. Therefore a_n does not vanish, if A is not singular. Premultiplying (33) by $a_n^{-1} \cdot A^{-1}$, we obtain the following expression for A^{-1}:

$$A^{-1} = -(A^{n-1} + a_1 A^{n-2} + \cdots + a_{n-2}A + a_{n-1}I)/a_n.$$

Thus, in the case of the matrix A in our example

$$A^{-1} = (A^2 + A - 21I)/45 = \frac{-1}{15}\begin{pmatrix} 4 & -2 & 3 \\ -2 & 1 & 6 \\ 1 & 2 & 2 \end{pmatrix}$$

and this agrees well with the result of a direct computation of A^{-1}.

With the aid of (33) a matrix M depending on A and expressed in terms of A by an infinite series

$$M = F(A) = c_0 I + c_1 A + c_2 A^2 + \cdots + c_m A^m + \cdots = \sum_0^\infty c_m A^m,$$

or by a polynomial in A of degree greater than $n-1$, can be reduced to a polynomial in A of degree $n-1$, provided A is of order $n \times n$.

Take, as an example, $M = A^5 - 4A^4 + 3A^3 - A^2 + 7A - I$, where $A = I + J$, that is $A = \begin{pmatrix} 1 & 1 \\ -1 & 1 \end{pmatrix}$. The order of A is 2×2, so that the characteristic equation of A is of second degree. We have $A^2 = I^2 + J^2 + 2IJ = 2J$ for $J^2 = -I^2 = -I$. Thus, $I^2 + J^2 = \emptyset$ and $A^2 = 2J = 2(A - I)$. Computing A^3, A^4, A^5 with the aid of the characteristic equation $A^2 = 2A - 2I$, one finds that $A^3 = 2A - 4I$, $A^4 = -4I$ and $A^5 = -4A$. Now the definition of M is simplified to $M = 7A + 5I$, so that $M = \begin{pmatrix} 12 & 7 \\ -7 & 12 \end{pmatrix}$.

Now here is the second proof of the Hamilton-Cayley theorem.

SECOND PROOF. The elements of A^{-1}, provided $\det |A| = D \neq 0$, are defined by $(A^{-1})_{ij} = F_{ji}/D$, where F_{ji} denotes the cofactor of the element a_{ji} of D. The matrix (F_{ji}) is called *associate* to A. Denoting it by $\mathscr{A}$, we have $\mathscr{A} = A^{-1} \cdot \det |A|$, if A^{-1} exists. But the associate matrix $\mathscr{A}$ does exist even when $\det |A| = 0$ and there is no reciprocal A^{-1}. The relation $A \cdot \mathscr{A} = I \cdot \det |A|$ is a corollary of the definition of $\mathscr{A}$, if $\det |A| \neq 0$ and A^{-1} does exist. But this relation still holds when $\det |A|$ vanishes: the product $A \cdot \mathscr{A}$ is a diagonal matrix the diagonal elements of which are equal to $\det |A|$ and therefore $A \cdot \mathscr{A} = \emptyset$, if $\det |A| = 0$, which shows that $A \cdot \mathscr{A}$ is always equal to $I \cdot \det |A|$.

Consider now the matrix $\mathscr{M}$ associate to the matrix $M(\lambda) = \lambda I - A$. The elements of $\mathscr{M}$ are cofactors of those in the *transposed* determinant $\det |\lambda I - A|$ and therefore they are polynomials in λ of degree at most equal to $n-1$. We denote them by M_{ij}.

Let us denote by E_{ij} the matrix which has only one non-vanishing element located in the ith row and jth column, all other $n^2 - 1$ elements being equal to zero. The element in the ith row and jth column by definition of E_{ij} is equal to one. With the aid of matrices E_{ij} any matrix $A = (a_{ij})$ can be represented as a sum of n^2 matrices $a_{ij}E_{ij}$:

$$A = (a_{ij}) = \sum_{i=1}^{n} \sum_{j=1}^{n} a_{ij}E_{ij} \quad \text{and, in particular,} \quad \mathscr{M} = \sum_{i=1}^{n} \sum_{j=1}^{n} M_{ij}(\lambda) \cdot E_{ij}.$$

But each $M_{ij}(\lambda)$ is a polynomial in the variable λ the coefficients of which are pure numbers. Performing the double summation in the expression of $\mathscr{M}$ in terms of matrices E_{ij}, we obtain

$$\mathscr{M}(\lambda) = M_{n-1} \cdot \lambda^{n-1} + M_{n-2} \cdot \lambda^{n-2} + \cdots + M_1\lambda + M_0,$$

where the coefficients M_k of powers λ^k are matrices with numerical elements. These matrices, therefore, do not contain the variable λ. They could be defined as follows: $M_0 = \mathscr{M}(0)$ and then by recurrence formula

$$M_{k+1} = \lim_{\lambda=0} \left[\mathscr{M}(\lambda) - \sum_{i=0}^{k} M_i \cdot \lambda^i \right] \Big/ \lambda^{k+1} \qquad (0 \leqslant k \leqslant n - 2)$$

Since $\det |\lambda I - A| = \det |M(\lambda)| = f(\lambda)$, the relation between $M(\lambda)$ and its associate matrix $\mathscr{M}(\lambda)$ is

$$M \cdot \mathscr{M} = f(\lambda) \cdot I = I \cdot \sum_{k=0}^{n} c_k \lambda^k \qquad (c_n = 1) \qquad (34)$$

But $M = \lambda I - A$ and $\mathscr{M} = \sum_{0}^{n-1} M_k \cdot \lambda^k$, so that (34) becomes

$$\sum_{0}^{n-1} M_k \cdot \lambda^{k+1} - \sum_{0}^{n-1} A M_k \cdot \lambda^k = \sum_{0}^{n} c_k I \cdot \lambda^k. \qquad (35)$$

Two identically equal polynomials have the same coefficients. Thus, $n + 1$ matricial identities are obtained comparing the coefficients of like powers of λ in both members of (35);

$$M_{k-1} - A M_k \equiv c_k I \qquad (0 \leqslant k \leqslant n) \qquad (36)$$

Naturally, in (36) M_{-1} and M_n must be replaced by zero matrix $\emptyset$.

Premultiplying (36) by A^k and summing up in k from $k = 0$ to $k = n$, the lefthand members cancel, all of them, while the sum of righthand members gives the matrix $f(A)$. The result is the characteristic equation

$$f(A) = \emptyset$$

and the theorem is proved without any limitation imposed on the nature of the matrix A.

Medians and Altitudes
of Non-Euclidean Triangles

THEOREM I. Three medians of a Non-Euclidean, spherical or hyperbolic, triangle are concurrent straight lines.

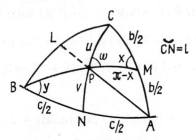

Fig. 1

PROOF. (a) *Spherical triangle.* Applying the sine law to triangles BPN, CPM and AMB (Fig. 1), the following three relations are obtained:

$$\text{Sin} \, (v/\text{R}) \, \text{Sin} \, \omega = \text{Sin} \, y \cdot \text{Sin} \, (c/2\text{R}) \qquad (1)$$

$$\text{Sin} \, (u/\text{R}) \, \text{Sin} \, \omega = \text{Sin} \, x \cdot \text{Sin} \, (b/2\text{R}) \qquad (2)$$

$$\text{Sin} \, x \, \text{Sin} \, (b/2\text{R}) = \text{Sin} \, y \cdot \text{Sin} \, (c/\text{R}) \qquad (3)$$

where $u = \overset{\frown}{\text{PC}}$, $v = \overset{\frown}{\text{PN}}$, $\omega = \overset{\frown}{\text{CPM}}$, $x = \overset{\frown}{\text{PMC}}$, $y = \overset{\frown}{\text{PBA}}$, $b = \overset{\frown}{\text{AC}}$, $c = \overset{\frown}{\text{AB}}$, the points L, M, N being the midpoints of the sides $\overset{\frown}{\text{BC}}$, $\overset{\frown}{\text{CA}}$, $\overset{\frown}{\text{AB}}$ respectively.

Multiplying both members of the first relation by $2 \, \text{Cos} \, (c/2\text{R})$, we rewrite it as follows

$$2 \, \text{Cos} \, (c/2\text{R}) \, \text{Sin} \, (v/\text{R}) \, \text{Sin} \, \omega = \text{Sin} \, y \cdot \text{Sin} \, (c/\text{R}) \qquad (4)$$

since $2 \, \text{Sin} \, t \cdot \text{Cos} \, t = \text{Sin} \, (2t)$. On the other hand, comparing (2) and (3), we have

$$\text{Sin} \, y \cdot \text{Sin} \, (c/\text{R}) = \text{Sin} \, (u/\text{R}) \, \text{Sin} \, \omega \qquad (5)$$

Denoting the length of the median $\overset{\frown}{CN}$ by l, we have $v = l - u$, so that

$$\text{Sin}(v/R) = \text{Sin}(l/R - u/R) = \text{Sin}(l/R)\,\text{Cos}(u/R) - \text{Cos}(l/R)\,\text{Sin}(u/R). \quad (6)$$

Thus, comparing (4) and (5) and dividing both members of the resulting relation $2\text{Cos}(c/2R)\,\text{Sin}(v/R)\,\text{Sin}\,\omega = \text{Sin}(u/R) \cdot \text{Sin}\,\omega$ by their common factor, $\text{Sin}\,\omega$, we obtain

$$\text{Sin}(u/R) = 2\text{Cos}(c/2R)\,\text{Sin}(v/R) \qquad\qquad (7)$$

Replacing in the righthand member of (7) $\text{Sin}(v/R)$ by the expression (6), we finally form the following trigonometric equation for the unknown distance $\overset{\frown}{PC} = u$, where the point P on the median $\overset{\frown}{CN}$ is defined as the intersection-point of this median with another median $\overset{\frown}{MB}$:

$$2\text{Cos}(c/2R)\,[\text{Sin}(l/R)\,\text{Cos}(u/R) - \text{Cos}(l/R)\,\text{Sin}(u/R)] = \text{Sin}(u/R).$$

Dividing through by $\text{Cos}(u/R)$ and solving for $\text{Tan}(u/R)$, we obtain

$$\text{Tan}(u/R) = 2\text{Sin}(l/R)\,\text{Cos}(c/2R)/[1 + 2\text{Cos}(l/R)\,\text{Cos}(c/2R)]$$

and therefore

$$u = R \cdot \text{Arctan}\,\{2\text{Sin}(l/R)/[\text{Sec}(c/2R) + 2\text{Cos}(l/R)\} \qquad (8)$$

Since the expression (8) of the distance $\overset{\frown}{PC} = u$ depends only on the length l of the median $\overset{\frown}{CN}$ and the side c, the location of P does not vary when the second median $\overset{\frown}{BM}$ is replaced by $\overset{\frown}{AL}$ and this proves Theorem I.

(b) *Hyperbolic triangle.* As we know the sine law also holds in hyperbolic geometry, replacing the radius R of the sphere by the characteristic constant k and the trigonometric functions by hyperbolic ones. Therefore, for a triangle in Lobatchevsky's plane we obtain the following result

$$u = k \cdot \text{Argtanhyp}\,\{2\text{Sh}(l/k)/[\text{Sech}(c/2k) + 2\text{Ch}(l/k)]\} \qquad (9)$$

which again proves Theorem I since u does not vary when $\overset{\frown}{BM}$ is replaced by $\overset{\frown}{AL}$.

When R or k become infinite, the spherical or hyperbolic geometry degenerates into Euclidean geometry. It is interesting to verify that at the limit for $R = \infty$ and $k = \infty$, the formulas (8) and (9) give $u = 2l/3$ as it must be in the Euclidean case. Since the triangle remains finite the arguments $c/2R$, $c/2k$, l/R and l/k vanish at the limit and the functions secant, cosine, hyperbolic secant, and hyperbolic cosine must be replaced by 1 since Sec 0

$= \mathrm{Cos}\, 0 = \mathrm{Sech}\, 0 = \mathrm{Ch}\, 0 = 1$; the denominators of the arguments of Arc-tan and Argtanhyp being equal to $1 + 2 = 3$. On the other hand, Sin x, tan x, Sh x and Tanh x can be replaced by x for $x \to 0$. Therefore, the right-hand member in (8) for $R \to \infty$ is approximately equal to $R \cdot \mathrm{Arctan}\,(2l/3R)$ and thus its limit is $2l/3$ since $\lim_{z=0} \mathrm{Arctan}\, z/z = 1$. The same conclusion holds for (9).

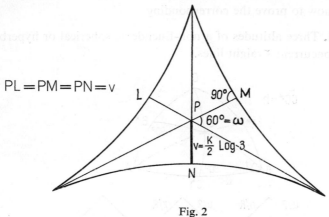

PL = PM = PN = v

$90°$ M

P

$60° = \omega$

$v = \frac{K}{2}\, \mathrm{Log}\, 3$

N

Fig. 2

We deduce from Theorem I an interesting corollary which yields the interpretation of the characteristic length k. We know that three mutually parallel lines form the largest hyperbolic triangle whose area is finite, namely, equal to πk^2; the sides are infinite and the angles equal to zero. This largest triangle is equilateral and its three medians form at their common intersection-point P (Fig. 2) six equal angles of 60°, so that $\omega = 60°$. By reason of symmetry the medians are at the same time perpendicular bisectors of sides and altitudes, so that $x = 90°$. Therefore, equation (3), which in the hyperbolic case takes the form Sh $(b/2k) \cdot$ Sin $x =$ Sin $y \cdot$ Sh (c/k), for an equilateral triangle with finite $a = b = c$, becomes $(x = 90°)$

$$1 = 2 \cdot \mathrm{Sin}\, y \cdot \mathrm{Ch}\,(c/2k) \qquad (10)$$

since Sh $(c/k)/$Sh $(c/2k) = 2$ Ch $(c/2k)$.

On the other hand, the relation (1) (that is, Sh (v/k) Sin $\omega =$ Sin y $\times$ Sh $(c/2k)$), for an equilateral triangle becomes (Sin $\omega =$ Sin 60° $= \sqrt{3}/2$)

$$\sqrt{3} \cdot \mathrm{Sh}\,(v/k) = 2 \cdot \mathrm{Sin}\, y \cdot \mathrm{Ch}\,(c/2k) \cdot \mathrm{Tanh}\,(c/2k) = \mathrm{Tanh}\,(c/2k). \quad (11)$$

The relation (11) holds for any equilateral hyperbolic triangle. Applied to the largest triangle with $c = \infty$, it gives $\sqrt{3} \cdot$ Sh $(v/k) = 1$ since Tanh $\infty = 1$.

Now, $Ch\,(v/k) = [1 + Sh^2\,(v/k)]^{1/2} = (1 + \tfrac{1}{3})^{1/2} = 2/\sqrt{3}$, so that

$$e^{v/k} = Ch(v/k) + Sh(v/k) = 2/\sqrt{3} + 1/\sqrt{3} = 3/\sqrt{3} = \sqrt{3}\,.$$

Taking the logarithms, we obtain $v/k = \tfrac{1}{2}\mathrm{Log}\,3$ and, therefore, $k = 2v/\mathrm{Log}\,3$, where the segment v denotes the distance of the point P from a side: $v = NP$.

The altitudes are concurrent in the spherical and hyperbolic triangles, too, and we wish now to prove the corresponding

THEOREM II. Three altitudes of a non-Euclidean, spherical or hyperbolic, triangle are concurrent straight lines.

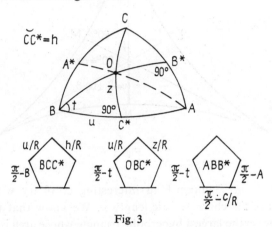

Fig. 3

The proof is based on the relations in a right triangle.

(a) *Spherical triangle.* Let us consider the two altitudes $\overset{\frown}{BB^*} \perp \overset{\frown}{AC}$ and $\overset{\frown}{CC^*} \perp \overset{\frown}{AB}$. Denoting their intersection-point by O (Fig. 3), we wish to evaluate the distance $\overset{\frown}{OC^*}$ of this point from the side $\overset{\frown}{AB} = C$. Considering the three right triangles BCC*, OBC* and ABB*, we introduce the following notations: $\overset{\frown}{OBC^*} = t$, $\overset{\frown}{BC^*} = u$, $\overset{\frown}{CC^*} = h$, $\overset{\frown}{OC^*} = z$ and apply Napier's pentagons (Fig. 3). Thus, we obtain the three relations

$$\mathrm{Sin}\,(u/R) = \mathrm{Tan}\,(h/R) \cdot \mathrm{Cotan}\,B \tag{12}$$

$$\mathrm{Sin}\,(u/R) = \mathrm{Tan}\,(z/R) \cdot \mathrm{Cotan}\,t \tag{13}$$

$$\mathrm{Cos}\,(c/R) = \mathrm{Cotan}\,A \cdot \mathrm{Cotan}\,t \tag{14}$$

Eliminating $\mathrm{Sin}\,(u/R)$ and $\mathrm{Cotan}\,t$ between them, we find

$$\mathrm{Tan}\,(z/R) = \mathrm{Tan}\,(h/R)\,\mathrm{Cotan}\,A \cdot \mathrm{Cotan}\,B \cdot \mathrm{Sec}\,(c/R). \tag{15}$$

The expression of the $\mathrm{Tan}\,(z/R)$ depends on the length h of the altitude $\widehat{CC^*}$, on the side $c = \widehat{AB}$ and on the two angles A and B. These two angles play different roles in the definition of the point O: the second altitude $\widehat{BB^*}$, whose intersection with the altitude $\widehat{CC^*}$ defines the point O, passes through the vertex B of the angle B. Nevertheless, the angles A and B play the same role in the righthand member of the expression (15). Therefore, if we define the intersection-point O' of the altitude $\widehat{CC^*}$ with that $\widehat{AA^*}$ and denote its distance $\widehat{O'C^*}$ from the side $\widehat{AB}$ by z', we will find for the tangent $\mathrm{Tan}(z'/R)$ the same expression (15) as for $\mathrm{Tan}\,(z/R)$. This proves the theorem because $z = z'$, if $\mathrm{Tan}\,(z/R) = \mathrm{Tan}\,(z'/R)$, both z/R and z'/R being two positive angles not exceeding $180°$.

(b) *Hyperbolic triangle*. The same reasoning yields a similar result this time also:

$$\mathrm{Tanh}\,(z/k) = \mathrm{Tanh}\,(h/k) \cdot \mathrm{Cotan}\,A \cdot \mathrm{Cotan}\,B \cdot \mathrm{Sech}\,(c/k) \qquad (16)$$

To check this result we observe that for the largest triangle we must have $z = v = k\,\mathrm{Log}\,3^{1/2}$, so that $\mathrm{Tanh}\,(z/k) = \mathrm{Tanh}\,(v/k) = \mathrm{Sh}\,(v/k)/\mathrm{Ch}\,(v/k) = \frac{1}{2}$. And we find, indeed, that for $a = b = c \to \infty$ at the limit $\mathrm{Tanh}\,(z/k) = \frac{1}{2}$. Applying to an equilateral triangle formula (10), we observe that by reason of symmetry the angle y is equal to $\frac{1}{2}B$; thus $A = B = C$ and we have $\mathrm{Sin}\,\frac{1}{2}A = \mathrm{Sin}\,\frac{1}{2}B = \frac{1}{2}\,\mathrm{Sech}\,(c/2k)$. When $a = b = c \to \infty$, the angles $A = B = C$ tend to zero and therefore $\mathrm{Cotan}\,A = \mathrm{Cotan}\,B = (1 + e)/A$, $\lim\,(e) = 0$. Now $\frac{1}{2}A = \mathrm{Sin}\,\frac{1}{2}A \cdot (1 + e') = \frac{1}{2}\,\mathrm{Sech}\,(c/2k) \cdot (1 + e')$ and, thus, the reciprocal $1/A$ is equal to $\mathrm{Ch}\,(c/2k) \cdot (1 + e'')$ with $\lim\,(e'') = 0$. Therefore, the product $\mathrm{Cotan}\,A \cdot \mathrm{Cotan}\,B = (\mathrm{Cotan}\,A)^2$ can be expressed as $(1 + e)^2/A^2 = \mathrm{Ch}^2\,(c/2k) \cdot (1 + g)$ with $\lim g = 0$. This discussion leads us to the following expression of $\mathrm{Tanh}\,(z/k)$ for an equilateral triangle increasing without limit:

$$\mathrm{Tanh}\,(z/k) = \mathrm{Tanh}\,(h/k) \cdot \mathrm{Ch}^2\,(c/2k)\,(1 + g)/\mathrm{Ch}\,(c/k).$$

Now, when c becomes infinite, the length h of the altitude is also infinite, so that $\lim\,[\mathrm{Tanh}\,(h/k)] = \mathrm{Tanh}\,(\infty) = 1$. On the other hand, $\lim_{x=\infty}\,[\mathrm{Ch}^2\,(x/2)/\mathrm{Ch}\,x] = \frac{1}{2}$. Therefore, passing to the limit for $c/k = \infty$, we obtain

$$\lim_{c=\infty}\,\mathrm{Tanh}\,(z/k) = \tfrac{1}{2}.$$

APPENDIX 8 (CHAPTER 17)

Angle of Parallelism

We wish to deduce in this appendix Lobachevsky's formula for the angle of parallelism A which in hyperbolic geometry is a function of the distance OP $= x$ between the point P through which passes the line PC parallel to OD, and the line OD (Fig. 1). The angle A $= \overset{\frown}{OPC}$ might be represented by

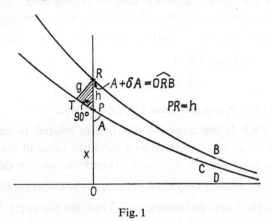

Fig. 1

$f(x)$, where f is the symbol of an unknown function of the variable distance OP $= x$. To find this unknown function $f(x)$ we use calculus; therefore the proof of the formula

$$\text{Tan} (\tfrac{1}{2}A) = e^{-x/k} \qquad (1)$$

given in this appendix is aimed at readers who have studied calculus.

In our proof we use the expression of the area of a triangle, and also the theorem which states that two straight lines parallel in the same direction to a third line are parallel to each other. Considering a point R at an infinitesimal small distance PR $= h$ above P on the straight line OP perpendicular to OD at O, we draw through R a perpendicular RT to the straight line PC as well as the line RB parallel to OD and, therefore, parallel also to PC.

If this line RB is considered as parallel to OD, the angle $\overset{\frown}{ORB}$ it makes with the line OR is equal to $f(x + h)$. On the other hand, the same line RB is a parallel to PC and, therefore, the angle $\overset{\frown}{TRB}$ it makes with the perpendicular TR to PC is equal to $f(g)$, where $g =$ TR is a leg of the infinitesimal small right triangle PRT with the hypotenuse PR $= h$ and the acute angle A opposite the leg TR $= g \approx h \cdot$ Sin A with a negligible error w which vanishes together with h. Thus, we can write TR $= g = h \cdot$ Sin A $\cdot (1 + w)$, where $\lim_{h=0} w = 0$.

Computing the area of the triangle PRT, we have K $(180° - 90° - A - \overset{\frown}{TRP})$, where K is a coefficient of proportionality, the second factor being the defect of the triangle. On the other hand, an infinitesimal small triangle of hyperbolic geometry can also be considered approximately as an Euclidean triangle; thus the same area PRT can be represented by the expression $\frac{1}{2}$PT $\cdot$ RT $= \frac{1}{2}h$ Cos A $\cdot h$ Sin A $= \frac{1}{4}h^2$ Sin 2A with a negligible error. The resulting equality 4K $(90° - \overset{\frown}{TRP} - A) = h^2$ Sin 2A yields the following expression for the angle $\overset{\frown}{TRP}$:

$$\overset{\frown}{TRP} = 90° - A - c \cdot h^2, \tag{2}$$

where the coefficient c is less than $\frac{1}{4}$/K: $c < 1/4$K.

The angle $\overset{\frown}{PRB}$ is the angle of parallelism related to the distance OR $= x + h$ and it can be considered as a modified value of the angle A, when the variable x increases up to $x + h$. Therefore, we can denote the angle $\overset{\frown}{PRB}$ by A $+ \delta$A, where the symbol δA means the variation of the function A when the variable x gets an increment h. Thus, for the angle $\overset{\frown}{TRB}$, we obtain the following expression:

$$\overset{\frown}{TRB} = \overset{\frown}{TRP} + \overset{\frown}{PRB} = 90° - A - c \cdot h^2 + A + \delta A = 90° + \delta A - ch^2 \tag{3}$$

On the other hand, TRB $= f(g) = f[h \cdot$ Sin A $(1 + w)]$ and $90° = f(0)$ since for $x = 0$ the parallel PC tends to become an Euclidean parallel and therefore tends to become perpendicular to OP. Inserting these values in (3) and forming the difference $f(g) - f(0) = \overset{\frown}{TRB} - 90°$, we obtain

$$f(g) - f(0) = \delta A - ch^2 \tag{4}$$

Now, by the Mean-Value Theorem of calculus, we also have

$$f(g) - f(0) = g \cdot f'(\theta g) = g \cdot [f'(0) + w']$$
$$= h \cdot \text{Sin A} \cdot (1 + w) [f'(0) + w'] \tag{5}$$

where $\lim\limits_{h=0} w' = 0$. Combining (4) and (5), we obtain

$$\delta A = h \cdot \text{Sin } A \cdot [f'(0) + w'] \cdot (1 + w) + ch^2$$

Dividing on both sides by h, we form the quotient $\delta A/h$ whose limit for $h = 0$ is the derivative dA/dx of the function $A = f(x)$. Passing to the limit for $h = 0$ which makes w and w' vanish, we find

$$dA/dx = \lim_{h=0} \delta A/h = f'(0) \cdot \text{Sin } A.$$

Since $f(x)$ is equal to 90° for $x = 0$, but is an acute angle for $x > 0$, the angle $A = f(x)$ is a decreasing function of x for $x = 0$, that is, the deriva-tive dA/dx is negative for $x = 0$. It is the reciprocal of a length and, therefore, denoting a constant length by k, we can express $f'(0)$ as $-1/k : f'(0) = -1/k$. Thus, the function $f(x) = A$ can be found, integrating the following simple differential equation

$$dA/\text{Sin } A = \text{Sec}^2 \frac{A}{2} \, d\left(\frac{A}{2}\right)\bigg/ \text{Tan } \frac{A}{2} = -dx/k,$$

where k denotes an arbitrary but constant length. The solution of this equa-tion is given by

$$\log \text{Tan } (\tfrac{1}{2}A) = C - x/k,$$

where C is the constant of integration. Substituting $x = 0$ and $A = 90°$ in this result, we prove that $C = 0$. We obtain indeed $\log \text{Tan } 45° = \log 1 = 0 = C$.

Therefore, $\log \text{Tan } (\tfrac{1}{2}A) = -x/k$; that is, $\text{Tan } (\tfrac{1}{2}A) = e^{-x/k}$ which is Lo-bachevsky's formula (1) for the angle of parallelism A.